W9-AOC-555

SMITHSONIAN INSTITUTION

UNITED STATES NATIONAL MUSEUM

BULLETIN 186

THE BIRDS OF NORTHERN THAILAND

BY

H. G. DEIGNAN

UNITED STATES

GOVERNMENT PRINTING OFFICE

WASHINGTON : 1945

For sale by the Superintendent of Documents, U. S. Government Printing Office

Washington 25, D. C. - Price $1.25

ADVERTISEMENT

The scientific publications of the National Museum include two series, known, respectively, as *Proceedings* and *Bulletin.*

The *Proceedings* series, begun in 1878, is intended primarily as a medium for the publication of original papers, based on the collections of the National Museum, that set forth newly acquired facts in biology, anthropology, and geology, with descriptions of new forms and revisions of limited groups. Copies of each paper, in pamphlet form, are distributed as published to libraries and scientific organizations and to specialists and others interested in the different subjects. The dates at which these separate papers are published are recorded in the table of contents of each of the volumes.

The series of *Bulletins*, the first of which was issued in 1875, contains separate publications comprising monographs of large zoological groups and other general systematic treatises (occasionally in several volumes), faunal works, reports of expeditions, catalogs of type specimens, special collections, and other material of similar nature. The majority of the volumes are octavo in size, but a quarto size has been adopted in a few instances in which large plates were regarded as indispensable. In the *Bulletin* series appear volumes under the heading *Contributions from the United States National Herbarium*, in octavo form, published by the National Museum since 1902, which contain papers relating to the botanical collections of the Museum.

The present work forms No. 186 of the *Bulletin* series.

ALEXANDER WETMORE,
Secretary, Smithsonian Institution.

CONTENTS

ILLUSTRATIONS

PLATES

MAPS

BINGHAM'S WHITE-HEADED ASHY BULBUL (MICROSCELIS THOMPSONI).
An endemic species of northern Thailand and the Southern Shan States.

THE BIRDS OF NORTHERN THAILAND

[AN ACCOUNT OF THE BIRDS OF CHIANG RAI PROVINCE AND THOSE PARTS OF THE PROVINCES OF MAE HONG SON, CHIANG MAI, LAMPHUN, LAMPANG, PHRAE, AND NAN LYING NORTH OF LATITUDE 17°47′ N.]

By H. G. DEIGNAN

ORNITHOLOGICAL EXPLORATION OF NORTHERN THAILAND

THE story of ornithological exploration of the area discussed in these pages opens in 1859, when Sir ROBERT HERMANN SCHOMBURGK (1804–1865), during his tenure of office as H. B. M. Consul at Bangkok, undertook a long and arduous journey to visit the Lao cities on the Mae Ping. Leaving Bangkok on December 12, he arrived at Rahaeng, the southernmost of the Lao settlements, on January 9, 1860. At this point sending his boats back to Bangkok, he continued the journey on elephants, reaching Chiang Mai, via Lamphun, on February 11. After a short stay here he made his way to Moulmein in Burma by the trade route that passed from Chiang Mai through Muang Hot and Mae Sariang.

Sir Robert published in The Ibis for 1864 (pp. 246–268) a paper entitled "Cursory Notes on Some of the Birds of Siam." Although most of his observations concern birds at Bangkok, a number of forms are stated to have been seen during the trip up-country, and two (*Streptopelia orientalis* and *Kittacincla malabarica*) are definitely mentioned as occurring at Chiang Mai. No northern specimens are known to have been included in Schomburgk's small collection of Thai birds, which was sent to John Gould, from whose possession it passed into that of the British Museum.

No student of birds visited northern Thailand again until 1912. Count NILS CARL GUSTAF FERSEN GYLDENSTOLPE (1886–) arrived at Bangkok in November, 1911, as a member of the delegation representing the Court of Sweden at the Coronation of H. S. M. King Maha Vajiravudh (Rama VI). With the ceremonies completed, he spent the latter half of December collecting in the neighborhood of Bangkok and the period from January 5 to 21, 1912, in the vicinity of Khorat on the eastern plateau. On January 25 he left Khorat by rail for the North. The collecting localities and dates that concern us here are as follows:

January 27–29, 1912, Khao Phlung.
January 31, 1912, Ban Huai Hom, Den Chai.
February 1–5, 1912, Den Chai.
February 6–7, 1912, Ban Huai Hom.
February 8–9, 1912, Den Chai.
February 10, 1912, Den Chai, Mae Raem.
February 11, 1912, Den Chai, Ban Huai Hom.
February 12–13, 1912, Ban Huai Hom.
February 14–15, 1912, Den Chai.
February 16–20, 1912, Pak Pan.
February 21, 1912, Pak Pan, Den Chai.
February 22–25, 1912, Ban Huai Hom.
February 26, 1912, Mae Yom river near Phrae.
February 27, 1912, Mae Yom river near Phrae, Mae Raem.
February 28–29, 1912, Phrae.
March 1–3, 1912, Phrae.
March 7–11, 1912, Mae Raem.
March 18, 1912, Pak Pan.
March 19–23, 1912, "Vang Nun."
March 25–26, 1912, Ban Huai Hom.

Departing from Ban Huai Hom on March 27, Gyldenstolpe visited Tha Lo near Phitsanulok and then went on to southeastern Thailand and the shores of the Inner Gulf of Siam. On May 9 he left Thailand for Europe, taking with him his collections to be deposited in the Royal Natural History Museum in Stockholm.

In mid-February 1914, Gyldenstolpe arrived at Bangkok to undertake his second and more important expedition to Thailand. After a stay of some weeks in the capital, he made the two-day trip to the railhead of the Northern Line at Pak Mae Ta, reaching this point on March 11. After a few days he removed to Pha Kho, the residence of a divisional engineer, where he spent almost a month. On April 18 he set out for Khun Tan, the residence of the engineer Eisenhofer (discussed in the following pages), who was in charge of construction of the Khun Tan tunnel. With Khun Tan as his headquarters, he worked out in all directions until the middle of June, at which time he moved on to Chiang Mai to make arrangements for a trip to the more northern districts. On June 21 he left Chiang Mai for Doi Pha Sakaeng, where he passed several weeks at a forest bungalow of the Borneo Company Limited. Near the end of July he made a difficult crossing of the mountains to Chiang Rai; the conditions of travel in the rains and an outbreak of anthrax among his pack ponies caused great hardship to the party. Spending a week at Chiang Rai, he left on August 8 to travel by boat down the Mae Kok to Chiang Saen Kao; thence, after a week, he returned on foot to Chiang Rai. During his absence the rest of his ponies had succumbed to disease, and it was not until August 18 that he was able to set out, accompanied by 48 bearers, for Chiang Mai, via Wiang Pa Pao. Almost exhausted, he reached his destination on August 26 and rested there until September 2. He next returned to Khun Tan where he was to work until about the 25th. Then going back to Chiang Mai he engaged boats to transport him down the Mae Ping to Pak Nam Pho and, on October 2, set off for Central Thailand and the upper part of the Malay Peninsula.

The valuable collections that resulted from the expedition were deposited in the museum at Stockholm.

Gyldenstolpe's northern collecting localities and dates during this journey are as follows:

March 11–13, 1914, Pak Mae Ta.
March 14–31, 1914, Pha Kho.
April 1–8, 1914, Pha Kho.
April 9–11, 1914, Pha Kho, Pha Hing.
April 13–18, 1914, Pha Kho.
April 22–24, 1914, Sop Tui.
April 28–30, 1914, Khun Tan.
May 1–31, 1914, Khun Tan, Tha Chomphu, Pang Hua Phong.
June 2–8, 1914, Khun Tan.
June 24, 1914, Ban Mae Na.
June 28–29, 1914, Doi Pha Sakaeng.
July 3, 1914, Nong Bia.
July 5, 1914, Hua Muang.
July 9–12, 1914, Doi Pha Sakaeng.
July 13, 1914, "Doi Vieng Par".
July 14–23, 1914, Doi Pha Sakaeng.
July 27, 1914, "Meh Nja Min."
July 28, 1914, Near Chiang Rai.
August 1–7, 1914, Chiang Rai, Nong Mae Rua.
August 8, 1914, Nong Mae Rua.
August 9–10, 1914, Chiang Saen.
August 15–16, 1914, Chiang Rai.
August 22, 1914, Mae Chedi.
August 24, 1914, Pang Kia.
August 25, 1914, Pong Pa O.
September 5–25, 1914, Khun Tan.

At the time of Gyldenstolpe's expedition of 1912, the Northern Line of the Royal State Railways extended no farther than Mae Phuak. The German divisional engineer in charge of construction, EMIL EISENHOFER, had his bungalow at Ban Huai Hom, and Gyldenstolpe stayed with him during the month of February, working out in all directions from that locality. Eisenhofer had already, as early as 1910, began to collect bird skins, sending specimens, with no more data than "Siam" and the year, to the museum at Munich. Evidently as a result of Gyldenstolpe's visit, he became much more active as a collector and began, at least on occasion, to write full information on his labels; the earliest of such specimens date from February 7, 1912.

In 1913 he sent to the Provinzial-Museum (now the Landesmuseum) at Hannover a sizable collection; this material was handed over to Gyldenstolpe for identification, but no list seems ever to have been published. In 1939 I examined 266 specimens in Hannover, all of which probably came from the North; among them were 6 presented by the Munich museum (perhaps the entire lot sent there by Eisenhofer) and 15 from "Siam" (3 with the dates December 12, 17, and 24, 1912) accredited to BRIECKE, who was probably an associate of Eisenhofer. The latter continued to collect sporadically, in the North until June 1913, and later in southwestern Thailand; his ornithological career came to an end in 1917 as a result of the Thai declaration of war upon Germany. Gyldenstolpe, during his expedition of 1914–15, published a briefly annotated list of Eisenhofer's northern specimens, as of that date, in the Journal of the Natural History Society of Siam, vol. 1, 1915, pp. 163–172, 229–236. Some years later Eisenhofer "presented his private collection of 1450 birds to the [Royal Natural History] Museum [at Stockholm], but because he was a German citizen the collection was sequestered by the Siamese authorities, and the Museum in 1920, had to pay a comparatively high price to redeem its own property" (*cf.* Lönnberg, Auk, 1926, p. 444).

A study of the labels of Eisenhofer's specimens, both in Stockholm and in Hannover, shows his northern collecting localities and dates to have been as follows:

February 7, 1912, Ban Huai Hom.
February 8, 1912, Ban Huai Hom, Den Chai.
February 9, 1912, Den Chai.
February 10, 1912, Den Chai, Mae Phuak.
February 11–13, 1912, Ban Huai Hom.
February 14, 1912, Den Chai.
February 16–20, 1912, Pak Pan.
February 22–24, 1912, Ban Huai Hom.
April 20–22, 1912, Pang Puai.
April 23–30, 1912, Pha Hing.
May 1–12, 1912, Pha Hing.
May 20–31, 1912, Huai Pu.
June 2–5, 1912, Huai Pu.
June 23–27, 1912, Huai San.
May 25, 1913, Khun Tan.
June 1–11, 1913, Khun Tan.

(Sir) WALTER JAMES FRANKLIN WILLIAMSON (1867—), although he never made a personal visit to the North, sent an Asiatic collector of birds to these provinces in at least two different years. No complete report on Sir Walter's large Thai collection has yet been published, but a few of his more unusual northern specimens have been noticed in the Journal of the Natural History Society of Siam.

These scattered records show that the collector visited the Muang Song forest in April 1916; Doi Nga Chang (Doi Khun Tan) in February 1917; Chiang Mai in June 1917; and Muang Wang in September, October, and November 1917. Doubtless many other northern localities are represented in the collection, which, in 1939, was stored at the British Museum (Natural History) and will probably eventually be incorporated into the museum's series. One of Sir Walter's specimens was taken October 4, 1915, at Mae Mo by E. W. TROTTER.

KENNETH G. GAIRDNER collected on Doi Suthep, March 31, 1919, the first Thai specimen of *Syrmaticus humiae burmannicus* and, later in the same year, published the record in the Journal of the Natural History Society of Siam.

The American ichthyologist HUGH MCCORMICK SMITH (1865–1941) went to Thailand in 1923 as adviser in fisheries to the Siamese Government. Smith's investigations took him, during the subsequent 11 years, to every part of the Kingdom, and he was accompanied on these excursions by the Dyak collector LAYANG GADDI, who made extensive collections of birds and other animals for the United States National Museum. The following résumé of Smith's collecting localities in the northern provinces has been compiled from his field catalogs:

November 15–17, 1928, Lampang.
November 19–23, 1928, Khun Tan.
November 24–27, 1928, Chiang Mai.
November 29–30, 1928, Chom Thong.
December 1, 1928, Ban Mae Klang.
December 2–9, 1928, Doi Ang Ka.
December 10, 1928, Chom Thong.
December 13–15, 1928, Doi Suthep.
October 16–28, 1929, Khun Tan.
April 10–11, 1930, Phrae.
April 13–16, 1930, Nan.
April 18–23, 1930, Ban Nam Khian.
April 26–28, 1930, Phrae.
August 23–31, 1930, Khun Tan.
September 1–10, 1930, Khun Tan.
November 2–22, 1930, Doi Langka.
April 22–30, 1931, Doi Langka.
May 1–6, 1931, Doi Langka.
January 28–31, 1932, Chiang Dao.
February 1, 1932, Chiang Dao.
February 3, 1932, Doi Suthep.
February 4, 1932, Chiang Mai.
February 6–8, 1932, Mae Khan.
February 13–29, 1932, Khun Tan.
March 1–4, 1932, Khun Tan.
December 20, 1932, San Pa Yang.
December 21, 1932, Sop Phung.

December 22, 1932, Sop Phung, "Ban Phradieng".
December 23, 1932, "Ban Phradieng," "Ban Ta Pai," Huai Lak.
December 24, 1932, Huai Mae Lao, Huai Mae Sae.
December 25, 1932, "Doi Kiew Koh Ma," Doi Buak Hua Chang, Doi Pata.
December 26, 1932, Tin Doi Pata, Muang Pai.
December 27–28, 1932, Muang Pai.
December 29, 1932, Muang Pai, Doi Musoe, Doi Pa Mai Daeng.
December 30, 1932, Doi Mana, Doi Kiu Wai.
December 31, 1932, Um Mong valley, Mae Lang valley.
January 1, 1933, Mae Lang valley, Doi Kiu Chong.
January 2, 1933, Mae Suya valley, Huai Salop.
January 3, 1933, Huai Salop, Mae Hong Son.
January 4–10, 1932, Mae Hong Son.
January 11, 1933, Burmese reach of the Mae Pai.
January 12–13, 1933, Burmese bank of the Salwin.
January 14, 1933, "Hang Nor Wu".
January 15, 1933, "Hang Tum Kai".
January 16–18, 1933, Thattafang.
January 19, 1933, Mae Kong Ka valley.
January 20, 1933, Mae Kong Ka valley, Song Khwae valley, Mae Sariang.
January 21–23, 1933, Mae Sariang.
January 25–26, 1933, Mae Kong Ka valley.
May 9–18, 1933, Khun Tan.
August 1–6, 1934, Doi Pha Cho [=Doi Langka].
August 12–31, 1934, Doi Hua Mot.
September 1–6, 1934, Doi Hua Mot.

The Swiss-American Baron Rodolphe Meyer de Schauensee (1901—), collecting in the interests of the Academy of Natural Sciences of Philadelphia, made his initial visit to Thailand in the hot season of 1928; between March 9 and 19 inclusive he made a small collection of birds in the vicinity of Chiang Mai and on Doi Suthep to 4,500 feet.

Returning in the following winter, he worked again chiefly on Doi Suthep and the Chiang Mai plain but in January made a short trip into Chiang Rai Province, traveling by motorcar from Lampang as far as Chiang Saen Kao and the Shan border. His collecting localities during this second expedition are as follows:

December 4–31, 1928, Chiang Mai and Doi Suthep.
January 1–2, 1929, Chiang Mai.
January 3, 1929, Chiang Mai to Lampang (train).
January 4, 1929, Pang La.
January 5–7, 1929, Chiang Rai.
January 8, 1929, Chiang Rai, Chiang Saen.
January 9–13, 1929, Chiang Saen Kao.
January 14, 1929, Chiang Saen, Mae Sai.
January 15, 1929, Mae Chai, Phayao, "Pa Tai".
January 16, 1929, Lampang to Ciang Mai (train).
January 17–20, 1929, Chiang Mai, Mae Rim, Doi Suthep.

At the close of 1932 de Schauensee revisited northern Thailand, where, assisted by four Asiatic collectors, he brought together extensive series of birds and other animals, again for the Academy of Natural Sciences. With the exception of a week spent in the Southern Shan State of Kengtung, three months were devoted to collecting in the provinces of Chiang Mai, Lampang, and Chiang Rai, as follows:

December 9, 1932, Chiang Mai.
December 10–12, 1932, Doi Suthep.
December 13, 1932, Chiang Mai.
December 14, 1932, Mae Taeng, Chiang Dao.
December 16–18, 1932, Chiang Mai.
December 19, 1932, Mae Taeng.
December 20, 1932, Chiang Mai.
December 21–29, 1932, Doi Suthep.
December 31, 1932, Chiang Mai.
January 1–3, 1933, Khun Tan, Doi Suthep.
January 4–5, 1933, Doi Suthep.
January 7–8, 1933, Chiang Dao.
January 9, 1933, Ridge south of Doi Chiang Dao.
January 10, 1933, Ridge opposite Doi Chiang Dao.
January 11–22, 1933, Doi Chiang Dao.
January 23, 1933, Chiang Dao.
January 24–26, 1933, Chiang Mai.
January 27, 1933, "Tung Sio".
January 28, 1933, "Tung Sio," Chiang Mai.
January 29, 1933, Chiang Mai.
January 30, 1933, Chiang Mai, Mae Rim.
January 31, 1933, Chiang Mai.
February 1, 1933, Chiang Mai.
February 2–7, 1933, Doi Suthep.
February 10, 1933, 55 km. northeast of Lampang.
February 11–13, 1933, Chiang Saen Kao.
February 14–20, 1933, Kengtung State (extra-limital).
February 21–23, 1933, Chiang Rai.
February 25–28, 1933, Doi Suthep.
March 1–3, 1933, Doi Suthep.

During the years 1933–1938, northern Thailand was visited at least three times by Asiatic collectors in de Schauensee's employ. The first of these brief trips was made by Y. Siah, a well-known taxidermist of Bangkok, who took birds on Doi Suthep from July 4 to 23, 1933. In March and April 1935, Layang Gaddi went to Kengtung State and collected a limited number of specimens in the Ban Chong hills, the low mountains that are visible to the north from the Chiang Rai-Chiang Saen highway. In January and February 1938, Lucas Bah made an interesting collection on the ornithologically unknown mountain Doi Pha Hom Pok.

The present writer resided at Chiang Mai as a master at the Prince Royal's College from November 21, 1928, to the end of March 1932. During this period no birds at all were collected before the middle of September 1930; thereafter a small collection was made in the interest of the Princeton Museum of Zoology, the specimens coming almost without exception from Chiang Mai, Doi Suthep, Doi Ang Ka, and Doi Chiang Dao.

Returning to his former position on April 20, 1935, and with financial assistance from the United States National Museum, he collected extensively throughout the northern provinces (and elsewhere) until April 15, 1937, sending all zoological material to the Museum at Washington. During this time he had the full-time assistance of the Chinese collector CHARLES TAN (known also as L. K. A. CHARLES). The northern collecting localities and dates of the two are shown in the following schedules:

DEIGNAN

April 19–30, 1935, Chiang Mai, Doi Suthep, Sop Khap.
May 1–31, 1935, Chiang Mai, Doi Suthep.
June 1–30, 1935, Chiang Mai, Doi Suthep.
July 1–31, 1935, Chiang Mai, Doi Suthep, Chom Thong, Mae Rim, Doi Mon Khwam Long.
August 1–28, 1935, Chiang Mai, Doi Suthep, Chiang Dao.
August 30, 1935, Chom Thong, Mae Klang.
August 31, 1935, Mae Klang, Doi Ang Ka.
September 1–10, 1935, Doi Ang Ka.
September 11, 1935, Chom Thong.
September 12–28, 1935, Chiang Mai, Doi Suthep.
October 1–31, 1935, Chiang Mai, Doi Suthep, San Sai Luang, Chiang Dao.
November 1–30, 1935, Chiang Mai, Doi Suthep, Doi Kham, Chom Thong.
December 1–18, 1935, Chiang Mai, Doi Suthep, Mae Dok Daeng Nai.
December 19, 1935, Chom Thong, Nong Khiat.
December 20, 1935, Sop Huai Khieo, Huai Muang.
December 21, 1935, Tha Nong Luang.
December 22, 1935, Wang Lung.
December 23, 1935, Ban Aen, Ban Noi, Mut Ka.
January 1–31, 1936, Chiang Mai, Doi Suthep, Sam Kamphaeng.
February 1–29, 1936, Chiang Mai, Doi Suthep, Ban Pong, San Sai Luang.
March 1–25, 1936, Chiang Mai, Pa Muat, Mae Dok Daeng Nai, Doi Kham, Chiang Dao.
March 29, 1936, Nan.
March 30, 1936, Nan, Huai Som Poi, Pha Tup.
March 31, 1936, San Pa Haeng, Wang Mo, Pha Khwang.
April 1, 1936, Pha Khwang, Wang Pa, Pang Kho, Ton Hang.
April 2, 1936, Pua, Pong Sanuk, Na Ko.
April 3, 1936, Ban Don.
April 4–17, 1936, Phu Kha.
April 18, 1936, Phu Kha, Din Tok.
April 19, 1936, Pua, Na Ko.
April 20, 1936, Pua, Ban Khana.
April 21, 1936, Ban Khana, Nam O, Bu, Lae.
April 22, 1936, Thung Ao, Ban Sala, Nam Sun, Ngop.
April 23, 1936, Ngop.
April 24, 1936, Ngop, Doi Lom, Don Chai.
April 25, 1936, Don Chai, Ban Lap, Din Tok, Doi Up Fa.

April 26, 1936, Nam Puat.
April 27, 1936, Nam Puat, Ban Tham, Ban Pao.
April 28, 1936, Ban Sathan, Ban Mai, Hua Muang.
April 29, 1936, Na Ban, Doi Chang Kong, Ban Sa.
May 1, 1936, Rong Chiang Laeng, Salaeng, Ngao.
May 2, 1936, Mai Tong Hong.
May 3, 1936, Mae Tak, Savannas of the Nam Ing.
May 4, 1936, Tong Yang, Pong Fa.
May 5, 1936, Hong Khaeo, Ton Yang.
May 6–8, 1936, Chiang Rai.
May 9–10, 1936, Mae Chai.
May 12, 1936, Chiang Mai.
May 13, 1936, Khun Tan.
May 15–31, 1936, Chiang Mai, Doi Suthep.
June 1–30, 1936, Chiang Mai, Pa Muat, Mae Cho, Ban Chang, Nong Phung.
July 1–31, 1936, Chiang Mai, Doi Suthep, Ban Pong.
August 1–31, 1936, Chiang Mai, Doi Suthep.
September 1–3, 1936, Chiang Mai.
September 7, 1936, Pa Lao.
September 8–9, 1936, Sa-iap.
September 10, 1936, Mae Ten, Ban Mang.
September 11, 1936, Bo Thong, Tha Fa.
September 12, 1936, Tha Fa, Muang Pong.
September 13, 1936, Muang Pong.
September 14, 1936, Hat Faen, 62 km. east of Phayao.
September 15, 1936, 62 km. east of Phayao, 50 km. east of Phayao, Ban Pin.
September 16, 1936, Mae Ka Huai Khian.
September 18-31, 1936, Chiang Mai, Doi Suthep.
October 1–31, 1936, Chiang Mai, Doi Suthep, Pa Muat.
November 1–30, 1936, Chiang Mai, Doi Suthep, Pa Muat.
December 1–15, 1936, Chiang Mai, Choeng Doi, Doi Suthep.
December 16, 1936, Ping Kong.
December 19, 1936, Huai Chang Tai.
December 20, 1936, Pang Makham Phong, San Pa Pao, Huai Tak, Hong Tan.
December 21, 1936, San Sai Mun, Mae Sun.
December 22, 1936, Ton Phung, Mae Mao.
December 23, 1936, Muang Sum, Headwaters of Mae Mao.
December 24, 1936, Headwaters of Mae Mao, Nong Thong, Muang Sum.
December 25–26, 1936, Muang Sum.
December 27, 1936, Muang Sum, Hua Fai, Mae Mao, Mae Chai Tai, Mon Pin.
December 29, 1936, Ban Ai, Hong Tan, Pang Makham Phong.
December 30, 1936, Pang Makham Phong.
January 1–31, 1937, Chiang Mai, Doi Suthep, Pa Muat.
February 1–28, 1937, Chiang Mai, Doi Suthep, Mae Rim.
March 1–8, 1937, Chiang Mai.
March 16–17, 1937, Mountain south of Doi Chiang Dao.
March 18–20, 1937, Doi Chiang Dao.
March 21, 1937, Doi Chiang Dao, Muang Chiang Dao.
March 22–24, 1937, Doi Suthep.
March 28, 1937, Huai Ki, Pai Ton, Huai Som.
March 29, 1937, Huai Som.
March 30, 1937, Huai Som, Thap Man, Pha Lai, San Tha.

March 31, 1937, San Tha.
April 1, 1937, San Tha, Ban Oi, Kiu Nak.
April 2, 1937, Na Noi.
April 3, 1937, Na Noi, Bo Kaeo.
April 4, 1937, Bo Kaeo, Huai Oi.
April 5, 1937, Huai Oi, Pak Li.
April 6–7, 1937, Pak Li.
April 8, 1937, Ban Hua Oi, Hat Sam Khwae, Hat La, Huai Pa Khan.
April 12–15, 1937, Chiang Mai.

Charles

July 20, 1935, Doi Dok Daeng.
July 21, 1935, Between Doi Dok Daeng and Wiang Pa Pao.
July 22–31, 1935, Wiang Pa Pao, Pang Ai, Doi Khrang.
August 1–4, 1935, Wiang Pa Pao, Doi Khrang.
August 5, 1935, Tha Ko.
August 6, 1935, Mae Suai.
August 7, 1935, Chiang Rai.
October 21–30, 1935, Doi Suthep.
November 1–13, 1935, Chom Thong, Nong Khiat.
November 22–30, 1935, Samoeng, Doi Samoeng.
December 2, 1935, Between Samoeng and Mae Rim.
December 7–17, 1935, Doi Suthep.
January 7, 1936, Chom Thong.
January 8, 1936, Mae Soi, Pa Pua.
January 9–18, 1936, Sop Mae Chaem, Thung Som Poi, Chom Thong.
January 19, 1936, Mae Soi.
January 26–31, 1936, Doi Suthep.
February 1–10, 1936, Doi Suthep.
February 19–28, 1936, Sala Mae Tha.
May 24–31, 1936, Tha Wang Luang, Na Noi, San Tha, Phu Chae, Doi San Huai Wai.
June 1–21, 1936, Doi San Huai Wai, Doi Ta Kong, Na Noi, Doi San Ho, Doi San Pa Bong, Huai Nam Lom, San Tha, Phu Het, Huai Thae, Huai Som.
June 22–23, 1936, Huai Ki.
July 2, 1936, Chiang Dao.
July 3, 1936, Huai Chang Tai, Tao Phun, Fang.
July 5–25, 1936, Fang.
August 15–31, 1936, Mae Mo.
September 1–2, 1936, Mae Mo.
September 26, 1936, Thung Ma Num, Doi Phrabat.
September 28, 1936, Huai Pa Phai.
September 29, 1936, Doi Khang Ma, Doi Pha Lat.
September 30, 1936, Bo Luang, Doi Mae Thian.
October 1, 1936, Bo Sali, Mae Wen, Huai Mae Lit.
October 4, 1936, Huai Mae Ka Nai, Mae Ho, Doi Lak Saen, Doi Mae Lai.
October 5, 1936, Doi Mae Lai.
October 6–8, 1936, Mae Sariang.
October 9–10, 1936, Mae Kong Ka valley.
October 11–16, 1936, Thattafang.

NONG HO, A POND NEAR CHIANG MAI.

A, Looking toward the west during the rains (September); at places such as this the little grebe is common. B, Looking toward the east in the cold weather (December); wagtails and pipits abound at this season along the shore. C, *Pa daeng* at the edge of the *nong*, home of *Crypsirina vagabunda* and *Dissemurus paradiseus*.

RICEFIELDS.

A, Setting out the young plants; at this season almost no birds are seen in the fields. B, Standing rice, haunt of bitterns, rails, and prinias. C, Stubble, with garden bamboo to the right, *pa daeng* to the left; at such places munias glean in flocks of hundreds.

CHARACTERISTIC BIRD HABITATS.

A, Marshy areas in fields after harvest attract wagtails, pipits, herons, and rails. B, Teak logs at edge of mixed-deciduous forest; white-crested laughing thrushes and racquet-tailed drongos occur along the tracks. C, Northern rivers flow for most of their courses between precipitous banks; the shrub growing in midstream is *takrai nam* (*Homonoia riparia*); at such places the black-capped kingfisher may be seen.

CHARACTERISTIC BIRD HABITATS.

A, Groves of *mai kwao* (*Butea frondosa*) hold a special attraction for *Dryobates m. longipennis* and *Sturnus malabaricus*. B, Flocks of *Nettapus* and *Dendrocygna* rest upon pools of open water in drying marshes. C, Jaçanas and crakes hide among the leaves of the sacred lotus.

October 17–23, 1936, Mae Kong Ka valley, Doi Mae Kong Ka.
October 24–31, 1936, Mae Sariang, Nong Mae La.
November 1, 1936, Mae Sariang.
November 3, 1936, Bo Sali.
November 4, 1936, Doi Mae Thian.
November 19–30, 1936, Doi Chiang Dao.
December 1–9, 1936, Doi Chiang Dao.
December 28, 1936, Mae Sao, Pa Bong.
December 29, 1936, Tha Ton, San Pa Khoi.
December 30, 1936, Pang Thoem, Wiang Khae, Pong Nam Ron.
January 1–2, 1937, Doi Mae Chan, Huai Mae Chan.
January 3, 1937, Huai Mae Chan, Pang Khwai, Pong Peng.
January 4–5, 1937, Huai Mae Chan.
January 8–19, 1937, Chiang Saen Kao.
January 20, 1937, Chiang Saen Kao, Mae Sai.
January 21, 1937, Mae Sai.
January 24, 1937, Nong Bua.
January 25–28, 1937, Chiang Rai.
January 30, 1937, Phayao.
February 9, 1937, Chom Thong.
February 10–13, 1937, Mae Klang.
February 21, 1937, Mae Wan.
February 22, 1937, Mae Dok Daeng Nai.
February 25, 1937, San Pa Sak.
February 26, 1937, Na Noi.
February 27, 1937, Pang An.
February 28, 1937, Doi Nang Kaeo.
March 1–2, 1937, Doi Nang Kaeo.
March 3–4, 1937, Doi Langka.
March 5, 1937, Pak Tang Huai Mo.
March 6, 1937, San Pa Sak.

A collection of birds at Cornell University, presented by Luang Sri Vijjakich (1902–), includes 9 or 10 from northern localities: Chiang Mai, Mae Klang, Lampang, Phayao, and Nan. Their dates run through 1928, 1929, and 1930, and it is not possible to work out from them the collector's routes. The two skins from Nan (March 21 and 27, 1930) are very probably from the collection made there by Alexander, inasmuch as it is known that Vijjakich was not at Nan during the period of Alexander's stay.

(Edward) Gordon Alexander (1901–), who was at the time visiting professor of biology at Chulalongkon University, made a brief visit to the North in 1930, in the course of which he collected 32 bird skins, about 25 of which are now at Princeton University, while the remainder are probably at Chulalongkon University. His collecting localities are:

February 21–22, 1930, Chiang Rai.
February 23, 1930, Chiang Saen Kao.
February 24, 1930, Chiang Rai.
March 21–29, 1930, Nan.

Carl Johan (Ove Mønster) Aagaard (1882–), a longtime Danish resident of Thailand, made two trips to the North to collect chiefly birds and mammals: The first, to Chiang Mai and Doi Suthep, in February and March 1931; the second, to Doi Ang Ka, about one year later. The nearly 400 bird skins obtained on Doi Suthep were discussed by Chasen and Boden Kloss in 1932 (Journ. Siam Soc. Nat. Hist. Suppl., vol. 8, No. 4, pp. 231–248), but nothing was ever published concerning the fruits of the Ang Ka expedition, among which is the only specimen of *Cinclus* yet taken in the Kingdom. Aagaard's specimens are widely scattered among the museums of the world, but his most important finds remained in his private collection, which eventually came into possession of Chulalongkon University in Bangkok.

In 1937, at the Raffles Museum in Singapore, I examined a small collection of bird skins, from the vicinity of Chiang Mai and Chiang Dao, that had been sent for purchase by one Nai Kaeo (1906?–), a resident of Ban Den, an out-village of Chiang Mai. The birds seen had been taken in 1936 and 1937, and it is probable that later sendings arrived at Singapore. Among them were several forms not previously recorded from the district, mention of which is made at the proper places in my text.

The Asiatic Primate Expedition spent the period between February 16 and April 30, 1937, in the province of Chiang Mai, and one of the party, J. A. Griswold, Jr., with the assistance of Asiatic collectors, during that time took more than 1,000 specimens of birds that were later to be deposited in Cambridge at the Museum of Comparative Zoology. A report on a part of this material was brought out by J. C. Greenway, Jr., in 1940 (Bull. Mus. Comp. Zool., vol. 87, No. 3, pp. 167–194). The pertinent collecting localities and dates are as follows:

February 16–26, 1937, Chiang Mai, Chiang Dao, Doi Saket.
February 26–April 27, 1937, Doi Ang Ka.
April 8–23, 1937, Doi Nang Kaeo.
April 26–28, 1937, Chiang Dao.
April 29, 1937, Chiang Mai.

In March and April 1938, the Swedish Film Industry Expedition, under the leadership of Dr. P. Fejos, a Hungarian, engaged Deignan's old collector, Charles Tan, to make a collection of bird skins for the Royal Museum of Natural History in Stockholm. Some 90 skins were taken, among them two specimens of the short-eared owl, which had not previously been known from our area. The whole collection seems to have come from Chiang Mai Province; the pertinent localities and dates are as follows:

March 12–14, 1938, Chiang Mai.
March 17, 1938, Chiang Mai, Huai Chang.

March 18, 1938, Huai Chang.
March 20, 1938, Doi Suthep.
March 23, 1938, Huai Mae Ta Man.
March 24, 1938, Huai Mae Ta Man, Muang Koet.
March 25–26, 1938, Huai Mae Ta Man.
March 27, 1938, Mae Taeng.
March 28, 1938, Chiang Mai.
April 1–4, 1938, Chiang Mai.
April 5–8, 1938, Doi Suthep.
April 10–11, 1938, Chiang Mai.
April 14–19, 1938, Doi Chiang Dao.

Between November 1938 and March 1939, the VIIe Expédition Ornithologique en Indochine Française, under the leadership of JEAN (–BAPTISTE THÉODORE ALEXANDRE) DELACOUR (1890–), accompanied by JAMES COWAN GREENWAY, Jr. (1903–), visited the western parts of Haut-Laos and traveled along the left bank of the Mae Khong opposite Chiang Rai Province. While at no time did the party collect in Thai territory, yet several unusual birds were added to the northern Thai list by their having been discovered on the bars and islands of the river between the two countries; these forms are noted in their proper places in my text.

GEOGRAPHY

Northern Thailand, as it is to be understood in the following pages, embraces all pre-war Thailand north of a somewhat arbitrary line drawn due east and west at about latitude 17° 47′ N., at the point where the Mae Yuam enters the Mae Moei (Thaungyin) just south of the latter's confluence with the Salwin. (Map 1.) This area then includes the whole of Chiang Rai Province and large parts of the provinces of Mae Hong Son, Chiang Mai, Lamphun, Lampang, Phrae, and Nan. Owing to the absence of natural boundaries between Chiang Mai and Lamphun, the latter is consistently treated as simply a part of Chiang Mai and will never be mentioned again in this study. The area covered is something considerably under 35,000 square miles and thus smaller than the State of Maine; its population is perhaps 1,500,000 and very unequally distributed.

At latitude 20° N., where the great rivers Salwin and Mae Khong part company to make room on the map for Thailand, the main ridge of mountains between them broadens and, with the name Daen Lao, becomes the greater part of the boundary between Thailand and the Shan States of Burma. The Daen Lao at the same time divides into a number of roughly parallel ranges running in general from north-northeast to south-southwest. The westernmost, called the Thanon Thong Chai, continues southward under various names, at last to form the backbone of the Malay Peninsula. The next to the east, the Khun Tan range, is followed by the Western and Eastern Phi Pan

Nam ranges, and these by the Phetchabun mountains, which, in this region, are the boundary hills between Thailand and the territories of the French.

Between each couple of these north-south ranges lies the valley of a river that finally, after dropping through a constricted gorge to the great plain of Central Thailand, unites its waters with those of its sister streams and others to form the Mae Nam Chao Phaya, the chief river of the Kingdom. The river flowing between the Thanon

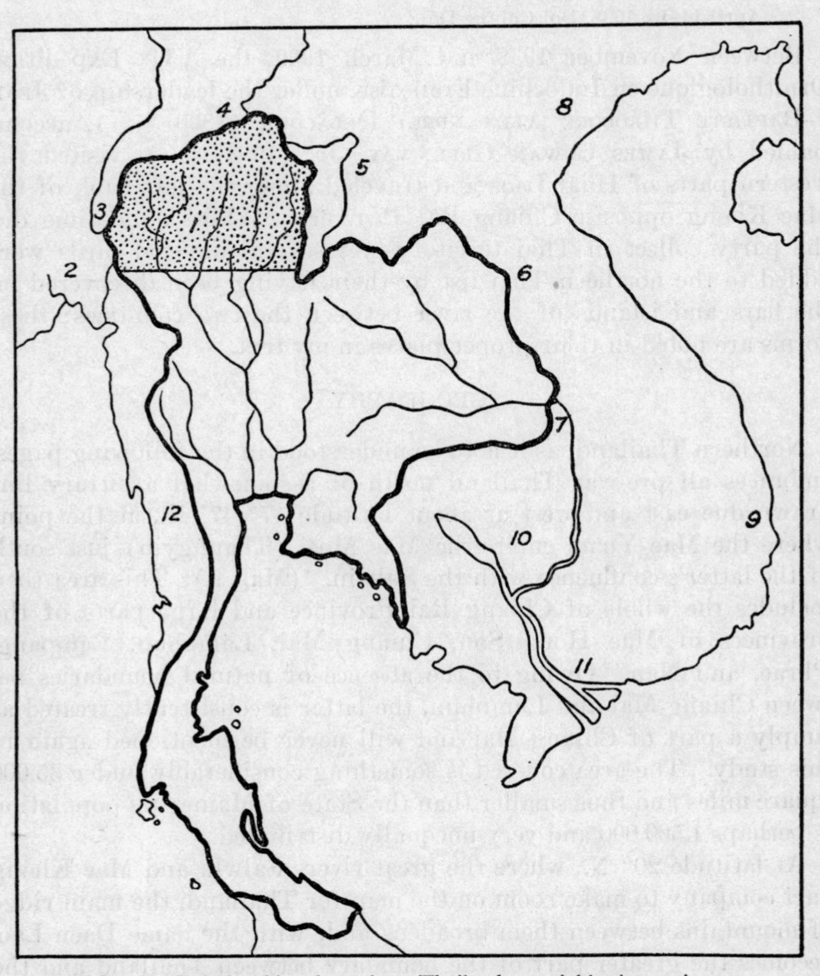

Map 1.—Relationship of northern Thailand to neighboring regions:

1. Northern Thailand.
2. Pegu.
3. Karen-ni.
4. Kengtung.
5. Haut-Laos.
6. Moyen-Laos
7. Bas-Laos.
8. Tongking.
9. Annam.
10. Cambodia.
11. Cochin-China.
12. Tenasserim.

Thong Chai and Khun Tan ranges is the Mae Ping; the one between the Khun Tan and Western Phi Pan Nam hills, the Mae Wang; the one between the two ranges of the Phi Pan Nam, the Mae Yom; the last one to the east, the Mae Nan. These four must be understood to belong to a single drainage system, quite unrelated to the systems of the Salwin and the Mae Khong. (Map 2.)

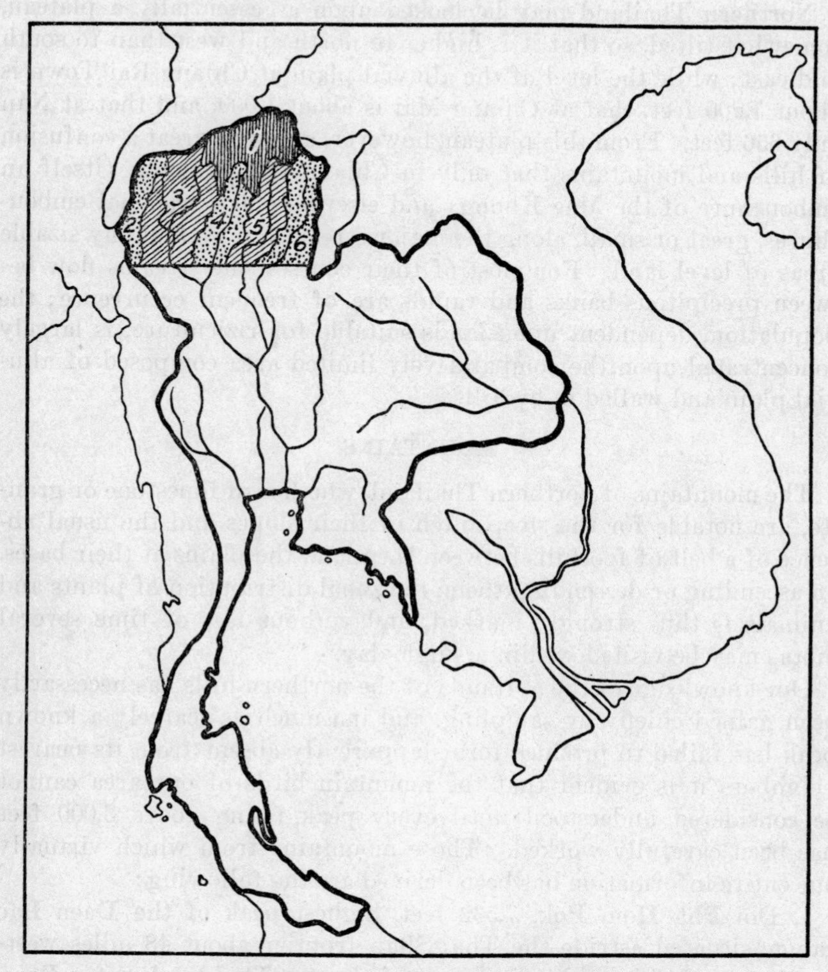

Map 2.—Drainage systems of northern Thailand:

1. Mae Khong.
2. Salwin.
3. Mae Ping.
4. Mae Wang.
5. Mae Yom.
6. Mae Nan.

The watersheds of the six main rivers of Northern Thailand are almost exactly equivalent to the six principal political divisions so far as they lie within our limits; so close is this correspondence that, throughout this study, I have found it convenient to treat Mae Hong

Son Province as identical with the Salwin drainage, Chiang Mai Province as equal to that of the Mae Ping, Lampang Province as equal to that of the Mae Wang, Phrae Province as equal to that of the Mae Yom, Nan Province as equal to that of Mae Nan, and Chiang Rai Province as equivalent to all northern territory drained by the Mae Khong.

Northern Thailand may be looked upon as essentially a plateau, somewhat tilted, so that it is higher to north and west than to south and east; while the level of the alluvial plain at Chiang Rai Town is about 1,200 feet, that at Chiang Mai is about 1,000, and that at Nan only 656 feet. From this plateau, however, arises so great a confusion of hills and mountains that only in Chiang Rai Province (itself an embouchure of the Mae Khong) and elsewhere at occasional embouchures, great or small, along the major streams do we find any sizable areas of level land. For most of their courses, the streams flow between precipitous banks and rapids are of frequent occurrence; the population, dependent upon lands suitable for riziculture, is largely concentrated upon the comparatively limited area composed of alluvial plain and walled in by hills.

MOUNTAINS

The mountains of northern Thailand, whether of limestone or granite, are notable for the steep pitch of their slopes and the usual absence of a belt of foothills between them and the plains at their bases. In ascending or descending them, the zonal distribution of plants and animals is thus strongly marked, and without loss of time several biotas may be visited within a single day.

Our knowledge of the avifauna of the northern hills has necessarily been gained chiefly by sampling, and inasmuch as scarcely a known peak has failed to produce forms apparently absent from its nearest neighbors it is evident that the mountain birds of our area cannot be considered understood until every peak rising above 3,000 feet has been carefully worked. Those mountains from which virtually our entire information has been derived are the following:

1. Doi Pha Hom Pok, 7,532 feet, highest peak of the Daen Lao range, situated astride the Thai-Shan frontier about 48 miles west-northwest of Chiang Rai; it is the only known Thai locality for *Bambusicola*, *Dryobates cathpharius*, *Garrulax merulinus*, and other forms common to the northward.

2. Doi Chiang Dao, 7,160 feet, second highest peak of the Thanon Thong Chai range, situated about 40 miles north by west of Chiang Mai; it is a solid block of limestone rising from a base elevation of only 1,312 feet.

3. Doi Suthep, 5,500 feet, a classical collecting ground of the Thanon Thong Chai range, situated just west of Chiang Mai.

4. Doi Ang Ka (Doi Inthanon), 8,400 feet, highest peak of the Thanon Thong Chai range, situated about 35 miles west-southwest of Chiang Mai; it is the only known Thai locality for *Siva strigula*, and *Aethopyga nipalensis angkanensis* is probably endemic at its summit.

5. Doi Langka (Doi Pha Cho), 6,601 feet, highest mountain of the Khun Tan range, situated about 32 miles east-northeast of Chiang Mai.

6. Doi Hua Mot, 6,047 feet, situated just northwest by north of Doi Langka and forming part of the same complex.

7. Doi Saket (Doi Lan), 5,958 feet, situated just southwest by south of Doi Langka and forming part of the same complex.

8. Doi Khun Tan (Doi Nga Chang), 4,422 feet, a classical collecting ground, situated about 29 miles southeast by south of Chiang Mai.

9. Khao Phlung, a low mountain at the southern extremity of the Eastern Phi Pan Nam range, situated about 20 miles south-southwest of Muang Phrae.

10. Phu Kha, 5,577 feet, mountain of the Phetchabun range, situated about 28 miles northeast of Muang Nan; it is the only known Thai locality for numerous montane forms common to the eastward.

CLIMATE

Northern Thailand is subject to the typical monsoonal climate of southeastern Asia, by which the prevailing winds, from October to May, blow from the northeast and, during the rest of the year, from the southwest. There are three distinct seasons—the cold weather, the rains, and the hot weather. The first extends, at Chiang Mai, from the middle of November to the middle of March; the third from about the middle of March to the onset of the rains in May; the rains cover the remaining months.

Meteorological observations made by Dr. A. F. G. Kerr at Chiang Mai during the years 1909–1915 show the extreme minimum temperature of the air in the shade to have been 41.3° F. (February 8, 1911) and the extreme maximum to have been 109.8° F. (April 1913). Official observations made at the same place from 1927 to 1929 give the former measurement as 48.56° F. (December 13, 1927), the latter as 103.60° F. (April 23, 1927). Official observations made there in the years 1931–1932 give the mean minimum as 47.50° F. (December 16 and 17, 1932), the mean maximum as 104.90° F. (April 18, 1931).

The following remarks are taken from the valuable contribution by Kerr (Journ. Siam Soc., vol. 17, pt. 1, 1923, pp. 26–27):

> The summit of Doi Sutep is 4500 feet (1350 metres) above the level of Chiengmai and is, naturally, very considerably cooler.
>
> The first meteorological observations taken on the top of Doi Sutep to be published were those of Dr. C. C. Hosseus who made temperature records there for 4 days in the first half of December 1904. These observations, together with others made by Dr. Hosseus elsewhere in Siam, were the subject of a paper by Dr. Gerbing, "Das Klima von Siam und die Ergebnisse der von Dr. Hosseus

angestellten meteorologischen Beobachtungen" published in Petermann's Geographische Mitteilung, 1909, No. 6. Dr. Hosseus gives an extract relating to Doi Sutep from this paper in his book, "Durch König Tschulalongkorns Reich." The following is a summary of this extract.

Temperatures were taken simultaneously in Chiengmai and on the top of Doi Sutep from 2 P. M. on December 10th, till 7 A. M. on December 14th. When these temperatures are tabulated it is seen the mean decrease in temperature between Chiengmai and the top of Doi Sutep for the four days is at 7 A. M. 2.45° C (4.4° F), at 2 P. M. 13.3° C (23.90° F) and at 9 P. M. 6.2° C (11.2° F). This gives a mean fall for each 100 metres altitude of 0.533° C, which accords with the value for decrease of temperature with height found in mountains elsewhere, namely 0.56° C for every 100 metres (about 1° F to 300 feet). The difference in temperature at night is not so great owing to the heavy cold collecting in the valley.

Taking it for granted that December is the coolest month in Chiengmai and April the hottest it may be assumed that the mean temperature on the top of Doi Sutep for December will be 12.2° C (54° F) and for April 22.3° C (72.1° F). May, which falls in the rains when the decrease of temperature with height is less, will have the same mean temperature as April.

Combining all the results it may be predicted that the Winter months on the top of Doi Sutep will have a temperature resembling that of our [German] Spring months, though night frosts are hardly to be expected. The hottest months, April and May, on the other hand will have a mean temperature which we rarely reach in the [German] Summer months.

Since the above paper was written a good many temperature records have been made on the top of Doi Sutep and these bear out, in the main, the predictions of Dr. Gerbing. It may be mentioned here that night frosts are not unknown in N. Siam, and at lower altitudes than the top of Doi Sutep. I myself experienced a frost one night in a small valley on the Baw Sali plateau in January 1904, the altitude being about 3,000 feet. I believe these frosts occur in valleys at fairly high altitudes and sufficiently enclosed to act as pockets for cold air. Such a valley, however, is not to be found on Doi Sutep, whose slopes are steep, so night frosts there are improbable.

Rain may fall in any month of the year in our provinces, but when it does so outside the limits of the rainy season it usually falls only as showers, though occasionally in the dry season there may be two or three days of continuous rain. Kerr's observations from 1909 to 1915 gave the mean annual rainfall at Chiang Mai as 42.629 inches; official measurements there from 1927 to 1929 gave 43.358 inches; on the other hand, the Meteorological Bureau recorded there only 17.350 inches in 1931 and 36.920 inches in 1932.

BREEDING SEASONS

It is probable that there is no time of the year when some species of bird is not breeding within our provinces; it may be added, however, that I have no record for any species' breeding in the month of October, and only the barn owl has been found breeding in November; this latter month therefore may perhaps be considered the first of the annual cycle. The number of forms known to be breeding increases thereafter month by month, reaches a high point in April and May, falls off in June, and then begins to rise again to another high point in September (when many waterfowl are nesting).

The great majority of species have a definite nesting season of fairly short duration, but some others have a very protracted one, with certain individuals breeding in the hot weather and others during the rains.

Comparatively few birds' nests have ever been found within our area; my information has been gained almost wholly from a study of gonadial condition and the collection of young birds.

MIGRATION

Hosts of migratory birds from more northern latitudes find in Thailand during even the cold weather the abundance of vegetable and insect life required by their economy; as a result, birds are more numerous, both in species and individuals, during the winter months than at any other season.

The earliest arrivals among these visitors appear late in August and early in September, and the latest stayers leave toward the end of May, but the great migratory waves, bringing most of the wintering species, appear in October and leave in March (before the individuals have assumed the nuptial plumage or have begun to sing). The provenience of our visitors cannot yet be told with any certainty, but a study of subspecific differences indicates that one large group is formed of species that breed in the mountains of northwestern Yunnan and southwestern Szechwan, while another more probably comes from notheastern China, Korea, Manchuria, and southeastern Siberia.

A form that winters on the mountains is not likely to occur also on the plains and the reverse is equally true. In certain cases, however, such as the tree pipit, birds racially indistinguishable occur commonly in both environments, and the two populations have different dates of arrival and departure. In all such cases we find that we are dealing with a form of extensive breeding range, and it is logical to assume that we are concerned with wintering populations that have come from distinct portions of that range by different routes.

In addition to normal north-south migration, we have indications of other kinds of movements among our native birds. These are:

1. The appearance of a few species, such as *Merops s. philippinus*, from farther south, apparently to breed in our provinces, since they are seen there only in summer.

2. The arrival of summer (rains) visitors to breed on marshes that have been dry during the cold and hot seasons; this type of migration is shown by many herons and rails.

3. The appearance in September, presumably from the more southern parts of Thailand, of immature green herons and night herons; these birds are present only for a short period before again disappearing.

4. The descent of individuals of numerous species in greater or smaller numbers from the mountains to the adjacent plains during the cold weather.

5. The extensive wanderings of parrots, hornbills, bulbuls, and other frugivores in accordance with the ripening of fruits and the flowering of ornithophilous trees.

FAUNISTICS

Following Boden Kloss's zoogeographical divisions for Thailand (Journ. Nat. Hist. Soc. Siam, vol. 1, 1915, pp. 250–251, map), it has been generally accepted that all Thai territory north of an east-west line at latitude 17°47′ N. belonged to a single faunal area, named by Kloss "Northern Siam." Kloss's decision was based almost entirely upon the material brought together by Gyldenstolpe during his first visit to the North; a glance at his itinerary will show that the entire collection was made in the lower parts of Phrae Province and was naturally wholly homogeneous.

My own researches have shown clearly that within Kloss's "Northern Siam" we are concerned with no less than three distinct, although related, faunas. The first of these is restricted to the territory watered by the Mae Khong and its tributaries (Chiang Rai Province); the second, to the systems of the Salwin and the Mae Ping (Mae Hong Son and Chiang Mai Provinces); the third, to the provinces drained by the Mae Wang, the Mae Yom, and the Mae Nan (Lampang, Phrae, and Nan). (Map 3.)

NORTH

The province of Chiang Rai, most northern of all Thailand, lies completely in the basin of the Mae Khong and is nothing more nor less than a purselike extension of the river valley, clearly and completely demarcated from its more southern sister-provinces by forest-clad ranges that probably at no point are lower than 3,000 to 3,500 feet.

The greater part of the province consists of great marshes and savannas, the characteristic inhabitants of which are birds, chiefly aquatic forms, that have reached their present home by way of the river from districts farther south and east and which, since the stream here leaves Thai territory temporarily, appear again in Thailand only much farther south. Among them may be mentioned *Pelecanus roseus*, *Dissoura e. episcopus*, *Xenorhynchus a. asiaticus*, *Leptoptilos dubius*, *Pseudibis p. davisoni*, and *Ploceus m. peguensis*. All are common and widely distributed on the Chiang Rai marshes but are quite unknown from other northern provinces, entry to which has been denied from the north by Chiang Rai's barrier wall of mountains, from the south by the narrow gorges through which all rivers of the Chao Phaya system flow between the northern plateau and Thailand's central plain.

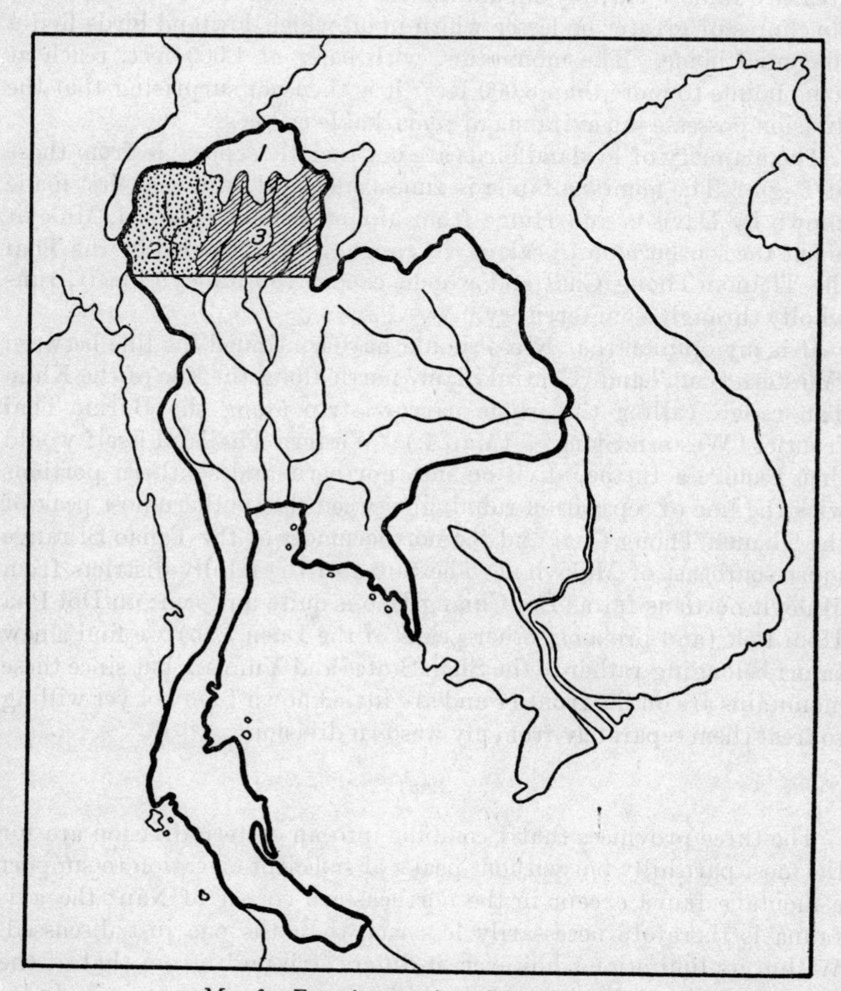

MAP 3.—Fanual areas of northern Thailand:

1. Northern division.
2. Western division.
3. Eastern division.

Chiang Rai also possesses a small number of forms that have presumably evolved in this part of the Indo-Chinese [1] peninsula and find within that province their entire *Thai* range; some of them are *Aegithina t. styani* and *Garrulax m. schauenseei*.

WEST

The two provinces that together form the western division of our area are almost entirely mountainous, but along the rivers are embouchures of greater or lesser width upon which lowland birds find a congenial home. The mountains, with bases at 1,000 feet, reach at some points to more than 8,000 feet; it is then not surprising that the division possesses an avifauna of remarkable richness.

The majority of lowland birds are not racially separable from those of Pegu. The montane fauna is almost identical with that first made known by Davison and Hume from Mount Muleyit; indeed, Muleyit is but the southernmost peak of the range, which is called by the Thai the Thanon Thong Chai and which, except for Muleyit itself, runs wholly through Thai territory.

It is my opinion that Kloss should have continued his line between "Western Siam" and "Central Siam" north along the line of the Khun Tan range, calling the whole narrow strip along the Burmo-Thai frontier "Western Siam." (Map 4.) Western Thailand itself would then require a further division into northern and southern portions with the line of separation running between the southernmost peak of the Thanon Thong Chai and the northernmost of the Tanao Si range (just southeast of Muleyit). The fauna of these hilly districts from Muleyit north as far as Doi Chiang Dao is quite uniform; on Doi Pha Hom Pok (and probably other peaks of the Daen Lao) we find a new fauna belonging rather to the Shan States and Yunnan, but since these mountains are on the frontier and are little known I am not yet willing to treat them separately from my western division.

EAST

The three provinces that I combine into an eastern division are for the most part hilly but without peaks of sufficient elevation to support a montane fauna except in the northeastern corner of Nan; the avifauna is therefore necessarily less rich than the one just discussed. Within its limitations, however, it differs strikingly from that of the western division by completely lacking many characteristic Indo-Burmese *species*, by the possession of many characteristic Indo-Chinese *species*, and by the fact that, in such species as range continuously from eastern Burma to Laos and are represented in the two

[1] I have consistently used the name Indo-China for the entire peninsula, the name Indochine for those territories governed by the French.

countries by distinct forms, we find here the Lao race. The last point is illustrated by the following list:

	W	E
Sphenurus apicauda	*apicauda*	*laotianus*
Harpactes erythrocephalus	*erythrocephalus*	*annamensis*
Picus chorolophus	*burmae*	*laotianus*
Picus flavinucha	*lylei*	*archon*
Crypsirina vagabunda	*kinneari*	*sakeratensis*
Paradoxornis gularis	*transfluvialis*	*laotiana*
Pteruthius erythropterus	*aeralatus*	*yunnanensis*
Siva castaniceps	*striata*	*torqueola*
Pomatorhinus schisticeps	*ripponi*	*humilis*
Napothera epilepidota	*bakeri*	*laotiana*
Aethopyga siparaja	*seheriae*	*cara*

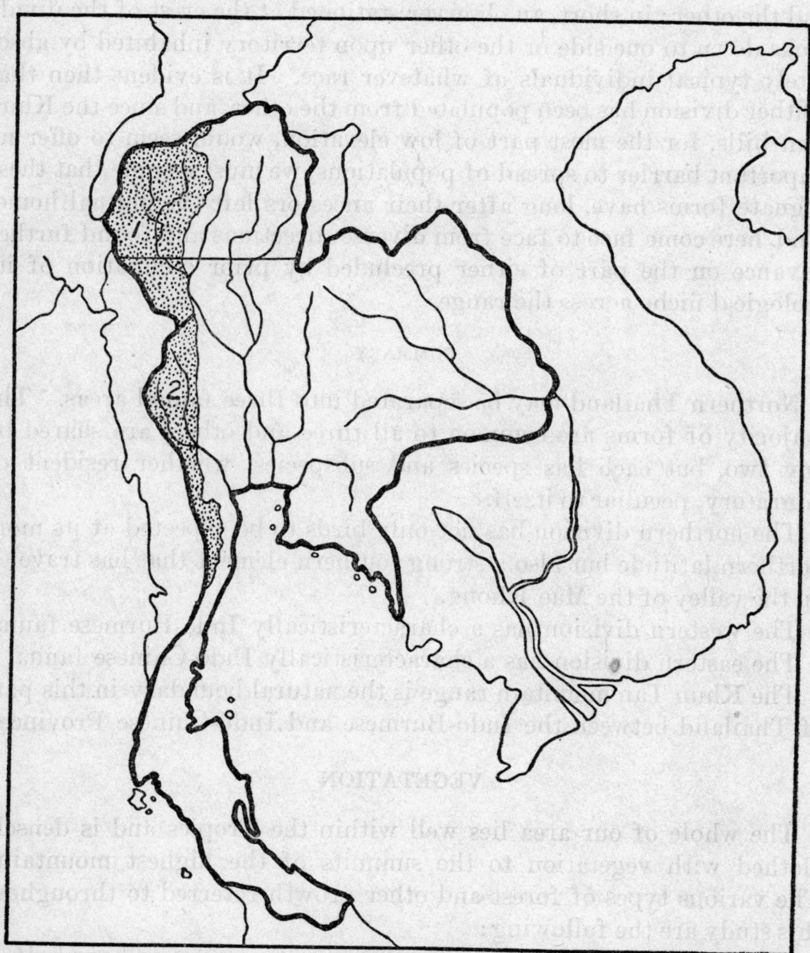

MAP 4.—Western Thailand, the Thai portion of the Indo-Burmese Province of the Indo-Chinese Subregion:

1. Northwestern Thailand.
2. Southwestern Thailand.

The dividing line between the two areas is the Khun Tan chain, which in one case may be inhabited by a western race, in another by an eastern race, and thus cannot be said definitely to belong to either division; however, since many eastern species not found at all farther west extend their range to the western foot of these mountains (*cf. Cyanops faiostricta*), they have perhaps a stronger claim to be included with the eastern provinces.

The importance of the Khun Tan range as a zoogeographical boundary between the Indo-Burmese and Indo-Chinese Provinces of the Indo-Chinese Subregion is highlighted by the interesting fact that in lowland species, distinct races of which occur right to its eastern and western bases, we find no sign of intergradation between one form and the other; in short, an observer stationed at the crest of the divide looks down to one side or the other upon territory inhabited by absolutely typical individuals of whatever race. It is evident then that neither division has been populated from the other, and since the Khun Tan hills, for the most part of low elevation, would seem to offer no important barrier to spread of populations, we must assume that these cognate forms have, long after their ancestors left the mutual homeland, here come face to face from diverse directions and found further advance on the part of either precluded by prior occupation of its ecological niche across the range.

SUMMARY

Northern Thailand may be separated into three faunal areas. The majority of forms are common to all three and others are shared by any two, but each has species and subspecies, whether resident or migratory, peculiar to itself.

The northern division has not only birds to be expected at its more northern latitude but also a strong southern element that has traveled up the valley of the Mae Khong.

The western division has a characteristically Indo-Burmese fauna.

The eastern division has a characteristically Indo-Chinese fauna.

The Khun Tan mountain range is the natural boundary in this part of Thailand between the Indo-Burmese and Indo-Chinese Provinces.

VEGETATION

The whole of our area lies well within the Tropics and is densely clothed with vegetation to the summits of the highest mountains. The various types of forest and other growth referred to throughout this study are the following:

1. *Pa daeng* ("red jungle"), an association covering perhaps half of the forested portions of all Thailand north of the Isthmus of Kra. It

is a deciduous open forest of small or medium-sized trees (the dominant species being *Shorea obtusa* and *Pentacme siamensis* of the family Dipterocarpaceae), with an abundant herbaceous undergrowth, chiefly of grasses. It is usually found at elevations below 2,500 feet on rather poor lateritic, sandy, or rocky soils. Its avifauna is limited; characteristic forms are *Picus erythropygius*, *Cyanops lineata*, and *Garrulax monileger*.

2. Mixed-deciduous, an association highly developed at low elevations in the larger valleys of our provinces, replacing *pa daeng* where the soil is richer and moister. It possesses many valuable timber trees, for the most part deciduous in hot weather; among them are the teak (*Tectona*), redwood (*Xylia*), *pradu* (*Pterocarpus*), and mango (*Mangifera*). Characteristic species of the not extensive avifauna are *Dissemurus paradiseus* and *Garrulax leucolophus*.

3. Evergreen, a forest that fits the popular conception of a tropical jungle. It contains an astonishing variety of lofty trees, often interspersed with palms, and all are bound together with rattans and other lianas. In certain parts of Nan and Chiang Rai Provinces such growth occurs in extensive stands at the lowest elevations; where water is plentiful it is the normal forest on the mountains above 3,500 feet in all the northern districts. Its avifauna is one of almost incredible richness, and scarcely a nonaquatic family fails to be represented therein.

4. Open hill-forest, an association composed almost wholly of various species of chestnuts and oaks with an undergrowth of grasses, mainly lalang (*Imperata*). It is restricted to dry mountain slopes at elevations above 3,500 feet. A characteristic bird of the limited fauna is *Prinia atrogularis*.

5. Pine forest, chiefly of *Pinus merkusii* but with some *P. khasya*; it grows on the mountains of the Thanon Thong Chai and Khun Tan ranges on dry slopes above 3,500 feet but, along the Daen Lao range, at lower elevations. The trees are widely spaced and have an undergrowth of lalang. Characteristic forms of its avifauna are such boreal types as *Mycerobas melanozanthos* and *Parus major*.

6. Bamboo brakes, which, in one species or another, cover large areas of all our provinces at any elevation. Between the dense clumps there is heavy shade and, as a result, virtually no undergrowth. Characteristic birds are *Gecinulus viridis* and *Sasia ochracea*.

The writer has frequently used the word *hai*. This refers to a tract cleared from the forest for cultivation and later, after a harvest or two, to be abandoned; in time it becomes a tangled mass of *Eupatorium*, *Rubus*, *Imperata*, and other weedy growth.

In many districts it is customary for the people to facilitate travel through the more arid types of forests by setting fire to the undergrowth after cessation of the rains; such incendiarism may result in damage to the vegetation of a wide area. Many birds collected in winter have the light portions of the plumage more or less discolored by contacts with charred wood and leaves, a fact that must always be taken into account by the taxonomist.

ACKNOWLEDGMENTS

It would be difficult indeed to give fair credit to the numerous individuals who have aided me during the more than 15 years that have passed since I first began the study of Thai ornithology. Perhaps first credit is due Charles H. Rogers, curator of the Princeton Museum of Zoology, to whom I am indebted for financial assistance in the earliest period of my collecting, and to the authorities of the United States National Museum for similar subvention during the years 1935–1937. For the gift of specimens, many of great importance, my thanks are due almost countless friends in Thailand, both Thai and European; among them I recall at once Hilda Cuniff Pontius, S. T. Queripel, W. Leigh Williams, C. J. Aagaard, T. W. Bevan, A. R. Buchanan, and the teachers and students of the Prince Royal's College. For encouragement and moral assistance in my work I am indebted to the late Dr. A. F. G. Kerr and other members of the Thailand Research Society (Siam Society); to the members of the Siam Mission of the Presbyterian Church in the U. S. A. (who ever received me hospitably in my travels throughout the Kingdom); and particularly to Dr. and Mrs. William Harris of Chiang Mai, from whom I received every opportunity to carry on my favorite studies.

Special mention must be made of the faithful and cheerful services rendered me by my collector, L. K. A. Charles (Charlie Tan), his assistant, Nai Wan, and our cook-boy, Nai Sang.

For the opportunity to visit the museums of Europe and there to examine Thai materials, I am indebted to the American Association of Museums for a grant-in-aid and to the trustees of the Walter Rathbone Bacon Traveling Scholarship for a similar grant. To my wife, Stella Leche Deignan, I am indebted not only for encouragement in my work but also for many hours spent in painstaking copying of data from the registers of the museums visited.

Ornithological material has been courteously placed at my disposal by the authorities of the following institutions:

1. Princeton Museum of Zoology, Princeton, N. J.
2. Academy of Natural Sciences of Philadelphia, Philadelphia, Pa.
3. Museum of Comparative Zoology, Cambridge, Mass.
4. American Museum of Natural History, New York, N. Y.
5. Chicago Natural History Museum, Chicago, Ill.

THE PEAK DOI CHIANG DAO, A REMARKABLE GEOLOGICAL FORMATION

A, This massive block of limestone rises more than 6,000 feet above the plain; at its summit grow representatives of such temperate genera as *Primula*, *Gentiana*, *Androsace*, *Cotoneaster*, and *Delphinium;* the type of *Garrulax e. schistaceus* was taken at the top of the peak farthest to the left. B, A hill village situated in a *hai;* the blooming plant in the foreground is *ya muang wai* (*Eupatorium odoratum*), a native of Brazil; this clump is the type locality of *Potamorhinus e. celatus*. C, View from the ridge west of the same village; in these pines were found *Parus major* and *Siphia s. aestigma.*

CHARACTERISTIC BIRD HABITATS.

A, At such cataracts as this occur *Myophonus c. eugenei*, *Enicurus schistaceus*, *Motacilla cinerea*, *Cinclus*, and the two water redstarts. B, Bamboo brakes cover great areas in northern Thailand and give shelter to a specialized fauna in which woodpeckers are prominent. C, Steep limestone hills are to be seen in one part or another of every northern province; they are without water, and their only peculiar bird is *Napothera crispifrons*.

FOREST TYPES ON DOI SUTHEP.

A, *Pa daeng* (1,500 feet), the home of *Garrulus* and *Chloropsis aurifrons*. B, Clearings in the evergreen (3,500 feet) are walled by creepers, among which *Rhopodytes* makes its squirrellike way. C, Open hill-forest of oaks and chestnuts (4,000 feet); here the mountain silver pheasant comes to feed at evening.

CHARACTERISTIC BIRD HABITATS.

A, Where evergreen meets the open hill-forest, epiphytes march along the branches, inviting sunbirds and flowerpeckers. B, In tall pines on knifelike ridges are seen *Sitta e. montium* and *Mycerobas*. C, A greenish light comes through moss-decked trees at the summit of Doi Ang Ka; in this forest live the indigo-blue shortwing and the Ang Ka green-throated sunbird.

6. Laboratory of Ornithology, Cornell University, Ithaca, N. Y.
7. Museum of Zoology, University of Michigan, Ann Arbor, Mich.
8. British Museum (Natural History), London.
9. Muséum d'Histoire Naturelle, Paris.
10. Zoologisches Museum der Universität, Berlin.
11. Naturhistoriska Riksmuseum, Stockholm.
12. Landesmuseum, Hannover.
13. Naturhistorisches Museum, Vienna.
14. Raffles Museum, Singapore.

Among the many ornithologists who have given me especial aid and advice must be mentioned Dr. Alexander Wetmore, Dr. Herbert Friedmann, and the late J. H. Riley, my colleagues at the United States National Museum; Rodolphe M. de Schauensee, of the Philadelphia Academy of Natural Sciences, who relinquished in my favor his prior claim to the investigation of northern Thai ornithology and has ever been most generous in sharing with me his discoveries; Dr. Ernst Mayr, of the American Museum of Natural History; Jean Delacour, of the New York Zoological Society, whose knowledge of Indo-Chinese birds is unexcelled; F. N. Chasen, of the Raffles Museum; Charles H. Rogers, of the Princeton Museum of Zoology; James C. Greenway, Jr., and James L. Peters, of the Museum of Comparative Zoology; the late Dr. C. B. Ticehurst, who was my host for a memorable ornithological weekend at his home in England; Sir Walter J. F. Williamson, C. M. G., of London; Count Nils Gyldenstolpe of the Riksmuseum at Stockholm; Dr. Erwin Stresemann, the renowned authority on birds at the University of Berlin.

The photographs used on plate 3 were purchased from Tanaka, a commercial photographer; the one used for plate 8, C, was taken by Kenneth E. Wells; for all others I owe thanks to David H. Dickason.

Finally, my gratitude is due those who have given me clerical help, especially Miss Hilda Schmaltz of the division of birds, United States National Museum, who has handled the trying tasks involved in preparing the final draft of my work.

ANNOTATED LIST OF BIRDS

The order of families followed in subsequent pages is almost identical with that proposed by Wetmore; the order of genera is based largely upon my personal views but, in some families, also those of Mayr and Delacour. Throughout I have been governed by conservatism in the use of generic names, by liberalism in the recognition of subspecies.

In certain cases I have been compelled to adopt the concept of the superspecies. Inasmuch as, under the rules of the International Code which has been used, no provision is made for proper nomenclatorial representation of this concept, I have everywhere used as specific name that of the earliest described section of the group; thus, considering *Sitta europaea* and *Sitta castanea* joint members of a superspecies, I have placed all races of the latter under the name *europaea.*

Order PODICIPITIFORMES

Family PODICIPITIDAE

PODICEPS RUFICOLLIS POGGEI (Reichenow)

CHINESE LITTLE GREBE

Colymbus nigricans poggei REICHENOW, Journ. für Orn., vol. 50, 1902, p. 125 (Chihli Province, China).

Podiceps ruficollis capensis, DE SCHAUENSEE, Proc. Acad. Nat. Sci. Philadelphia, 1929, p. 588 (Chiang Mai).—DEIGNAN, Journ. Siam Soc. Nat. Hist. Suppl., 1931, p. 174 (Chiang Mai).

Poliocephalus ruficollis capensis, DEIGNAN, Journ. Siam Soc. Nat. Hist. Suppl., 1936, p. 72 (Chiang Mai).

This species is a locally common resident in the northern provinces but may be absent from some districts during the months of drought.

The grebe is a shy and wary little bird, haunting small lakes and large ponds where open water is bounded by dense stands of rushes and sedges and where aquatic plants grow so thickly beneath the surface that passage is impossible for man or boat. At such places it may often be found in numbers, swimming about in pairs or small parties. At the least alarm it moves rapidly toward the nearest reeds, sinks out of sight, or scuds away over the water before diving headlong. A shot is sufficient to cause every grebe within hearing to vanish, after which heads cautiously reappear at quite different places or the birds come up behind the vegetation and are not seen again. Owing to its short wings and weak feet, the grebe can arise from water only after running across the surface, and on land it is helpless. A female collected by me at Chiang Mai in December 1931 had alighted upon a pool so small that it was unable to escape and was easily captured by hand.

Of the breeding season in our area nothing definite is known, but in the neighborhood of Chiang Mai birds in nuptial plumage may be seen from August to March, and during these months the love song of the species is heard frequently from the reed beds.

A female in breeding dress had the irides yellow; the maxilla black, with a small light-brown mark at the middle on each side, the extreme tip pale gray; the mandible black, mottled toward the base with light brown, beneath light green, the extreme tip pale gray; the rictus light yellow; the outer side of the tarsi black, the inner side olive mottled with black; the toes black, with olive lobes; the soles black; the claws horny black, tipped horny white.

The grebe is a swimming bird (smaller than any Thai duck) which is apparently tailless and has a pointed bill. In nuptial dress it has the entire upperparts dark brown; a conspicuous white area in the outspread wing; the chin blackish; the throat and foreneck rufous; the remaining underparts silvery white, more or less mixed, especially on the sides of the body, with dark brown. In the nonbreeding season the rufous disappears from the neck.

Birds from our provinces agree perfectly with a topotype of *poggei*.

Order PELECANIFORMES

Family PELECANIDAE

PELECANUS ROSEUS Gmelin

SPOTTED-BILLED PELICAN

[*Pelecanus*] *roseus* GMELIN, Systema naturae, vol. 1, pt. 2, 1789, p. 570 (Manila, Luzón, P. I.).

Pelecanus philippensis, GYLDENSTOLPE, Kungl. Svenska Vet.-Akad. Handl., 1916, p. 132 (Chiang Rai, Chiang Saen) ; Ibis, 1920, p. 776 ("Northern Siam").

This species has been reported from our area only by Gyldenstolpe, who says he found it several times during the summer of 1914 on the lakelike swamps near Chiang Rai and Chiang Saen. Besides the two specimens he lists from Chiang Rai, there is a third in the museum at Stockholm, taken at Chiang Saen, August 10, 1914.

I have visited the same localities in May, shortly before the beginning of the rains, when the lakes were greatly reduced in area, and failed to see anything of these birds, which makes it seem probable that the pelican is merely a seasonal visitor, arriving from farther south by way of the Mae Khong valley. It is not likely to occur at all in the other northern provinces.

The pelican is a huge, short-legged, large-billed swimming bird, which can be confused with no other in northern Thailand. It has the body plumage largely white; the primaries and primary coverts blackish; the secondaries, scapulars, and tail silvery brown; the bill flesh-colored on the basal half, otherwise orange, with a row of blackish spots on each side near the commissure.

Family PHALACROCORACIDAE

PHALACROCORAX CARBO SINENSIS (Blumenbach)

CHINESE CORMORANT

Pelecanus sinensis BLUMENBACH, Abbildungen naturhistorischer Gegenstände, Heft 3, 1798, pl. 25 and text (China).

The Chinese cormorant is known from our area only along the Mae Khong from Chiang Saen to Chiang Khong, where Delacour and Greenway found it in small numbers (L'Oiseau et la Revue Française d'Ornithologie, 1940, p. 25). It is not likely to occur on the smaller rivers of the North.

From the little cormorant this species may always be known by its much greater size. The adult is black and in nuptial plumage has white filaments upon the head and neck and a broad patch of white on each flank. The immature bird has the upperparts brown and the underparts largely white.

PHALACROCORAX NIGER (Vieillot)

LITTLE CORMORANT

Hydrocorax niger VIEILLOT, Nouv. Dict. Hist. Nat., nouv. éd., vol. 8, 1817, p. 88 (East Indies=Bengal, *apud* Peters).

Phalacrocorax javanicus, GYLDENSTOLPE, Kungl. Svenska Vet.-Akad. Handl., 1913, p. 71 (Mae Raem).

Phalacrocorax pygmaeus javanicus, GYLDENSTOLPE, Kungl. Svenska Vet.-Akad. Handl., 1916, p. 133 ("Northern Siam"); Ibis, 1920, p. 775 ("Along the rivers and creeks of northern Siam").

Phalacrocorax niger, DEIGNAN, Journ. Siam. Soc. Nat. Hist. Suppl., 1931, p. 172 (Chiang Mai); 1936, p. 72 (Chiang Mai).

All specimens of this bird are from the provinces of Chiang Mai and Lampang, but it may be expected to occur at suitable places anywhere in our area at one season or another. At Chiang Mai it is a rare visitor to the ponds and marshes from July to December, after which month there is not enough water for its needs. During the cold weather I have found it near Ban Tha Nong Luang and have collected it on the Mae Klang, a mountain torrent, at the foot of Doi Ang Ka, where it is seen regularly in winter.

The little cormorant is rather an inactive species, perching quietly, often with outspread wings, upon snags or stakes that jut out of the water. On the Mae Klang it occurred in small flocks, which rested on rocks and boulders in the stream for some hundreds of feet up the mountain slope. It swims low in the water and is an expert diver.

Cormorants are short-legged, long-necked waterfowl with a comparatively long, hooked bill. The adult of the present species has the plumage black, with silver-gray about the shoulders; in nonbreeding dress it has a white patch on the upper throat at the base of the bill. Immature birds have the plumage brown, with the underparts largely white. From the Chinese cormorant this form may be known by its lesser size and by the fact that it is the only species likely to be found on small ponds and streams.

Family ANHINGIDAE

ANHINGA RUFA MELANOGASTER Pennant

INDIAN DARTER

Anhinga melanogaster PENNANT, Indian zoology, 1769, pp. 13–14, pl. 12 (Ceylon and Java).

Plotus melanogaster, GYLDENSTOLPE, Kungl. Svenska Vet.-Akad. Handl., 1916, p. 133 (Nong Mae Rua, Mae Kok river) ; Ibis, 1920, p. 775 ("Throughout the whole country").

Anhinga melanogaster, DEIGNAN, Journ. Siam. Soc. Nat. Hist. Suppl., 1936, p. 132 (Ban Tha Nong Luang).

Although it has been recorded from but few localities, the darter may be expected to occur in any of our provinces. Gyldenstolpe found it very common at Mae Rua, a few miles southwest of Chiang Saen, and saw it also along the Mae Kok and other rivers. I observed one at Nong Luang, below Chom Thong, in December 1935, and collected a female at Muang Ngop, on the upper Mae Nan, in April 1936.

The darter lives at marshes edged by trees or along rivers with forested banks; at such places it may be found perched upon a snag or a branch overhanging the water, often with its wings outspread in the manner of a cormorant. It sometimes swims with the body submerged and only the head and neck protruding from the water. In flight it bears a marked resemblance to a cormorant but may always be recognized by a peculiar kink near the middle of the neck.

A specimen taken by Gyldenstolpe had the irides brownish yellow; the bill yellowish green, with the culmen horn; the feet brownish yellow.

The darter is similar to a cormorant but has a sharp, pointed bill and a longer, more slender neck. Our species has the head and neck light brown; the chin and throat and a streak from the eye down the side of the upper neck, white; the body black, with the scapulars and a conspicuous shoulder area silvery gray. The tail is comparatively long and, in flight, is spread like a fan.

Order CICONIIFORMES

Family ARDEIDAE

ARDEA CINEREA RECTIROSTRIS Gould

EASTERN GRAY HERON

Ardea rectirostris GOULD, Proc. Zool. Soc. London, 1843, p. 22 (New South Wales, error; Stone suggests "=India?," Austral Avian Rec., vol. 1, 1913, p. 142).

Ardea cinerea jouyi, GYLDENSTOLPE, Kungl. Svenska Vet.-Akad. Handl., 1916, p. 136 (Nong Mae Rua).—DE SCHAUENSEE, Proc. Acad. Nat. Sci. Philadelphia, 1929, p. 586 (Chiang Saen) ; 1934, p. 279 (Chiang Mai).

Ardea cinerea rectirostris, DEIGNAN, Journ. Siam Soc. Nat. Hist. Suppl., 1931, p. 173 (Chiang Mai) ; 1936, p. 72 (Chiang Mai).

The status of this species is uncertain; it is probably chiefly a winter visitor, but a few birds, perhaps sterile individuals, seem to pass the summer in our region. I found it rather common at Chiang Mai from October 19 (1931) to March 29 (1929) but have also seen it there as early as September 23 (1936) and as late as May 26 (1930). Gyldenstolpe took a specimen at Mae Rua, August 7, 1914. I have collected it on the Salwin, at Thattafang, October 16, 1936, and on the Mae Ping, just above Chom Thong, November 23, 1935. A bird in the collection of Cornell University was taken by Vijjakich at Lampang, in April 1929.

The gray heron is a solitary species, which may be seen at sloughs in the ricefields, on the marshes, at the edge of woodland ponds, and on the sandbars of the great rivers. Specimens whose stomachs I examined had been feeding on fishes.

Members of the heron family may be recognized in flight at any distance by the deliberate strokes of their broad wings, the long legs extending behind beyond the tail, and by their carrying the head drawn back and resting over the lower neck. The present species is the largest of the northern herons and in the field appears generally dark gray; it has the neck and underparts white with some black markings and a long, black crest of narrow feathers. Immature birds, which are commoner than adults, are colored more brownish gray.

ARDEA PURPUREA MANILENSIS Meyen

EASTERN PURPLE HERON

Ardea purpurea var. *manilensis* MEYEN, Observationes zoologicae in itinere circum terram institutae, *in* Nova Acta Academiae Caesareae Leopoldino-Carolinae Naturae Curiosorum, vol. 16, suppl. 1, 1834, pp. 102–103 (Manila, P. I.).

Pyrrherodias manillensis, GYLDENSTOLPE, Kungl. Svenska Vet.-Akad. Handl., 1916, p. 136 ("Northern Siam").

Ardea purpurea manillensis, DEIGNAN, Journ. Siam Soc. Nat. Hist. Suppl., 1931. p. 173 (Chiang Mai) ; 1936, p. 73 (Chiang Mai).

The paucity of records for the purple heron is no doubt due to the absence of observers from its haunts during the rainy season. Gyldenstolpe considered it fairly common on "the swamps of northern Siam" (presumably Chiang Rai Province), sometimes in the ricefields, but usually in swamps overgrown with reeds. I found it only in very small numbers on the large marshes south of Chiang Mai from September 5 to November 12. On the lake at Phayao, August 24, 1929, I flushed a single bird from a stand of tall reeds.

It is a much wilder bird than the gray heron and is not likely to be seen near human habitations.

The purple heron is second in size only to the preceding species, from which it may be readily distinguished by its having the head, neck, and underparts largely rufous or buff; adults have the back and wings gray, but immature specimens have the feathers of these parts broadly margined with rufous.

BUTORIDES STRIATUS AMURENSIS von Schrenck

AMUR GREEN HERON

[*Ardea* (*Butorides*) *veriscens*] var. *amurensis* VON SCHRENCK, Reise and Forschungen in Amur-lande, vol. 1, pt. 2, 1860, p. 441 (Amurland).

The Amur green heron occurs in North Thailand as an uncommon winter visitor. I have three specimens that may be attributed to this northern form: An immature female from the foot of Doi Mae Kong Ka, October 10, 1936, an adult female from Ban Muang Sum, December 27, 1936; and an adult male from the Mae Klang Waterfall, February 11, 1937. The flattened wing of each of these birds measures about 198 mm.

All my examples were taken at mountain torrents, in wild and uninhabited country.

The Amur green heron can be distinguished from the other races occurring in our area only by its wing length, which ranges from 195 to 215 mm.

BUTORIDES STRIATUS ACTOPHILUS Oberholser

SOUTH CHINA GREEN HERON

Butorides javanicus actophilus OBERHOLSER, Smithsonian Misc. Coll., vol. 60, No. 7, 1912, p. 1 (North Pagi Island, off the western coast of Sumatra).

Butorides javanica, GYLDENSTOLPE, Kungl. Svenska Vet.-Akad. Handl., 1916, p. 137 (Tha Chomphu).

Butorides striatus javanica [*partim*], GYLDENSTOLPE, Ibis, 1920, p. 769 ("Northern districts").

Gyldenstolpe reported seeing three green herons along the Mae Tha, near Tha Champhu, one of which, in fully adult plumage, was collected, May 4, 1914. Since the wing of this specimen measured 186 mm., it must be attributed to this race. I place here also two unsexed, undated skins taken by Eisenhofer at Khun Tan, which are in the museum at Stockholm and which have wings of 185 and 186 mm.

While no other examples have been collected in our area, I believe this heron is a rather rare resident in the northern provinces. I have more than once, during the summer months, seen green herons, which probably belonged to this race, along quiet jungle streams, but did not then realize the importance of taking a specimen.

Gyldenstolpe records that his bird had the irides yellow, the maxilla black, the mandible yellowish green, the feet and toes yellowish brown.

The South China green heron, like the preceding form, is distinguishable only by its wing length, which ranges from 180 to 195 mm.

Mayr suggests (Emu, vol. 43, 1943, pp. 11–12) that the Chinese forms of the green heron never reach Sumatra in winter and that the name *actophilus* must be synonymized with that of some race resident in the Malaysian islands. If his view be correct, the bird here discussed will be known as *Butorides striatus connectens* Stresemann (Orn. Monatsb., vol. 38, 1930, pp. 48–49).

BUTORIDES STRIATUS JAVANICUS (Horsfield)

Javanese Green Heron

Ardea Javanica Horsfield, Trans. Linn. Soc. London, vol. 13, 1821, p. 190 (Java).

Butorides striatus javanicus, de Schauensee, Proc. Acad. Nat. Sci. Philadelphia, 1929, p. 587 (Chiang Mai).—Deignan, Journ. Siam Soc. Nat. Hist. Suppl., 1931, p. 173 (Chiang Mai); 1936, p. 73 (Chiang Mai).

This form of the green heron appears in small numbers in the northern provinces at the end of the rains, apparently as a result of a northward movement after breeding in more southern districts. A similar phenomenon has been observed in numerous species of herons in other parts of the world.

At Chiang Mai it is found along the river and occasionally at sloughs in the ricefields, from September 20 to October 16; an exceptionally late bird was taken by de Schauensee, January 2, 1929. I have one specimen which was collected at Thattafang, October 11, 1936. All northern examples which I have examined have been birds of the year; their wing length varied from 174 to 180 mm.

This seems to be the only green heron likely to occur in settled districts and along the large rivers. On the Mae Ping I used to find it settled quietly on rocks and snags under the shelter of the high banks, where it was difficult to observe except from a boat. When disturbed, it utters a loud squawk and flaps slowly and low over the water to a similar hiding place farther along the stream.

Immature specimens taken by me had the irides yellow; the eyelids greenish yellow; the lores yellow-green; the maxilla black, with a greenish-yellow patch under each nostril; the mandible yellowish green, with the upper half black at the base; the feet and toes greenish yellow; the soles yellow; the claws horn.

This is a small, squat heron, which sits with its head drawn in so that it seems to have no neck. It has the crown and a long crest black; the neck and underparts gray; the upperparts chiefly a bronzed green, which may look bluish in the field. Immature specimens appear largely brownish gray. The wing length of the present subspecies ranges from 165 to 180 mm.

ARDEOLA BACCHUS (Bonaparte)

CHINESE POND HERON

B[uphus] bacchus BONAPARTE, Conspectus generum avium, vol. 2, 1855, p. 127 (Malay Peninsula).

Ardeola grayii, GYLDENSTOLPE, Ibis, 1920, p. 769 ("Throughout the whole country").—DE SCHAUENSEE, Proc. Acad. Nat. Sci. Philadelphia, 1928, p. 578 (Chiang Mai); 1929, p. 587 (Mae Rim).—DEIGNAN, Journ. Siam Soc. Nat. Hist. Suppl., 1931, p. 173 (Chiang Mai); 1936, p. 73 (Chiang Mai).

Ardeola bacchus, GYLDENSTOLPE, Kungl. Svenska Vet.-Akad. Handl., 1913, p. 73 (Den Chai); Journ. Nat. Hist. Soc. Siam, 1915, p. 236 (listed); Kungl. Svenska Vet.-Akad. Handl., 1916, p. 138 (Pha Kho); Ibis, 1920, p. 769 ("Northern Siam").—DEIGNAN, Journ. Siam Soc. Nat. Hist. Suppl., 1931, p. 173 (Chiang Mai); 1936, p. 73 (Chiang Mai).

This is one of the commonest and most familiar of northern birds, occurring anywhere in the lowlands at some time of the year: on the ricefields or the marshes, along streams both large and small, in roadside ditches, at wet places in the deciduous forests, and even for some distance up the mountain slopes along the wider torrents. In addition to the localities listed above, there are definite records for Khun Tan (six specimens without data in Stockholm, taken by Eisenhofer); for Wiang Pa Pao, where I saw it in April, 1929; for Phayao, where I observed it, August 28, 1929; and for Ban Pak Li, a village on the Nan river, where I took a specimen, April 7, 1937.

The seasonal movements of this bird require further study. At Chiang Mai, where alone continuous observations have been made over a period of years, the species is rare or absent from March to August, the very time when water is most plentiful and other herons are most numerous. Since these are the months when it wears full nuptial plumage, it is clear that it goes elsewhere, perhaps farther north, to breed. All my specimens had the gonads inactive, with the sole exception of a female, taken April 9, which had the ovaries slightly enlarged.

Examples collected by me had the irides deep golden-yellow; the eyelids edged bright yellow; the orbital skin and lores yellow-green, sometimes with a blackish mark in front of the eye; the culmen and a diagonal line from its base to the corner of the mouth black; the maxilla yellow, tipped black; the mandible with the basal half bluish green, the rest yellow, except for a black patch on each side near the tip; the tarsi bright yellow-green, more yellow behind; the toes bright yellow-green; the soles bright yellow; the claws horny brown, tinged olive or yellowish at the tips.

The pond heron is the well-known brown bird with streaked head and neck that roosts on the bamboos or sits hunched up at the margin of some wet place, often invisible until it startles the observer by flying up with a squawk and a flashing of pure white wings. In nuptial plumage, which will be less often seen, it has the head and neck dark chestnut, the back covered with dark slaty-blue plumes.

Despite numerous reports of *Ardeola grayii* in North Thailand, the actual occurrence of this species must be held very doubtful. Upon examining the specimens upon which the records have been based, I have discovered that they are, without exception, birds in nonbreeding dress, and I have found no satisfactory criteria that serve to distinguish between *grayii* and *bacchus* in this plumage. Moreover, every specimen in full or partial nuptial plumage is obviously *bacchus*. My own records for *grayii* were based upon a misunderstanding of what constitutes the breeding dress and are hereby withdrawn.

BUBULCUS IBIS COROMANDUS (Boddaert)

Eastern Cattle Egret

Cancroma Coromanda Boddaert, Table des planches eluminéez d'histoire naturelle, 1783, p. 54 (Coromandel, *ex* D'Aubenton, pl. 910).

Bubulcus coromandus, Gyldenstolpe, Kungl. Svenska Vet.-Akad. Handl., 1916, p. 139 (Chiang Rai); Ibis, 1920, p. 769 ("Throughout the whole country").

Bubulcus ibis coromandus, Deignan, Journ. Siam Soc. Nat. Hist. Suppl., 1931, p. 173 (Chiang Mai); 1936, p. 73 (Chiang Mai).

The cattle egret is common and generally distributed throughout the northern lowlands, but appears to be only a winter visitor. At Chiang Mai it arrives in numbers about August 9 and finally disappears about April 12. Gyldenstolpe collected a specimen at Chiang Rai, August 15, 1914; I saw flocks at Phayao, August 28, 1929, and took an example at Ban Mae Mo, August 22, 1936. Our birds may come in from southern China, as true migrants, but more probably reach our districts as northward wanderers from southern Thailand, where this species is known to breed in many localities. The specimen from Mae Mo is a male in worn nuptial plumage, and many birds in nuptial dress may be seen in March, but the great majority will be in the pure white nonbreeding plumage.

The cattle egret has habits that make it less dependent upon the presence of water than any other of our herons, and it does not usually like to get more than its toes wet. At the edge of the marshes and in damp pastures, where the buffaloes are turned out to graze, flocks of these beautiful birds may be seen, stalking about among the cattle and frequently resting upon their backs in pursuit of insects frightened up by the herd. A specimen taken at Chiang Mai had the stomach distended with grasshoppers.

The irides are light yellow; the orbital region olive-green; the lores pale dull orange; the bill yellow, with the extreme tip and basal half of the culmen horny; the feet, toes, and claws black; the soles dull olive-green.

In nuptial plumage this species is unmistakable, having the head, neck, and long dorsal plumes orange-buff and the remainder of the plumage pure white. In nonbreeding dress the whole bird is white and is then likely to be confused with other, similar species. From the large and intermediate egrets it may be known by its lesser size, thicker neck, and shorter bill; from the little egret by the different colors of bill and feet.

EGRETTA ALBA MODESTA (J. E. Gray)

INDIAN LARGE EGRET

Ardea modesta, J. E. GRAY, Zoological miscellany, 1831, pp. 19–20 (India).

Herodias alba, GYLDENSTOLPE, Kungl. Svenska Vet.-Akad. Handl., 1916, p. 137 ("Northern Siam").

Herodias alba modesta, GYLDENSTOLPE, Ibis, 1920, p. 168 ("Throughout Siam").

Egretta alba modesta, DEIGNAN, Journ. Siam Soc. Nat. Hist. Suppl., 1931, p. 173 (Chiang Mai).

Casmerodius albus modestus, DEIGNAN, Journ. Siam Soc. Nat. Hist. Suppl., 1936, p. 73 (Chiang Mai).

Although this egret is probably common and generally distributed throughout the northern provinces, the only specimen known from our area is a male in nonbreeding plumage collected by me at Ban Hat Sam Khwae, on the Nan river, April 8, 1837.

At Chiang Mai a bird that was either this species or the intermediate egret was found every month in the year but was rather rare during the driest period. In the rainy season, however, it became very common, and hundreds could be seen at once on the large marshes between Chiang Mai and Lamphun.

In nuptial plumage this largest of the white herons wears long, filamentous dorsal plumes, which extend some inches beyond the tail; it has the bill, feet, and toes black. In nonbreeding dress the plumes are shed and the bill becomes yellow; in this plumage it can be distinguished from the intermediate egret only by shooting and measuring the specimen. *E. a. modesta* has the wing length over 350 mm. and the length of tarsus over 160; *E. i. intermedia* has the wing under 350 mm. and the tarsus under 150.

EGRETTA GARZETTA GARZETTA (Linnaeus)

INDIAN LITTLE EGRET

[*Ardea*] *Garzetta* LINNAEUS, Systema naturae, ed. 12, vol. 1, 1766, p. 237 ("in Oriente," *ex* Brisson).

Egretta garzetta garzetta, DEIGNAN, Journ. Siam Soc. Nat. Hist. Suppl., 1931, p. 173 (Chiang Mai); 1936, p. 73 (Chiang Mai).

This is a common bird at Chiang Mai and probably is equally so in other districts. The only specimen known from the North is a female in nuptial plumage collected by me at Chiang Mai, May 24, 1935. The ovaries were not enlarged.

Like the large egret, this species becomes rare or absent during the season of drought and returns in great numbers during the rains. It is then generally distributed over the countryside, occurring not only on the marshes but also in the ricefields and even along the irrigation canals beside the highways.

My specimen had the irides yellow; the eyelids yellowish green, edged bright yellow; the lores yellowish green; the bill black, with the basal half of the mandible plumbeous-white; the feet black; the toes greenish yellow; the soles yellow; the claws yellowish horn.

The little egret, in nuptial livery, wears a white crest, breast plumes, and dorsal plumes extending beyond the tail, all of which are lost after the breeding season. It is the smallest of the pure white herons and is easily recognized by its blackish bill and its greenish-yellow toes (which are conspicuous when it takes to flight).

EGRETTA INTERMEDIA INTERMEDIA (Wagler)

INDIAN INTERMEDIATE EGRET

A[*rdea*] *intermedia* WAGLER, Isis, 1829, p. 659 (Java).

Egretta intermedia intermedia, DE SCHAUENSEE, Proc. Acad. Nat. Sci. Philadelphia, 1929, p. 587 (Chiang Saen).

Mesophoyx intermedia intermedia, DEIGNAN, Journ. Siam Soc. Nat. Hist. Suppl., 1936, p. 73 (Chiang Mai).

The intermediate egret may be common throughout our area, but there are few definite records. De Schauensee took a specimen at Chiang Saen, January 10, 1929; I collected a male at Chiang Mai, October 17, 1931, and another male, in full nuptial plumage, at Chiang Rai, January 27, 1937.

The Chiang Mai specimen had the irides light yellow; the orbital region and lores bright yellow; the bill yellow, with maxilla tipped horny brown; the feet, toes, and claws black.

This species, in nuptial dress, wears ornamental plumes upon the upper breast, as well as long dorsal plumes. In the nonbreeding season the aigrettes are lost, and it becomes indistinguishable in life from the large egret.

NYCTICORAX NYCTICORAX NYCTICORAX (Linnaeus)

EURASIAN NIGHT HERON

[*Ardea*] *Nycticorax* LINNAEUS, Systema naturae, ed. 10, vol. 1, 1758, pp. 142–143 ("in Europa australi").

Nycticorax nycticorax nycticorax, DEIGNAN, Journ. Siam Soc. Nat. Hist. Suppl., 1931, p. 173 (Chiang Mai); 1936, p. 74 (Chiang Mai).—DE SCHAUENSEE, Proc. Acad. Nat. Sci. Philadelphia, 1934, p. 279 (Chiang Mai).

The status of this bird is uncertain; at Chiang Mai it appears to be an uncommon winter visitor from late in August to the beginning of February, but the only other northern locality where it has been found is Ban Hat La, on the Nan river, where I took an adult pair, April 8, 1937. Chiang Mai specimens are usually immature and may be wanderers from breeding localities farther south.

The night heron is almost completely nocturnal, spending the daylight hours concealed at the heart of some dense clump of giant bamboo and venturing forth at dusk to feed along the river or at marshy spots in the ricefields. I frequently saw it over the Mae Ping at Chiang Mai, flapping heavily through the gathering darkness, and often heard its loud squawk falling from the sky, even above the streets of the town.

An immature female from Chiang Mai had the irides golden-orange; the orbital skin and lores green; the maxilla black with a green streak along the side; the mandible green, tipped blackish; the rictus greenish yellow; the feet and toes green, bright yellow behind the upper tarsal joint; the soles bright yellow; the claws horny brown, with apical half black. Adults differ chiefly in having the irides blood red.

The head of this species seems to be disproportionately large, and the neck is short and thick. Old birds have the crown, nuchal crest, and back black, with a greenish gloss; the wings and tail gray; the underparts gray or white; sometimes two or three long, narrow, white feathers in the crest. Immature examples are quite different in appearance: above they are brown streaked with whitish (on the wings the streaks are enlarged to conspicuous spots) and below whitish streaked with brown.

GORSACHIUS MELANOLOPHUS MELANOLOPHUS (Raffles)

SUMATRAN BLACK-CRESTED TIGER BITTERN

Ardea melanolopha RAFFLES, Trans. Linn. Soc. London, vol. 13, 1822, p. 326 (Sumatra; type locality restricted to Benkulan, by Kinnear and Robinson, Bull. Brit. Orn. Club, vol. 47, 1927, p. 130).

Gorsachius melanolophus, WILLIAMSON, Journ. Nat. Hist. Soc. Siam, 1918, p. 41 (Phrae).—GYLDENSTOLPE, Ibis, 1920, p. 768 ("Northern Siam").

The tiger bittern seems to be a bird of extreme rarity in the northern provinces, and Williamson's specimen, a female collected at Phrae in May, 1916, constitutes the sole record. If the species is really a resident of the North, rather than a mere straggler, it should be expected to occur in Nan Province also.

This is a nocturnal species that lives in dense evergreen forest. In coloration it looks something like a huge cinnamon bittern (*Ixobrychus cinnamomeus*). It has a long black crest; the upperparts cinnamon, vermiculated everywhere with wavy, black bars; the tail and a large area near the tip of the wing black; the underparts rufous, mottled with black and buff.

IXOBRYCHUS SINENSIS SINENSIS (Gmelin)

CHINESE YELLOW BITTERN

[*Ardea*] *Sinensis* GMELIN, Systema naturae, vol. 1, pt. 2, 1789, pp. 642–643 (China, *ex* Latham).

Ardetta sinensis, GYLDENSTOLPE, Kungl. Svenska Vet.-Akad. Handl., 1916, p. 139 (Chiang Rai).

Ixobrychus sinensis, GYLDENSTOLPE, Ibis, 1920, p. 769 ("Throughout Siam").

Ixobrychus sinensis sinensis, DEIGNAN, Journ. Siam Soc. Nat. Hist. Suppl., 1931, p. 173 (Chiang Mai); 1936, p. 74 (Chiang Mai).

The yellow bittern appears in numbers during the rains and is probably found at that season throughout the northern provinces. I considered it common on the large marshes between Chiang Mai and Lamphun, but rare in the ricefields, from June 28 to October 13. Gyldenstolpe found it not uncommon in August in the neighborhood of Chiang Rai. It occurs sporadically during the cold weather at suitably wet places, for an immature specimen was brought to me at Chiang Mai, January 17, 1936, and I myself saw two or three at a small marsh near the town between January 30 and February 11, 1936. I have also taken an immature bird at Ban Pa Som, on the Nan river just south of our limits, April 9, 1937.

This tiny heron is said to be largely nocturnal in habits, but I found it active enough during the dark, cloudy days of the rainy season and easy to flush by walking along the elevated bunds which border the marshes. It hides among the sedges and, when not actually in motion, is extraordinarily well concealed among the lanceolate leaves. It may try to escape observation by climbing quietly away through the reeds or may fly a short distance across the marsh to vanish again into thick cover.

Gyldenstolpe noted that his specimens had the irides yellow; the bill yellowish green, with culmen brown; the feet and toes yellowish green.

The cinnamon bittern will be found at the same places as the present species, but there is no need to confuse them, for the latter wholly lacks the cinnamon hue. The adult has the top of the head black;

the upperparts light vinaceous-brown; the tail black; the underparts pale buff; the wing coverts buff and the apical half of the wing black. The immature is streaked above and below with rufous and buff, but, like the adult, is recognizable by the distinctive wing pattern.

IXOBRYCHUS EURHYTHMUS (Swinhoe)

VON SCHRENCK'S BITTERN

Ardetta eurhythma SWINHOE, Ibis, 1873, p. 74, pl. 2 (Amoy and Shanghai, China).
Ixobrychus eurhythmus, DEIGNAN, Journ. Siam. Soc. Nat. Hist. Suppl., 1936, p. 169 (Ban Mai Tong Hong).

Von Schrenck's bittern is a species that breeds in Japan and northern China and winters in the Malay Peninsula and the Malaysian islands; its main migration route is coastal. The only specimen known from the interior of Thailand is a female taken by me, May 2, 1936, near Ban Mai Tong Hong, a village near Muang Thoeng. Whether this unexpected occurrence signifies that the species regularly migrates in small numbers up the valley of the Mae Khong, or whether my bird was merely a straggler, cannot yet be decided.

The specimen was collected beside what seemed to be an abandoned gem pit in the midst of an extensive mixed-deciduous forest—a highly improbable place for a member of this genus.

The male is entirely dark chestnut above and buff below. The wing pattern is like that of *sinensis*, but the apical half of the wing is dark gray rather than black and the inner primaries and outer secondaries are narrowly tipped with white. The female has the upperparts dark chestnut, conspicuously spotted with white on back and wings, and the underparts buff, streaked with blackish.

IXOBRYCHUS CINNAMOMEUS (Gmelin)

CINNAMON BITTERN

[*Ardea*] *cinnamomea* GMELIN, Systema naturae, vol. 1, pt. 2, 1789, pp. 643–644 (China).
Ardetta cinnamomea, GYLDENSTOLPE, Journ. Nat. Hist. Soc. Siam, 1915, p. 236 (Khun Tan); Kungl. Svenska Vet.-Akad. Handl., 1916, p. 139 (Chiang Rai).
Ixobrychus cinnamomeus, DEIGNAN, Journ. Siam Soc. Nat. Hist. Suppl., 1931, p. 173 (Chiang Mai); 1936, p. 74 (Chiang Mai).

At Chiang Mai this heron appears about the middle of January and thereafter is common (even abundant during the rains) until about October 23. Gyldenstolpe found it very common about Chiang Rai in August 1914, and I saw many at Phayao between August 24 and 28, 1929. An undated specimen in Stockholm was collected by Eisenhofer at Khun Tan. I have taken it at Ban Pang Ai, July 23, 1935; at Ban Huai Som, March 29, 1937; at Doi Ta Kong, June 1,

1936. Although the bird is evidently common in all our provinces at some time during the year, there is still no record for its presence in November and December anywhere in the North.

The cinnamon bittern is found not only on the larger marshes, but everywhere in the paddy-fields and even at the tiniest pools after the countryside begins to dry up. At Chiang Mai I have frequently seen it flying low over the city streets.

While it has not yet been found breeding in our area, I have no doubt that it nests with us during the summer months. I took a male with the testes enlarged May 5, and specimens with the gonads greatly enlarged were collected on May 21 and 31, June 28, and July 2 and 3.

I witnessed a courtship performance May 30, 1930: the male flew slowly before the female with slow, stiff wing beats, calling *ek—ek—ek*, then perched at the top of a low tree and sang *gook-gook-gook-gook-gook-gook-gook-gook*, with each of the first five notes louder than the one before it, and the last three pitched three or four tones lower.

My birds had the irides golden-yellow; the eyelids, orbital region, and lores light green or greenish yellow; the culmen black (sometimes horny brown at the base), the rest of the maxilla horny brown, the commissure edged bright yellow; the mandible yellow, the commissure edged horny brown; the tibiae and tarsi light green, bright yellow behind; the toes light green; the soles bright yellow; the claws horny brown or greenish horn.

The adult male is entirely cinnamon-colored, paler below and usually with a blackish mesial stripe from the base of the bill to the upper abdomen; there is a streak of pure white at each side of the throat. Adult females and immature birds have the upperparts dark brown, with many obsolescent buffy bars and spots and the underparts buffy, everywhere heavily streaked with blackish. Any example of this species may readily be known by its having the apical half of the wing cinnamon, not black or dark gray.

DUPETOR FLAVICOLLIS FLAVICOLLIS (Latham)

INDIAN BLACK BITTERN

[*Ardea*] *flavicollis* LATHAM, Index ornithologicus, vol. 2, 1790, p. 701 (India).

Dupetor flavicollis, GYLDENSTOLPE, Kungl. Svenska Vet.-Akad. Handl., 1913, p. 73 (Ban Huai Hom).

Dupetor flavicollis flavicollis, GYLDENSTOLPE, Ibis, 1920, p. 769 ("Several parts of the country").—DEIGNAN, Journ. Siam Soc. Nat. Hist. Suppl., 1931, p. 173 (Chiang Mai); 1936, p. 74 (Chiang Mai).

During my first stay in Thailand, 1929–1932, I considered the black bittern not uncommon on the marshes between Chiang Mai and Lamphun, from July 26 (1930) to September 19 (1931); during my second visit, 1935–1937, I never once recorded it. A specimen taken near Chiang Mai, November 24, 1931, was probably a late straggler. The only other northern locality from which the species is known is Ban Huai Hom, where Gyldenstolpe collected a male beside a small pool, March 25, 1912.

This bittern has nocturnal habits and, during the day, conceals itself in dense growths of reeds, unless the sky be dark and clouded. I usually saw it when it flew across the marsh after being frightened by the report of a gun, or when I waded waist-deep in water through the thick vegetation. One of my specimens had a fish, 4½ inches long, in its stomach. No Chiang Mai bird showed evidence of breeding.

A male from Chiang Mai had the irides red-brown; the eyelids plumbeous; the orbital skin and lores pinkish brown; the rictus and skin of the throat rose; the bill purplish brown, darker on the culmen, lighter on the underside of the mandible, and whitish toward the tip; the feet and toes dark brown; the claws black. An adult female differed chiefly in having the irides golden-yellow, while an immature female had them golden-yellow, mottled with dull brown.

Adults have the upperparts entirely slaty black with a bluish sheen; the sides of the neck bright buff; the foreneck and breast streaked slaty black, chestnut, and white. Immature birds have the upperparts dark brown, with light rufous edgings to the feathers. The bluish cast of the upperparts of old birds is very evident in the field.

BOTAURUS STELLARIS STELLARIS (Linnaeus)

Eurasian Great Bittern

[*Ardea*] *stellaris* Linnaeus, Systema naturae, ed. 10, vol. 1, 1758, p. 144 (Europe; type locality restricted to Sweden, *apud* Hartert).

Botaurus stellaris stellaris, Deignan, Journ. Siam Soc. Nat. Hist. Suppl., 1931, p. 174 (Chiang Mai).

Botaurus stellaris, Deignan, Journ. Siam Soc. Nat. Hist. Suppl., 1936, p. 74 (Chiang Mai).

The great bittern is a rare, but doubtless regular, winter visitor to North Thailand. I collected one, February 14, 1931, at a small marsh near Chiang Mai, and at a similar place nearby saw another on several occasions between January 14 and February 14, 1936. The only other northern record is based upon a bird taken by me at Ban Mae Sai, near Chiang Saen, January 21, 1937.

These birds were found only by chance when frightened from the heavy stands of rushes in which they were hiding. The Chiang Mai specimen had the remains of fish in its stomach.

A female had the irides yellow; the orbital skin mixed olive-green and lavender; the lores dark brown; the culmen dark brown, becoming blackish at the tip; the bill otherwise dull olive-green; the feet and toes green; the soles yellowish; the claws horn brown.

This heron has the whole crown and nape, and a line from the gape below each cheek, black; the upperparts bright buff, heavily streaked and barred with rufous and black; the underparts bright buff, streaked with dark rufous; the apical half of the outspread wing pinkish rufous, barred with black.

Botaurus stellaris orientalis Buturlin is considered unrecognizable by Hartert and Peters. A pair of topotypes of this race in Washington are strikingly larger and darker than all specimens from other localities I have examined; it would seem either that the bird of northeastern Asia is indeed separable, or, if it be identical with Swedish specimens (which I have not seen), that a smaller, more southern race must be recognized.

Family CICONIIDAE

ANASTOMUS OSCITANS (Boddaert)

ASIATIC OPENBILL

Ardea oscitans BODDAERT, Table des planches enluminéez d'histoire naturelle, 1783, p. 55 (Pondicherry, *ex* D'Aubenton, pl. 932).

Anastomus oscitans, DEIGNAN, Journ. Siam Soc. Nat. Hist. Suppl., 1931, p. 172 (Chiang Mai); 1936, p. 74 (Chiang Mai).

On the marshes south of Chiang Mai the openbill occurs in flocks from early in September to the beginning of November, and at Chiang Mai I saw a solitary bird above the town, June 10, 1930. On December 19, 1935, a small flock was found roosting in the dead top of an enormous tree along the river just south of Chom Thong, and from this group a male in nonbreeding plumage was collected. Otherwise the species is not recorded from North Thailand, although I have no doubt that it is widely distributed during the rains, especially in Chiang Rai Province.

I found it a very shy bird and was never able to approach within gunshot of the feeding flocks. Much of its time seems to be spent soaring in circles high in the air. The example from Chom Thong had been feeding on a species of snail.

This is the only stork likely to be seen in the North outside of Chiang Rai Province. It differs from all other Thai birds in having an open space in the middle between the two parts of the bill. In nuptial dress it has the scapulars, tail, and apical half of the wing black, glossed with green and purple; the rest of the plumage pure white. Nonbreeding dress differs in having the white replaced by soft gray.

DISSOURA EPISCOPUS EPISCOPUS (Boddaert)

INDIAN WHITE-NECKED STORK

Ardea Episcopus BODDAERT, Table des planches enluminéez d'histoire naturelle, 1783, p. 54 (Coromandel coast, *ex* D'Aubenton, pl. 906).
Dissoura episcopa episcopa, DE SCHAUENSEE, Proc. Acad. Nat. Sci. Philadelphia, 1934, p. 279 (Chiang Saen).

The white-necked stork has reached northern Thailand from the South by way of the Mae Khong basin, and, while it is widely distributed over the plains of Chiang Rai, it has been prevented by the surrounding mountain barriers from extending its range into the other provinces. A specimen was taken by de Schauensee at Chiang Saen in February 1933, and another by me at Muang Fang in July 1936. I also saw this bird north of Wiang Pa Pao in April 1929, on the plains between Muang Thoeng and Chiang Rai in May 1936, and on the marsh at Mae Chai during the same month.

It is normally a solitary bird, but where conditions are satisfactory many individuals may be seen at once. It is conspicuous at the margins of the large "pong" and may also be found in the ricefields after the harvest, especially at marshy spots. During the heat of the day it spends much of its time roosting in neighboring trees. When alarmed it may fly directly out of sight but quite often rises into the air and, beyond gunshot, begins to sail in wide circles overhead, gradually ascending with scarcely a visible motion of the wings until lost to the eye in the brilliant sunshine.

This stork is not likely to be confused with any other species. It has the crown and whole body black; the neck (covered with short, woolly feathers), tail, and lower abdomen white.

CICONIA NIGRA (Linnaeus)

BLACK STORK

[*Ardea*] *nigra* LINNAEUS, Systema naturae, ed. 10, vol. 1, 1758, p. 142 ("in Europa boreali"; type locality restricted to Sweden, *apud* Peters).

The status of this stork is uncertain; it is perhaps a regular winter vistor to the Mae Khong basin. It was discovered by Delacour and Greenway on the Mae Khong during the winter of 1938–39; they reported (L'Oiseau et la Revue Française d'Ornithologie, 1940, p. 26) seeing a flock of 17 on a large sandbank in the river about 20 km. below Ban Huai Sai, Laos, December 27, and finding them again at the same spot, January 20. In addition, a solitary bird was observed along the river between Ban Nam Khuang and Huai Sai, January 19. Otherwise there are no records for this species in the Indo-Chinese countries.

This large stork has the lower breast, abdomen, and under tail coverts white; the rest of the plumage black (glossed with purple and green); the bill and feet bright red.

XENORHYNCHUS ASIATICUS ASIATICUS (Latham)

INDIAN BLACK-NECKED STORK

[*Mycteria*] *asiatica* LATHAM, Index ornithologicus, vol. 2, 1790, p. 670 (India).
Xenorhynchus asiaticus, GYLDENSTOLPE, Kungl. Svenska Vet.-Akad. Handl., 1916, p. 140 (Chiang Saen); Ibis, 1920, p. 766 ("On the swamps of northern Siam").

This strikingly marked stork, like *Dissoura*, occurs only in Chiang Rai Province, where, while not numerous, it seems to be widely distributed. Gyldenstolpe found a few near Chiang Saen in August 1914. In May 1936 I saw it at Mae Chai and on the plains between Muang Thoeng and Chiang Rai, near the Nam Ing. Delacour and Greenway reported it on the Mae Khong about 20 km. below Ban Huai Sai, January 20, 1939. No specimen has yet been taken anywhere in our area.

The black-necked stork can be identified as far as it can be seen. It has the head and neck black, glossed with greenish blue; the scapulars, inner secondaries, greater and median wing coverts black, glossed with bronze-green; the rest of the plumage white. A bird seen flying overhead will show a broad black band diagonally across the wing. The long bill is black, with the lower edge of the mandible curved upward, and the feet are bright red.

LEPTOPTILOS DUBIUS (Gmelin)

LARGER ADJUTANT

[*Ardea*] *dubia* GMELIN, Systema naturae, vol. 1, pt. 2, 1789, p. 624 (India).
Leptoptilus dubius, GYLDENSTOPLE, Kungl. Svenska Vet.-Akad. Handl., 1916, p. 140 (Chiang Saen); Ibis, 1920, p. 766 ("Throughout the whole country").

The only specimen from our area was taken by Gyldenstolpe at Chiang Saen, August 10, 1914. I saw a pair at the Mae Chai marsh in May 1936. It is a form that occurs only in Chiang Rai Province, where Gyldenstolpe considered it rather common, but it is so extremely wary that it is rarely possible to get within gunshot of it.

This is a gigantic stork with large, massive bill and a gular pouch, which can be inflated like a child's balloon. The head and neck are naked except for a few scattered black feathers on the nape and numerous thin, curly, hairlike feathers; the skin of the head is pinkish brown, that of the neck and pouch yellow or pinkish yellow. The bird has a ruff of white feathers around the base of the neck; the underparts white; the upperparts wholly black; the inner secondaries and greater wing coverts gray during the nuptial season (then forming a broad and conspicuous wing band).

Family THRESKIORNITHIDAE

PSEUDIBIS PAPILLOSA DAVISONI (Hume)

DAVISON'S BLACK IBIS

Geronticus Davisoni HUME, Stray Feathers, vol. 3, 1875, p. 300 ("on the banks of the Pakchan Estuary in the extreme south of the Tenasserim Provinces").

The black ibis is confined to Chiang Rai Province, and the only northern specimen yet known is a male collected by me at Chiang Saen Kao, January 12, 1937. This was one of a flock of five or six birds that occurred upon a large sandbar in the Mae Khong. They were exceedingly wild, and it was possible to take an example only by stalking them from a boat at nightfall.

Ibises in general may be known from herons by their long, sickle-shaped bill. The present species has the head naked, black in color except for a pale blue area on the nape; the plumage black, glossed purple and green, with the exception of a white patch on the inner lesser wing coverts; the feet red.

Order ANSERIFORMES

Family ANATIDAE

DENDROCYGNA JAVANICA (Horsfield)

JAVANESE WHISTLING TEAL

Anas Javanica HORSFIELD, Trans. Linn. Soc. London, vol. 13, 1821, pp. 199–200 (Java).

Dendrocygna javanica, GYLDENSTOLPE, Kungl. Svenska Vet.-Akad. Handl., 1916, p. 135 (Chiang Rai); Ibis, 1920, p. 773 ("Throughout the whole country").—DEIGNAN, Journ. Siam Soc. Nat. Hist. Suppl., 1931, p. 174 (Chiang Mai); 1936, pp. 74, 131–132 (Chiang Mai, Ban Nong Khiat, Ban Tha Nong Luang).

The whistling teal is by far the commonest and best known of Thai ducks and is present throughout the year in all our provinces. During the rains it abounds everywhere, on the marshes and at pools in the ricefields; in the dry months it congregates, often in vast numbers, at woodland ponds and in the swamps. Gyldenstolpe found it abundant at Chiang Rai in August 1914; I considered it abundant at Chiang Mai from June 28 (1930) to September 19 (1931) and locally common during the rest of the year. I saw it in numbers at Phayao in August 1929 and at Muang Fang in July 1936. It was locally common at Chom Thong in January 1936. In December 1935 I observed a flock of about 100 at Nong Khiat and over 1,000 at Nong Luang. The "millions of ducks" reported to occur in winter in Chiang Rai Province are largely of this species.

A bird shot at Muang Fang, July 5, and another taken at Chiang Mai, August 14, were carrying oviduct eggs ready to be laid.

This duck has a characteristic appearance in flight, which assists in identification: against the sky it seems to be black, and the outstretched neck is depressed to form an angle with the plane of the back. Its call is a shrill whistle, which may be heard while the bird is flying or perched in a tree.

My specimens had the irides dark brown; the eyelids plumbeous, edged yellow; the maxilla slaty, bluish toward the base, with the nail blackish, and the commissure edged fleshy; the mandible below bluish fleshy, tipped and edged with dark slate; the interior of the mouth white; the feet and toes plumbeous-gray, with the webs darker; the claws slaty black, lighter at the base.

The whistling teal has the head brown with a dark cap; the back dark brown, the feathers margined with rufous; the rump black; the upper tail coverts dark rufous; the tail black; the underparts unmarked rufous; the wings black with a large chestnut area at the shoulder; the underwing solid black.

SARKIDIORNIS MELANOTOS (Pennant)

Indian Comb Duck

Anser melanotos Pennant, Indian zoology, 1769, pp. 12–13, pl. 11 (Ceylon).

Sarcidiornis melanolota, Gyldenstolpe, Kungl. Svenska Vet.-Akad. Handl., 1916, p. 134 ("Northern Siam").

Sarkidiornis melanotus melanotus, Gyldenstolpe, Ibis, 1920, p. 772 ("Somewhere in northern Siam").

Sarcidiornis melanota, Riley, U. S. Nat. Mus. Bull. 172, 1938, p. 39 ("Nan River, near Kampang, northern Siam"=Mae Wang river, near Lampang).

Gyldenstolpe saw specimens of this duck in the garden of H. H. Chao Kaeo Nawarat na Chiang Mai and was told that they had been captured somewhere in "Upper Siam, probably at the neighbourhood of Muang Pra Yao." As recently as 1937, I myself saw descendants of these birds in the aviary of the late Chao.

Riley recorded a specimen as taken by Dr. Hugh M. Smith at the "Nan River, near Kampang, northern Siam." This is incorrect! The bird, a female, was killed by W. Leigh Williams, Esq., on the Mae Wang, near Lampang, March 21, 1928, and was presented to Dr. Smith by E. Chapple, Esq. It is the only wild-taken example I have seen from North Thailand.

While I have never observed this duck, I have no doubt that it is widely distributed in our provinces. It is well known to the northern people everywhere as *pet hong* ("swan duck"). A man who lived beside a marsh between Chiang Mai and Lamphun told me that he had once shot one there, and it was reported to occur at times on a large woodland pond near Ban Pa Muat, some miles north of San Sai Luang. At a swamp near Ban Nong Khiat people said that it bred commonly during the rains, but when I visited this place no ducks of any kind were seen, owing to the presence of fishermen in some numbers. Finally, at Phayao I was informed that it is often found on the lake there.

This is one of the largest of Thai ducks. The male has the head and neck white, thickly spotted with black (glossed purple and green); the lower neck, all around, and the entire underparts white; the lower back gray; the remaining upperparts black, beautifully glossed with bronze, purple, and green; an erect fleshy growth at the base of the bill, which becomes greatly swollen in the breeding season. The female differs in having the black parts much less glossed and in lacking the "comb." Birds of both sexes have a spur at the bend of the wing.

ASARCORNIS SCUTULATA (S. Müller)

White-winged Wood Duck

Anas scutulata S. Müller, Verhandelingen over de Natuurlijke Geschiedenis der Nederlandsche overzeesche bezittingen . . . Land- en Volkenkunde [=vol. 1], 1839–1844 [=1842], p. 159, footnote (Java).

I met with a flock of five or six of these ducks at about 5,000 feet on Doi Ang Ka during the first week of September 1935. I had been alone to the summit of the mountain, had lost the trail for hours, and finally was hurrying, drenched to the skin and bleeding from hundreds of leech-bites, along a small brook through a stand of dense evergreen, hoping to arrive at camp before the path was obliterated by darkness. Suddenly, with loud cries, one of these gooselike birds arose from my very feet, quickly followed by others. I was too startled to aim my gun and within seconds they were lost to sight in the gloom among the trees.

Inquiry of the local White Karens revealed that they knew a large duck that lived in the forest, but they felt that its rarity and the irregularity of its appearances would not justify making a special search for it. I never met with it again in northern Thailand.

That a bird of this sort should be found at so high an altitude seems remarkable, but it is not more so than the discovery of *Rallina eurizonoides nigrolineata* in 1931 at virtually the same spot.

The present species is about equal to the comb duck in size. It has the head and upper neck white, thickly spotted with black; the upperparts brown, glossed with green; the underside of the lower neck black and the remaining underparts chestnut-brown; the wing with an extensive area of pure white at the shoulder and a large speculum of blue-gray bordered above by a broad black band.

CASARCA FERRUGINEA (Pallas)

RUDDY SHELDRAKE

Anas (*ferruginea*) PALLAS, *in* Vroeg's Beredeneerde catalogus, Adumbratiunculae, 1764, pp. 5–6 (no locality given=Tartary, *ex* "Tartarysche Gans" and "*Anser Tataricus ferrugineus*" in Catalogus, p. 25).

Casarca ferruginea, DEIGNAN, Journ. Siam Soc. Nat. Hist. Suppl., 1936, p. 132 ("Opposite the village of Ban En").

A ruddy sheldrake was seen by me, December 23, 1935, on a lagoon just behind the left bank of the Mae Ping, opposite Ban Aen, a village between Chom Thong and Mut Ka. The bird flew out onto an enormous expanse of exposed sand and could not be approached within gunshot.

This species normally occurs on broad streams with wide stretches of sand and may be expected to be found sooner or later along any of the major northern rivers.

The sheldrake is about the size of the comb duck. The male has the top of the head buff; the neck, back, scapulars, and entire underparts bright orange-brown; the tail and upper tail coverts black; the speculum of the wing glossy purplish green; a large white area at the shoulder, above and below, and the remainder of the wing black. The female is similar, but has the head and neck paler, almost buffy white.

ANAS POECILORHYNCHA HARINGTONI (Oates)

BURMESE SPOT-BILLED DUCK

Polionetta haringtoni OATES, Journ. Bombay Nat. Hist. Soc., vol. 17, No. 3, 1907, pp. 558–559 (Shan States).

Anas poecilorhyncha haringtoni, DEIGNAN, Journ. Siam Soc. Nat. Hist. Suppl., 1936, p. 169 (Mae Chai).

The spotbill is thus far known only from Chiang Rai Province, where it seems to be rather common during the cold weather and quite possibly throughout the year. I saw at least 50 on the marsh at Mae Chai, May 9 and 10, 1936; a specimen was taken at Chiang Saen Kao, January 17, 1937, another at Ban Mae Sai, January 20, and numerous others were observed at the two latter localities.

This duck occurred in small flocks upon open pools surrounded by tall rushes. It was very wild and, owing to the noise made in breaking through the stiff vegetation, one could only with great difficulty approach within gunshot range of it. It behaved exactly like a mallard and uttered the same loud quack when startled.

The bill is black with a broad band of orange-yellow just behind the tip; the feet are coral-red. The red spot at the base of the bill on each side, from which this duck derives its name, is obsolescent or absent in the present subspecies.

The spotbill is about the size of a small mallard, and the sexes are alike in plumage. It has the upperparts generally dark brown, each feather edged with light gray-brown; the tail black; the underparts buffy white, spotted profusely everywhere (except on the neck) with dark brown; the speculum of the wing glossy green, edged inwardly by a narrow black bar followed by a rather broader bar of white; the underwing with a large area of pure white at the base.

ANAS QUERQUEDULA Linnaeus

Eurasian Garganey

[*Anas*] *Querquedula* Linnaeus, Systema naturae, ed. 10, vol. 1, 1758, p. 126 ("in Europae aquis dulcibus"; type locality restricted to Sweden, *apud* Hartert).

Querquedula querquedula, Deignan, Journ. Siam Soc. Nat. Hist. Suppl., 1936, p. 75 (Chiang Mai).

This teal occurs regularly at Chiang Mai in small numbers between October 24 (1931) and February 20 (1936), and I have specimens from there and from Lamphun. It will without doubt be found eventually in all our provinces.

It settles even at quite small marshes, where the water may be completely hidden by floating plants. In such places it remains motionless and invisible until one is almost upon it, when the flock will burst into the air at great speed. It is one of the fastest fliers among the ducks.

My examples had the irides bright brown; the maxilla slaty, becoming plumbeous-blue on the basal half; the mandible violet, tipped brownish slate; the rictus and edges of the commissure plumbeous-blue; the interior of the mouth bluish white; the feet and toes plumbeous-blue, with the webs slaty; the claws horny slate.

The old male has the crown and nape glossy black, bordered by a broad white stripe above the eye; the neck and sides of the head chocolate, narrowly streaked everywhere with white; the upperparts blackish brown, each feather margined with pale brown; the chin black; the entire breast light brown, thickly marked with wavy blackish bars; the abdomen white; the speculum glossy green, edged above and below by white bars; a large shoulder patch blue-gray. The female lacks the broad superciliary stripe and the conspicuous markings of the breast; she has the blue-gray of the shoulder duller in color and the speculum almost unglossed. Immature males, which are common in Thailand, resemble the female but have brighter colors on the wing.

ANAS CRECCA CRECCA Linnaeus

EURASIAN GREEN-WINGED TEAL

[*Anas*] *Crecca* LINNAEUS, Systema naturae, ed. 10, vol. 1, 1758, pp. 126–127 ("in Europae aquis dulcibus"; type locality restricted to Sweden, *apud* Hartert).
Nettion crecca, ROGERS and DEIGNAN, Proc. Biol. Soc. Washington, 1934, p. 92 (Chiang Mai); Journ. Siam Soc. Nat. Hist. Suppl., 1936, p. 75 (Chiang Mai).

The greenwing is an uncommon winter visitor, known only from Chiang Mai and Chiang Rai Provinces, but is probably generally, if locally, distributed in the North. I have found it at Chiang Mai from December to February and have specimens from Chiang Saen Kao, taken January 14 and 19, 1937.

It occurs at the same places as the garganey and sometimes at pools in open, swampy woods; I have seen as many as 100 individuals in a single flock. The flight of this species is extremely swift.

A female had the irides brown; the maxilla slaty, flecked with black, the tip and edges of the commissure black; the mandible light brown, tipped darker; the feet and toes gray with a brownish tinge; the webs dark gray; the claws dark brown.

The drake has the head and neck chestnut, with a broad band of glossy green running back from the eye; the upperparts finely vermiculated black and white; the underparts white, with black spots on the breast and black vermiculations on the sides of the body; the wings gray, with a speculum, partly black and partly glossy green, edged above with a white bar. The female differs in having the entire upperparts brown, each feather edged with rufous-buff; the underparts white, with obsolescent spots on the breast.

ANAS ACUTA Linnaeus

PINTAIL

[*Anas*] *acuta* LINNAEUS, Systema naturae, ed. 10, vol. 1, 1758, p. 126 ("in Europae maritimis"; type locality restricted to Sweden, *apud* Hartert).
Dafila aquta [*sic*], GYLDENSTOLPE, Kungl. Svenska Vet.-Akad. Handl., 1916, p. 135 (Phayao); Ibis, 1920, p. 774 (Phayao).
Dafila acuta acuta, DEIGNAN, Journ. Siam Soc. Nat. Hist. Suppl., 1931, p. 174 (Chiang Mai); 1936, p. 75 (Chiang Mai).

The pintail is probably present in greater numbers than any other species of northern duck that reaches Thailand in the cold weather. I found it uncommon but regularly present at Chiang Mai from October to late in February, chiefly on the large marshes, but sometimes at quite small pools among the ricefields and on woodland ponds. I have seen as many as 50 birds in a single flock over the marshes between Chiang Mai and Lamphun.

Two females had the irides dark brown; the maxilla plumbeous, with the culmen, edges of commissure, and corners of mouth slaty; the mandible slaty, tinged fleshy at the base; the interior of the mouth plumbeous; the feet and toes plumbeous-gray, darker at the joints; the webs and claws slaty.

The pintail may be known in flight at a great distance by its rakish build, its slender neck, and, in the case of the full-plumaged male, by the greatly elongated, pointed tail feathers (but such males seem to occur with us only rarely).

The drake has the whole head umber-brown; the upper side of the neck, the upperparts, and the sides of the body gray, finely vermiculated with blackish; the underparts white, the white of the underneck extending as a white stripe into the brown on each side of the head; the under tail coverts black; the long, pointed scapulars brownish gray with wide, black shaft streaks; the speculum glossy bronze-green, edged above with a dull rufous stripe and below by a white one. The duck has the upperparts generally dark brown, barred and speckled with white; the underparts buffy white, barred and streaked everywhere with brown.

ANAS PENELOPE Linnaeus

EURASIAN WIGEON

[*Anas*] *Penelope* LINNAEUS, Systema naturae, ed. 10, vol. 1, 1758, p. 126 ("in Europae maritimis et paludibus"; type locality restricted to Sweden, *apud* Hartert).

Three or four examples of this distinctively marked species were seen by me with a flock of *Anas acuta*, at a woodland pond near Ban Pa Muat (north of San Sai Luang), November 23, 1936, but I was unable to take a specimen. The wigeon may occur in winter anywhere in our provinces in the same localities as the pintail.

The drake has the crown buff, the rest of the head and neck chestnut, the throat more or less marked with black; the upperparts finely vermiculated black and white (gray in the field); the breast vinaceous-pink; the under tail coverts black; the remaining underparts pure white; a large shoulder patch pure white; the speculum metallic green, edged above and below with black; the underwing gray. The duck has the plumage generally dark brown, the feathers edged with rufous, gray, and buffy white; the breast and abdomen white; a dull brown speculum, edged above by buffy white.

NETTAPUS COROMANDELIANUS COROMANDELIANUS (Gmelin)

INDIAN COTTON TEAL

[*Anas*] *coromandeliana* GMELIN, Systema naturae, vol. 1, pt. 2, 1789, pp. 522–523 (Coromandel, India).

Nettopus coromandelianus, GYLDENSTOLPE, Kungl. Svenska Vet.-Akad. Handl., 1916, p. 135 (Chiang Rai); Ibis, 1920, p. 773 ("Throughout the whole country").

Nettapus coromandelianus, DE SCHAUENSEE, Proc. Acad. Nat. Sci. Philadelphia, 1929, p. 587 (about 19 miles south of Chiang Rai).—DEIGNAN, Journ. Siam Soc. Nat. Hist. Suppl., 1931, p. 174 (Chiang Mai).
Cheniscus coromandelianus, DEIGNAN, Journ. Siam Soc. Nat. Hist. Suppl., 1936, pp. 74, 131 (Chiang Mai, Ban Nong Khiat).

The cotton teal, or pygmy goose, is common and generally distributed, particularly during the rains, on marshes, large or small, on ponds, and even in ditches beside public roads. Gyldenstolpe found it common at Chiang Rai in August 1914. At Chiang Mai I considered it common from June 1 (1929) to October 3 (1935) and rare during the cold weather. I recorded it at Phayao, August 24, 1929, and took specimens at Chom Thong, November 13, 1935, and at Ban Mae Sariang, October 8, 1936. In Stockholm there is an undated specimen collected by Eisenhofer at Khun Tan.

I usually found this tiny duck in pairs but sometimes also in flocks of a dozen or so. On the marshes it was often completely concealed by the vegetation and seen only when startled from one's very feet, when it would fly rapidly away, looking exactly like a gigantic bee. It rides high in the water and is capable of diving well.

The adult male has the crown brown, the rest of the head and neck white; at the base of the neck a complete collar, black glossed with green; the underparts, and a collar on the hindneck below the black collar, white; the under tail coverts black; the upperparts black, glossed purple and green; the wing dark glossy green, with a broad white band across it near the tip, above and below. The female and immature male have a dark brown bar through the eye and a white eyebrow; the upperparts dark brown; the underparts brownish white, with more or less indistinct wavy bars of dark brown on the breast and lower neck.

AYTHYA FERINA (Linnaeus)

WHITE-BACKED POCHARD

[*Anas*] *ferina* LINNAEUS, Systema naturae, ed. 10, vol. 1, 1758, p. 126 ("in Europae maritimis"; type locality restricted to Sweden, *apud* Hartert).

I saw a male example of the white-backed pochard at Nong Khiat, south of Chom Thong, November 28, 1931, in company with *Aythya baeri*. I was unable to take the specimen but have no hesitation in adding this easily identified form to our list.

The adult male has the whole head and neck bright rufous; the upper breast and upper back black; the upper and under tail coverts black; the remainder of both upperparts and underparts pale gray, finely vermiculated with black. The adult female has the head, neck, upper breast, and upper back dull brown, more blackish on the crown and whitish on the throat and lower side of upper neck; the upperparts grayish brown, more or less vermiculated with pale gray; the underparts dull brownish gray.

In the field the drake is recognizable at a glance by its bright reddish head and neck and its apparently white back.

AYTHYA BAERI (Radde)

Eastern White-eyed Pochard

Anas (Fuligula) Baeri Radde, Reisen im Süden von Ost-Siberien, vol. 2, 1863, pp. 376–378, pl. 15 (Middle Amur, southeastern Siberia).

Nyroca baeri, Deignan, Journ. Siam Soc. Nat. Hist. Suppl., 1936, pp. 75, 131 (Chiang Mai, Ban Nong Khiat).

The eastern white-eyed pochard occurs regularly in winter, at least in Chiang Mai Province, but always in small numbers. I found it comparatively common only at the woodland pond at Ban Pa Muat (north of San Sai Luang), where it was present throughout the cold weather of 1936–37, in company with other ducks. I have specimens taken at Chiang Mai, March 3 and November 23, 1936, and one taken at Ban Nong Khiat, below Chom Thong, December 19, 1935.

A female had the irides dark brown; the bill slaty; the feet and toes plumbeous, the joints slaty; the claws slate. An immature male had the irides pale gray; the feet plumbeous, with the webs and joints black.

I have never seen an adult male *baeri* in Thailand. If such a bird should be shot, it may be recognized by its having the head and neck greenish black, changing gradually to a ring of unglossed black at the base of the neck; a rather large, well-marked white chin spot; the breast and upper belly dark rufous and the remaining underparts white; the upperparts blackish brown; a broad white wing band and a brownish-white area near the tip of the opened wing; the underwing largely white.

Females and young males have a white chin, an indistinct patch of dark rufous on the sides of the head at the base of the bill, and the rest of the head and neck blackish brown, almost black on top of the head; the upperparts blackish brown; the breast and upper belly dull rufous (adults) or dark brown (immatures), somewhat mottled with blackish, whitish, or light brown; the remaining underparts light brown or sullied white; the wing like that of the adult male, but the light area near the tip less whitish, more brownish.

AYTHYA NYROCA (Güldenstädt)

Western White-eyed Pochard

Anas nyroca Güldenstädt, Nov. Comm. Acad. Sci. Imper. Petropol., vol. 14, pt. 1, 1769, pp. 403–408 ("in regionibus Tanaicensibus inter gradum 54 et 55 latitudinis").

Nyroca nyroca nyroca, Rogers and Deignan, Proc. Biol. Soc. Washington, 1934, p. 91 (Chiang Mai).

Nyroca nyroca, Deignan, Journ. Siam Soc. Nat. Hist. Suppl., 1936, p. 75 (Chiang Mai).

A young male was shot at Chiang Mai, November 22, 1931, by W. Leigh Williams, Esq., who kindly presented me the skin. Since northwestern Thailand is at the periphery of the known winter range of this duck, it may be expected to occur only rarely within our limits.

This specimen had the irides gray; the maxilla slate-blue, with tip and culmen black; the mandible fleshy, with tip and edges of commissure mottled blackish; the feet dark slaty; the toes plumbeous; the webs dark slaty; the claws black.

The adult male has a well-marked white chin spot, the whole head and neck otherwise dark rufous, concolorous with the breast, but with a tendency toward a blackish ring around the base of the neck; other parts as in *baeri*.

The female and immature male are rather difficult to distinguish from *baeri*, and it is probably not possible in the field. I have compared six such skins of *nyroca* with four of *baeri*, and found these differences:

1. *A. baeri* has the head and neck blackish brown, almost black on the crown, and with an indistinct area of dark rufous on the sides of the head at the base of the bill. *N. nyroca* has the head and neck uniformly dull rufous.

2. *A. baeri* has a rather large, well-marked white chin spot. *N. nyroca* has the whole chin and throat whitish, maculated with dull rufous (3 specimens), wholly dull rufous (1 specimen), or dull rufous with a few whitish feathers at the extreme point of the chin (2 specimens).

3. *A. baeri* is a rather larger bird in all its parts (wing length 186–196 mm.) and has a somewhat broader bill. The wing length of *N. nyroca* is 171–184 mm. But in identifying these birds, size should be employed only in combination with other characters.

Any pochard taken in Thailand should have the head and wing, even if not the whole skin, preserved for critical examination, since a number of species, not yet recorded at all from the Kingdom, are to be expected in winter.

Order FALCONIFORMES

Family ACCIPITRIDAE

ELANUS CAERULEUS VOCIFERUS (Latham)

INDIAN BLACK-WINGED KITE

[*Falco*] *vociferus* LATHAM, Index ornithologicus, vol. 1, 1790, p. 46 (India; type locality restricted to Coromandel Coast, *ex* Sonnerat, *apud* Hartert).

Elanus caeruleus vociferus, DEIGNAN, Journ. Siam Soc. Nat. Hist. Suppl., 1935, p. 64 (Chom Thong).

I have only twice seen this beautiful little kite in North Thailand: once at Phayao, August 24, 1929, and once along the highway about

2 km. north of Chom Thong, September 11, 1935; in neither case was I able to take the specimen. Since the species is rather common on the plains to the south of our area and, furthermore, is known to make occasional irruptions into territory where it has not been seen before, it is likely to occur at some time anywhere in the northern lowlands, except in heavily forested districts.

The Chom Thong bird was in a tract from which the jungle had only recently been cleared and where there were still numerous dead trees, upon which it perched. At Phayao I found it among low second-growth trees, at the edge of the taller forest. The latter bird was observed to hover in a curious manner, with the wings pointed almost straight upward and the tail depressed.

This kite has the irides (in adults) deep red; the bill black; the cere and rictus yellow; the feet and toes yellow; the claws black.

It is a small, graceful hawk with pure-white underparts; the posterior lores and a line over the eye black; the forehead white, shading into the blue-gray of the upperparts; a large black shoulder patch and the wings blackish toward the tip; the central tail feathers pale gray, the outer ones white; the basal half of the underwing pure white, the rest dark gray. The wing is pointed and very long, when folded extending beyond the tip of the tail.

Recent authors have been inclined to merge the race *vociferus* with *caeruleus* of Africa. The latter is supposed to have a blue-gray wash on the breast, rarely seen in the Asiatic birds, and to be slightly darker above. The presence or absence of the blue-gray wash seems to be a very inconstant character, but I find that the two forms are easily separable by the difference in the tone of gray of the upperparts, a distinction that is especially well marked on the head.

AVICEDA LEUPHOTES (Dumont)

BLACK-CRESTED BAZA

Falco leuphotes DUMONT, Dict. Sci. Nat., vol. 16, 1820, p. 217 (Pondicherry).

Baza lophotes, GYLDENSTOLPE, Journ. Nat. Hist. Soc. Siam, 1915, p. 234 (listed); Kungl. Svenska Vet.-Akad. Handl., 1916, p. 130 (Pha Kho, Pang Hua Phong, Khun Tan); Ibis, 1920, p. 750 ("Throughout the whole country").

Baza euphotes [*sic*], DE SCHAUENSEE, Proc. Acad. Nat. Sci. Philadelphia, 1928, p. 576 (Doi Suthep).

Aviceda leuphotes, DEIGNAN, Journ. Siam Soc. Nat. Hist. Suppl., 1936, p. 75 (Doi Suthep).

The baza is well distributed in the provinces of Chiang Mai, Lampang, and Phrae, at least in the hilly districts, and should be watched for in the remaining northern provinces. Gyldenstolpe found it not uncommon at Pha Kho in March and at Khun Tan in June. Eisenhofer sent to Stockholm one bird taken at Huai Pu, May 28, 1912; one taken at Khun Tan, June 8, 1913; and no less than 18 others, including a juvenile, with no data but Khun Tan. On the lower slopes of Doi Suthep, de Schauensee took a specimen, March 12, 1928, and I saw four, March 20, 1936. I have found it near Ban Pong, a village at the southern foot of Doi Suthep, February 15, 1936; in the deciduous jungle near Ban Choeng Doi in March; and between Ban Choeng Doi and Wiang Pa Pao in April, 1929. During the latter half of August, 1936, I collected six specimens at Mae Mo and there observed many others. Finally, I have often seen this species from the train while passing through the hill-forests between Chiang Mai and Uttaradit.

There is a strong likelihood that this hawk is migratory. Chasen has remarked (Birds of the Malay Peninsula, vol. 4, 1939, p. 47) that all specimens he has seen from the Peninsula have been collected from November to March. With us, it has so far been recorded only from February to August. The presence of the species on Doi Suthep only in March implies that it has arrived from elsewhere and then moves on.

The baza is found both in the evergreen and in the deciduous forest, but never at really high elevations. When not breeding, it is usually seen in parties of from 3 to 5 individuals, but sometimes the small groups band together into loose flocks of as many as 20 birds. It is more active at dusk and during the heat of the day perches quietly in the top of a high tree, where it would be overlooked if it did not periodically fly out after passing insects. Sometimes it is very tame, at others exceedingly wild and difficult to approach. When alarmed it utters a soft, tremulous scream and begins to soar in small circles above the treetops. The long crest is held vertically when the bird is at rest. In flight it flaps frequently and looks exactly like a small black and white crow.

The crest and upperparts are black, the feathers of the back with white bases which show through in places; the scapulars are black and chestnut, with white bases which show as large white patches; the throat is black; a broad white band across the breast is succeeded by another broad band of mixed black and chestnut; the sides of the body are buffy, barred with chestnut; the center of the abdomen and the under tail coverts are black; the wings are black, with a large area of white, mixed with chestnut, near the end of the secondaries; the axillaries are black and the rest of the underwing is gray, darker toward the tip.

PERNIS PTILORHYNCUS RUFICOLLIS Lesson

INDIAN HONEY BUZZARD

Pernis ruficollis LESSON, Traité d'Ornithologie, livr. 1, 1830, p. 77 ("Patrie inconnue"=Bengal, *fide* Kirke Swann).

Pernis apivorus ruficollis [*partim*], DEIGNAN, Journ. Siam Soc. Nat. Hist. Suppl., 1936, p. 75 (Chiang Mai).

Pernis apivorus orientalis [*partim*], DEIGNAN, Journ. Siam Soc. Nat. Hist. Suppl., 1936, p. 75 (Chiang Mai).

With this migratory form I place three specimens from Chiang Mai: An adult female and an immature of the same sex, respectively taken October 19 and 20, 1935, and an adult male collected May 12, 1936.

The two October examples are molting both remiges and rectrices. The third specimen, shot at a surprisingly late date, had the gonads quite inactive and doubtless represents a delayed north-bound migrant.

The adult female had the irides red-orange; the cere and maxilla black; the mandible slaty black, plumbeous at the base; the rictus pale yellow; the feet and toes yellow; the claws horny slate. The immature differed only in having the irides olive-yellow.

A general description of the plumages of this species will be found under the following race. *P. p. ruficollis* is distinguishable from *gurneyi* only by its greater size.

Stresemann, in his revision of the genus *Pernis* (Archiv für Naturgeschichte, 1940, pp. 137–193), states that *ruficollis* has the "tail-wing index" (length of tail multiplied by 100 and divided by length of wing) usually under 65 mm.; the "wing-tip" (distance from tip of longest secondary to tip of longest primary) usually under 110 mm.; the wing length from 392 to 460 mm. My adult male has the "index" 61 mm., the "wing-tip" 106 mm., the wing length 446 mm.; the adult and immature females respectively have the "index" 61 and 58 mm., the "wing-tip" 78 and 97 mm., the wing length 423 and 444 mm. Owing to the fact that both females are molting the quills of wings and tail, their measurements are misleadingly short, yet great enough to place them under this name without question.

PERNIS PTILORHYNCUS GURNEYI Stresemann

BURMESE HONEY BUZZARD

Pernis ptilorhynchus gurneyi STRESEMANN, Arch. für Naturg., new ser. Abt. B, vol. 9, No. 2, 1940, pp. 168–170 (Lamaing, near Mandalay, Burma).

Pernis apivorus ruficollis [*partim*], DEIGNAN, Journ. Siam Soc. Nat. Hist. Suppl., 1936, p. 75 (Chiang Mai).

Pernis apivorus orientalis [*partim*], DEIGNAN, Journ. Siam Soc. Nat. Hist. Suppl., 1936, p. 75 (Chiang Mai).

At Chiang Mai I obtained specimens of this small subspecies October 1 and December 13, 1935; February 25, 1936; January 20, February 4 and 6, 1937. Others reached me from Ban San Kamphaeng, January 4, 1936, and Doi Suthep (3,500 feet), December 16, 1935. With *P. p. gurneyi* may be placed also an undated adult male in Stockholm, taken by Eisenhofer at Khun Tan; this is the bird discussed by Lönnberg (Ibis, 1924, p. 321). Finally, I have seen in Hannover an unsexed example, collected by Eisenhofer in "Siam," March 9, 1911, which probably is of this race and may well have come from some northern locality.

Most of the honey buzzards in my collection were shot in village gardens by the indignant owners of hives of bees. Some examples had the stomach filled with honey, bees, and their larvae. Since honey was to be found easily only near human habitation and since these large birds were very tame and rather sluggish, they were readily killed. On November 1, 1935, I saw six at one time soaring lazily above Chiang Mai, and during that winter I frequently observed them perched upon low trees beside the highways and close to houses.

An adult male of October 1 is molting both remiges and rectrices; another of February 6, the remiges; a subadult female of February 25, the rectrices. Stresemann has suggested that *gurneyi* may breed in Thailand, but I took only winter birds with inactive gonads and Riley's specimen of May 4 from Pak Chong may have been a migrant (as is my example of *ruficollis* of even later date).

An adult male had the irides deep orange; the cere black above, olive-green at the sides; the maxilla black, olive-green on the sides at the base; the mandible slaty at the tip, then plumbeous, with the extreme base yellow-green; the rictus pale yellow; the feet and toes yellow; the claws horny slate.

Hawks of this genus may always be known in the hand by their having the lores and sides of the head closely covered with small, scalelike feathers, instead of the usual bristles and naked skin. In plumage the individual variation is so great that the species may be described as polymorphic. It usually has the upperparts dark brown; the head more or less whitish, owing to the white bases of the feathers showing through; the lores and sides of the head some shade of gray; the underwing whitish, with broad, irregular bars of blackish; the upper surface of the tail barred blackish brown and light brown or whitish, the dark and light bands of subequal breadth (adults) or the dark bars much narrower than the pale ones, the latter crossed by numerous narrow medium brown bands (immatures); the lower surface of the tail similarly but rather less distinctly marked; the underparts various, light brown with narrow black streaks, white barred everywhere with brown, white, or buffy marked with black or brown drops, plain dark brown, or any combination of these colors and markings; the throat usually of some light color, often set off by black borders and a black mesial streak.

According to Stresemann's diagnosis (*loc. cit.*), this form agrees with *ruficollis* in having the "tail-wing index" usually under 65 mm. and the "wing-tip" usually under 110 mm., but differs in its shorter wing length (from 363 to 400 mm.). Of three nonmolting specimens before me, two immature females have the "index" 66 and 63 mm., the "wing-tip" 83 and 85 mm., the wing length 399 and 390 mm.; an immature male, the "index" 67 mm., the "wing-tip" 62 mm., the wing length 345 mm. Of my three examples in molt, of which the measurements are necessarily somewhat inexact, the two adult males have the "index" 66 and 65 mm., the "wing-tip" 70 and 85 mm., the wing length 382 and 381 mm.; the subadult female, the "index" 62 mm., the "wing-tip" 77 mm., the wing length 390 mm.

MILVUS MIGRANS LINEATUS (J. E. Gray)

BLACK-EARED KITE

Haliaetus lineatus J. E. GRAY, *in* Hardwicke, Illustrations of Indian zoology, vol. 1, pt. 8, 1830–1832 [= 1831], pl. 18 (China).

Milvus migrans lineatus, DEIGNAN, Journ. Siam Soc. Nat. Hist. Suppl., 1931, p. 166 (Chiang Mai.)

Milvus lineatus, DEIGNAN, Journ. Siam Soc. Nat. Hist. Suppl., 1936, p. 75 (Chiang Mai).

This kite is a well-known winter visitor, which occurs chiefly along the larger rivers; at Chiang Mai it was common from October 20 (1931) to March 21 (1929). My specimens were collected at Chiang Mai, November 16, 1931, and at Doi Mae Kong Ka, October 23, 1936.

The black-eared kite is a familiar sight at Chiang Mai, over the river and above the city streets. It seems to spend most of its waking hours in the air, where it is able to soar for long periods with only slight movements of the wings and turning of the forked tail to one side or the other.

One of my specimens, a female, had the irides bright brown; the orbital skin plumbeous-blue; the bill black, plumbeous-blue at the base; the cere pale yellow; the feet and toes grayish yellow; the claws black.

The stomach of this bird contained small lizards, but much of its food must consist of offal gathered from the surface of the water.

This is a large, long-winged hawk, with a distinctly forked tail, the central tail feathers being from an inch to an inch and a half shorter than the outermost. Adults are generally very dark brown, with a large, noticeable white patch near the middle of the underwing. Immature birds have the plumage dark brown with whitish streaks on the head, upper back, and underparts, whitish spots on the shoulders, whitish tips to the feathers of the lower back and tail, and the underwing marked as in the adult. The ear coverts are not really black but are blackish brown, rather darker than the neighboring areas.

HALIASTUR INDUS INDUS (Boddaert)

INDIAN BRAHMINY KITE

Falco Indus BODDAERT, Table des planches enluminéez d'histoire naturelle, 1783, p. 25 (Pondicherry, *ex* D'Aubenton, pl. 416, and Buffon, vol. 1, p. 490).

Haliastur indus, GYLDENSTOPLE, Kungl. Svenska Vet.-Akad. Handl., 1916, p. 128 (Nong Mae Rua).

Haliastur indus indus, GYLDENSTOLPE, Ibis, 1920, p. 747 ("Northern Siam").—DE SCHAUENSEE, Proc. Acad. Nat. Sci. Philadelphia, 1929, p. 578 (Chiang Mai); 1934, p. 270 (Chiang Mai).—DEIGNAN, Journ. Siam Soc. Nat. Hist. Suppl., 1931, p. 166 (Chiang Mai); 1936, p. 76 (Chiang Mai).

The Brahminy kite is very common, especially along the larger rivers and on the great marshes, and is a familiar bird in towns and villages. At Chiang Mai it was present throughout the year except during the month of April, when it was rare or absent. In January 1936 I took specimens at Chiang Mai, Ban Sop Mae Chaem, and Ban Thung Som Poi. Gyldenstolpe collected one in August near Chiang Saen, and I recorded it at Phayao in August 1929.

This kite is always to be seen from the bridges at Chiang Mai, in winter accompanied by *Milvus*, with which it shares the refuse floating down the river. A common call, sometimes uttered while circling high in the air, is a shrill *chee—ăăăăă*. At nightfall it repairs to some solitary tree in the ricefields and roosts together with others of its kind. I knew such a tree near the river below Chiang Mai which was used by the kites at least for several years.

Gyldenstolpe's specimen from Mae Rua had the irides brownish yellow; the bill yellowish green; the feet yellow.

The Brahminy kite has the wing and tail rounded. When adult, it has the plumage bright red-brown, with the head, neck, upper back, and forehalf of the underparts white (with blackish shaft streaks) and the apical half of the wing black. The immature bird has the head, neck, and underparts dull light brown, redder on the lower abdomen; the apical half of the wing blackish; the rest of the plumage dark brown.

The only northern specimens extant are from Chiang Mai and Chiang Rai Provinces, and these are quite typical *indus*, agreeing perfectly with specimens from India in the heavy streaking of the head and underparts.

ACCIPITER GENTILIS KHAMENSIS (Bianchi)

TIBETAN GOSHAWK

Astur palumbarius khamensis BIANCHI, Bull. Brit. Orn. Club, vol. 16, 1906, pp. 70–71 ("in terra Kham dicta, Tibet, merid.-orient."; type from "basin of the headwaters of Mekong, Lun-tok-ndo, north of Chamdo, southeastern Tibet," *fide* Sushkin, Proc. Boston Soc. Nat. Hist., vol. 39, 1928, p. 27; locality further limited to the Re-tschu river, *apud* Kirke Swann).

Accipiter gentilis schvedowi, ROGERS and DEIGNAN, Proc. Biol. Soc. Washington, 1934, p. 91 (Chiang Mai=Doi Suthep).—DEIGNAN, Journ. Siam Soc. Nat. Hist. Suppl., 1936, p. 76 (Chiang Mai=Doi Suthep, ?Doi Chiang Dao).

This fine hawk is definitely known as a Thai bird only by a single immature male, which came into my possession on November 29, 1931; it had been shot a day or two before by a Lao watchman at the bungalow of H. B. M. Consulate, on Doi Suthep at about 3,500 feet. The skin is now deposited in the collection of the Princeton Museum of Zoology. The species may be less rare than is indicated by the paucity of records: I believe that I saw a pair on Doi Chiang Dao in December 1931, and on several occasions in winter, over the topmost ridge of Doi Suthep, I have observed birds that may well have been of this form.

Adults are dark slaty above, with white bases of the feathers showing through on the nape; they have black ear coverts and a white eyebrow; the rounded tail narrowly white-tipped and crossed by indistinct blackish bars; the underparts white, closely barred everywhere with narrow blackish bands. Immature birds are brown above, with the tail narrowly white-tipped and narrowly barred light and dark; below buffy white, heavily streaked with brown.

This genus is recognizable among hawks by its relatively short, rounded wing and long tail. The present form differs from its Thai congeners by its great size and the lack of a definite mesial line on the throat, but, because of the variation in size and color among individuals of all these species, no record for this bird should be held valid without a specimen.

In default of suitable comparative material and with only one immature bird from Thailand, the true subspecific identity of my specimen must remain in doubt. *A. g. khamensis*, the supposed breeding form of southeastern Tibet and Szechwan, is, if separable from *schvedowi*, the race most likely, on a basis of analogies, to occur in winter among the mountains of northwestern Thailand.

ACCIPITER BADIUS POLIOPSIS (Hume)

BURMESE SHIKRA

Micronisus poliopsis HUME, Stray Feathers, vol. 2, 1874, p. 325 (northern Pegu; type locality restricted to Thayetmyo, *ex* Hume, Stray Feathers, vol. 3, 1875, p. 24).

Astur poliopsis, GYLDENSTOLPE, Kungl. Svenska Vet.-Akad. Handl., 1913, p. 63 (Pak Pan).

Astur badius poliopsis, GYLDENSTOLPE, Journ. Nat. Hist. Soc. Siam, 1915, p. 234 (Khun Tan); Kungl. Svenska Vet.-Akad. Handl., 1916, p. 124 (Khun Tan, Pha Kho, Pang Hua Phong, Pak Ta); Ibis, 1920, p. 747 ("Throughout Siam").—DE SCHAUENSEE, Proc. Acad. Nat. Sci. Philadelphia, 1929, p. 579 (Chiang Mai, Chiang Rai, Chiang Saen).—DEIGNAN, Journ. Siam Soc. Nat. Hist. Suppl., 1931, p. 166 (Chiang Mai).

Accipiter gularis, GYLDENSTOLPE, Kungl. Svenska Vet.-Akad. Handl., 1916, p. 125 (Pha Kho, Khun Tan) ; Ibis, 1920, p. 746 (Pha Kho, Khun Tan).

Astur trivirgatus indicus, DE SCHAUENSEE, Proc. Acad. Nat. Sci. Philadelphia, 1934, p. 270 (Chiang Mai).

Accipiter badius klossi, DE SCHAUENSEE, Proc. Acad. Nat. Sci. Philadelphia, 1934, p. 270 (Chiang Mai).

Accipiter trivirgatus indicus, DEIGNAN, Journ. Siam Soc. Nat. Hist. Suppl., 1936, p. 76 (Chiang Mai).

Accipter badius poliopsis, DEIGNAN, Journ. Siam Soc. Nat. Hist. Suppl., 1936, p. 76 (Chiang Mai).—RILEY, U. S. Nat. Mus. Bull. 172, 1938, p. 46 (Chiang Dao).

Accipter gularis nisoides, DEIGNAN, Journ. Siam Soc. Nat. Hist. Suppl., 1931, p. 175 (Doi Suthep, Chiang Mai).

Accipiter virgatus nisoides, DEIGNAN, Journ. Siam Soc. Nat. Hist. Suppl., 1936, p. 76 (Doi Suthep).

The shikra is a very common permanent resident throughout northern Thailand. In the vicinity of Chiang Mai it occurred everywhere on the plain and ascended Doi Suthep, along the trails and in the more open forest, to 3,500 feet. A specimen in Hannover was taken by Eisenhofer at Pha Hing. The same collector sent to Stockholm one example from Huai Pu, and no less than 19 from Khun Tan. I took it at Chom Thong, Ban Nong Khiat, Ban Tha Nong Luang, Chiang Saen Kao, Ban Noi, Ban San Sai Mun, Ban Mae Dok Daeng Nai, Chiang Mai, and Doi Suthep and have seen it in Nan Province.

This is a fearless little hawk, more often observed in the neighborhood of human habitation than in wilder areas. One frequently seen in my compound at Chiang Mai used to conceal itself in the crown of a coconut palm, whence it would dash out after some unsuspecting myna; a great chase would then take place, the pursuer and pursued wheeling and dodging among the trees until the starling at last found shelter in the dense heart of a palm or fell victim to the bandit. One of my specimens, a large female, was shot while in the act of tearing to pieces a dove (*Streptopelia c. tigrina*), and de Schauensee (1929) took examples that had fed, one on a small bird, another on a small rodent; most stomachs examined, however, have contained insects, frogs, and lizards. A bird observed in northern Nan Province was beating the edge of an extensive grass fire, catching grasshoppers and other insects as they tried to escape the flames.

Apparently no birds in actual breeding condition have been taken in our area. Eisenhofer took juveniles at Huai Pu, June 4, 1912, and at Khun Tan, June 6, 1913, while Gyldenstolpe took similar examples at Pang Hua Phong, May 26 and 27, 1914. A number of my specimens had paired ovaries.

An adult male, taken by me on August 15, retains a few traces of the brown subadult plumage on the head and back. The third primary on each side has been molted and the new feather is still in sheath.

Adult males have the irides orange or orange-red; the bill black, plumbeous or slaty blue at the base; the cere green, or yellow with yellow-green at the sides; the feet and toes yellow; the claws black. Adult females differ only in having the irides golden-yellow. Immature birds are like the adults, but have the irides light yellow.

Adults have the upperparts from brownish slate to blue-gray, depending upon the age of the specimen; the visible portion of the rounded tail crossed by four black bands, rather indistinct in older birds; the throat white with a more or less distinct gray mesial stripe; the under tail coverts white; the remaining underparts closely barred everywhere pinkish rufous and white. Immature birds have the upperparts dark brown, with the white bases of the feathers showing through on head and nape; the throat white with a dark brown mesial stripe; the remaining underparts white, heavily marked with streaks and drops of rufous and dark brown. The fourth primary is longest, the third subequal.

My synonymy of this bird is based upon personal examination of all the specimens from our area in the museums of Europe and America.

The alleged characters of *klossi*, described by Kirke Swann from South Annam, are not constant even in a topotypical series. The name *Astur bifasciatus* of Peale cannot be used for the Indo-Chinese race, as has been done by Chasen (Birds of Malay Peninsula, vol. 4, 1939, p. 25). I have examined the type specimen in the U. S. National Museum and find it to be an immature female of *Accipiter virgatus gularis* Temminck and Schlegel.

ACCIPITER SOLOENSIS (Horsfield)

HORSFIELD'S SPARROW HAWK

Falco Soloensis HORSFIELD, Trans. Linn. Soc. London, vol. 13, 1821, p. 137 (Java).
Accipiter soloensis, GYLDENSTOLPE, Kungl. Svenska Vet.-Akad. Handl., 1916, p. 125 (Pha Kho); Ibis, 1920, p. 746 (Pha Kho).

Horsfield's sparrow hawk is likely to occur in winter anywhere in our provinces, but so far there are only three definite records: Gyldenstolpe took a female at Pha Kho, April 14, 1914; I collected an adult female at Ban Huai Mae Lit, October 1, 1936, and an adult male at Ban Huai Ki, March 28, 1937.

Gyldenstolpe has recorded that his bird was found perched upon a clump of bamboo near the banks of an almost dry creek. My specimen from Huai Ki was on a dead tree beside a small stream at the edge of light evergreen forest. The species seems to occur only in wild, uninhabited places.

The male had the irides dark brown; the bill black, plumbeous at the rictus; the cere orange; the feet and toes orange-yellow; the claws black. Gyldenstolpe's female had the irides yellow and the bill horn.

Adults have the upperparts dark slate, the scapulars with large white spots; the rounded tail with four obsolescent dark bands, the central feathers often immaculate; the throat white or rufous-white, each feather with a narrow dark gray shaft streak; the under tail coverts white; the remaining underparts varying, according to age of specimen, from pinkish rufous with indistinct, narrow buffy bars to immaculate vinaceous-pink; the under wing coverts white, washed with buff. Immature birds have the crown brownish slate; the remaining upperparts dark brown; the exposed portion of the tail with four indistinct dark bars; the throat white, with a narrow dark brown mesial line; the remaining underparts white, boldly marked on the breast with rufous-brown streaks and drops, which change to bars on the abdomen. The third primary is longest, the fourth subequal.

ACCIPITER TRIVIRGATUS INDICUS (Hodgson)

NORTHERN CRESTED GOSHAWK

[*Astur*] *Indicus* PARBATTIAH [=HODGSON], Bengal Sporting Mag., new ser., vol. 8, 1836, p. 177 (Nepal).

Lophospizias trivirgatus, GYLDENSTOLPE, Journ. Nat. Hist. Soc. Siam, 1915, p. 234 (listed).

Astur trivirgatus rufitinctus, GYLDENSTOLPE, Kungl. Svenska Vet.-Akad. Handl., 1916, p. 124 (Pha Kho); Ibis, 1920, p. 747 ("Northern . . . Siam").

Lophospizias trivirgatus rufitinctus, DE SCHAUENSEE, Proc. Acad. Nat. Sci. Philadelphia, 1929, p. 578 (Chiang Saen).

Lophospiza indica, RILEY, U. S. Nat. Mus. Bull. 172, 1938, p. 48 (Khun Tan, Doi Langka).

This large accipitrine is not common but seems to be generally distributed in the northern provinces throughout the year. A female in the Stockholm Museum, taken by Eisenhofer at Khun Tan in 1914, is probably the bird listed by Gyldenstolpe in 1915; a specimen in Hannover was taken by the same collector at Pha Hing, May 4, 1912. I obtained a male about 6 km. south of Muang Chiang Dao, August 17, 1935.

Gyldenstolpe has observed that the species seems to avoid evergreen jungles and the lower valleys with their dense vegetation, and it was met with only in the deciduous forest or in thin tree jungle. My own experience has been precisely the same. The stomach of my specimen contained small frogs.

The bird had the irides golden-orange; the orbital region and lores greenish yellow; the cere and rictus yellow; the maxilla black; the mandible plumbeous, tipped black; the feet and toes bright yellow; the claws black.

Adults have the crown and short nuchal crest brownish black; the upperparts dark brown; the exposed portion of the rounded tail crossed by four blackish bars; the throat white with a broad blackish mesial streak; the remaining underparts white, with broad rufous-brown streaks on the breast, rufous-brown bars elsewhere. Immatures have the feathers of the head and nape edged pale rufous; the underparts buffy white, with a blackish mesial stripe on the throat, broad blackish streaks on the breast, and similar streaks of brown on the sides of the body; the thighs thickly barred brown and buffy. The fourth primary is longest, the fifth subequal.

ACCIPITER VIRGATUS AFFINIS Hodgson

NEPALESE BESRA

[*Accipiter*] *affinis* PARBATTIAH [=HODGSON], Bengal Sporting Mag., new ser. vol. 8, 1836, p. 179 (Nepal).

I have twice taken this bird at Chiang Mai: an immature male, November 25, 1935, and an adult male, February 29, 1936. It is probably only a winter visitor.

The immature specimen had the irides deep yellow; the eyelids yellow; the cere, lores, and rictus olive-green; the bill black, plumbeous at the base; the tarsi dull olive in front, bright yellow behind; the toes bright yellow; the claws black. The adult had the irides orange, but I have no record of the colors of other soft parts.

The adult male has the upperparts dark slate; the exposed portion of the *square*-tipped tail with four broad blackish bands, the basal sometimes concealed by the coverts; the throat white, with a broad blackish mesial stripe; the upper breast pale rufous, barred with white in the center; the remaining underparts white, with fairly broad pale rufous bars; the under tail coverts white. The adult female differs in having the upperparts dark brown, blackish on the head and nape. Immatures have the upperparts dark brown with four broad blackish bands across the tail; the throat white, with a broad blackish mesial stripe; the remaining underparts boldly streaked black and dull rufous on the breast, barred dull rufous on the abdomen. The fourth and fifth primaries are longest and equal.

ACCIPITER VIRGATUS GULARIS (Temminck and Schlegel)

JAPANESE BESRA

Astur (*Nisus*) *gularis* TEMMINCK and SCHLEGEL, *in* Siebold, Fauna Japonica, Aves, 1850 [=1844], pp. 5–6, col. pl. 2 (Japan).

Accipiter virgatus, GYLDENSTOLPE, Journ. Nat. Hist. Soc. Siam, 1915, p. 234 (listed).

Accipiter virgatus virgatus, GYLDENSTOLPE, Ibis, 1920, p. 746 (Khun Tan).

The specimen upon which Gyldenstolpe's record is based is in Stockholm; it is an adult male, taken by Eisenhofer at Khun Tan in 1914. The only other example known from our area is an adult male, collected for de Schauensee at Chiang Saen Kao, April 20, 1935, and now deposited in Philadelphia.

Adult males have the upperparts dark slate, almost black, with four blackish bands across the exposed portion of the *square*-tipped tail; the throat white, with a mere hairstreak of blackish down the center; the remaining underparts white, with ill-defined pale rufous barring everywhere. Adult females have the upperparts blackish brown; the mesial stripe of the throat broader than in the male; the remaining underparts barred distinctly everywhere with white and dull brownish rufous. Immature specimens are colored like the corresponding age of *solöensis*, but are distinguishable by their longer, slenderer tarsi and toes, and the different wing formula. The fourth primary is longest, then come the third and the fifth.

BUTASTUR INDICUS (Gmelin)

GRAY-FACED BUZZARD EAGLE

[*Falco*] *indicus* GMELIN, Systema naturae, vol. 1, pt. 1, 1788, p. 264 (Java, *ex* Latham).

Butastur indicus, GYLDENSTOLPE, Journ. Nat. Hist. Soc. Siam, 1915, p. 234 (listed); Ibis, 1920, p. 748 (Khun Tan).—DE SCHAUENSEE, Proc. Acad. Nat. Sci. Philadelphia, 1929, p. 578 (Doi Suthep); 1934, p. 270 (Chiang Mai).—DEIGNAN, Journ. Siam Soc. Nat. Hist. Suppl., 1931, p. 166 (Doi Suthep); 1936, p. 76 (Doi Suthep, Chiang Mai).

This buzzard eagle, which breeds in Japan and northern China, is a regular but rather uncommon winter visitor to the plains and foothills of northern Thailand. A specimen in Hannover was taken by Eisenhofer at Pha Hing, April 26, 1912; I believe that Gyldenstolpe's record for Khun Tan (1920) refers to the same specimen and that the locality is erroneous as published. De Schauensee's birds from Chiang Mai and Doi Suthep (1,500 feet) were taken December 26, 1928, and January 25 and 29, 1933. I collected an adult female about 21 km. west of Ban Mae Rim, December 2, 1935, and an immature male at Ban Na Noi (Nan Province), April 2, 1937.

This is a tame and somewhat sluggish species. The Mae Rim bird was shot from a low tree at a clearing beside a jungle road; the Na Noi specimen was perched upon a bush growing in a dry and fallow ricefield. De Schauensee found his birds in dry deciduous forest at the base of Doi Suthep. The Na Noi specimen had a large centipede in its stomach.

My birds had the irides golden-yellow; the orbital skin pale yellow; the bill black, yellow at the base; the cere and rictus yellow; the feet and toes yellow; the claws black.

Adults have the lores and a patch on each side of the forehead white; the sides of the head brownish gray; the upperparts dark brown, the feathers of the crown and upper back tipped and edged rufous, the upper tail coverts tipped white; the exposed portion of the tail crossed by three black bars; the throat white, with a broad black mesial stripe; the breast grayish rufous-brown with white spots; the under tail coverts white; the remaining underparts barred white and grayish rufous-brown. Immatures have the upperparts brown, washed with rufous; the underparts white, on the breast streaked with rufous-brown, on the abdomen barred with the same color; the other parts as in the adults.

BUTASTUR LIVENTER (Temminck)

Rufous-winged Buzzard Eagle

Falco liventer Temminck, Nouveau recueil de planches coloriées d'oiseaux, livr. 74, 1827, pl. 438 (Celebes, Sumatra, Java, and India).

Butastur liventer, Gyldenstolpe, Journ. Nat. Hist Soc. Siam, 1915, p. 234 (listed); Ibis, 1920, p. 747 (Khun Tan).—de Schauensee, Proc. Acad. Nat. Sci. Philadelphia, 1929, p. 578 (Chiang Saen).—Deignan, Journ. Siam Soc. Nat. Hist. Suppl., 1931, p. 166 (Doi Suthep); 1936, p. 76 (Doi Suthep).

The rufous-winged buzzard eagle is a not uncommon permanent resident of the deciduous forests of the plains and the lower hills (to 2,700 feet). A specimen in Stockholm was taken by Eisenhofer at Khun Tan and is probably the one mentioned by Gyldenstolpe. I have observed the species near Wiang Pa Pao in April and have collected it at Chiang Mai in September and January and at Ban Salaeng, May 1, 1936.

Near Chiang Mai, in March, I watched a pair that were doubtless about to breed. They were in hot, leafless woods, and one pursued the other from treetop to treetop, or followed it up into the air, where they swooped and dived, both uttering a loud and continuous squealing.

The stomach of one of my specimens was filled with crabs.

Owing to the coarse, hard leaves of the type of jungle inhabited by these birds, the plumage becomes very worn and the color washed out. My May specimen has the feathers very frayed. The bird of September 24 has the second primary on each side partly ensheathed and the second rectrix from outside on each side not fully grown.

An adult male had the irides lemon-yellow; the orbital skin, lores, and cere deep yellow; the basal half of the bill horny yellow, the rest black; the feet and toes deep yellow; the claws black.

Mature birds in fresh plumage have the feathers of the head and upper back light brownish gray with blackish shafts; the remaining upperparts rufous with black shafts; the tail deep rufous with a blackish subterminal band and about three narrow, incomplete bars of black; the throat mixed white and gray; the breast light brownish gray with dark shafts to the feathers, changing sometimes to indistinct white and pale rufous barring on the abdomen; the remaining underparts pure white; an indistinct pale rufous-gray area on the shoulder; the primaries deep rufous, barred and broadly tipped with black; the edge of the wing and the under wing coverts pure white.

A smallish hawk with gray head and breast, rufous wings and tail, and most of the face and bill deep yellow, this species is unmistakable.

SPIZATEUS NIPALENSIS FOKIENSIS W. L. Sclater

CHINESE CRESTED HAWK EAGLE

Spizaetus nipalensis fokiensis W. L. SCLATER, Bull. Brit. Orn. Club, vol. 40, 1919, p. 37 (Fuhkien Province, South China).

Spizaetus limnaetus, GYLDENSTOLPE, Journ. Nat. Hist. Soc. Siam, 1915, p. 233 (listed).

Spizaetus cirrhatus limnaetus, GYLDENSTOLPE, Ibis, 1920, p. 743 (Khun Tan).

Spizaetus nipalensis fokiensis, DE SCHAUENSEE, Proc. Acad. Nat. Sci. Philadelphia, 1934, p. 270 (Doi Suthep).—DEIGNAN, Journ. Siam Soc. Nat. Hist. Suppl., 1936, p. 77 (Doi Suthep).

The status of this large hawk is uncertain. De Schauensee took a female on Doi Suthep at 4,500 feet, February 27, 1933, and Eisenhofer sent to Stockholm two skins without other data than Khun Tan; otherwise there are no definite records. In the jungle on Doi Suthep I frequently saw birds that may have been this form but was never able to take specimens for verification.

An adult specimen from southeastern Thailand has the feathers of the head pale brown, more pale rufous on the nape, with blackish centers; the long, narrow crest feathers black with pale, narrow tips; the upperparts dark brown; the tail crossed by four blackish bands; the throat rufous-white, with a conspicuous black mesial stripe and a black stripe at each side; the underparts fulvous-brown on the breast, chocolate-brown on the abdomen and thighs, spotted with black and white on the throat and breast, barred with white elsewhere; most of the underwing boldly barred black and white, but a large area about the center barred gray and white; the tarsi densely feathered onto the base of the toes. Immature birds differ chiefly in having the head, neck, and underparts fulvous-white.

I have examined the specimens in Stockholm upon which Gyldenstolpe based his northern record for *Spizaetus cirrhatus limnaeetus* and have decided that they must be referred to the present form. Both have much more highly developed crests and heavier, stronger claws than *limnaeetus*.

HIERAAËTUS KIENERII FORMOSUS Stresemann

SOUTHERN RUFOUS-BELLIED HAWK EAGLE

Hieraaëtus kieneri formosus STRESEMANN, Orn. Monatsb., vol. 32, 1924, pp. 108–109 (North Celebes.)

Hieraaëtus kienerii kienerii, DEIGNAN, Journ. Siam Soc. Nat. Hist. Suppl., 1936, p. 76 (Doi Suthep).

The rufous-bellied eagle seems to be a bird of considerable rarity in Thailand. I have three sight records for the species: One at 5,500 feet on Doi Suthep, February 1, 1936; one at 4,000 feet, February 6, 1937, on the same mountain; one in the foothills to the south of Suthep, February 15, 1936. The only northern Thai specimen was taken by the Asiatic Primate Expedition in 1937 on Doi Ang Ka; the data for this bird have not yet been published.

The adult has the long, narrow crest feathers, the sides of the head, and the entire upperparts black; the throat white, with a few black streaks at each side; the remaining underparts bright rufous, with black shaft streaks; the under wing coverts rufous; the rest of the underwing barred blackish and gray, but a large area at the center pale gray, the bars being obsolescent; the tarsi feathered. The immature is quite different and entirely lacks rufous coloration.

All Thai birds probably belong to the southern race, *formosus*, which is distinguished from the typical form (Himalayas) only by smaller dimensions. Stresemann states that the wing length of *kienerii* varies from 356 (male) to 444 mm. (female); of *formosus*, from 324 (male) to 382 mm. (female). James C. Greenway, Jr., of the Museum of Comparative Zoology, has informed me in a letter that the Ang Ka specimen is a female with a wing length of 369 mm.

AQUILA RAPAX VINDHIANA Franklin

INDIAN TAWNY EAGLE

Aquila Vindhiana FRANKLIN, Proc. Comm. Sci. Corr. Zool. Soc. London, 1830–1831 [=1831], p. 114 (Vindhya Hills, central India).

Aquila rapax vindhiana, DE SCHAUENSEE, Proc. Acad. Nat. Sci. Philadelphia, 1929, p. 577 (Chiang Mai).—DEIGNAN, Journ. Siam Soc. Nat. Hist. Suppl., 1931, p. 165 (Chiang Mai); 1936, p. 77 (Chiang Mai).

A female taken by de Schauensee at Chiang Mai, December 20, 1928, constitutes the only definite record for the tawny eagle in Thailand.

This specimen had the apical half of the maxilla horny black, the basal half olive-gray; the mandible olive-gray, tipped black; the cere olive-yellow; the toes yellow; the claws black.

This is a very large species which exhibits great individual variation in coloration. An adult example in Washington has the general plumage light brown; the primaries blackish; the blackish brown secondaries and the greater wing coverts tipped fulvous-white, giving the appearance of two narrow, light wing bars; the upper tail coverts tipped fulvous-white; the tarsi feathered to the toes; the nostril elliptical, higher than broad.

AQUILA CLANGA Pallas

GREATER SPOTTED EAGLE

Aquila Clanga PALLAS, Zoographia Rosso-asiatica, vol. 1, 1811, pp. 351–352 (Russia and Siberia to Kamchatka).

Aquila nipalensis, DE SCHAUENSEE, Proc. Acad. Nat. Sci. Philadelphia, 1929, p. 577 (Chiang Mai).

Aquila nipalensis nipalensis, DEIGNAN, Journ. Siam Soc. Nat. Hist. Suppl., 1931, p. 165 (Chiang Mai); 1936, p. 77 (Chiang Mai).

A male taken by de Schauensee at Chiang Mai, December 20, 1928, is the only definite record for our area.

This specimen had the irides brown, mixed with yellow; the apical half of the maxilla black and the basal half gray-green; the cere olive-yellow, brighter at the rictus; the claws black.

Adults are in general dark chocolate-brown. Immature birds differ in having the upper tail coverts mixed with brownish white; the upper wing coverts with brownish white or light brown tips; the ends of the secondaries mottled with light brown or brownish white, which sometimes forms a broad wing bar; the underparts streaked everywhere with light brown. The tarsi are feathered to the toes and the nostril is round, as broad as high.

De Schauensee and I have reexamined together the specimen upon which his record of *A. nipalensis* was based and agree that it must be referred to *clanga*.

ICTINAËTUS MALAYENSIS (Temminck)

MALAYAN BLACK EAGLE

Falco malayensis "Reinw." TEMMINCK, Nouveau recueil de planches coloriées d'oiseaux, livr. 20, 1822, pl. 117 ("dans toutes les îles du grand archipel des Indes . . . principalement à Java et à Sumatra"; type locality restricted to Java, by Kirke Swann, Synopsis of the Accipitres, ed. 2, 1922, p. 115).

Ictinaëtus malayensis perniger, DEIGNAN, Journ. Siam Soc. Nat. Hist. Suppl., 1931, p. 175 (Doi Suthep).—DE SCHAUENSEE, Proc. Acad. Nat. Sci. Philadelphia, 1934, p. 270 (Doi Suthep).

Ictinaëtus malayensis, DEIGNAN, Journ. Siam Soc. Nat. Hist. Suppl. 1936, p. 77 (Doi Suthep).

I collected a male on Doi Suthep, 5,500 feet, June 13, 1931; de Schauensee took a female at the same locality, February 20, 1933. I have seen the species soaring over Doi Chiang Dao at 5,000 and 7,000 feet, and the members of the Asiatic Primate Expedition found it on Doi Ang Ka. It is probably generally distributed over our provinces wherever the mountains reach great elevations.

A family of these fine birds used to be a familiar sight at the summit of Suthep, swooping low over the bungalows and soaring gracefully out over the mountain slopes. In April 1931 a pair nested and produced two young in a high tree just below and in sight of the windows of one of the cabins. When I left Thailand in 1937 at least two individuals were still in evidence in the neighborhood, although the old nest had not been used again.

My specimen had the irides brown; the eyelids white; the lores gray; the cere and rictus yellow; the bill black, with a plumbeous zone adjacent to the cere; the feet and toes yellow; the claws black.

This is a large blackish-brown eagle, with a noticeable whitish area from the base of the bill to and around the eye. Immature birds are colored a lighter brown.

ICTHYOPHAGA ICHTHYAETUS ICHTHYAETUS (Horsfield)

INDIAN GREATER FISHING EAGLE

Falco Ichthyaetus HORSFIELD, Trans. Linn. Soc. London, vol. 13, 1821, pp. 136–137 (Java).

Polioaëtus ichtyaëtus, GYLDENSTOLPE, Kungl. Svenska Vet.-Akad. Handl., 1916, p. 123 (Nong Mae Rua).

Polioaëtus ichthyaëtus, GYLDENSTOLPE, Ibis, 1920, p. 750 ("Along the larger rivers of northern Siam").

The only specimen from our provinces is a male in Stockholm, taken by Gyldenstolpe at Nong Mae Rua (near Chiang Saen Kao), August 6, 1914. I used to see solitary individuals occasionally on the large marshes between Chiang Mai and Lamphun, and recorded one at Nong Khiat, November 29, 1931, and another at Mae Chai, May 9 and 10, 1936. Gyldenstolpe considered it to be fairly common at suitable localities.

As Gyldenstolpe has observed (1916), this eagle "inhabits well wooded tracts where large rivers and swamps abound." At such places it may often be seen quietly resting on the marsh, but it takes off with slow, heavy flight long before one comes within gunshot range of it.

Gyldenstolpe notes that his bird had the irides yellowish white; the bill horn color, plumbeous at the base; the feet and toes whitish gray.

The adult of this huge species has the head and neck gray, more brownish above; the upperparts dark brown; the tail white, with the apical third black; the breast and upper abdomen brown; the remaining underparts pure white. The immature has the white parts mottled with brown.

ICTHYOPHAGA NANA NANA (Blyth)

MALAYAN LESSER FISHING EAGLE

Icthyaetus nanus BLYTH, Journ. Asiat. Soc. Bengal, vol. 11, 1842, p. 202 (Malay Peninsula; type locality restricted to Singapore, *apud* Stuart Baker).

Polioaëtus humilis, GYLDENSTOLPE, Journ. Nat. Hist. Soc. Siam, 1915, p. 234 (listed); Ibis, 1920, p. 750 (Khun Tan).

The only definite record for northern Thailand is based upon a female specimen taken by Eisenhofer at Khun Tan and now deposited in the museum at Stockholm.

This is said to be a bird of forested waterways and not to occur on marshes and ricefields as does the preceding species. Doubtless it will be found to be not uncommon along our larger rivers.

It is a much smaller bird than the last and differs in color chiefly by having the central rectrices entirely brown and the lateral ones mottled brown and white on the basal two-thirds (sometimes wholly brown in very old specimens).

I have examined the skin in Stockholm and find that the flattened wing measures 401 mm. (its arc, 392 mm.); so small a female clearly belongs with the Malayan race.

SARCOGYPS CALVUS (Scopoli)

INDIAN KING VULTURE

Vultur (*calvus*) SCOPOLI, Deliciae florae et faunae insubricae, pt. 2, 1786, p. 85 (Pondicherry, *ex* Sonnerat).

Otogyps calvus, GYLDENSTOLPE, Kungl. Svenska Vet.-Akad. Handl., 1916, p. 132 ("Northern Siam").—DE SCHAUENSEE, Proc. Acad. Nat. Sci. Philadelphia, 1928, p. 576 (Den Chai).

Sarcogyps calvus, DEIGNAN, Journ. Siam Soc. Nat. Hist. Suppl., 1931, p. 164 (Chiang Mai, Doi Suthep); 1936, p. 77 (Chiang Mai, Doi Suthep).—DE SCHAUENSEE, Proc. Acad. Nat. Sci. Philadelphia, 1934, p. 269 (Khun Tan).

The king vulture is common everywhere in our provinces; it occurs chiefly on the plains but may also be seen soaring above even the highest peaks. It may be found feeding with *Pseudogyps* wherever there is carrion, but always in comparatively small numbers.

At Chiang Mai this species repaired to the trees on the lower slopes of Doi Suthep to roost; only occasionally were individuals observed to pass the night in the trees of the town.

In spite of the commonness of this bird, I have only once found evidence of its breeding: On Doi Suthep at 1,800 feet, May 31, 1930, I took a fully grown immature that was perched beside a large nest of sticks about 60 feet from the ground in a dipterocarp.

An adult female had the irides light yellow; the bill dark brown, the mandible lighter; the cere rose-pink; the bare skin of the head and neck mottled pink and white, with black macules; the wattles pink; the bare skin on the sides of the abdomen and inside the thighs livid white; the feet and toes mottled pink and white; the soles light brown; the claws black.

An immature specimen differed in having the irides dull brown; the cere blue-gray; the maxilla dark horn-brown; the mandible blue-gray, horny at the tip; the naked skin of the head livid white; the feet and toes livid white; the claws black.

This vulture has very broad wings and a comparatively short wedge-shaped tail. The naked head and wattled neck, the feet, and a bare area on the inner thigh are reddish and conspicuous in flight.

The adult is generally black, with a large chest patch of pure white down, continued up the sides of the neck to meet a ruff of black feathers on the back of the neck; it has a similar patch of white down along either flank. The immature has the general plumage brown and the head and neck covered with white down.

PSEUDOGYPS BENGALENSIS (Gmelin)

INDIAN WHITE-BACKED VULTURE

[*Vultur*] *bengalensis* GMELIN, Systema naturae, vol. 1, pt. 1, 1788, pp. 245–246 (Bengal).

Pseudogyps bengalensis, GYLDENSTOLPE, Kungl. Svenska Vet.-Akad. Handl., 1916, p. 131 (Chiang Mai); Ibis, 1920, p. 743 ("Throughout the whole country").—DE SCHAUENSEE, Proc. Acad. Nat. Sci. Philadelphia, 1928, p. 576 (Den Chai).—DEIGNAN, Journ. Siam Soc. Nat. Hist. Suppl., 1931, p. 164 (Chiang Mai, Doi Suthep); 1936, p. 77 (Chiang Mai, Doi Suthep).

The white-backed vulture is very common throughout our area, but, unlike the preceding species, it has not been observed at high altitudes.

While the vultures are feeding they can be closely approached, and the sight of a large number of these birds, together with a few king vultures, devouring a dead cow or buffalo, is a familiar but wholly repulsive one. The heavier and stronger *Sarcogyps* takes its fill first, while the white backs wait respectfully; the leaving of the king is a signal for the impatient hordes to crowd forward over the cadaver. They are quarrelsome birds, and the beating of wings, the craning of long snaky necks, the growling and hissing that take place, especially when two individuals begin to devour a strip of entrals from the opposite ends, are horrible beyond description. As the observer comes too near, they spread the great wings and cover the ground with clumsy leaps; they seem incapable at any time of taking to the air without this preliminary, and when gorged are highly unwilling, if not unable, to leave the ground. After the feast has been devoured to the bones, the banqueters stand torpidly about the remains or move off only to the branches of the nearest trees, which they line while digestion takes place.

583136—45——6

The vultures are inactive on dark days and in the morning before the warmth of the sun is felt, but at other times they are rarely out of sight somewhere in the sky. At Chiang Mai the present species roosted in some numbers in trees on the lower slopes of Suthep and, in addition, had certain favorite tall trees in the city, where numbers slept together.

The whiteback often breeds in the neighborhood of villages, if there are trees sufficiently large. Gyldenstolpe reported seeing several nests near Chiang Mai. I saw a bird on a nest along the Chiang Mai–Ko Klang road, March 8, 1937, and another brooding near Chiang Rai, May 5, 1936.

A male from Chiang Mai had the irides yellowish brown; the eyelids plumbeous-blue; the skin of the head dusky gray; the neck plumbeous, mottled with dusky gray; the bill slaty, with the base of the culmen olive-plumbeous; the cere black; the feet and toes black, the scutes edged with gray; the claws black.

The adult has the upperparts brown, with lower back and rump white; the primaries and tail blackish; a white ruff around the neck, not connected across the chest; the underparts light brown, with flanks white. The immature has the upperparts dark brown; the underparts dark brown with light brown shaft streaks; the ruff, flanks, and lower back white, as in the adult; the under wing coverts pure white, forming a large area conspicuous in flight; the head and neck covered with white down.

CIRCUS MELANOLEUCOS (Pennant)

PIED HARRIER

Falco melanoleucos PENNANT, Indian zoology, 1769, p. 2, pl. 2 (Ceylon).

Circus melanoleucus, GYLDENSTOLPE, Journ. Nat. Hist. Soc. Siam, 1915, p. 234 (listed); Kungl. Svenska Vet.-Akad. Handl., 1916, p. 123 (Khun Tan, Mae Tha river, Nong Bia); Ibis, 1920, p. 748 ("Northern Siam").—DE SCHAUENSEE, Proc. Acad. Nat. Sci. Philadelphia, 1929, p. 579 (Chiang Mai, Chiang Saen, 30 km. north of Chiang Rai).—DEIGNAN, Journ. Siam Soc. Nat. Hist. Suppl., 1931, p. 166 (Chiang Mai); 1936, p. 77 (Chiang Mai).

The pied harrier is a common and widely distributed winter visitor from October 4 (Chiang Mai) to April 15 (Chiang Dao). The latter date is based upon a specimen in Stockholm taken by Dr. P. Fejos. I have collected it at Chiang Mai, Chom Thong, Mae Sariang, and Ban Mae Chai Tai and have observed it at numerous other lowland localities.

Of the three harriers now known from northern Thailand, only the present species occurs in great numbers. It is to be seen flying low over the ricefields and marshes, a graceful, long-winged, long-tailed hawk, which systematically quarters the ground and occasionally hovers at one spot, then dives to the kill. De Schauensee has recorded that one of his specimens had a lizard in its stomach; stomachs I examined usually contained frogs, but once a small snake and once a munia (*Lonchura* sp.).

Specimens taken in Thailand show no gonadal activity. In at least some cases, the female of this species has paired ovaries.

An immature male, taken at Chiang Mai, January 14, is acquiring the central tail feathers of the adult; they are about four-fifths grown. An adult female from Ban Mae Chai Tai, December 27, has also molted the central rectrices: one of the new feathers is about four-fifths grown, the other one-half.

I have noted that an adult male had the irides dark brown; the bill brownish black; the feet and toes chrome-yellow. De Schauensee records that an immature male had the irides light yellow; the cere olive-yellow; the bill black, gray at the base; the rictus green above, blue below; the interior of the mouth dark slaty blue; the feet and toes bright yellow; the claws black.

The adult male is an unmistakable bird, with the head, throat, breast, back, outer scapulars, quills, and median upper wing coverts black; the rump and a large shoulder patch grayish white; the tail, inner scapulars, and greater wing coverts silvery gray; the underparts pure white; the under wing coverts white, the remaining underwing black. The adult female has the upperparts brown, streaked on the head and the coverts along the forearm with rufous and white; the upper tail coverts white with rufous-brown markings along the shafts; the tail crossed by about five darker brown bars; the underparts white, heavily streaked with brown. Immature birds are dark brown above, with the upper tail coverts white, marked with brown; dark brownish rufous below.

CIRCUS AERUGINOSUS AERUGINOSUS (Linnaeus)

Western Marsh Harrier

[*Falco*] *aeruginosus* Linnaeus, Systema naturae, ed. 10, vol. 1, 1758, p. 91 (Europe; type locality restricted to Sweden, *apud* Hartert).

Circus aeruginosus, de Schauensee, Proc. Acad. Nat. Sci. Philadelphia, 1929, p. 579 (Chiang Mai).

Circus aeruginosus aeruginosus, Deignan, Journ. Siam Soc. Nat. Hist. Suppl., 1931, p. 166 (Chiang Mai); 1936, p. 77 (Chiang Mai).

An undated female specimen in Stockholm was taken by Eisenhofer at Khun Tan; otherwise the only definite records for our area are based upon a female collected by de Schauensee at Chiang Mai, December 25, 1928, and two specimens taken by me at the same locality, December 5, 1931. The species is only a winter visitor to northern Thailand, where it probably occurs in small numbers in all the provinces.

My specimens, which I supposed to be immature Brahminy kites, were taken on one of the large marshes south of Chiang Mai. The stomach of one contained fishes; that of the other, fishes, a small snake, and feathers of a grebe.

These birds had the irides brown; the orbital skin, lores, and eyelids plumbeous-blue; the maxilla black; the mandible black, with the basal half plumbeous-blue; the rictus and interior of the mouth plumbeous-blue; the cere yellow; the feet and toes yellow; the claws black.

This is a large, heavy harrier, whose flight is much less buoyant than that of *melanoleucos*. The adult male has the head, hindneck, throat, breast, and coverts along the forearm light rufous to buffy white, heavily streaked with black or dark brown; the remaining underparts rufous with black shaft streaks; the back, scapulars, and most wing coverts dark brown, edged rufous; the upper tail coverts mixed white, gray, and rufous; the tail silvery gray; the primaries black; the secondaries and greater wing coverts silvery gray, forming a broad band across the wing; the basal half of the underwing pure white, the rest black. The adult female has the head, hindneck, and upper back dark brown, heavily streaked with white; the back, coverts, and scapulars dark brown with rufous edgings; the upper tail coverts white, with rufous spots or bars; the tail gray-brown, crossed by about five more or less distinct dark bars; the underparts white, streaked everywhere with rufous, the streaks more brownish on the throat and breast. Immatures are generally dark chocolate-brown above and below, sometimes dark rufous on the abdomen, with the throat, crown, and hindneck white to buffy, with or without blackish shaft streaks, but there are many intermediate stages between the immature and adult plumages.

SPILORNIS CHEELA BURMANICUS Kirke Swann

BURMESE SERPENT EAGLE

Spilornis cheela burmanicus KIRKE SWANN, A synoptical list of the Accipitres, 1920, p. 81 (Jobin, Thayetmyo, Pegu, Burma).

Spilornis cheela rutherfordi, GYLDENSTOLPE, Kungl. Svenska Vet.-Akad. Handl., 1913, p. 62 (Mae Yom river); 1916, p. 127 (Khun Tan); Journ. Nat. Hist. Soc. Siam, 1915, p. 234 (listed).

Spilornis cheela burmanicus, GYLDENSTOLPE, Ibis, 1920, p. 745 ("Throughout the country").—GREENWAY, Bull. Mus. Comp. Zool., 1940, p. 194 (Chiang Mai).

Spilornis cheela ricketti, DE SCHAUENSEE, Proc. Acad. Nat. Sci. Philadelphia, 1929, p. 577 (Doi Suthep, Chiang Mai).

Haematornis cheela ricketti, DEIGNAN, Journ. Siam Soc. Nat. Hist. Suppl., 1931, p. 165 (Chiang Mai, Doi Suthep).

Haematornis cheela burmanicus, DEIGNAN, Journ. Siam. Soc. Nat. Hist. Suppl., 1936, p. 78 (Chiang Mai, Doi Suthep).

From the plains to the mountain summits, the serpent eagle is a common permanent resident in forested districts throughout the northern provinces. In Stockholm are eight adults and two juveniles, without dates, all taken by Eisenhofer at Khun Tan. I have collected this bird at Chiang Mai, on Doi Suthep, along the Mae Sa river (about 15 km. northwest of Chiang Mai), at Wiang Fa Pao, and at Muang Ngop and have observed it at many other localities.

This magnificent eagle may be seen quietly perched in a tree at the edge of a path or clearing in the jungle, but it spends much of its time wheeling high in the air above the forest canopy, its presence made known by a characteristic plaintive scream, which can be heard even when the bird (or birds, for they are usually in pairs) is invisible in the sky.

The stomach of one of my specimens, taken on Doi Suthep, contained crabs and a small snake; the latter has been identified by Dr. Doris M. Cochran, of the U. S. National Museum, as *Simotes* (*Holarchus*) *violaceus*.

A male taken by me at San Sai Luang, near Chiang Mai, February 27, had the gonads slightly enlarged.

Birds taken in July were found to be in molt. An adult of July 6 has the second primary largely ensheathed, one central rectrix half-grown, the other somewhat shorter. An adult of July 27 has the first primary only half-grown.

Adult examples had the irides golden-yellow; the lower eyelid livid white, edged bright yellow; the upper eyelid, orbital region, lores, rictus, and cere bright yellow; the bill plumbeous with the apical half black; the feet and toes yellow; the claws black.

This is one of the most easily identifiable of our large hawks. When a perching individual is alarmed, the crest is erected so as to frame the face with a beautiful black and white ruff. From below, a flying bird may be known at once by the broad whitish bar, edged by two black bands, across the primaries, and by the broad whitish bar across the middle of the blackish tail.

The adult has the crown and a full, rounded nuchal crest black, with the basal half of each feather pure white, these bases showing through in places when the crest is not raised; the upperparts dark brown; the coverts along the forearm with small white spots, the other coverts like the back; the visible portion of the tail feathers black, with the base brown, a broad band across the center brownish white, the extreme tip whitish; the throat and sides of the head grayish brown; the remaining underparts brown, with blackish-bordered white ocellations on the abdomen, changing to bars on the thighs and under tail coverts; the primaries black, with a broad gray-brown band near the end and two other gray-brown bands near the base, these mottled with white on the inner web; the underwing broadly barred black and white. The immature is quite different: it has the feathers of the crown and crest fulvous-white with a blackish-brown subapical bar; the upperparts brown, each feather brownish white at the base and narrowly tipped whitish; the tail with three comparatively narrow blackish bands and three light bands, mottled brown and whitish; the underparts fulvous-white with narrow blackish-brown shaft streaks on the breast and abdomen; the primaries with broad gray-brown bars, separated by much narrower blackish-brown bands.

The wing lengths of three nonmolting adults are 428 mm. (male), 444 and 457 mm. (females). The largest female was taken June 15, and must be considered an example of the resident form. Gyldenstolpe has recorded (1916) a male from Khun Tan with a wing of only 300 mm., but this must certainly be an error.

Family PANDIONIDAE

PANDION HALIAETUS HALIAETUS (Linnaeus)

EURASIAN OSPREY

[*Falco*] *Haliaetus* LINNAEUS, Systema naturae, ed. 10, vol. 1, 1758, p. 91 (Europe; type locality restricted to Sweden, *apud* Hartert).

Pandion haliaetus haliaetus, DEIGNAN, Journ. Siam Soc. Nat. Hist. Suppl., 1931, p. 164 (Chiang Mai); 1936, pp. 78, 132 (Chiang Mai, Ban Mut Ka).

While the osprey is common enough on the great rivers of Central Thailand, it seems to be quite rare in the northern provinces, although it might occur occasionally almost anywhere along the major streams. I saw an adult at a small pond near the Mae Ping at Chiang Mai from December 29, 1930, to January 2, 1931; another at the woodland pond near Ban Pa Muat, November 23, 1936; a third at some extensive cliffs on the left bank of the Mae Ping just north of Ban Mut Ka, December 23, 1935. Delacour and Greenway found the species common along the Mae Khong, so it must occur at Chiang Khong and Chiang Saen. The locality nearest our area where the bird has actually been taken is Rahaeng; a specimen in Washington was collected there by Gairdner, February 26, 1916.

The osprey is normally observed over bodies of water, for its diet is composed almost entirely of fish. When a fish is sighted from above, the bird hovers at one point in the air, in the manner of a kestrel, then plunges with closed wings upon its victim. The call, which is uttered frequently, whether the bird is perched or in flight, is a series of sharp, shrill whistles, rapidly given, such as I have heard from no other Thai species.

The adult has the head and neck white, broadly streaked on the crown and nape with dark brown; a broad dark brown band from the eye down the side of the neck, joining with the dark brown of the upperparts; the lower plumage white, more or less heavily marked with brown on the breast; the under wing coverts mixed brown and white. The immature is similar, but has the feathers of the upperparts boldly edged whitish and the head and neck more heavily marked with dark brown.

The osprey might be confused with the immature serpent eagle, which is sometimes seen near water. The latter is crested, does not hover, has a quite different call, and has the wing and tail broadly and very conspicuously barred.

Family FALCONIDAE

FALCO PEREGRINUS HARTERTI Buturlin

SIBERIAN PEREGRINE

Falco peregrinus harterti BUTURLIN, Psovaia i Ruzheinaia Okhota, vol. 13, 1907, p. 100 (Lower Lena to Anadyr, common on the Kolyma).[2]

Falco peregrinus calidus, DE SCHAUENSEE, Proc. Acad. Nat. Sci. Philadelphia, 1929, p. 576 (Chiang Rai).—DEIGNAN, Journ. Siam Soc. Nat. Hist. Suppl., 1931, p. 165 (Chiang Mai); 1936, p. 78 (Chiang Mai).

The only specimen from within our limits was collected by de Schauensee at Chiang Rai, January 6, 1929. I saw one near Chom Thong, November 29, 1931. For Chaing Mai I have four sight records: one, November 8, 1930; two flying steadily northward, March 7, 1931; one, October 24, 1936; one, November 5, 1936. Its status seems to be that of a rather rare winter visitor along the valleys of the larger rivers.

De Schauensee reports that his bird was taken near a house, from which it had been stealing fowls. This specimen had the irides brown; the orbital region and cere pale olive-yellow; the bill olive-gray, tipped black; the feet and toes bright yellow, tinged greenish; the claws black.

An adult male from Ban Wang Mo, near Rahaeng, has the upperparts generally bluish slate, the centers of the feathers darker, the head more blackish, the lower back and upper tail coverts more bluish with black bars; on the side of the head a black patch below the eye and another similar patch from the nape, each extending into the white of the throat; the underparts pale creamy white, with narrow black shaft streaks on the breast, which change to spots on the abdomen, to bars on the flanks and thighs. An immature male from Ban Wang Muang, near Rahaeng, has the upperparts dark brown; the underparts buffy white, heavily streaked with dark brown.

Falcons may be distinguished from hawks by their long, pointed wings and by their having a tooth at the edge of the maxilla just behind the hooked tip. The present species is the largest falcon known to occur in our area.

After Stegmann's researches on the Asiatic peregrines (Journ. für Orn., 1934, pp. 222–236), which indicate that a number of races must

[2] Original not seen; reference taken from Peters.

winter in India, it appears to be impossible to allocate Latham's name *calidus*. In default of suitable comparative material, I follow Friedmann (MS.) in employing the name *harterti* for Thai birds. An adult male in Washington, taken by Oates near Pegu, February 2, 1877, agrees perfectly with a similar specimen from Thailand.

A resident form of the peregrine, the shahin, *F. p. peregrinator*, with ferruginous underparts, may be found eventually in the mountains of western Thailand; it should be watched for especially in the gorges of the Mae Ping.

FALCO SEVERUS SEVERUS Horsfield

RUFOUS-BELLIED HOBBY

Falco severus HORSFIELD, Trans. Linn. Soc. London, vol. 13, 1821, p. 135 (Java).
Falco severus severus, DEIGNAN, Journ. Siam Soc. Nat. Hist. Suppl., 1931, p. 165 (Doi Suthep); 1936, p. 78 (Chiang Mai, Doi Suthep).—DE SCHAUENSEE, Proc. Acad. Nat. Sci. Philadelphia, 1934, p. 269 (Chiang Mai).

This pretty hobby seems to be a rather rare permanent resident, although perhaps restricted to the more western provinces. I saw one at 1,800 feet on Doi Suthep, June 14, 1930; de Schauensee took a male at Chiang Mai, December 23, 1932; I collected a subadult female at Ko Klang, near Chiang Mai, October 14, 1935. The "small unidentified falcon sometimes seen in the summer months" at Chiang Mai, which in 1936 I supposed to be a kestrel, probably belongs to the present species.

The stomach of my specimen contained feathers of an unidentifiable bird.

I have noted that it had the irides brown; the orbital region yellow; the cere yellow; the maxilla slaty black; the mandible yellow-horn, tipped slaty; the rictus yellowish flesh; the feet and toes deep yellow; the claws black.

The adult has the crown, sides of the head, nape, and upper back slaty black, changing to slaty blue on the remaining upperparts; the throat and sides of the neck white, more or less washed with rufous; the remaining underparts deep rufous. The immature differs chiefly in having the underparts boldly streaked with black everywhere except on the throat and neck.

FALCO TINNUNCULUS TINNUNCULUS Linnaeus

EUROPEAN KESTREL

[*Falco*] *Tinnunculus* LINNAEUS, Systema naturae, ed. 10, vol. 1, 1758, p. 90 (Europe; type locality restricted to Sweden, *apud* Hartert).

Two of my specimens, a male taken at Chom Thong, November 8, 1935, and a female shot at the roadside about 21 km. north of Chom Thong, November 16, 1935, are distinguishable by their pale coloration from all other Thai examples of this species I have seen, but they cannot be separated from a series of European birds.

The comments and description given under the following race will serve equally well for the present one, which differs only in its generally paler hues.

FALCO TINNUNCULUS INTERSTINCTUS McClelland

HIMALAYAN KESTREL

Falco interstinctus McCLELLAND, Proc. Zool. Soc. London, 1839 [=1840], p. 154 (Assam).

Cerchneis tinnunculus, DEIGNAN, Journ. Siam Soc. Nat. Hist. Suppl., 1931, p. 165 (Chiang Mai, Doi Suthep).

Cerchneis tinnunculus saturatus, DE SCHAUENSEE, Proc. Acad. Nat. Sci. Philadelphia, 1934, p. 270 (Chiang Mai).

Falco tinnunculus saturatus, DEIGNAN, Journ. Siam Soc. Nat. Hist. Suppl., 1936, p. 78 (Chiang Mai, Doi Suthep).

The kestrel occurs uncommonly at Chiang Mai from October 13 (1931) to February 1 (1930), and I have seen two specimens from there that belong to the present race: One (in the Princeton Museum of Zoology) taken by S. T. Queripel in November 1931; one taken by de Schauensee, January 25, 1933. I saw it on Doi Suthep at 3,300 feet, October 18, 1929, and on Doi Ang Ka at 4,500 feet in the latter part of April 1931. Since it reaches the southernmost districts of Thailand, we may expect to find it eventually anywhere in the northern provinces.

This falcon is found only at places from which the forest has been well cleared, such as the ricefields, where it perches on the scattered bushes or upon the bunds. It has a characteristic method of hunting from the air its prey of insects and small mammals, frequently halting its flight and hovering with the wings rapidly beaten and the tail depressed and spread, then making a slanting stoop. When it returns to a perch after flight its beats the tail violently up and down several times. The usual call is a shrill *killy-killy-killy*.

The male has a blackish streak under the eye from the base of the bill; the forehead creamy white; the crown, sides of the head, rump, and upper tail coverts soft blue-gray; the tail blue-gray, with narrow whitish tip and broad black subterminal band; the remaining upperparts light red-brown with black spots; the underparts vinaceous-buff with black streaks on the breast, black spots on the abdomen. The female has the upperparts light rufous, the head streaked, the rest banded, with blackish; the underparts pale buffy, boldly streaked with dark brown.

Of the eight Thai specimens of the kestrel I have examined, six have proved to belong to the dark eastern race, and I assume that most of my sight records must apply to the same form. In addition to the specimens listed above, I place here a bird taken by Abbott in Trang Province, two taken by H. M. Smith at Bangkok, and one collected at Ko Lak by Gyldenstolpe, all of which have been recorded in print as *saturatus*.

MICROHIERAX CAERULESCENS BURMANICUS Kirke Swann

BURMESE RED-LEGGED FALCONET

Microhierax caerulescens burmanicus KIRKE SWANN, A synoptical list of the Accipitres, 1920, p. 116 (Thayetmyo, Burma).

Microhierax eutolmus, GYLDENSTOLPE, Kungl. Svenska Vet.-Akad. Handl., 1913, p. 64 (Den Chai, Pak Pan) ; Journ. Nat. Hist. Soc. Siam, 1915, p. 234 (listed).

Microhierax caerulescens, GYLDENSTOLPE, Kungl. Svenska Vet.-Akad. Handl., 1916, p. 130 (Pha Kho, Pang Hua Phong, Khun Tan, Doi Pha Sakaeng) ; Ibis, 1920, p. 749 ("Throughout northern and north-western Siam").

Microhierax caerulescens burmanicus, DE SCHAUENSEE, Proc. Acad. Nat. Sci. Philadelphia, 1928, p. 576 (Doi Suthep) ; 1929, p. 577 (Doi Suthep) ; 1934, p. 269 (Mae Taeng, Doi Suthep, Chiang Dao).—DEIGNAN, Journ. Siam Soc. Nat. Hist. Suppl., 1931, p. 165 (Chiang Mai, Doi Suthep).—CHASEN and BODEN KLOSS, Journ. Siam Soc. Nat. Hist. Suppl., 1932, p. 233 (Doi Suthep).—DEIGNAN, Journ. Siam Soc. Nat. Hist. Suppl., 1936, p. 78 (Chiang Mai, Doi Suthep).—RILEY, U. S. Nat. Mus. Bull. 172, 1938, p. 57 (Mae Khan, Mae Hong Son, Doi Pata).

The diminutive falconet is a common permanent resident throughout the North. Eisenhofer sent to Stockholm no less than 40 specimens from Khun Tan! I have taken it at Ban Mae Mo and Wiang Pa Pao and have observed it at many other localities. On Doi Suthep it occurred to the summit but was most numerous below the evergreen forest belt.

It is a bird of jungle clearings and deciduous forest and may often be seen upon a dead tree beside a highway or soaring in small circles just above the treetops. Its usual prey is large insects, captured on the wing or by a pounce, but Gyldenstolpe saw one attack and kill an oriole, a bird much larger than itself. Its call is a shrill *kee-kee-kee*.

Its breeding season seems to be March and April, when it may be seen going in and out of the deserted nest holes of the smaller barbets and woodpeckers. These holes must be employed again during the cold weather as sociable retreats, for de Schauensee at Chiang Dao in January watched a number of individuals entering and leaving such a hole.

Gyldenstolpe and de Schauensee note that their specimens had the irides dark brown; the bill black, plumbeous at the base; the cere horny gray; the feet and toes plumbeous.

This is one of the smallest raptorial birds in the world. The adult has the forehead, supercilium, sides of the head, and a broad collar over the upper back white; the remaining upperparts glossy black; many white spots on the expanded wing and tail; a broad line back from the eye black; the throat, thighs, and under tail coverts ferruginous; the remaining underparts white, washed with ferruginous on the abdomen. The immature has the forehead and supercilium pale ferruginous and the throat pure white.

NEOHIERAX INSIGNIS CINEREICEPS (Stuart Baker)

TENASSERIMESE WHITE-RUMPED FALCON

Polihierax insignis cinereiceps STUART BAKER, Bull. Brit. Orn. Club, vol. 47, 1926, pp. 101–102 (Myawadi, Tenasserim).

Poliohierax insignis, GYLDENSTOLPE, Journ. Nat. Hist. Soc. Siam, 1915, p. 234 (listed); Kungl. Svenska Vet.-Akad. Handl., 1916, p. 131 (Khun Tan); Ibis, 1920, p. 749 ("Northern Siam").

Neohierax insignis cinereiceps, DE SCHAUENSEE, Proc. Acad. Nat. Sci. Philadelphia, 1929, p. 577 (Doi Suthep); 1934, p. 269 (Mae Taeng, Chiang Mai).—DEIGNAN, Journ. Siam Soc. Nat. Hist. Suppl., 1931, p. 165 (Doi Suthep); 1936, p. 78 (Doi Suthep).—RILEY, U. S. Nat. Mus. Bull. 172, 1938, p. 58 (Doi Ang Ka).

The pretty white-rumped falcon is apparently restricted to the dry lowland deciduous forests (*pa daeng*) of Mae Hong Son, Chiang Mai, and Lampang Provinces, where it is locally fairly common. Eisenhofer sent to Stockholm five specimens from Khun Tan; I collected it at Ban Sop Mae Chaem, Chom Thong, Doi Pha Lat, Ban Mae Mo, and about 27 km. north of Chiang Mai. I have found it in some numbers in the neighborhood of Ban Mae Klang (at the foot of Doi Ang Ka) and along the highway north of Chom Thong. At Chiang Mai it appears uncommonly in winter at the base of Doi Suthep, where I have seen it between October 23 (1930) and January 28 (1933).

This is one of the tamest of raptorial birds. I have often found it perched on a low branch of a leafless tree or even upon a pile of the material used to metal the roads and have thrown handfuls of stones and gravel all around it without causing it to fly. From its post of observation it makes swift dashes to the ground, where it remains to eat its prey, which is usually grasshoppers. De Schauensee took a bird whose stomach contained only charcoal; it may be noted that charcoal kilns are numerous in the type of forest in which it dwells. The flight of this falcon is dipping, like that of a woodpecker, and quite unlike that of other Thai species.

The feathers become very abraded from the coarse leaves of the dry forest, and then the dark portions of the plumage become distinctly brownish. A specimen taken on December 2 has one fresh black central rectrix in the otherwise brownish black tail.

My specimens had the irides brown; the orbital region, lores, and cere yellow; the maxilla black, with the basal half yellow; the mandible yellow, with a blackish patch on each side near the tip; the feet and toes yellow; the claws black.

This is a slender, graceful bird, with comparatively long legs and tail. The adult male has the head and upper neck soft gray, streaked with blackish; the back and exposed portions of the wings slaty gray; the rump and upper tail coverts pure white; the tail feathers blackish; the outspread wings and tail with many white spots; the entire underparts immaculate white. The adult female differs in having the head, nape, and upper back chestnut. The immature has the top of the head colored like the back and a broad white collar across the hindneck.

Order GALLIFORMES

Family PHASIANIDAE

FRANCOLINUS PINTADEANUS (Scopoli)

CHINESE FRANCOLIN

Tetrao (*Pintadeanus*) SCOPOLI, Deliciae florae et faunae insubricae, pt. 2, 1786, p. 93 (China, *ex* Sonnerat).

Francolinus chinensis, GYLDENSTOLPE, Journ. Nat. Hist. Soc. Siam, 1915, p. 235 (listed); Ibis, 1920, p. 735 ("Throughout Siam").

Francolinus pintadeanus phayrei, DEIGNAN, Journ. Siam Soc. Nat. Hist. Suppl., 1931, p. 168 (Chiang Mai, Doi Suthep); 1936, p. 79 (Chiang Mai, Doi Suthep).—DE SCHAUENSEE, Proc. Acad. Nat. Sci. Philadelphia, 1934, p. 276 (Chiang Mai).

The francolin is seldom seen but seems to be fairly common in suitable territory, at least in Chiang Mai Province, whence all the northern specimens have come. Eisenhofer sent to Stockholm a male from Khun Tan. I have taken it on Doi Ang Ka (Pha Mon) at about 5,000 feet, near Chom Thong, and at Chiang Mai. On Doi Suthep it occurs up to 4,600 feet.

It is confined to the dry, deciduous jungle of the plains, to the open hill-forest, and to those often extensive areas on the mountains where the evergreen has been destroyed and supplanted by *Eupatorium* and lalang grass. In such places the guttural song *kă-kă'—kă-kă'-ă* may be heard on all sides, yet only rarely can the singers be raised. The flesh is a favorite article of diet, and the birds are often seen alive in the markets; such individuals are virtually always males that have been ensnared by means of a male decoy. The decoy is kept, when not at work, in a wicker cage suspended from a window, and the song of such a bird is a familiar sound in almost every village, at least in the breeding season. A specimen taken on May 7 was found to have the gonads greatly enlarged.

Male examples, taken in May, had the irides bright brown; the bill black; the eyelids dull olive-greenish; the feet and toes golden-orange; the claws horny brown. An October female had the irides bright brown; the eyelids plumbeous; the maxilla dark horn brown; the mandible fleshy, more horny at the tip; the rictus fleshy; the feet and toes deep yellow; the claws light horny brown.

The plumage of this species is somewhat variable, especially in the extent of the different colors. The male may be described as having the crown light brown, marked in the center with black; the front, supercilium, and a line from the base of the bill below the ear coverts black; the upper back black, spotted with white; the lower back and tail narrowly barred black and white; the shoulder coverts and scapulars chestnut, marked with black and white; the rest of the wing black, with white spots and bars; the throat and ear coverts pure white; the breast and upper abdomen black, closely covered with roundish white spots; the lower abdomen plain buff; the under tail coverts chestnut. The female is similar to the male, but is duller everywhere, and has the underparts, excepting the white throat, barred black and buffy white.

COTURNIX COTURNIX JAPONICA Temminck and Schlegel

JAPANESE MIGRATORY QUAIL

Coturnix vulgaris japonica TEMMINICK and SCHLEGEL, *in* Siebold, Fauna Japonica, Aves, 1849, p. 103, pl. 61 (Japan).
Coturnix coturnix japonica, DEIGNAN, Journ. Siam Soc. Nat. Hist. Suppl., 1936, p. 79 (Chiang Mai).

The Japanese quail seems to be a species of extreme rarity in Thailand; the only northern example is a female taken by me at Chiang Mai, October 31, 1935.

My bird was found on a patch of short grass surrounded by standing rice and, when started, flew off rapidly, to be dropped by a wing shot. The stomach contained only seeds.

It had the irides bright brown; the bill horn-brown; the feet and toes flesh; the claws dark horn.

In the male of this quail, the feathers at the sides of the throat are soft and rounded at the tip; in the female, they are somewhat elongated, acute, and stiff.

The male has the upperparts mixed rufous, brown, and black, with a narrow, longitudinal creamy streak bisecting the crown, and many elongated, lanceolate creamy streaks elsewhere; the face and throat vinaceous; the breast rufous-buff with whitish shaft streaks; the remaining underparts pale buff, with broad rufous streaks along the flanks. The female has the upperparts as in the male; the underparts pale buff, the breast more deeply colored and spotted with rufous and black.

In the field the Japanese quail might easily be mistaken for a hemipode; in the hand it can be recognized by its flesh-colored feet and the presence of a hindtoe, as well as by the differences in color pattern.

EXCALFACTORIA CHINENSIS CHINENSIS (Linnaeus)

CHINESE BLUE-BREASTED QUAIL

[*Tetrao*] *chinensis* LINNAEUS, Systema naturae, ed. 12, vol. 1, 1766, p. 277 ("in China, Philippinis"; type locality restricted to Nanking, China, *ex* Edwards *apud* Peters).

Excalfactoria chinensis chinensis, DEIGNAN, Journ. Siam Soc. Nat. Hist. Suppl., 1931, p. 168 (Chiang Mai); 1936, p. 78 (Chiang Mai).

While the blue-breasted quail is common enough in southern Thailand and is known to breed near Bangkok, in the North it seems to occur only as a rare migrant. The sole specimen from our provinces is a male taken by me at Chiang Mai, February 28, 1931.

This bird was collected among the stubbles of a fallow ricefield. It flew up from my very feet, to drop again to the ground a short distance away.

It had the irides deep crimson; the bill plumbeous, with the culmen and tip of the mandible blackish; the feet and toes bright yellow; the claws horn.

The male of this species is so brightly colored that it need be confused with no other small game bird in our area; it has the upperparts rufous-brown with black spots and narrow bars; the throat black; the lower neck and a streak below the eye pure white; the breast and flanks slaty blue; the remaining underparts deep chestnut. The female has the upperparts similar to those of the male; the throat buffy; the remaining underparts vinaceous-buff, barred with blackish on the breast and sides of the body.

The bright yellow feet will distinguish this quail from all similar forms except the yellow-legged hemipode, which, however, has no hindtoe.

ARBOROPHILA RUFOGULARIS TICKELLI (Hume)

TENASSERIMESE RUFOUS-THROATED HILL PARTRIDGE

A[*rboricola*] *tickelli* HUME, *in* Hume and Marshall, The game birds of India, Burmah, and Ceylon, vol. 2, 1879 [=1880], p. 78, footnote, col. pl. [11], fig. of head (Mount Muleyit, Tenasserim).

Arboricola rufogularis, DE SCHAUENSEE, Proc. Acad. Nat. Sci. Philadelphia, 1928, p. 575 (Doi Suthep).

Arborophila rufogularis rufogularis, DE SCHAUENSEE, Proc. Acad. Nat. Sci. Philadelphia, 1929, p. 581 (Doi Suthep).

Arborophila rufogularis, DEIGNAN, Journ. Siam. Soc. Nat. Hist. Suppl., 1931, p. 168 (Doi Suthep).

Arborophila rufogularis tickelli, DE SCHAUENSEE, Proc. Acad. Nat. Sci. Philadelphia, 1934, p. 275 (Doi Suthep).—DEIGNAN, Journ. Siam Soc. Nat. Hist. Suppl., 1936, p. 79 (Doi Suthep).—RILEY, U. S. Nat. Mus. Bull. 172, 1938, p. 62 (Doi Ang Ka, Doi Suthep, Doi Langka, Doi Hua Mot).

This partridge is very common in the evergreen forest above 4,500 feet in the Thanon Thong Chai and Khun Tan chains, but its possible distribution within our area is pretty well limited to the mountains named above.

On Doi Suthep, coveys of about a dozen individuals lived in ravines and on the steepest slopes, where they could be heard clucking and cheeping to one another as they scratched among the dead leaves, but they could not be seen through the dense foliage. When flushed they frequently took refuge high up in a tree and were well concealed by the leaves. They seemed always to roost in a tree, the whole group huddled together on the same branch.

Few melodies of the Thai mountains surpass the evening song of the hill partridges. It is a sweet, clear, double whistle, repeated again and again, each time on a higher note and with a briefer pause between the phrases. As one bird stops, another begins. The sound carries for a great distance through the still air and may be heard from all parts of the mountain at once.

In 1931 I attributed these lovely calls to the brown-breasted partridge, but now believe that I was in error, unless, indeed, the song is common to both species.

The nesting season in our hills is not certainly known, but specimens with the spotted breast of young birds have been taken in June and August.

De Schauensee states that adults had the irides dark brown; the orbital region crimson; the bill black; the feet and toes crimson; the claws deep flesh. I have recorded that an immature male had the irides gray-brown; the bill horny red, with the basal half black; the orbital region, rictus, and interior of the mouth pink; the feet and toes salmon-rose; the claws horny salmon.

The plumage of this species is rather variable in minor details. In general, the adult has the upperparts olive-brown, with black spots on the lower back, rump, and tail, chestnut and black markings on the scapulars and some wing coverts; the throat and neck all around orange-rufous with black spots, which are smaller on the throat, larger on the collar; the breast and flanks deep gray, the belly paler, the concealed sides of the body mixed with chestnut; the thighs and under tail coverts olive-brown, more or less barred with black. Younger specimens have buffy spots on the wings and the gray underparts more brownish and spotted with buff and white.

ARBOROPHILA BRUNNEOPECTUS BRUNNEOPECTUS (Blyth)

TENASSERIMESE BROWN-BREASTED HILL PARTRIDGE

Arboricola brunneopectus "Tickell" BLYTH, Journ. Asiat. Soc. Bengal, vol. 24, 1855, p. 276 ("Mountainous interior of Tenasserim").

Arboricola brunneipectus, GYLDENSTOLPE, Kungl. Svenska Vet.-Akad. Handl., 1916, p. 156 ("Doi Vieng Par"=Doi Chom Hot).

Arboricola brunneopectus brunneopectus, GYLDENSTOLPE, Ibis, 1920, p. 735 ("Doi Vieng Par"=Doi Chom Hot).

Arboricola brunneopectus, DE SCHAUENSEE, Proc. Acad. Nat. Sci. Philadelphia, 1928, p. 575 (Doi Suthep).

Arborophila brunneopectus brunneopectus, DE SCHAUENSEE, Proc. Acad. Nat. Sci. Philadelphia, 1929, p. 582 (Chiang Saen); 1934, p. 275 (Doi Suthep, Doi Chiang Dao).—DEIGNAN, Journ. Siam Soc. Nat. Hist. Suppl., 1931, p. 168 (Doi Suthep).—CHASEN and KLOSS, Journ. Siam Soc. Nat. Hist. Suppl., 1932, p. 232 (Doi Suthep).—DEIGNAN, Journ. Siam Soc. Nat. Hist. Suppl., 1936, p. 79 (Doi Suthep).—RILEY, U. S. Nat. Mus. Bull. 172, 1938, p. 63 (Khun Tan, Doi Hua Mot).

The brown-breasted partridge, like the rufous-throated, is a bird of the evergreen and replaces the latter at lower elevations. On Doi Suthep it is very common from 3,500 feet (below which elevation the jungle is unsuitable) to 4,500 feet, where it meets *rufogularis*. On Doi Chiang Dao, where the evergreen stops at about 4,500 feet, *rufogularis* is unknown but *brunneopectus* is extremely common. On Doi Khun Tan, the highest point of which is about 4,500 feet and where the evergreen is restricted in area, only *brunneopectus* is known and then is not numerous. De Schauensee's record from Chiang Saen indicates that the present species reaches the plains where there is suitable forest. On Phu Kha it seemed to be the only partridge and was not common, but the game birds of that mountain have been much persecuted by the local tribes.

As might be expected from the summary of distribution, the habits of this species seem to differ in no important way from those of its congener. De Schauensee records (1929) that its "note is a musical three note whistle repeated on a descending scale. The skin of the throat is distended while the whistle is being delivered, plainly showing the brick red color of the skin."

De Schauensee states that a male had the irides sandy brown, with a broad outer ring dark gray; the orbital region crimson; the skin of the chin and throat, between the feathers, brick-red; the bill black; the feet and toes deep flesh; the claws fleshy horn. A male taken by me had the irides brown; the eyelids and orbital region crimson-lake; the bill black; the skin of the chin and throat deep rose-red; a fleshy ring around the vent rose-pink; the feet and toes old rose, tinged orange, the tarsi golden-yellow behind; the claws horny orange.

This bird has the upperparts similar to those of the preceding form but closely barred everywhere with black; the scattered feathers of the throat and foreneck white or buffy white with black tips; the remaining underparts bright buff, whitish on the belly and barred black and white along the sides. The plumage shows considerable variation in minor ways among different individuals.

I am skeptical of the validity of *henrici*, which, *fide* Delacour, is the subspecies of French Laos, and which has been reported by Delacour and Greenway from a locality just across the Mae Khong from Chiang Saen Kao. De Schauensee's specimen from Chiang Saen is typical *brunneopectus*, as is my bird from Phu Kha, where, judged from analogous cases, a Lao race should occur if such be distinct from the Tenasserimese. De Schauensee mentions (1934) that a skin from French Laos "is very close to Siamese birds and differs only in having the ground color of the chin and throat tinged with buff." Individuals with buff-tinged throats are common in western Thailand in the same flocks as white-throated examples. Either *henrici* is not a distinct form or the birds so named from western Laos are extremely close to, or identical with, *brunneopectus*.

TROPICOPERDIX CHLOROPUS CHLOROPUS Blyth

TENASSERIMESE GREEN-LEGGED HILL PARTRIDGE

Tropicoperdix chloropus "Tickell" BLYTH, Journ. Asiat Soc. Bengal, vol. 28, 1859, p. 415 ("Mountainous interior of the Tenasserim provinces").

Tropicoperdix chloropus, GYLDENSTOLPE, Kungl. Svenska Vet.-Akad. Handl., 1913, p. 67 (Ban Huai Hom, Khao Phlung) ; 1916, p. 156 (Khun Tan) ; Journ. Nat. Hist. Soc. Siam, 1915, p. 235 (listed).

Arboricola chloropus chloropus, GYLDENSTOLPE, Ibis, 1920, p. 735 (Ban Huai Hom, Khao Phlung, Khun Tan).

Tropicoperdix chloropus olivacea, DE SCHAUENSEE, Proc. Acad. Nat. Sci. Philadelphia, 1929, p. 583 (Chiang Saen).—RILEY, U. S. Nat. Mus. Bull. 172, 1938, p. 65 (Khun Tan, Mae Lang valley).

Tropicoperdix chloropus chloropus, DE SCHAUENSEE, Proc. Acad. Nat. Sci. Philadelphia, 1934, p. 276 (Doi Suthep).—DEIGNAN, Journ. Siam Soc. Nat. Hist. Suppl., 1936, p. 79 (Doi Suthep).

This partridge has been found in all our provinces; it is common in the lowland evergreen forest of the more eastern districts but rather rare in the western hills, where it must compete with the two species of *Arborophila*. In Stockholm are five specimens collected by Eisenhofer at Khun Tan. From Doi Suthep it is known by only two examples, one taken by me at 3,500 feet, the other by de Schauensee at 4,500 feet. I have collected it also at Chiang Rai, Ban Huai Som, and on Doi Chiang Dao.

The habits of the green-legged partridge, as I have observed them, seem not to differ markedly from those of the other northern hill partridges. The only indication we have of the breeding season is the fact that my specimen from Doi Suthep, collected August 24, 1935, is a juvenile.

De Schauensee records that adult specimens had the irides dark brown; the basal half of the bill deep crimson, the apical half olive, tipped yellow; the orbital region crimson; the feet, toes, and claws dark olive or olive-yellow. My juvenile bird had the irides brown;

the eyelids edged brown; the orbital skin slaty; the maxilla blackish at the base, greenish horn at the tip, otherwise blackish olive; the mandible horny; the skin of the throat fleshy pink; the feet, toes, and claws very pale green.

The adult has the upperparts olive-brown, all feathers except those of the crown narrowly edged and barred with black; the throat with black spots; a complete collar around the neck bright ferruginous with black spots; a broad olive-brown band across the upper breast; the remaining underparts bright ferruginous, much paler on the abdomen and marked with black on the under tail coverts and the sides of the body. The juvenile has the upperparts and wings dark reddish brown, narrowly barred with black everywhere except on the head; the throat and neck pale brown; the breast band and sides of the body reddish brown, the feathers with white shafts and tips; the upper abdomen pale buff with broad black streaks; the remaining underparts whitish.

I agree with Riley and de Schauensee that all Thailand (north of the Peninsula), from the borders of Karen-ni to the Cambodian frontier, is inhabited by but one race of this species and that it agrees well with Delacour's *olivacea*, but am not convinced that *olivacea* is separable from typical *chloropus*. The tone of brown of the upperparts and breast band varies among individuals and perhaps with age of specimen; the ferruginous of the lower breast shows equal variation. Certain skins from western Thailand could be called *olivacea*, while others from extreme eastern districts are *chloropus*.

T. c. cognacqi of Cochinchine is a well-marked form of the species. The buff shaft streaks of the upperparts are not present in all individuals and appear also in some specimens of *chloropus;* the real characters are the darker brown of the upperparts and breast band and the pale, washed-out collar.

BAMBUSICOLA FYTCHII FYTCHII Anderson

YUNNANESE BAMBOO PARTRIDGE

Bambusicola fytchii ANDERSON, Proc. Zool. Soc. London, 1871, p. 214 (Ponsee, western Yunnan).

Bambusicola fytchii fytchii, DE SCHAUENSEE, Proc. Acad. Nat. Sci. Philadelphia, 1938, p. 30 (Doi Pha Hom Pok).

The bamboo partridge is known within our limits only from Doi Pha Hom Pok, where at 6,400 feet de Schauensee's collectors took five males and one female in February 1938. It is not likely to occur elsewhere in the northern provinces unless upon other high peaks of the Daen Lao range.

This bird has a proportionately much longer tail than other northern partridges. The adult has the crown dull rufous-brown; a collar on the hindneck, the quills, and tail feathers rufous; the remaining upperparts gray-brown, the upper back, scapulars, and wing coverts marked with chestnut-bordered black drops or spots; a black or rufous stripe back from the eye, edged above by a white supercilium; the throat and sides of the neck buff; the breast rufous, mottled with buffy white; the remaining underparts buffy or whitish, boldly spotted and barred with black.

GENNAEUS CRAWFURDII LINEATUS (Vigors)

Peguan Lineated Pheasant

Phasianus lineatus "Lath. Mss." Vigors, Proc. Comm. Sci. Corr. Zool. Soc. London, pt. 1, 1830–1831 [=1831], p. 24 (Straits of Malacca, error; East Pegu Hills designated as type locality, by Ticehurst, Journ. Bombay Nat. Hist. Soc., vol. 36, 1933, p. 936).

Gennaeus lineatus sharpei, Riley, U. S. Nat. Mus. Bull. 172, 1938, p. 67 (Mae Sariang).

The range of the lineated pheasant is apparently restricted to the lower elevations of the hilly districts of western Thailand. The only specimen known to me from the northern provinces is a male taken by Dr. Hugh M. Smith at Mae Sariang, January 20, 1935. I have another male example, collected and kindly presented to me by T. W. Bevan, Esq., from Kaeng Soi (in the Mae Ping Gorges, just beyond our limits), on the right bank of the river, March 16, 1936.

Dr. Smith records that his bird had the irides hazel; the bare skin at the sides of the head red; the bill horn; the feet and toes sepia.

An attempt should be made to preserve, however crudely, together with pertinent data, any lineated or silver pheasant shot in Thailand, as an aid to solution of the perplexing problems of distribution of the various forms.

The adult male has the crown and long crest black with a greenish or bluish gloss; the remaining upperparts finely vermiculated black and white, giving a slaty-gray appearance; the inner webs of the central tail feathers almost wholly unmarked white; the underparts black with scattered white shaft streaks, which are broader and more numerous at the sides of the body. The adult female has the upperparts golden-brown, with V-shaped white or buffy marks on the neck and upper back, white or buffy shaft streaks on the rest of the mantle; the tail beautifully barred and mottled with black, white, and red-brown; the throat plain light brown; the remaining underparts mixed rufous and dark brown, with broad white shaft streaks everywhere.

I have elsewhere given my reasons for the adoption of the specific name *crawfurdii* (*cf.* Diegnan, Auk, 1943, pp. 88–89).

GENNAEUS NYCTHEMERUS RIPPONI Bowdler Sharpe

YUNNANESE SILVER PHEASANT

Gennaeus ripponi BOWDLER SHARPE, Bull. Brit. Orn. Club, vol. 13, 1902, p. 29 ("Southern Shan Hills"; type specimen from Mawkmai, *fide* Peters, Check-list of birds of the world, vol. 2, 1934, p. 114).

G[ennaeus] nycthemerus ripponi, GYLDENSTOLPE, Kungl. Svenska Vet.-Akad. Handl., 1916, p. 157 (Doi Pha Sakaeng).

Gennaeus sp., DEIGNAN, Journ. Siam Soc. Nat. Hist. Suppl., 1931, p. 168 (Doi Suthep).

Gennaeus nycthemerus rufipes, CHASEN and KLOSS, Journ. Siam Soc. Nat. Hist. Suppl., 1932, p. 232 (Doi Suthep).

Gennaeus nycthemerus ripponi, RILEY, Journ. Siam Soc. Nat. Hist. Suppl., 1933, p. 154 (Doi Langka).—DEIGNAN, Journ. Siam Soc. Nat. Hist. Suppl., 1936, p. 80 (Doi Suthep).—DE SCHAUENSEE, Proc. Acad. Nat. Sci. Philadelphia, 1934, p. 274 (Doi Chiang Dao, Doi Suthep).—RILEY, U. S. Nat. Mus. Bull. 172, 1938, p. 69 (Doi Langka, Khun Tan).

The silver pheasant seems to be rather common on all the higher peaks of the North, occurring indifferently in the evergreen, the open hill-forest, and in the pinewoods. It is ordinarily not found below 4,500 feet, but Smith took it on Khun Tan at 3,000 feet and de Schauensee on Doi Chiang Dao at 2,500 feet. In April 1936 I picked up a primary of this bird on Phu Kha at 5,000 feet. In Stockholm are two males taken by Eisenhofer in 1916 at Khun Tan.

Where all sunlight is shut out by the forest canopy and every rock and tree trunk is draped with ferns and mosses, it is a beautiful sight to watch an apparently snow-white cock skulk through the shadow and vanish into what appears to be impassable thicket. At dusk and dawn, when the silvers come out in small flocks to feed along the paths which follow the ridges, the plumage is much less striking and more concealing. They are shy and wary birds, and usually the only indication of their presence in the forest will be a distant crowing, not unlike that of the common pheasant.

Riley has noted that Smith's two females from Doi Khun Tan, taken May 15, had bare incubation patches.

A male collected by me in May had the irides red-brown; the orbital skin deep crimson; the bill horny olive; the feet and toes bright coral-red; the spurs horny white; the soles light brown; the claws horny white, tinged pink at the base.

The adult male has the crown and long crest steel blue; the upperparts white with narrow black bars which follow the outline of the feather and are broader on the wings; the central tail feathers almost wholly unmarked white; the sides of the neck unmarked white; the underparts black, glossed with blue on the breast and sides of the body. The adult female has the upperparts rich brown, the crest tipped steel blue and the tail feathers marked with irregular light brown or black-edged white streaks and bars; the underparts changing gradually from rich brown to blackish brown, with white or buff bars, which follow the outline of the feather, giving a squamated appearance.

It is worthy of note that *ripponi* in Thailand is a quite stable form, exhibiting only the slightest individual variation. This is doubtless connected with the fact that its distribution overlaps that of no other member of the genus.

DIARDIGALLUS DIARDI (Bonaparte)

Diard's Fire-backed Pheasant

Euplocomus diardi "Temm." Bonaparte, Compt. Rend. Acad. Sci. Paris, vol. 43, 1856, p. 415 (no locality given=Cochinchine).

Lophura diardi, Gyldenstolpe, Kungl. Svenska Vet.-Akad. Handl., 1913, p. 67 (Mae Raem river); Journ. Nat. Hist. Soc. Siam, 1915, p. 235 (listed); Ibis, 1920, p. 737 (Mae Raem).

The fireback has not yet been reported anywhere west of the Khun Tan mountains but is widely distributed in the low hilly country east of them as far as the borders of Laos. Gyldenstolpe reported (1913) seeing skins of birds shot "in the forests at the Meh Lem river" (Phrae Province). I have examined in Hannover a mounted cock, for which the exact data have been lost but which was taken by Eisenhofer in "Siam" in 1912; this specimen almost certainly came from Phrae Province, where Eisenhofer collected from February 7 to June 27, 1912. The species is well known to the people of Nan Province, where I saw, but could not collect, a male at Huai Oi (about 14 km. north of Ban Pak Li), April 5, 1937.

This bird dwells in the densest cover—lowland evergreen, bamboo brakes, and the areas of deserted cultivation usurped by *Eupatorium* and thorns. As a result it is rarely seen, and nothing has been recorded of its habits in our provinces. The cock observed by me in Nan Province was feeding on a road with a small flock of junglefowl in a hot and waterless district covered with leafless trees and bamboos.

The male has the crown black; the crest feathers steel blue; the upper back and wings finely vermiculated black and white, giving a steel-gray appearance; the upper portion of the scapulars with irregular black bars edged with white; the feathers of the lower back with vermiculated bases, which are concealed by broad golden-buff tips; the rump and upper tail coverts steel blue, tipped maroon; the tail feathers black, glossed with green; the throat with scattered black feathers; the breast vermiculated like the back, the remaining underparts black, glossed with steel blue. The female has the crown dull brown; the upper back ferruginous; the lower back and the wings broadly and irregularly barred black and buffy white; the rump and upper tail coverts coarsely vermiculated black and buffy white; the central rectrices black with broad, broken buffy-white bars; the outer rectrices chestnut-red; the throat with scattered buffy feathers; the remaining underparts ferruginous with many of the feathers narrowly edged white and the center of the abdomen dirty white.

GALLUS GALLUS GALLUS (Linnaeus)

Red Junglefowl

[*Phasianus*] *Gallus* Linnaeus, Systema naturae, ed. 10, vol. 1, 1758, p. 158 ("in India Orientali: Pouli candor, etc."; type locality restricted to Pulau Kondor, off the delta of the Mae Khong).

Gallus ferrugineus, Gyldenstolpe, Kungl. Svenska Vet.-Akad. Handl., 1913, p. 67 (Mae Raem, Ban Huai Hom); Journ. Nat. Hist. Soc. Siam, 1915, p. 235 (listed).

Gallus gallus, Gyldenstolpe, Kungl. Svenska Vet.-Akad. Handl., 1916, p. 157 (Khun Tan, Pha Kho); Ibis, 1920, p. 737 ("Throughout the whole country").

Gallus gallus gallus, de Schauensee, Proc. Acad. Nat. Sci. Philadelphia, 1928, p. 575 (Doi Suthep).—Deignan, Journ. Siam Soc. Nat. Hist. Suppl., 1936, p. 79 (Chiang Mai, Doi Suthep).—Riley, U. S. Nat. Mus. Bull. 172, 1938, p. 71 (Mae Kong Ka valley).

Gallus gallus robinsoni, de Schauensee, Proc. Acad. Nat. Sci. Philadelphia, 1929, p. 580 (Chiang Saen, Chiang Rai); 1934, p. 273 (Doi Suthep, Doi Chiang Dao, Mae Rim).

Gallus bankiva robinsoni, Deignan, Journ. Siam Soc. Nat. Hist. Suppl., 1931, p. 167 (Chiang Mai).

In spite of persecution the junglefowl is common throughout our provinces, occurring in *pa daeng*, bamboo brakes, mixed-deciduous forest, and the evergreen, from the plains to at least 4,500 feet. Eisenhofer sent to Stockholm 14 skins from Khun Tan. I have specimens from Doi Ang Ka, Ban Mae Klang, and Muang Fang and have heard or seen the species at numerous other localities.

The *kai pa* spend the heat of the day hidden in the depths of the jungle, but early in the morning and again at evening they may often be seen feeding at the edge of the forest or in clearings. They are wary birds and at the least alarm run, with outstretched neck, to cover, sometimes, especially on a slope, leaving the ground and sailing at a low elevation with wings stiffly set. The challenge of the male is rather different from the crow of the domesticated bird of the Occident: it is cut off sharply at the end and is delivered in the cracked voice of a western cockerel. Both sexes cackle wildly when frightened, and the hen keeps up a constant low clucking and cackling when leading a brood of chicks. Stomachs examined by me contained seeds and insects.

I found hens with half-grown chicks on Doi Ang Ka, April 6 and May 7, and took a juvenile male at Muang Fang, July 15.

The coloration of the soft parts varies somewhat in accordance with age of specimen. De Schauensee records that northern males had the irides reddish brown, sandy orange, or crimson; the facial skin, comb, and wattles crimson; the auricular region pinkish white; the bill horn, with the mandible paler; the feet, toes, and spurs gray or blue-gray. I have noted that an adult female had the irides bright orange; the eyelids plumbeous; the naked skin of the face pinkish gray; the rudimentary comb pink; the maxilla horny brown, tinged pink at the base; the mandible whitish, tinged fleshy at the base; the feet and toes slaty; the soles slaty brown; the claws horny flesh. A juvenile male had the irides brown; the naked skin of face and orbital region pink; the maxilla dark horny brown; the mandible fleshy, horny at the tip; the feet and toes olive-brown; the claws horny brown.

The wild junglefowl is so similar to the domesticated bird to be seen on every side in Thailand that no detailed description of plumages will be given. The downy white bases of the upper tail coverts of the adult male are conspicuous in flight and afford an excellent field mark.

Further collecting in Chiang Rai Province may show that the population of that area must be called *Gallus gallus jabouillei.*

SYRMATICUS HUMIAE BURMANNICUS (Oates)

BURMESE BARRED-BACKED PHEASANT

Calophasis burmannicus OATES, Ibis, 1898, pp. 124–125 (Ruby Mines district of Burma and Kalaw, Southern Shan States).

Phasianus humiae burmanicus, GAIRDNER, Journ. Nat. Hist. Soc. Siam, 1919, p. 229 (Doi Suthep).

Syrmaticus humiae burmanicus, DE SCHAUENSEE, Proc. Acad. Nat. Sci. Philadelphia, 1929, p. 581 (Doi Suthep); 1934, p. 274 (Doi Chiang Dao).—DEIGNAN, Journ. Siam Soc. Nat. Hist. Suppl., 1931, p. 168 (Doi Suthep).—CHASEN and BODEN KLOSS, Journ. Siam Soc. Nat. Hist. Suppl., 1932, p. 232 (Doi Suthep).—DEIGNAN, Journ. Siam Soc. Nat. Hist., Suppl., 1936, p. 79 (Doi Suthep).

Few specimens of this beautiful copper pheasant are known from Thailand, where it seems to be a species of considerable rarity. An adult male taken by Gairdner on Doi Suthep, 4,350 feet, March 31, 1919, constitutes the first record for the Kingdom. De Schauensee collected an adult male on Doi Suthep, 5,500 feet, December 29, 1928. One day later, I saw, at 5,100 feet on the same mountain, a male accompanied by three or four hens. At the same spot, May 11, 1930, I shot an adult male. Finally, a pair were taken by de Schauensee at 4,000 feet on Doi Chiang Dao, January 14, 1933. During my second visit to Thailand, 1935–1937, in spite of constant collecting on Suthep, I never once saw or heard of the species.

Like the silver pheasant, this bird seems to spend the middle of the day concealed in the dense evergreen of the upper slopes, coming out only at dusk and dawn to feed in the open hill-forest of oak or pine. The examples observed by me were along paths through the tall lalang grass which carpets such forest; when startled, they ran swiftly until out of sight around a bend or hurtled at once into the nearby evergreen.

My specimen had the irides brown; the orbital skin bright red; the bill pale olive; the feet and toes steel gray.

The male has the crown and ear coverts dull olive-brown; the chin and throat black, glossed steel blue; the neck, upper breast, and upper back steel blue; the middle back glossy copper red, the feathers tipped steel blue; the lower back and rump silvery white, barred black; the long, pointed tail soft gray with narrow, widely spaced black bars; the wings chestnut, with a broad white bar running from the lower back to the shoulder and a broad steel-blue bar and two broad white bars across them; the under tail coverts black; the remaining underparts chestnut. I have not seen the female; it may be known from other northern pheasants by its having the feet and toes gray, like the male.

POLYPLECTRON BICALCARATUM BICALCARATUM (Linnaeus)

BURMESE PEACOCK PHEASANT

[*Pavo*] *bicalcaratus* LINNAEUS, Systema naturae, ed. 10, vol. 1, 1758, p. 156 (China, error; Thoungyah, Burma, designated as type locality by Lowe, Ibis, 1925, p. 477).

Polyplectron bicalcaratus, GYLDENSTOLPE, Kungl. Svenska Vet.-Akad. Handl., 1913, p. 66 (Mae Raem).

Polyplectron malaccensis, GYLDENSTOLPE, Kungl. Svenska Vet.-Akad. Handl., 1916, p. 158 (Khun Tan).

Polyplectron bicalcaratum, GYLDENSTOLPE, Ibis, 1920, p. 737 ("Northern Siam").

The peacock pheasant is apparently rare, but I believe that this is due, not to actual scarcity, but to the extraordinary shyness of the bird and the impenetrable undergrowth in which it lives. It is now known from our provinces by but two skins, one in Stockholm from Khun Tan and the other from Doi Pha Hom Pok in Philadelphia. I never was able to find it at all but on Doi Chiang Dao and again on Phu Kha heard distant calls, which were attributed by the hillmen to this species.

This is a small pheasant. The cock has the throat white; the rest of the plumage dark brown, everywhere finely freckled with buffy white; the feathers of the mantle, the scapulars, wing coverts, inner secondaries, longer upper tail coverts, and tail feathers with a large, round ocellus near the tip, glossy blue or green and purple, framed in a buffy ring. The hen has the throat white; the remainder of the plumage brown, mottled with paler brown; the ocelli fewer and reduced in size and gloss, especially on the back and wings.

Northern Thai birds are inseparable from topotypical specimens of *bicalcaratum.*

The provenance of Lowe's *bailyi* (Ibis, 1925, p. 482) is unknown but is believed by the describer to lie somewhere in our provinces. The male of this form is said to have the ground color of a darker brown than *bicalcaratum* and the spotting almost pure white rather than buff. Northern birds I have seen do not fit this description, nor do the odd wing and tails from Lom Sak, just beyond our limits, mentioned (1938) by Riley.

PAVO MUTICUS MUTICUS Linnaeus

JAVANESE GREEN PEAFOWL

[*Pavo*] *muticus* LINNAEUS, Systema naturae, ed. 12, vol. 1, 1766, p. 268 (Japan, error; Java designated as type locality, by Hartert, Nov. Zool., vol. 9, 1902, p. 538).

Pavo muticus, GYLDENSTOLPE, Kungl. Svenska Vet.-Akad. Handl., 1913, p. 66 (Den Chai, Pak Pan); 1916, p. 159 (Chiang Saen); Ibis, 1920, p. 738 ("Throughout the country").

The peafowl is well distributed in the northern lowlands, except in the immediate vicinity of the larger towns, where it has been extirpated. Gyldenstolpe heard its calls in the deciduous forests near Den Chai and Pak Pan and later collected one at Chiang Saen. Eisenhofer sent to Stockholm two males, taken at Khun Tan in 1915. It is common in the neighborhood of Chiang Dao, where I took an adult female, January 1, 1932. It is said to occur in the dry forests at the foot of Doi Ang Ka. In Nan Province it appears to be common everywhere and is seen by all who travel down the Mae Nan by boat. In December 1935 I saw a flock at the edge of the Mae Ping near Ban Mut Ka.

These giant pheasants inhabit the deciduous jungle, the more open evergreen, and the second growth. If they must go uphill to escape danger, they run rapidly, making as much noise as deer in the dry leaves; on the level or downhill they leave the ground after a running start and fly strongly, sometimes taking refuge even in the highest trees. In December and January 1931–32, I found them in large bands along the Mae Ping east of Chiang Dao, coming down at dusk and dawn to feed and drink in the ricefields along the river and spending the hot hours of the day on the dry, low hills of the left bank, where they rested on the ground, concealed among the clumps of coarse grass.

Gyldenstolpe records that his immature male had the irides brown; the bill horn color; the feet and toes brown.

Since the peafowl are such familiar birds to residents of Thailand and only one species is likely to occur in the Kingdom, no detailed descriptions need be given.

Order GRUIFORMES

Family TURNICIDAE

TURNIX TANKI BLANFORDII Blyth

CHINESE YELLOW-LEGGED HEMIPODE

Turnix Blanfordii BLYTH, Journ. Asiat. Soc. Bengal, vol. 32, 1863, p. 80 (Thayetmyo, Pegu, Burma).
Turnix blanfordi, GYLDENSTOLPE, Journ. Nat. Hist. Soc. Siam, 1915, p. 235 (listed); Kungl. Svenska Vet.-Akad. Handl., 1916, p. 155 (Nong Bia).
Turnix tanki blanfordi, DE SCHAUENSEE, Proc. Acad. Nat. Sci. Philadelphia, 1928, p. 575 (Doi Suthep).
Turnix maculatus maculatus, DEIGNAN, Journ. Siam Soc. Nat. Hist. Suppl., 1931, p. 169 (Chiang Mai); 1936, p. 80 (Chiang Mai).—DE SCHAUENSEE, Proc. Acad. Nat. Sci. Philadelphia, 1934, p. 277 (Chiang Mai).
Turnix tanki blanfordii, RILEY, U. S. Nat. Mus. Bull. 172, 1938, p. 74 (Nan).

This hemipode seems to be, in northern Thailand, only a winter visitor, occurring commonly in suitable territory from October to April. Eisenhofer sent to Stockholm a pair without date from Khun Tan. I have taken one specimen at Sala Mae Tha and many at Chiang Mai. It is chiefly a bird of the plains, but de Schauensee found it in the open forest at 2,000 feet on Doi Suthep, and I took several in open country at 4,400 feet on Doi Ang Ka, in April 1931.

Its habits apparently differ in no way from those of the following species, and the two occur in the same places. Stomachs I examined contained only seeds and other vegetable matter.

My specimens had the irides white or creamy white; the maxilla dark brown or horny brown, with the edges of the commissure yellow on the basal two-thirds; the mandible yellow, tipped horn brown or fleshy; the feet and toes yellow, the joints of the toes horn brown; the claws horny flesh or yellowish flesh.

The female has the crown mixed black, rufous, and buff; a broad collar on the upper back ferruginous-red; the remaining upperparts brown, mottled with black, ferruginous, and buff; the throat whitish; the upper breast bright rusty; the remaining underparts buff; the sides of the breast, the flanks, and the upper wing coverts with rounded, black spots. The male, which is much smaller and rather less brightly colored, lacks the collar on the upper back.

TURNIX SUSCITATOR INTERRUMPENS Robinson and Stuart Baker

THAI GRAY-LEGGED HEMIPODE

Turnix suscitator interrumpens ROBINSON and STUART BAKER, Bull. Brit. Orn. Club, vol. 48, 1927, p. 60 (Krasom, Peninsular Thailand).
Turnix suscitator, DEIGNAN, Journ. Siam Soc. Nat. Hist. Suppl., 1931, p. 169 (Chiang Mai).

Turnix suscitator interrumpens, DE SCHAUENSEE, Proc. Acad. Nat. Sci. Philadelphia, 1934, p. 276 (Chiang Mai).—DEIGNAN, Journ. Siam Soc. Nat. Hist. Suppl., 1936, p. 80 (Chiang Mai).—RILEY, U. S. Nat. Mus. Bull. 172, 1938, p. 75 (Mae Sariang).

The gray-legged hemipode is a common permanent resident, at least in the provinces of Chiang Mai and Mae Hong Son, whence all specimens have come. A pair in Stockholm were taken in 1914 by Eisenhofer at Khun Tan. I have collected it at Chiang Mai, Mae Sariang, and on Doi Ang Ka at 4,500 feet.

The hemipodes live singly or in pairs at grassy places, especially where the grass is rather short and is dotted with bushes and thickets. At Chiang Mai I found them most common on the wastelands set aside for cremations and in the uncultivated areas around ruined pagodas in the fields.

Many of these little birds are snared for the market by the use of female decoys; when not employed, the decoys are kept in cages suspended in houses, since the presence of a hemipode is believed to be a safeguard against fire.

A male from Doi Ang Ka, April 6, had the gonads enlarged; females taken at Chiang Mai, July 12 and 21, had them slightly enlarged. Between these months the loud *khoom-khoom-khoom* of the female, from which the vernacular name is derived, may be heard constantly in the grasslands.

My birds had the irides white or creamy white; the bill plumbeous, with the culmen slaty gray; the feet and toes plumbeous; the claws fleshy.

There are two distinct phases of this bird: one in which the prevailing color of the upperparts is dark rufous, another in which it is gray-brown. The female differs from that of the preceding form in having no collar on the upper back; in having the throat and center of the upper breast black; the sides of the breast and the upper flanks with broken black bars; the remaining underparts deep buff. The male has the throat white; the breast buff with broken black bars; the remainder of the plumage like that of the preceding species.

I provisionally call northern examples *interrumpens* but am not sure that this alleged subspecies differs from *blakistoni*, which I have not seen. Robinson and Baker, in fact, call our birds *blakistoni* (Bull. Brit. Orn. Club, vol. 48, 1927, p. 61), but I find that, granting individual variation, northern skins agree well with a good series of *interrumpens* from the Peninsula. It seems that revisers have not made sufficient allowance for the existence of red, gray, and intermediate phases in a given locality.

Family GRUIDAE

GRUS ANTIGONE SHARPII Blanford

BURMESE SARUS CRANE

Grus (*Antigone*) *sharpii* BLANFORD, Bull. Brit. Orn. Club, vol. 5, 1896, p. 7 (Burma).

Antigone sharpei, GYLDENSTOLPE, Kungl. Svenska Vet.-Akad. Handl., 1916, p. 141 (Muang Fang).

Antigone sharpii, GYLDENSTOLPE, Ibis, 1920, p. 765 ("Throughout the whole country").

Antigone antigone sharpei, DE SCHAUENSEE, Proc. Acad. Nat. Sci. Philadelphia, 1929, p. 583 (about 10 km. north of Ban Chong).—DEIGNAN, Journ. Siam Soc. Nat. Hist. Suppl., 1931, p. 170 (Chiang Mai).

Antigone antigone sharpii, DEIGNAN, Journ. Siam Soc. Nat. Hist. Suppl., 1936, p. 80 (Chiang Mai).

The crane is a common permanent resident on the plains of Chiang Rai Province; at Chiang Mai it has been recorded only during the cold weather (December 8 to March 23), sailing high overhead in flocks of 8 to 40 birds.

Attention may be drawn to the cranes by their clarion calls, which can be heard when the migrating birds are almost invisible in the sky. On the Chiang Rai savannas they are often seen from the highways, stalking about the marsh in pairs or family parties. Because of the open country they inhabit and the wide range of vision commanded by such tall birds, it is seldom possible to approach within gunshot range of them. However, I have been told that when one of a pair is killed or wounded, its mate refuses to leave its side, so that both are usually destroyed. This is confirmed by de Schauensee, who writes (1929): "If one bird is wounded the others then seem to lose all fear and refuse to leave their companion. They run along with the wounded bird, if it is able to run, and take short circling flights above it, uttering their musical trumpet-like *Krrrrrr* call."

Gyldenstolpe records (1916) that he was shown a nest with a light-set egg near Muang Fang; this was probably in July 1914. He describes the nest as a large structure about one-half meter in diameter, made of grass and other vegetable matter, placed on a tuft and about 30 cm. from the ground. He quotes a number of curious observations or beliefs, in connection with the bird's behavior in the breeding season, told him by a Lao informant.

De Schauensee states that a male had the irides orange; the bare skin of the crown greenish gray; the skin of the rest of the head and the naked portion of the neck dusky crimson; the feet and toes crimson.

This is a huge bird, with the head and upper neck unfeathered and chiefly of a red color; it has the plumage generally soft gray, the primaries and primary coverts blackish.

Family RALLIDAE

RALLUS AQUATICUS INDICUS Blyth

INDIAN WATER RAIL

Rallus indicus BLYTH, Journ. Asiat. Soc. Bengal, vol. 18, 1849, p. 820 (Lower Bengal).

Rallus aquaticus indicus, DEIGNAN, Journ. Siam Soc. Nat. Hist. Suppl., 1936, p. 80 (Chiang Mai).

The water rail is apparently a rare migrant at Chiang Mai, where I observed one February 28, 1931, and took specimens February 4 and 10, 1936.

Like the other migratory rails, this species may most easily be found in spring, since by then the countryside is almost wholly dry and paludine forms are concentrated at the few small areas still wet enough to satisfy their needs. My birds were taken at dusk as they fed in the open just outside heavy stands of rushes and sedges; in the fading light they resembled small, blackish chickens.

In this species the bill is rather thin and as long as the head. The adult has the feathers of the upperparts black with broad olive-brown margins; a broad olive-brown band through the eye and an ashy-gray supercilium; the throat white; the sides of the head, the fore-neck, and the upper abdomen ashy gray, more or less washed with olive-brown, especially on the breast; the remaining underparts banded black, white, and buff.

RALLUS STRIATUS ALBIVENTER Swainson

INDIAN GRAY-BREASTED RAIL

Rallus albiventer SWAINSON, Animals in menageries [The Cabinet of Natural History, vol. 123], 1838, p. 337 (India).

Hypotaenidia striata striata, DEIGNAN, Journ. Siam Soc. Nat. Hist. Suppl., 1931, p. 169 (Chiang Mai).

Rallus striatus gularis, DEIGNAN, Journ. Siam Soc. Nat. Hist. Suppl., 1936, p. 80 (Chiang Mai).

I collected this rail at Chiang Mai in November 1930 and again June 23 and 28, 1935; otherwise, it has been found in our provinces only at Ban Mae Klang, where I saw one in September, 1935.

My specimens were shot in flooded ricefields. The two June birds are males with greatly enlarged gonads.

These examples had the irides orange-brown; the apical half of the bill light horny brown, the culmen darker, the basal half rose; the feet and toes fleshy gray-brown; the claws horny gray.

The adult has the crown and nape rufous, more or less streaked with black; the feathers of the remaining upperparts dark brown, edged olive-brown and crossed by narrow, wavy white bars; the throat white; the sides of the head, the foreneck, and the breast ashy gray; the remaining underparts barred dark brown and white.

There is considerable difference in size between *jouyi* of Kiangsu and *gularis* of Java. In this respect the resident birds of Thailand are intermediate between the two, and I follow Riley (1938) in using the name *albiventer* for our race.

RALLINA FASCIATA (Raffles)

Red-legged Banded Rail

Rallus fasciatus Raffles, Trans. Linn. Soc. London, vol. 13, 1822, p. 328 (Sumatra; type locality restricted to Benkulan, by Kinnear and Robinson, Bull. Brit. Orn. Club, vol. 47, 1927, p. 130).

Rallina fasciata, Gyldenstolpe, Journ. Nat. Hist. Soc. Siam, 1915, p. 235 (listed); Ibis, 1920, p. 763 (Khun Tan).

The only northern example of this species is an unsexed bird in Stockholm, taken by Eisenhofer at Khun Tan sometime prior to 1915 (probably in 1913).

This apparently rare rail has the head, neck, and breast bright rufous, somewhat paler on the throat; the remaining upperparts dark rufous; the primaries and upper wing coverts blackish brown with white bars; the remaining underparts broadly banded black and white.

RALLINA EURIZONOIDES NIGROLINEATA (G. R. Gray)

Slaty-legged Banded Rail

Zapornia nigrolineata G. R. Gray, Catalogue of . . . Mammalia and birds of Nepal and Thibet . . . British Museum, 1846, p. 143. In synonymy of *Rallus superciliaris* Eyton, *ex* Hodgson, Gray's Zoological Miscellany, 1844, p. 86, *nomen nudum* (Nepal).

Rallina superciliaris superciliaris, Rogers and Deignan, Proc. Biol. Soc. Washington, 1934, p. 92 (Doi Ang Ka).

I took the only northern specimen on Doi Ang Ka at about 5,000 feet, April 14, 1931. This bird, a female with inactive gonads, was shot at dusk among bamboos at the edge of wet, evergreen forest. The stomach contained insects.

It had the irides bright orange; the edges of the eyelids light orange; the maxilla green at the extreme base, then pale blue, otherwise blackish brown; the mandible pale blue at the extreme base, then green, otherwise plumbeous; the edges of the commissure horny; the feet and toes slate color; the claws dark brownish slate.

The adult has the throat white; the head, neck, and breast bright rufous; the remaining upperparts and the wings dark olive-brown; the remaining underparts banded black and white.

Our two species of *Rallina* are very similar in plumage. The present form has a proportionately much larger bill. They may, however, be most easily distinguished by the color of the feet, which in *fasciata* are always red but in *nigrolineata* are greenish gray, plumbeous, slaty, or black.

PORZANA PUSILLA PUSILLA (Pallas)

ASIATIC LITTLE CRAKE

Rallus pusillus PALLAS, Reise durch verschiedene Provinzen des russischen Reichs, vol. 3, 1776, p. 700 (Davuria).

Porzana pusilla pusilla, DEIGNAN, Journ. Siam Soc. Nat. Hist. Suppl., 1936, p. 81 (Chiang Mai).

This little bird, like the water rail, has been found only in the spring months, when the species is necessarily concentrated in the few areas which are still wet. It is known only from Chiang Mai, where I saw one, March 30, 1929, and took specimens, April 26, 1935, and February 4, 1936.

This crake may occasionally be seen at nightfall, feeding at the edge of the marsh vegetation, into which, when alarmed, it scuttles like a diminutive chicken. Considering its small size and the impenetrability of its habitat, one may suppose that it is much commoner than would appear from the few records. The stomach of one of my specimens contained small snails.

The bird of April 26 is of considerable interest. It has lost the four outermost primaries on each side, and the new feathers, just appearing from the sheaths, are so short that it is questionable whether it could fly. This fact, in connection with the late date, may indicate that the species stays in small numbers to breed with us. Since the coloration of this example does not quite agree with that of any other specimen I have seen, there is the further possibility that we are concerned with an undescribed race in Thailand.

The bird just discussed, a female with inactive ovaries, had the irides brown-orange; the bill dark olive-green, more slaty on the culmen; the feet and toes dark olive-green; the claws horny brown.

The adult has the crown, nape, a line through the eye, and the remaining upperparts rufous-brown, everywhere streaked with black, on the back, scapulars, and inner wing coverts irregularly flecked with white; the supercilium, sides of the head, the throat, breast, and upper abdomen soft gray (paler on the throat); the remaining underparts closely barred brown and white. The immature is similar but has the underparts largely white, more or less washed with brownish.

PORZANA FUSCA BAKERI Hartert

BAKER'S RUDDY CRAKE

Porzana fusca bakeri HARTERT, Nov. Zool., vol. 24, 1917, p. 272 (Bhim-tal, Kumaon).

Amaurornis fuscus bakeri, DEIGNAN, Journ. Siam Soc. Nat. Hist. Suppl., 1931, p. 169 (Chiang Mai).

Porzana fusca bakeri, DEIGNAN, Journ. Siam Soc. Nat. Hist. Suppl., 1936, p. 81 (Chiang Mai).

This is another species that has been recorded only during the driest months, when it may be found concentrated within small areas. At Chiang Mai it was of rather rare occurrence from January 28 (1936) to May 8 (1935); otherwise it is known only from Chiang Saen Kao, where I took specimens January 14 and 18, 1937.

The ruddy crake was observed in the same places as the other small rails and, like them, was seen only at dusk when it came out to feed at the edge of the marsh.

A male had the irides orange-red; the eyelids edged coral-red; the maxilla slate; the mandible olive-plumbeous; the feet and toes coral-red; the claws horny brown.

The adult has the forepart of the crown, the sides of the head and neck, the breast, and the upper abdomen vinaceous-chestnut; the chin and throat whitish; the remaining upperparts dark olive-brown; the remaining underparts dark brown, narrowly barred with white.

Judging by the variation in color exhibited by specimens in Washington, I question whether *bakeri* and *erythrothorax* be separable on any character other than size. On this assumption, seven Thai specimens (wing length 102.6 to 110.1 mm.) must be called *bakeri*, in spite of Stuart Baker's assertion in the "Fauna of British India, Birds" that *erythrothorax* is the form of all Indo-China and the Shan States.

AMAURORNIS PHOENICURUS CHINENSIS (Boddaert)

CHINESE WHITE-BREASTED RAIL

Fulica chinensis BODDAERT, Table des planches enluminéez d'histoire naturelle, 1783, p. 54 (China, *ex* D'Aubenton, pl. 896; type locality restricted to Hongkong, by Stresemann, Nov. Zool., vol. 20, 1913, p. 304).

Amaurornis phaenicurus, GYLDENSTOLPE, Kungl. Svenska Vet-Akad. Handl., 1913, p. 68 (Ban Huai Hom).

Amaurornis phoenicurus chinensis, GYLDENSTOLPE, Journ. Nat. Hist. Soc. Siam, 1915, p. 235 (listed).—DEIGNAN, Journ. Siam. Soc. Nat. Hist. Suppl., 1931, p. 169 (Chiang Mai); 1936, p. 81 (Chiang Mai).—DE SCHAUENSEE, Proc. Acad. Nat. Sci. Philadelphia, 1934, p. 277 (Chiang Mai).

Amaurornis phaenicura chinensis, GYLDENSTOLPE, Kungl. Svenska Vet.-Akad. Handl., 1916, p. 148 ("Northern provinces").

Amaurornis phoenicura chinensis, GYLDENSTOLPE, Ibis, 1920, p. 763 ("Throughout the whole country").—DE SCHAUENSEE, Proc. Acad. Nat. Sci. Philadelphia, 1928, p. 578 (Chiang Mai).—RILEY, U. S. Nat. Mus. Bull. 172, 1938, p. 79 (Ban Nam Khian, Muang Pai).

This very common bird occurs throughout the year in all our provinces. In addition to localities cited above, I have it from Ban Sop Mae Chaem, Muang Fang, and Wiang Pa Pao and have seen in Stockholm eight examples taken at Khun Tan by Eisenhofer.

The *nok wak* may be seen in the fields, in village gardens, along tiny streams in the deciduous forest, but especially where great clumps of bamboo overarch ditches or quiet pools. It is highly tolerant of a semiarid environment and, at Chiang Mai, I noted little diminution in its numbers during even the driest months, when it was often seen slinking across parched fields, where only the low bunds offered concealment. It has a particular fondness for the thorny types of bamboo, using them for roosting and nesting purposes, even when they are at some distance from the nearest water, to and from which it travels on foot. The vernacular name is derived from its song, the syllable *wak* repeated many times in a loud, harsh voice, heard chiefly during the rains and at night dominating even the unearthly din of the frogs. The breeding season seems to coincide with the rainy months, during which period I have often seen the black juveniles.

An adult female had the irides garnet; the frontal plate red; the bill green, with extreme tip violet-blue; the rictus violet-blue; the feet and toes chrome-yellow; the claws horn. A somewhat younger female differed only in having the irides bright brown.

The adult has the forehead, sides of the head, the throat, breast, and upper abdomen white; the lower abdomen fawn color; the upper flanks slate; the lower flanks and under tail coverts rufous; an indistinct black line bordering the white of neck and breast; the remaining plumage slaty olive, more slaty on the wings.

GALLICREX CINEREA CINEREA (Gmelin)

CHINESE WATERCOCK

[*Fulica*] *cinerea* GMELIN, Systema naturae, vol. 1, pt. 2, 1789, p. 702 (China).
Gallicrex cinerea, DEIGNAN, Journ. Siam Soc. Nat. Hist. Suppl., 1931, p. 169 (Chiang Mai); 1936, p. 81 (Chiang Mai).

At Chiang Mai individuals in the brown nonbreeding plumage appeared locally and in small numbers early in March, but the species was really common only during the rains; my extreme dates are March 5 (1931) and September 26 (1931). I have also seen the watercock at Muang Phayao late in August. Doubtless it occurs throughout our provinces during the wet weather.

This large rail may be found in the flooded ricefields and in some numbers amid the tangled vegetation of the larger marshes. When open water must be crossed, it swims well, riding high and rather resembling a duck. When alarmed it stretches up its neck and, at short intervals, raises the tail with rapid jerks. Stomachs I examined contained only seeds and other vegetable matter.

Two males taken May 26 were in full nuptial dress and had the gonads greatly enlarged; a juvenile collected July 25 is well grown but completely lacks remiges and rectrices.

The remarkable song is heard from the reedbeds all through the summer, but only once, June 23, 1930, did I witness the curious performance that accompanies its delivery. The bird, with swollen neck and bill pointed at the ground, uttered a series of short notes, *owgh-owgh-owgh*, then, dipping the head, continued with a hollow-sounding *gook-gook-gook-gook*, the tone exactly like that of *Botaurus*. At times the two kinds of notes were interspersed, and without exception the head was lowered to produce the second sound. A similar performance has been observed in Upper Burma by Stanford (Ibis, 1939, p. 231). Anatomical investigation may show that we have here yet another species that has the habit of inflating the gullet to serve as a vocal resonator.

Males in breeding condition had the irides brown; the frontal plate and the base of the bill blood red; the rest of the bill bright yellow or bright yellow-green; the fleshy prolongation of the frontal plate scarlet above, otherwise fleshy pink; the feet and toes bright olive-green; the claws horn-brown. A March male in brown plumage had the irides brown; the frontal plate and basal three-quarters of the culmen dark brown, the rest of the maxilla olive-green; the mandible horny yellow, tipped olive-green; the feet and toes brownish olive; the claws horn-brown. A male juvenile had the irides olive-brown; the maxilla dark horny brown; the edges of the commissure and the mandible horny flesh; the feet and toes gray-green; the claws horny brown.

The breeding male has the head and neck dark slaty; the upperparts blackish brown, each feather broadly edged slaty gray; the underparts slaty black, each feather narrowly tipped pale gray; a fleshy protuberance rising from the hind end of the frontal plate and resembling a horn. The female (and the nonbreeding male) is a light brown bird, with blackish brown centers to the feathers above, and faint, wavy dark brown bars everywhere below. The immature resembles the female but is rather buffier generally and less barred below.

I agree with Chasen (Handlist of Malaysian Birds, 1935, p. 28) that Malaysian examples of this species are sufficiently smaller than more northern birds to be properly separable under the name *plumbea*.

GALLINULA CHLOROPUS INDICA Blyth

INDIAN GALLINULE

Gallinula chloropus (?) var. *Indicus* [*sic*] BLYTH, Journ. Asiat. Soc. Bengal, vol. 11, 1842, p. 887 (Calcutta, Bengal).

Gallinula chloropus parvifrons, GYLDENSTOLPE, Ibis, 1920, p. 763 ("Northern Siam").

Gallinula chloropus indicus, DEIGNAN, Journ. Siam Soc. Nat. Hist. Suppl., 1931, p. 169 (Chiang Mai); 1936, p. 81 (Chiang Mai).—DE SCHAUENSEE, Proc. Acad. Nat. Sci. Philadelphia, 1934, p. 277 (Chiang Mai).

The gallinule is known in northern Thailand only as a winter visitor; at Chiang Mai my extreme dates were September 19 (1931) and March

30 (1929). I have collected it at Ban Mae Sai, Chiang Saen Kao, Chom Thong, and Chiang Mai and have seen it at Nong Khiat and in the neighborhood of Chiang Dao.

I found this bird on the marshes, where there were small areas of open water, and on quiet ponds overgrown with lotus and the water-hyacinth. It spends much of its time swimming about like a little duck but never ventures far from reeds or other water plants, among which it takes shelter at the least alarm.

A female specimen had the irides bright brown; the frontal plate coral-red; the basal two-thirds of the maxilla and the basal half of the mandible bright red, the rest of the bill greenish yellow; a ring around the tibia just below the feathers orange in front, red behind; the rest of the tibia bright yellow; the tarsus bright yellow-green in front, slaty green behind; the toes bright yellow-green, the joints and soles slaty gray; the claws slaty black.

The adult has the head and neck slaty black, gradually changing to slaty gray on the upper back, breast, flanks, and abdomen (the last more or less mottled with white); the central under tail coverts black, the others white; the remaining upperparts deep brown, strongly washed with olivaceous. The immature has the upperparts wholly brown; the underparts everywhere mottled gray, buffy, and white; the under tail coverts as in the adult, but the white sometimes washed with buff.

Practically all seen in our provinces will be immature individuals. Both old and young, however, may be readily known by the distinctively marked under tail coverts, which show as the bird swims with upturned tail.

PORPHYRIO PORPHYRIO POLIOCEPHALUS (Latham)

INDIAN PURPLE COOT

G[allinula] poliocephala LATHAM, Index ornithologicus, Suppl., 1801, p. lxviii (India).

Porphyrio poliocephalus, GYLDENSTOLPE, Kungl. Svenska Vet.-Akad. Handl., 1916, p. 149 (Chiang Rai).

P[orphyrio] poliocephalus, ROBINSON and BODEN KLOSS, Journ. Nat. Hist. Soc. Siam, 1921, p. 44 (Chiang Mai).

Porphyrio poliocephalus poliocephalus, GYLDENSTOLPE, Ibis, 1920, p. 764 ("Swampy plains of northern Siam").—DEIGNAN, Journ. Siam Soc. Nat. Hist. Suppl., 1931, p. 169 (Chiang Mai); 1936, pp. 81, 131 (Chiang Mai, Ban Nong Khiat).

This large and handsome rail occurs on the marshes near Chiang Mai in some numbers during the rains; I found it there from June 28 (1930) to November 23 (1936) and saw a solitary bird February 11, 1936. I have taken specimens at Chom Thong in November. At Muang Phayao it was common in August 1929, and near Ban Nong Khiat it was abundant at the end of December 1935.

One who ventures into the flooded marshes of summer will find the *nok khieo* not at all shy—feeding in quite open places, fluttering above the vegetation with dangling feet, climbing the reeds for a better view of the intruder, and uttering their loud, hoarse notes on every side.

Specimens taken on August 3 and 14 had the gonads greatly enlarged. On August 28, 1929, I watched one bird of a pair brooding on a nest, while its mate walked in a circle about it, with wings held stiffly vertically and tail upraised to expose the white area beneath.

An August male had the irides deep red; the bill brownish red, much darker at the base, whitish about the nares; the casque dark brownish red, darker at the center, more vermilion at the sides; the feet and toes light red, gray at the joints; the claws horny brown. Another August male differed chiefly in having the irides brown.

The adult has the head gray, more or less washed with blue, changing to purple-blue on the back and light greenish blue on the lower neck and breast; the flanks and belly purple-blue; the thighs light greenish blue; the under tail coverts pure white; the scapulars and exposed portions of the wings greenish blue.

At certain localities in Central Thailand, at the peripheries of their respective ranges, we find *poliocephalus* and *viridis* together in the breeding season. I do not for this reason believe that we are dealing with distinct species but think rather that we have here a case in which inosculation is absent, each individual appearing externally to be definitely of one or the other race.

FULICA ATRA ATRA Linnaeus

EURASIAN COOT

[*Fulica*] *atra* LINNAEUS, Systema naturae, ed. 10, vol. 1, 1758, p. 152 (Europe; type locality restricted to Sweden, *apud* Hartert).

Fulica atra atra, ROGERS and DEIGNAN, Proc. Biol. Soc. Washington, 1934, p. 91 (Chiang Mai).—DEIGNAN, Journ. Siam Soc. Nat. Hist. Suppl., 1936, p. 81 (Chiang Mai, "some fifty miles south of Chiengmai"=Nong Khiat).

A female in the collection of Cornell University, taken by Vijjakich at Lampang, August 13, 1930, seems to be the earliest example known from Thailand. In 1931 I acquired a specimen captured alive near Chiang Mai on November 17, collected another November 28 near Ban Nong Khiat, where it was very common, and a third at Chiang Mai on December 17. At Ban Pa Muat, north of San Sai Luang, a solitary bird was seen on October 23, 1936, and later dozens of individuals were noted on the same pond, at least until January 16, 1937.

The specimen taken at Lampang in August may indicate that some birds stay to breed in Thailand, at least occasionally.

My examples had the irides red or bright brown; the frontal plate ivory white or pinkish yellowish, edged white; the interior of the mouth fleshy white; the bill fleshy white or horny white, pinkish at the base of the culmen; the exposed portion of the tibiae wholly light orange, wholly bright olive-green, or orange behind and olive-green in front; the tarsi brown-olive or dull olive-green; the toes olive-green, duller or darker at the joints; the lobes of the toes olive-green, slaty below and at the edges above; the claws blackish slate.

The adult has the head and neck dull black; the entire upperparts blackish slate; the entire underparts slaty gray; the under tail coverts dull black. The immature is browner and has the underparts more or less mottled with white.

The coot is a swimming bird that occurs at the same places as the gallinule, from which it may at once be known by its larger size and its white, not red, bill and frontal plate. It is the only Thai rail having the phalanges of the toes edged with membranous lobes.

Family HELIORNITHIDAE

HELIOPAIS PERSONATA (G. R. Gray)

MASKED FINFOOT

Podica personata G. R. GRAY, Proc. Zool. Soc. London, 1848 [=1849], p. 90, Aves, pl. 4 (Malacca).

Heliopais personata, VIJJAKICH, Journ. Siam Soc. Nat. Hist. Suppl., 1934, p. 330 ("about fifteen miles [north of Lampang] along the Lampang-Chiengrai road").

The only northern record for the rare finfoot is the adult female taken by Vijjakich and deposited in the collection of Cornell University. The collector has published the date as November 11, 1930, but on the specimen label the date appears as "11.2.30." The species is perhaps only a straggler to our provinces.

Vijjakich states that his bird was swimming and was probably searching for food. An extralimital example, which I took at Tha Chalaep, near Chanthaburi, May 4, 1937, was found on mud flats among mangroves at low tide and had been feeding upon small crabs and mollusks.

My specimen had the irides brown; the eye ring yellow-green; the bill bright yellow, with the basal two-thirds of the culmen horny brown; the feet and toes green; the lobes of the toes greenish yellow; the claws horn.

The adult male has the forehead and sides of the crown, the sides of the head, the throat, and entire foreneck black, the last parts edged by a narrow white line beginning behind the eye; the remainder of the crown, the upper side of the neck, and the extreme upper back steel gray; the sides of the neck light olive-brown; the remaining upperparts olive-brown; the remaining underparts whitish, with the sides of the body and the under tail coverts dull brown, more or less barred with white. The adult female differs in having the center of the throat and foreneck white.

Order CHARADRIIFORMES

Family JACANIDAE

HYDROPHASIANUS CHIRURGUS (Scopoli)

BRONZE-WINGED JAÇANA

Tringa (*Chirurgus*) SCOPOLI, Deliciae florae et faunae insubricae, pt. 2, 1786, p. 92 ("in nova Guiana," error=Luzón, *ex* Sonnerat).

Hydrophasianus chirurgus, DEIGNAN, Journ. Siam Soc. Nat. Hist. Suppl., 1931, p. 170 (Chiang Mai); 1936, p. 82 (Chiang Mai).

At Chiang Mai this jaçana was present in some numbers from July 26 (1930) to March 26 (1929) and unknown during the rest of the year, except for a single individual seen on April 12, 1937. I found it common at Phayao in August 1929 and at Ban Nong Khiat in November and December. A specimen at Cornell University was collected by Vijjakich, February 11, 1930, at "Lampang," but perhaps came from the same locality as the finfoot of the same date. Finally, I took an example at Ban Mae Chai, May 9, 1936.

The present species occurs on the marshes where there are areas of open water surrounded by heavy vegetation and occasionally, as the countryside becomes drier, at the edges of comparatively small ponds. It feeds among the floating plants, walking with complete ease upon lotus pads and water-hyacinths. It swims well, riding high, and is able, when alarmed, to submerge the body until only the head is visible, in the manner of a grebe. A common call, often uttered during flight, is a plaintive *mee-a-ar*, rather like the mew of a cat.

The May bird from Mae Chai is acquiring breeding dress (the golden nuchal patch is present and dark feathers are appearing everywhere below) and already had the gonads enlarged; a Chiang Mai specimen of August 11 is in full nuptial plumage and had the ovaries greatly enlarged.

The breeding adult has the entire head and neck white, except for a shining golden-yellow patch on the nape and extreme upper back, edged by a narrow black line; the back and scapulars brown, glossed with purple and bronze; the rump, upper tail coverts, and greatly elongated tail dull black; most of the wing pure white; the underparts dark chocolate-brown. Nonbreeding adults have the crown and nape brown; a white supercilium continued down the side of the neck as a yellow band; a black band from the base of the bill, through the eye, continued down the neck below the yellow and connected with the one on the opposite side to form a broad breast band; the remaining underparts white; the short, pointed tail feathers brown; the other parts much as in the breeding dress, but the wing coverts more or less barred with brown.

METOPIDIUS INDICUS (Latham)

BRONZE-WINGED JAÇANA

[*Parra*] *indica* LATHAM, Index ornithologicus, vol. 2, 1790, p. 765 ("in Indiae paludosis").

Metopidius indicus, GYLDENSTOLPE, Kungl. Svenska Vet.-Akad. Handl., 1916, p. 142 (Chiang Rai, Nong Mae Rua); Ibis, 1920, p. 765 ("Throughout the whole country").—DE SCHAUENSEE, Proc. Acad. Nat. Sci. Philadelphia, 1929, p. 583 (Chiang Rai).—DEIGNAN, Journ. Siam Soc. Nat. Hist. Suppl., 1931, p. 170 (Chiang Mai); 1936, p. 81 (Chiang Mai).

At Chiang Mai the bronze-winged jaçana was rather more common that the preceding species; during the driest months it was very local in distribution, and, for no obvious reason, I never saw it in October and November. I found it common at Phayao in August and at Ban Nong Khiat in November and December. I have collected it at Chiang Rai in January and at Chom Thong in November and January.

Two downy young taken at Chiang Mai, September 5, 1930, were accompanied by a male with greatly enlarged gonads. The latter's stomach contained vegetable matter, mud, and tiny stones; another of my specimens had been feeding on small snails.

The breeding male had the irides brown; the frontal lappet gray; the bill greenish yellow, reddish at the base; the feet and toes greenish gray. The downy young had the irides brown; the bill gray, pinkish at the base; the feet and toes dark gray ringed with buffy ridges. Nonbreeding adults had the irides brown; the lappet and basal half of the culmen slaty green; the maxilla olive-yellow with an orange-yellow patch near the rictus; the mandible with the basal half pure yellow, otherwise olive-yellow; the feet and toes dull green; the claws slaty green.

The adult has a white supercilium from the eye to the nape; the crown glossy green; the upper back glossy blue and purple; the back, scapulars, and wing coverts glossy olive-bronze; the quills and under wing coverts black glossed with green; the rump and upper tail coverts chestnut glossed with blue; the under tail coverts and tail chestnut; the remaining underparts black glossed with green. The immature has the crown rufous; the tail light rufous barred with blackish; the throat, a short supercilium, and the sides of the head white; the breast and lower neck fawn; the remaining underparts white; other parts much as in the adult.

Family ROSTRATULIDAE

ROSTRATULA BENGHALENSIS BENGHALENSIS (Linnaeus)

Asiatic Painted Snipe

[*Rallus*] *benghalensis* Linnaeus, Systema naturae, ed. 10, vol. 1, 1758, p. 153 (Asia).

Rostratula capensis, Gyldenstolpe, Journ. Nat. Hist. Soc. Siam, 1915, p. 236 (listed); Kungl. Svenska Vet.-Akad. Handl., 1916, p. 147 (Khun Tan); Ibis, 1920, p. 762 ("Northern Siam").

Rostratula benghalensis benghalensis, Deignan, Journ. Siam Soc. Nat. Hist. Suppl., 1931, p. 170 (Chiang Mai); 1936, p. 82 (Chiang Mai).

At Chiang Mai the painted snipe occurred throughout the year but was common and generally distributed only during the rains. Eisenhofer sent to Stockholm an undated male from Khun Tan. Otherwise, it is definitely known only from Mae Sariang, where I took a male on October 24, 1936, but the species will doubtless be found to occur in all our provinces.

In its choice of habitat and manner of flight, this bird closely resembles a rail. It seems to be active chiefly at night, and during the dry season I have found small flocks passing the day concealed under some bush or clump of bamboo as much as a quarter of a mile from the nearest water. The stomach of one of my specimens contained gravel and a pellet of shot, of another a single snail.

As is well known, in this species the roles of the sexes are completely reversed, the larger and brighter female playing a dominant part in all sexual matters and being promiscuous besides. With us, at least, the males are greatly in excess of the females and there is apparently no definite season for breeding, for I have taken birds with greatly enlarged gonads on May 21 and October 7.

Male specimens had the irides brown; the bill fleshy brown, blackish at the tip, greenish or slaty blue at the base of the mandible; the feet and toes slaty blue or green, tinged plumbeous; the claws horny brown or black.

The adult male has the crown blackish, with a median stripe and a short streak behind the eye buff; some of the scapulars largely white, forming a white line down either side of the back; the remaining upperparts gray, barred with white and glossy olive-green; the quills ashy, barred with buff; the upper wing coverts olive-brown, barred and spotted with black and buff; the neck and breast brown mottled with white; a patch of brown at each side of the belly separated from the breast by a white band; the remaining underparts white. The adult female has a white circle around the eye, continued as a streak behind it; the crown dark brown with a buff median stripe; the throat and foreneck chestnut, continued as a band over the upper back; the remaining upperparts brownish, glossed with olive-green and narrowly vermiculated with blackish; the quills and tail as in the male; a broad blackish-brown pectoral band, followed by a white band and then a broken blackish-brown band; the remaining underparts white.

Family CHARADRIIDAE

MICROSARCOPS CINEREUS (Blyth)

GRAY-HEADED LAPWING

Pluvianus cinereus BLYTH, Journ. Asiat. Soc. Bengal, vol. 11, 1842, p. 587 (Calcutta, Bengal).

Microsarcops cinereus, DEIGNAN, Journ. Siam Soc. Nat. Hist. Suppl., 1931, p. 171 (Chiang Mai); 1936, p. 82 (Chiang Mai).

This migratory lapwing occurs fairly commonly in the neighborhood of Chiang Mai from September 8 (1930) to March 14 (1930), and I have seen it at Ban Nong Khiat in November, but otherwise, curiously enough, it has been overlooked in the northern provinces.

The present species is found in flocks of 6 to 10 birds at moist places in the ricefields after harvest and on the drying marshes, often accompanied by the next form, which it closely resembles in habits.

A female specimen had the irides deep red, more orange next to the pupil; the edges of the eyelids and the bare skin in front of the eye bright yellow; the wattles bright yellow; the bill bright deep yellow with the terminal third black; the feet, toes, and soles bright yellow; the claws black.

The adult has the head, neck, and breast brownish ashy, the last delimited by a blackish-brown pectoral band; the back, scapulars, and upper wing coverts light brown; the upper tail coverts and tail white, the last with a broad, black subterminal band; the outspread wing with the apical half black, the basal half white; the remaining underparts white.

LOBIVANELLUS INDICUS ATRONUCHALIS Jerdon

BURMESE RED-WATTLED LAPWING

L[obivanellus] atronuchalis "Blyth" JERDON, Birds of India, vol. 3, 1864, p. 648 (Burma).

Sarcogrammus atrinuchalis, GYLDENSTOLPE, Journ. Nat. Hist. Soc. Siam, 1915, p. 235 (listed).

Sarcogrammus indica atrinuchalis, GYLDENSTOLPE, Kungl. Svenska Vet.-Akad. Handl., 1916, p. 142 (Khun Tan).

Sarcogrammus indicus atronuchalis, GYLDENSTOLPE, Ibis, 1920, p. 755 ("Throughout the whole country").

Lobivanellus indicus atrinuchalis, DE SCHAUENSEE, Proc. Acad. Nat. Sci. Philadelphia 1929, p. 584 (Chiang Mai, Chiang Rai, Chiang Saen).

Lobivanellus indicus atronuchalis, DEIGNAN, Journ. Siam Soc. Nat. Hist. Suppl., 1931, p. 171 (Chiang Mai); 1936, p. 82 (Chiang Mai).

This is one of our most familiar birds, occurring in suitable territory throughout the northern provinces. Eisenhofer sent to Stockholm six undated specimens from Khun Tan. I have skins from Chiang Mai, Wiang Pa Pao, and Ban Na Noi (Nan Province).

The red-wattled lapwing haunts areas of barren soil or short grass, whether wet or dry. I have found it in pairs or small parties at the edge of ponds and marshes, on the ricefields after harvest, in pastures and meadows, and even in the more open *pa daeng*. It is an excitable and fearless bird, wheeling about the intruder upon its territory with loud, nasal cries, *did-he-do'-it*, *do-it*, *do-it*, *did-he-dare'-do-it*, and effectively alarming all other birds in the neighborhood. It is active after dark and on nights of bright moonlight often ascends high into the air to soar about, constantly calling. Uneducated people believe this nocturnal singing to be an omen of death; there is also a belief prevalent in all parts of Thailand that the bird sleeps on its back with feet upraised, lest the sky fall during the night. The stomach of one of my specimens was filled with beetles.

It has not yet been found breeding with us, but May specimens show the lateral brood patches. At this season I have observed birds seeking escape by lowering the head almost to the ground and silently slinking off in a zigzag path, and have no doubt that a nest was in the vicinity.

A Wiang Pa Pao specimen of July 26 is subadult; the feathers of the chin and throat are white with black shaft streaks and fresh central rectrices are about four-fifths grown.

A male had the irides brownish red; the eye ring, wattles, and basal half of the bill rose-red, the rest of the bill black; the feet yellow, tinged greenish at the "knee"; the toes dusky green; the claws black.

The adult has the sides of the head behind the eye white; the rest of the head, the neck, and upper breast black; the remaining underparts white, this color continued over the nape as a narrow band; the back and scapulars light brown, glossed with green; the upper wing coverts light brown, glossed with violet; the primaries and outer secondaries black; the inner secondaries partly or wholly white, forming a conspicuous white wing bar; the upper tail coverts and tail white, the latter with a broad, black subterminal bar.

HOPLOPTERUS DUVAUCELII (Lesson)

INDIAN SPUR-WINGED PLOVER

Charadrius Duvaucelii LESSON, Dict. Sci. Nat., éd. Levrault, vol. 42, 1826, p. 38 (Calcutta, Bengal).

Hoplopterus ventralis, GYLDENSTOLPE, Kungl. Svenska Vet.-Akad. Handl., 1913, p. 69 (Mae Yom river near Phrae, Mae Yom near "Vang Nun"); 1916, p. 143 (Mae Ping river, Khun Tan); Journ. Nat. Hist. Soc. Siam, 1915, p. 235 (listed); Ibis, 1920, p. 755 ("Along the larger rivers of the whole country").—DE SCHAUENSEE, Proc. Acad. Nat. Sci. Philadelphia, 1929, p. 584 (Chiang

Rai).—DEIGNAN, Journ. Siam Soc. Nat. Hist. Suppl., 1931, p. 171 (Chiang Mai).

Hoplopterus duvaucelii, DE SCHAUENSEE, Proc. Acad. Nat. Sci. Philadelphia, 1934, p. 278 (Chiang Saen Kao).—DEIGNAN, Journ. Siam Soc. Nat. Hist. Suppl., 1936, p. 82 (Chiang Mai).—RILEY, U. S. Nat. Mus. Bull. 172, 1938, p. 85 (Chom Thong, Thattafang).

Along our major streams, the abundant and conspicuous spurwing replaces the preceding form or, at least, greatly outnumbers it. It haunts the sand bars and shingly beaches of the Salwin, the Mae Ping, the Mae Tha, the Mae Wang, the Mae Yom, the Mae Nan, the Mae Kok, and the Mae Khong, only rarely leaving the edge of clear water to settle in the nearby fields.

The habits of this species are much like those of the red-wattled lapwing. When alarmed and caused to fly it utters a nasal *o͝onkh-o͝onkh-o͝onkh* or an equally nasal *chão, chão-chão*.

On the Nan river, near Ban Pa Luat (just south of our limits), April 9, 1937, while exploring a great sandy area at night with the aid of a torch, I was led by the outcries of the parents to discover three downy young, cowering together in the shingle of an anabranch's dry bed. One was collected; it has the upper half of the head rufous-buff, spotted with black; the posterior half of the crown edged with a continuous black band, beginning behind the eye; a white nuchal collar; the entire underparts white, somewhat tinged with buffy on the upper breast, lower flanks, and undertail; the apical half of the wing white; the rest of the wing and the remaining upperparts rufous-buff; the caudal down black.

My mature specimens had the irides dark brown; the bill and carpal spurs black; the feet and toes slate color; the claws slaty black.

The adult has the crown and long, full crest, the cheeks, throat, and center of the foreneck black, all edged with white; the back and scapulars light brown; the tail with the basal half white, the apical half black; the wing black, crossed by a broad, white bar; the underparts white, with a broad gray-brown pectoral band and a black horseshoe on the abdomen.

PLUVIALIS APRICARIA FULVA (Gmelin)

PACIFIC GOLDEN PLOVER

[*Charadrius*] *fulvus* GMELIN, Systema naturae, vol. 1, pt. 2, 1789, p. 687 (Tahiti).

Pluvialis dominicus fulvus, DEIGNAN, Journ. Siam Soc. Nat. Hist. Suppl., 1931, p. 171 (Chiang Mai); 1936, p. 83 (Chiang Mai).

I believed at one time that the golden plover wintered in northern Thailand, but reexamination of my records shows that it has been found with us only in the months of October and February. At Chiang Mai, the extreme dates are October 4 (1930) and February 17

(1932). The species is also known from Mae Sariang, where I took specimens on October 26 and 27, 1936.

I have found this bird only occasionally and in small flocks, among dry rice stubbles and on such grassy areas as the aviation field west of Chiang Mai.

One of my specimens had the irides dark brown; the bill black; the feet and toes slate color; the claws black.

Any example from our region will probably be in winter dress, when it has the upperparts dark brown or blackish, heavily spotted everywhere with whitish and golden-yellow; the underparts white, the throat and breast more or less washed with golden-buff and more or less streaked with brown. In nuptial plumage it has the forehead, supercilia, sides of neck, and breast white; the remaining underparts black; the other parts much as in winter but more deeply colored.

There is a slight chance that the European golden plover, *Pluvialis apricaria apricaria*, may some day be found in northern Thailand; it has the axillaries pure white, while the present form has them brownish gray. There is a much greater possibility that the gray plover, *Squatarola squatarola*, will occur in our provinces; it may be recognized by its black axillaries and the presence of a small hindtoe. The golden plovers have no hindtoe at all.

CHARADRIUS DUBIUS CURONICUS Gmelin

EURASIAN LITTLE RINGED PLOVER

[*Charadrius*] *curonicus* GMELIN, Systema naturae, vol. 1, pt. 2, 1789, p. 692 (Kurland, Russia).

Charadrius dubius jerdoni [*partim*], DEIGNAN, Journ. Siam Soc. Nat. Hist. Suppl., 1931, p. 171 (Chiang Mai [*partim*]); 1936, p. 82 (Chiang Mai [*partim*]).

I took two specimens of the Palearctic race of the little ringed plover on the Mae Ping at Chiang Mai, December 29, 1930, and a third on the same river at Chom Thong, November 7, 1935. It is probably often overlooked among the much more numerous individuals of the following form.

The bird of November 7, a female in first-winter plumage, has the outermost primary partly ensheathed (about two-thirds grown).

The specimens of December 29, a male and a female in the first winter dress, had the irides dark brown; the edges of the eyelids yellow; the bill black, yellow at the base of the mandible; the feet and toes fleshy yellow; the soles fleshy; the claws black.

It is perhaps not possible to identify this bird in the field with any certainty. It is extremely close to the resident race in plumage but has a longer wing and bill. Most Thai examples are young birds in the first winter plumage, wholly lacking a black band on the forecrown and having the breast band either black mixed with brown, the feathers edged buffy or white (males) or ash brown, the feathers with buff edges (females).

The wings of my specimens measure 115, 114.7, and 108 mm. The first is the molting bird already mentioned; the measurement has been made to the tip of the *second* primary. The last is unusually short for this race, but it should be noted that the outermost primaries are new and unworn and may not yet have attained their full length.

CHARADRIUS DUBIUS JERDONI (Legge)

JERDON'S LITTLE RINGED PLOVER

AE[*gialitis*] *jerdoni* LEGGE, Proc. Zool. Soc. London, 1880, pp. 38–39. New name for *AEgialitis minutus* "Pallas" Jerdon, 1864 ("in the Deccan, generally among hills; and also from the top of the Eastern Ghats inland from Nellore"), not *Charadrius minutus* Pallas, 1811.

AEgialites dubia, GYLDENSTOLPE, Journ. Nat. Hist. Soc. Siam, 1915, p. 235 (listed); Kungl. Svenska Vet.-Akad. Handl., 1916, p. 144 (Khun Tan).

AEgialitis dubia jerdoni, GYLDENSTOLPE, Ibis, 1920, p. 757 (Khun Tan).

Charadrius dubius jerdoni [*partim*], DEIGNAN, Journ. Siam. Soc. Nat. Hist. Suppl., 1931, p. 171 (Chiang Mai [*partim*]); 1936, p. 82 (Chiang Mai [*partim*]).

Charadrius dubius jerdoni, DE SCHAUENSEE, Proc. Acad. Nat. Sci. Philadelphia, 1928, p. 577 (Chiang Mai); 1929, p. 585 (Chiang Mai, Chiang Saen Kao).—RILEY, U. S. Nat. Mus. Bull. 172, 1938, p. 86 (Chiang Mai).

This little plover is rare and local in our provinces from April to August but extremely common during the rest of the year, when its numbers are augmented by visitors from other parts of its range. Eisenhofer sent to Stockholm 11 specimens without other data than "Khun Tan." I have collected it at Chiang Mai, Sala Mae Tha, Ban Mae Klang, Ban Sop Mae Chaem, and Ban Na Noi (Nan Province). The bird occurs at areas of sand and shingle along the major streams and, during the cold weather, in the fields wherever there is open water.

There is still no definite record for the nesting of this bird in northern Thailand, but I feel certain that it breeds, at least in small numbers, on the great sand bars near Wat Phranon, above Chiang Mai. A male taken there, January 12, had the gonads slightly enlarged. The nuptial season of this species, like that of our other riverside breeders, must necessarily fall in the early part of the year, so that the young may be on the wing before the breaking of the rains and the rising of the waters.

The plumage becomes much abraded, perhaps from the action of wind-blown sand; this is most marked in a bird of May 27. My only specimen with virtually unworn feathers is an adult female from Chiang Mai, November 27, which has presumably just completed the prenuptial molt.

Thai examples of this race have been recorded as having the irides brown; the eye ring yellow; the bill black, yellow at the base of the mandible; the feet and toes light brown or olive-flesh. The yellow around the eye and at the base of the bill is much more lasting and conspicuous in dried skins of *jerdoni* than of *curonicus*, but I do not know whether it is correspondingly brighter in life.

The adult has a band across the forecrown, the lores and the area about the eye, and a complete collar over the upper back and across the upper breast black; the forehead, supercilium, throat, nuchal collar connected with the throat, remainder of underparts, and the greater portion of the outer tail feathers white; the rest of the plumage ashy brown.

The young bird presumably has a plumage much like that described under the preceding form, but it is noteworthy that every Thai specimen of the little ringed plover in immature dress has proved to belong to the race *curonicus*.

I have not been able to compare Thai examples with indubitable *jerdoni* of South India. My specimens are small: the wings of five males measure 96.6–101.3 mm. (one, 104 mm.); of nine females, 101.4–104.3 mm. (one, 106.9 mm.). The wing lengths of *jerdoni* in India, as recorded by several authors, are considerably greater, but this appears to be due to the practice of lumping under a common name the rather larger birds of the Himalayas with the smaller birds of southern India, to which alone the name *jerdoni* properly should be applied. Thai birds agree well, in fact, with two males from southern India which have wing lengths of 102.4 mm., but are smaller than two Himalayan specimens with wings of 108.8 and 109 mm.

Since even the Palearctic *curonicus* has been taken at Bangkok as early as August 24 and as late as April 12, I suggest that some or all of the larger Indian examples believed to be typical *jerdoni* are, as a matter of fact, even though collected far south, early or late visitors from more northern breeding grounds. Comparison of series of *breeding* birds from the Himalayas with similar series from Ceylon and South India may make it desirable to place the former under a separate name.

CHARADRIUS ALEXANDRINUS ALEXANDRINUS Linnaeus

Western Kentish Plover

[*Charadrius*] *alexandrinus* Linnaeus, Systema naturae, ed. 10, vol. 1, 1758, p. 150 ("ad Ægypti ex Nilo canalem").

Leucopolius alexandrinus dealbatus, Deignan, Journ. Siam Soc. Nat. Hist. Suppl., 1931, p. 171 (Chiang Mai).

Charadrius alexandrinus dealbatus, Deignan, Journ. Siam Soc. Nat. Hist. Suppl., 1936, p. 82 (Chiang Mai).

At Chiang Mai I found the Kentish plover rather common from the beginning of October to the end of March and have seen it in small numbers in June and August; I have also taken it at Mae Sariang, October 26, 1936.

This species was found chiefly on the sand bars of the Mae Ping, less commonly at wet places in the fields, and was usually in company with the little ringed plover. The stomach of one of my birds contained tiny snails.

Three females had the irides dark brown; the bill black with the base of the mandible dusky flesh; the feet fleshy plumbeous (2 birds) or bluish plumbeous (1 bird); the "knees" and toes slaty; the claws black.

As seen in our provinces, this species has the forehead, short eyebrow, incomplete nuchal collar, underparts, and three outer pairs of rectrices white; the upperparts and an incomplete breast band ashy brown. It can be confused only with the little ringed plover, from which it may always be known by the heavy bill without yellow at the base, the plumbeous feet, and the broken breast band.

Six examples from northwestern Thailand are, somewhat hesitantly, placed with *alexandrinus*. The heaviest bill in my series can be matched by a bird from England, but, on the other hand, all my specimens are immature; adults would doubtless fall somewhere between *alexandrinus* and *nihonensis*.

CHARADRIUS PLACIDUS J. E. Gray and G. R. Gray

Long-billed Ringed Plover

Charadrius placidus J. E. and G. R. Gray, Catalogue of . . . Mammalia and birds of Nepal and Thibet . . . British Museum, ed. 2, 1863, pp. 70–71 (Nepal).

AEgialites placida, Gyldenstolpe, Journ. Nat. Hist. Soc. Siam, 1915, p. 235 (listed).

AEgialitis placida, Gyldenstolpe, Ibis, 1920, p. 757 (Khun Tan).

Charadrius placidus, de Schauensee, Proc. Acad. Nat. Sci. Philadelphia, 1929, p. 585 (Chiang Mai).—Deignan, Journ. Siam Soc. Nat. Hist. Suppl., 1931, p. 171 (Chiang Mai); 1936, p. 82 (Chiang Mai).

Only two examples of this plover are known from Thailand: An unsexed, undated specimen in Stockholm, taken by Eisenhofer at Khun Tan, and a female collected at Chiang Mai by de Schauensee, December 22, 1928.

I was with de Schauensee when his bird was taken and recall that it was found on a sand bar of the Mae Ping above Chiang Mai among a considerable number of Jerdon's ringed plover, in contrast with which its superior size was immediately apparent. During my subsequent winters in Thailand I looked for this bird without success.

De Schauensee notes that his specimen had the irides dark brown; the bill black; the feet and toes fleshy yellow; the claws black.

This species is considerably larger than any other ringed plover known from our provinces and normally would be seen under conditions that permit direct comparison of size. From *alexandrinus* it may be known also by its yellowish feet and unbroken breast band.

Family SCOLOPACIDAE

TRINGA GLAREOLA Linnaeus

WOOD SANDPIPER

[*Tringa*] *Glareola* LINNAEUS, Systema naturae, ed. 10, vol. 1, 1758, p. 149 (Europe; type locality restricted to Sweden, *apud* Hartert).

Totanus glareola, GYLDENSTOLPE, Journ. Nat. Hist. Soc. Siam, 1915, p. 236 (listed).

Rhyacophilus glareola, DE SCHAUENSEE, Proc. Acad. Nat. Sci. Philadelphia, 1928, p. 577 (Chiang Mai).—DEIGNAN, Journ. Siam. Soc. Nat. Hist. Suppl., 1936, p. 84 (Chiang Mai).—RILEY, U. S. Nat. Mus. Bull. 172, 1938, p. 91 (Nan).

Tringa glareola, DEIGNAN, Journ. Siam Soc. Nat. Hist. Suppl., 1931, p. 172 (Chiang Mai).—DE SCHAUENSEE, Proc. Acad. Nat. Sci. Philadelphia, 1934, p. 279 (Chiang Mai, Chiang Saen).

The wood sandpiper is an abundant winter visitor throughout the northern provinces. At Chiang Mai I recorded it from September 26 to March 14, and a single individual was seen July 11, 1931. At Ban Na Noi (Nan Province) I took a specimen on April 3, 1937. An undated bird in Stockholm was collected by Eisenhofer at Khun Tan. In addition, I have it from Chiang Saen Kao, Chom Thong, and San Sai Luang and have observed it at many other localities.

This species is much the commonest of our sandpipers, occurring singly or in loose flocks wherever there is mud and shallow water. At Chiang Mai many are snared and sold as game in the markets.

A male specimen had the irides brown; the bill black, dull olive at the base; the feet and toes dull brownish green; the claws black.

The wood sandpiper has the upperparts generally dark brown, most of the feathers spotted at the edges and narrowly tipped with white, the upper tail coverts largely pure white; the underparts white, sullied or indistinctly streaked with brown on the breast; the under wing coverts and axillaries white, lightly barred with brown.

TRINGA NEBULARIA (Gunnerus)

GREENSHANK

Scolopax nebularia GUNNERUS, *in* Leem, Beskrivelse over Finmarkens Lapper, 1767, p. 251 (District of Trondhjem, Norway).

Glottis nebularia, DE SCHAUENSEE, Proc. Acad. Nat. Sci. Philadelphia, 1929, p. 585 (Chiang Rai).—DEIGNAN, Journ. Siam Soc. Nat. Hist. Suppl., 1931, p. 172 (Chiang Mai).

Glottis nebularius, DEIGNAN, Journ. Siam Soc. Nat. Hist. Suppl., 1936, p. 84 (Chiang Mai).

The greenshank is a rather uncommon winter visitor in the North, ordinarily found along the larger rivers but occasionally, especially during the migrations, alighting at marshy areas in the fields and at the margins of ponds. At Chiang Mai I saw one on October 4, 1930, and two (together with five red-wattled lapwings) on September

20, 1935. De Schauensee collected a specimen on the Mae Kok at Chiang Rai, January 6, 1929. I took examples at Chom Thong, November 28, 1931; Chiang Saen Kao, January 8, 1937; and at Ban Pa Tao (on the Nan river, just south of our limits), April 10, 1937.

One of my specimens had the irides dark brown; the apical half of the bill black, the rest slaty blue; the feet and toes plumbeous-olive; the claws blackish brown.

The greenshank is much larger than any other sandpiper known from our provinces and has the bill distinctly recurved. As usually seen in Thailand, it has the upperparts generally gray-brown, the feathers with black shaft streaks and narrow white edges; the lower back, rump, and upper tail coverts white; the underparts white, sometimes with small blackish streaks on the breast.

TRINGA OCROPHUS Linnaeus

Green Sandpiper

[*Tringa*] *Ocrophus* Linnaeus, Systema naturae, ed. 10, vol. 1, 1758, p. 149 (Europe; type locality restricted to Sweden, *apud* Hartert).

Totanus ochropus, Gyldenstolpe, Kungl. Svenska Vet.-Akad. Handl., 1913, p. 69 ("Northern districts"); Journ. Nat. Hist. Soc. Siam, 1915, p. 236 (listed).

Tringa ochropus, de Schauensee, Proc. Acad. Nat. Sci. Philadelphia, 1929, p. 585 (Chiang Mai).

Tringa ocrophus, Deignan, Journ. Siam Soc. Nat. Hist. Suppl., 1931, p. 172 (Chiang Mai); 1936, p. 83 (Chiang Mai).

Tringa ochrophus, de Schauensee, Proc. Acad. Nat. Sci. Philadelphia, 1934, p. 278 (Chiang Mai).

The green sandpiper is a fairly common winter visitor to all our provinces, though much less so than the wood sandpiper. At Chiang Mai I recorded a single individual, July 11, 1931, but its stay there normally extended from September 26 to April 1. In Stockholm are six birds taken by Eisenhofer at Khun Tan, one collected by Gyldenstolpe at Dẹn Chai, and one by Fejos at Chiang Mai. I have specimens from Mae Sariang, Ban Mae Wan, Sala Mae Tha, Chiang Mai, and Ban Na Noi (April 2, 1937) and have observed it at numerous other places.

This species occurs on the plains wherever there is mud and shallow water, usually in company with the wood sandpiper, but in smaller numbers.

My specimens had the irides dark brown; the bill black, dark olive-green on the basal half; the feet and toes dull olive-green or slaty green; the claws black or horny brown.

The green sandpiper may be confused with the wood sandpiper. The former is a somewhat larger bird; it has the upperparts darker, usually more or less washed with oily olive-green, and the whitish markings less distinct; rather heavier streaking on the breast; the

583136—45——9

under wing coverts and axillaries blackish brown, narrowly barred with white.

ACTITIS HYPOLEUCOS (Linnaeus)

COMMON SANDPIPER

[*Tringa*] *Hypoleucos* LINNAEUS, Systema naturae, ed. 10, vol. 1, 1758, p. 149 (Europe; type locality restricted to Sweden, *apud* Hartert.).

Tringoides hypoleucos, GYLDENSTOLPE, Kungl. Svenska Vet.-Akad. Handl., 1913, p. 69 ("Northern Siam"); Journ. Nat. Hist. Soc. Siam, 1915, p. 236 (listed); Ibis, 1920, p. 759 ("Throughout the whole country").

Tringa hypoleuca, DE SCHAUENSEE, Proc. Acad. Nat. Sci. Philadelphia, 1929, p. 586 (Chiang Mai.)

Tringa hypoleucos, DEIGNAN, Journ. Siam Soc. Nat. Hist. Suppl., 1931, p. 172 (Chiang Mai).—DE SCHAUENSEE, Proc. Acad. Nat. Sci. Philadelphia, 1934, p. 279 (Chiang Mai).

Actitis hypoleucos, DEIGNAN, Journ. Siam Soc. Nat. Hist. Suppl., 1936, p. 83 (Chiang Mai).—RILEY, U. S. Nat. Mus. Bull. 172, 1938, p. 91 (Nan).

This is a very common winter visitor throughout the North. At Chiang Mai I recorded it from August 1 (1931) to April 3 (1931). Eisenhofer sent to Stockholm eight specimens from Khun Tan. I collected it at Chiang Mai, Mae Sariang, Thattafang, Chom Thong, and Chiang Saen Kao and have seen it almost everywhere in the lowlands.

The common sandpiper is well named, for it is found wherever there is water—in the ricefields, along streams, large and small, at village ponds, and in roadside ditches; it even ascends the mountains for some distance along the torrents.

This is an unmistakable little bird: in flight it may be known by its shrill *peet-weet*, *peet-weet*, and the peculiarly jerky action of its white-barred wings; at other times, whether walking or standing, it constantly bobs the hinder portion of its body up and down.

It has the upperparts brown, washed with oily olive-green, many of the feathers faintly barred darker and narrowly tipped whitish; the underparts white, more or less sullied with brown on the lower neck and breast; a conspicuous white bar in the outspread wing.

EROLIA TEMMINCKII (Leisler)

TEMMINCK'S STINT

Tringa Temminckii LEISLER, Nachtrage zu Bechsteins Naturgeschichte Deutschlands, 1812, pp. 64–73 (Hanau-am-Main, Germany).

Erolia minuta ruficollis, DE SCHAUENSEE, Proc. Acad. Nat. Sci. Philadelphia, 1929, p. 586 (Chiang Saen Kao).

Erolia temminckii, DEIGNAN, Journ. Siam Soc. Nat. Hist. Suppl., 1931, p. 172 (Chiang Mai).—DE SCHAUENSEE, Proc. Acad. Nat. Sci. Philadelphia, 1934, p. 279 (Chiang Mai).

Pisobia temminckii, DEIGNAN, Journ. Siam Soc. Nat. Hist. Suppl., 1936, p. 84 (Chiang Mai).—RILEY, U. S. Nat. Mus. Bull. 172, 1938, p. 95 (Chom Thong).

Temminck's stint is a common winter visitor, at least to Chiang Mai and Chiang Rai Provinces, and doubtless occurs throughout our area. In the neighborhood of Chiang Mai I recorded it only between November 1 (1935) and February 16 (1932), but I took a specimen at Chiang Rai on May 6, 1936, and another at Ban Mae Chai on May 9 of the same year.

This little sandpiper is found in flocks, often of 50 or more individuals, upon the marshes, at muddy places in the fields, and on the sandy bars and islands of the rivers.

My specimens had the irides dark brown; the bill black, olive or olive-brown at the base; the feet and toes olive-yellow or yellowish olive; the soles yellow; the claws black.

In winter this stint has the upperparts brownish gray, more or less glossed with olive-green, many of the feathers with obsolescent dark centers; the underparts white, sullied with brownish gray on the lower neck and breast; a narrow white bar in the outspread wing; the outer tail feathers white (visible in flight).

Late spring specimens have the upperparts browner, many of the feathers blackish with pale rufous margins; the breast more or less definitely streaked with brown and pale rufous.

EROLIA SUBMINUTA (Middendorff)

LONG-TOED STINT

Tringa subminuta MIDDENDORFF, Sibirische Reise, vol. 2, pt. 2, 1851, pp. 222–223, pl. 19, fig. 6 (western slopes of the Stanovoi Mountains and mouth of the Udâ, Siberia).

Limonites damacensis, GYLDENSTOLPE, Kungl. Svenska Vet.-Akad. Handl., 1916, p. 146 (Ban Sop Tui).

Limonites minutilla subminuta, GYLDENSTOLPE, Ibis, 1920, p. 760 (Ban Sop Tui).

Erolia subminuta, ROGERS and DEIGNAN, Proc. Biol. Soc. Washington, 1934, p. 92 (Chiang Mai).—DE SCHAUENSEE, Proc. Acad. Nat. Sci. Philadelphia, 1934, p. 279 (Chiang Mai).

Pisobia subminuta, DEIGNAN, Journ. Siam Soc. Nat. Hist. Suppl., 1936, p. 84 (Chiang Mai).

The long-toed stint seems to be a species of considerable rarity, and I know of only four specimens from our provinces: a female taken by Gyldenstolpe near Ban Sop Tui (Lampang Province), April 23, 1914; a male taken by me at Chiang Mai, January 30, 1932; a male taken by de Schauensee at Chiang Mai, January 26, 1933; a male collected by me at Ban Mae Chai, May 9, 1936.

Gyldenstolpe states that his bird was shot on a sand bar in the Mae Wang river, but both of my specimens were found on marshes; the Mae Chai example was associated with *Erolia temminckii.*

One of my birds had the irides brown; the bill black, olive-brown at the base of the mandible; the feet and toes olive-yellow; the claws black. Gyldenstolpe's specimen differed in having the feet and toes yellowish brown.

The diminutive size of this sandpiper will separate it from any other species known from the North except *Erolia temminckii;* from that bird it may be known by its having the feathers of the upperparts black, broadly edged with bright rufous and tipped with whitish, and the outer tail feathers brown, and by its lack of a wing bar.

CAPELLA GALLINAGO GALLINAGO (Linnaeus)

FAN-TAILED SNIPE

[*Scolopax*] *Gallinago* LINNAEUS, Systema naturae, ed. 10, vol. 1, 1758, p. 147 (Europe; type locality restricted to Sweden, *apud* Hartert).

Gallinago gallinago, GYLDENSTOLPE, Journ. Nat. Hist. Soc. Siam, 1915, p. 236 (listed); Ibis, 1920, p. 762 ("Throughout the whole country").

Capella gallinago, DE SCHAUENSEE, Proc. Acad. Nat. Sci. Philadelphia, 1928, p. 577 (Chiang Mai).

Capella gallinago gallinago, DE SCHAUENSEE, Proc. Acad. Nat. Sci. Philadelphia, 1929, p. 586 (Chiang Mai).—DEIGNAN, Journ. Siam Soc. Nat. Hist. Suppl., 1931, p. 172 (Chiang Mai); 1936, p. 83 (Chiang Mai).

The fantail is probably common in winter throughout our provinces. Eisenhofer sent to Stockholm three undated specimens from Khun Tan. I took a male at Thattafang, on the Salwin, October 13, 1936. At Chiang Mai it arrived in October and was present in some numbers until March.

I found it at the margins of ponds, at muddy places in the fields, and especially on the marshes, whether great or small. It conceals itself in the vegetation, from which when startled it bursts with rapid, zigzagging flight, uttering a characteristic note that resembles the syllable *scape*.

One of my specimens had the irides dark brown; the bill light horny brown, with the apical third and edges of the commissure brownish black; the feet and toes dull olive-green; the claws black.

The two closely related species of *nok som* are so well known to all residents of Thailand that no detailed description is necessary. From the pintail the present species is not distinguishable in the field; in the hand it may be known by the tail, of which the outer feathers are scarcely narrowed and not at all stiffened.

CAPELLA STENURA (Bonaparte)

PIN-TAILED SNIPE

Scolopax stenura "Kuhl" BONAPARTE, Ann. Stor. Nat. Bologna, vol. 4, 1830, pp. 335–336 (Sunda Islands, particularly the Island of Java).

Gallinago stenura, GYLDENSTOLPE, Journ. Nat. Hist. Soc. Siam, 1915, p. 236 (listed).

Gallinago sthenura, GYLDENSTOLPE, Ibis, 1920, p. 762 ("Throughout the whole country").

Capella megala, DEIGNAN, Journ. Siam Soc. Nat. Hist. Suppl., 1931, p. 172 (Chiang Mai).

Capella stenura, DE SCHAUENSEE, Proc. Acad. Nat. Sci. Philadelphia, 1929, p. 586 (Chiang Mai).—DEIGNAN, Journ. Siam Soc. Nat. Hist. Suppl., 1931, p. 172 (Chiang Mai); 1936, p. 83 (Chiang Mai).

The pintail is no doubt present in season at any suitable place in our districts. In Stockholm are two undated specimens collected by Eisenhofer at Khun Tan. I took examples at Ban Mae Klang, February 11 and 13, 1937, and at Ban Huai Pa Khan (on the Nan river), April 8, 1937. One was shot at 4,300 feet on Doi Ang Ka, April 21, 1931, at the same bog in which the wood snipe had been found a week earlier. At Chiang Mai I recorded it as early as August 22 (1931) and as late as April 25 (1935); it was very common during the months of migration but I never took it there in midwinter, which leads me to suspect that it occurs in our provinces only as a bird of passage.

The pintail occurs at the same wet areas as the fantail, but I have also discovered it occasionally in quite dry places at some distance from water, hiding in grass or under a bush. Its alarm note and manner of flight are much like those of the fantail. Stomachs I examined contained only vegetable matter.

A female had the irides brown; the apical half of the bill brownish black, the basal half of the maxilla light brown, of the mandible horny olive; the feet and toes dull olive-green, the joints slaty gray; the claws black.

The pintail chiefly differs from the fantail in having the eight outer tail feathers on each side very narrow and stiff, the outermost so much so as to be pinlike.

CAPELLA NEMORICOLA (Hodgson)

WOOD SNIPE

Gall[inago] nemoricola HODGSON, Proc. Zool. Soc. London, 1836, p. 8 (Nepal).

Capella nemoricola, ROGERS and DEIGNAN, Proc. Biol. Soc. Washington, 1934, p. 91 (Doi Ang Ka).

The rare wood snipe is known from Thailand by a single specimen, a male taken by me on Doi Ang Ka, 4,300 feet, April 13, 1931.

This bird was shot at a boggy area, overgrown with an alderlike shrub, near the upper end of the valley beneath Pha Mon. In September 1930 I flushed a large snipe, probably of this species, in the ricefields at the opposite end of the same valley.

My specimen had the irides dark brown; the maxilla light brown with a fleshy tinge, the tip blackish brown, the narial region and extreme base dark gray; the mandible with the apical half blackish brown, the basal half fleshy white; the feet and toes chalky fleshy (almost white); the soles dead white; the claws horn-brown.

The wood snipe is decidedly larger than our other snipes. In coloration it resembles *gallinago* and *stenura*, but whereas these two species have the center of the abdomen immaculate white, *nemoricola* has this part wholly barred with brown.

I have been unable to compare this skin with examples from Nepal.

SCOLOPAX RUSTICOLA RUSTICOLA Linnaeus

EURASIAN WOODCOCK

[*Scolopax*] *Rusticola* LINNAEUS, Systema naturae, ed. 10, vol. 1, 1758, p. 146 (Europe; type locality restricted to Sweden, *apud* Hartert).

Scolopax rusticola rusticola, GYLDENSTOLPE, Ibis, 1920, p. 762 ("Northern Siam").—DEIGNAN, Journ. Siam. Soc. Nat. Hist. Suppl., 1931, p. 172 (Chiang Mai); 1936, p. 83 (Chiang Mai).—RILEY, U. S. Nat. Mus. Bull. 172, 1938, p. 93 (Khun Tan).

The woodcock is not common but is probably generally distributed at suitable places in all our provinces during the cold weather. At Chiang Mai I have recorded it only from January 1 (1931) to March 3 (1932). A specimen from Mae Rim was taken on February 3, 1937, and another from Ban Dan (on the Nan River just south of our limits) was collected on April 10, 1937.

About Chiang Mai this species occurred yearly in small numbers at a well-watered coppice near Wat Suan Dok, and I have also seen it several times at marshy spots in the deciduous forest near the foot of Doi Suthep. The bird from Ban Dan was shot from a boat and was discovered in an extraordinary situation: resting in a dense clump of an aquatic willowlike shrub growing in swirling water at some distance from the river bank. The woodcock is chiefly active at night, spending the day concealed on the ground in thick vegetation, so that it will not often be observed. The stomach of one of my birds contained only mud and gravel.

A female had the irides dark brown; the bill with the basal half dusky flesh, the apical half dark brown, and the extreme tip horny; the feet and toes plumbeous-fleshy; the claws black. Another female differed in having the bill yellow-brown, becoming almost black on the apical third; the feet and toes brownish yellow; the claws dark horny brown.

The woodcock is a large and heavy wood-dwelling snipelike bird. It has the upperparts beautifully marked everywhere with black, rufous, and buff; the underparts buff, with narrow, wavy, blackish-brown cross bars.

Family RECURVIROSTRIDAE

HIMANTOPUS HIMANTOPUS HIMANTOPUS (Linnaeus)

EURASIAN BLACK-WINGED STILT

[*Charadrius*] *Himantopus* LINNAEUS, Systema naturae, ed. 10, vol. 1, 1758, p. 151 ("in Europa australiore").

Himantopus himantopus himantopus, DEIGNAN, Journ. Siam Soc. Nat. Hist. Suppl., 1936, p. 169 (Ban Mae Chai).

I watched a stilt on the marsh at Ban Mae Chai, May 9 and 10, 1936, but found it too wild to be collected. Since there is no other northern record, it is not possible to define the status of this species in our provinces.

A female with enlarged gonads, collected by me at Chanthaburi, April 22, 1937, had the irides red; the bill black; the feet and toes rose.

This is an unmistakable form. The male has the wings, scapulars, and a narrow band across the upper back black, slightly glossed with green; the rest of the plumage white, becoming smoky gray on the tail. The female differs only in having the scapulars and the band across the back brown. The pink legs are grotesquely long and, in flight, extend far beyond the tail.

Family BURHINIDAE

ESACUS MAGNIROSTRIS RECURVIROSTRIS (Cuvier)

INDIAN GREAT-BILLED THICK-KNEE

OEd[icnemus] recurvirostris CUVIER, Règne animal, nouv. éd., vol. 1, 1829, p. 500, note 2 (no locality given=Nepal, *apud* Stuart Baker).

Esacus recurvirostris, DE SCHAUENSEE, Proc. Acad. Nat. Sci. Philadelphia, 1929, p. 584 (Chiang Rai, Chiang Mai). — DEIGNAN, Journ. Siam Soc. Nat. Hist. Suppl., 1931, p. 170 (Chiang Mai); 1936, p. 84 (Chiang Mai).

The thick-knee is confined to the great bars of sand and shingle along our major rivers. De Schauensee took a female from a flock of six birds on the Mae Kok at Chiang Rai, January 6, 1929. I collected a pair on the Mae Khong at Chiang Saen Kao, January 9, 1937. In April 1937 I recorded the species at several places on the Mae Nan between Ban Pak Li and Ban Pa Luat. For Chiang Mai there is but one record: A solitary individual on the Mae Ping near Wat Phranon, December 15 and 22, 1928.

Along the Nan river I found the thick-knee concealing itself during the day in impenetrable thickets of a willowlike shrub which grew in hollows of the dunes. While camped upon a huge bar near Ban Pa Luat, April 9, 1937, I heard constantly during the night the sweet, mournful piping of this species. The wild excitement of the parents, invisible in the darkness, led to the discovery of a downy young one, flattening itself with outstretched neck against the shingle. This bird, which was collected, was probably less than one week old; it was able to run strongly and had been feeding on Orthoptera. A few feet away a second chick was found, about three-fourths the size of the first and still unable to stand.

De Schauensee's specimen had the irides creamy yellow; the orbital region olive-yellow; the bill black, with base, nares, and rictus olive-yellow; the feet and toes bluish olive. My juvenile had the irides yellow.

The juvenile has the upperparts generally pale sandy rufous (scapulars darker), streaked with black on crown and scapular tract, narrowly barred elsewhere, and with a pair of parallel black lines separating the center of the back from the scapulars and another similar pair at the sides of the rump; a black streak from the base of the mandible below the eye to the lower edge of the ear coverts; the throat buffy white; the lower neck and upper breast pale sandy rufous, indistinctly streaked blackish; the lower breast and flanks pinkish buff; the belly whitish, tinged buffy; the under tail coverts pale rufous; the quills and rectrices just beginning to appear from the sheaths, so that the wing is outwardly bordered by a white bar (coverts) which is inwardly edged black.

This is a huge ploverlike bird with a very heavy, somewhat recurved bill. It has the upperparts sandy brown; the wings sandy brown with the shoulder area blackish brown and a white patch at the center of the outer primaries; a streak above the white eyebrow, the ear coverts, and a mustachial streak black; the underparts white with a broad, indistinct brownish breast band.

Family GLAREOLIDAE

GLAREOLA PRATINCOLA MALDIVARUM J. R. Forster

INDIAN COLLARED PRATINCOLE

Glareola (*Pratincola*) *Maldivarum* J. R. FORSTER, Faunula Indica, ed. 2, 1795, p. 11 (open sea in the latitude of the Maldive Islands, *ex* Latham, General synopsis of birds, vol. 3, pt. 1, 1785, p. 224, Pratincole var. B).

Glareola maldivarum maldivarum, DEIGNAN, Journ. Siam Soc. Nat. Hist. Suppl., 1931, p. 170 (Chiang Mai).

Glareola maldivarum, DEIGNAN, Journ. Siam Soc. Nat. Hist. Suppl., 1936, p. 84 (Chiang Mai).

On the Chiang Mai plain the collared pratincole appeared rather irregularly and in small numbers between March 23 (1929) and June 27 (1931) (one seen, February 16, 1937) but was unknown at other seasons. At Ban Mae Chai I collected a male from a flock. Otherwise the species is unrecorded from our provinces, although it might be expected to occur on occasion almost anywhere in the lowlands.

This swallow-plover avoids the rivers and keeps to the fields (whether fallow or plowed) and moist areas overgrown with low grass. Here it may be seen in loose flocks: some individuals feed on the ground, making short running dashes after their insect prey; others wheel through the air with graceful flight, somewhat resembling huge swallows, constantly uttering a characteristic call, *kirri-kirri*. Stomachs I examined contained Coleoptera and Orthoptera.

At the season of its occurrence in northern Thailand, the species is known to be breeding in more southern districts, but all northern specimens have had the gonads quite inactive. On the other hand, an unsexed bird from Chiang Mai, June 6, 1931, is so young that it was almost certainly bred in the neighborhood.

This example had the irides dark brown; the bill black; the rictus and interior of the mouth yellow; the feet and toes dull brown; the claws dark brown.

The adult has the upperparts brown with an olivaceous wash and a pale rufescent collar across the hindneck; the upper tail coverts and the greater portion of the outer rectrices white; the throat and lower neck rufous-buff, bordered by a narrow black gorget which begins below the eye and is edged inwardly with white; the breast isabella color, changing to light rufous on the upper belly, which color in turn fades to white on the remaining underparts; the under wing coverts and axillaries deep rufous.

The wings are long and hirundine; the tail is distinctly forked.

GLAREOLA LACTEA Temminck

MILKY PRATINCOLE

Glareola lactea TEMMINCK, Manuel d'ornithologie, ed. 2, vol. 2, 1820, p. 503 (Bengal).

Glareola lactea, DEIGNAN, Journ. Siam Soc. Nat. Hist. Suppl., 1931, p. 171 (Chiang Mai); 1936, pp. 84, 132 (Chiang Mai, Ban Sop Huai Khieo).—DE SCHAUENSEE, Proc. Acad. Nat. Sci. Philadelphia, 1934, p. 278 (Chiang Saen Kao).

I once saw a pair of the milky pratincole at the edge of a pond with a pair of the collared species, but otherwise I have found it only on the bars of sand and shingle along the larger streams, where the other form does not occur. The flocks seem to wander up and down the rivers, so that the bird is only irregularly present at any one locality. At Chiang Mai I recorded it but three times, in March and December. It is also known from Ban Sop Huai Khieo (Mae Ping), Chiang Rai (Mae Kok), Chiang Saen Kao (Mae Khong), and Ban Na Noi (Nam Haeng).

The flocks may be quite small or composed of many dozens of individuals. Their coloration is very concealing as they stand on the sand facing the observer, and they keep their ground until danger is near, then fly, a few at a time, merely to the farther end of the bar to perch again. It seemed to me that less feeding is done on the wing than is the case with the larger species.

A specimen with enlarged ovaries was taken at Chiang Rai, May 6, 1936, and an immature bird was collected at Chiang Mai, December 8, 1931.

Adults had the irides dark brown; the bill black; the rictus coral-red; the interior of the mouth deep pink; the feet, toes, and claws black. The immature example differed only in having the feet and toes dark brown.

This species has the upperparts soft gray, slightly tinged brownish on the head; the upper tail coverts and the greater portion of the outer rectrices white; the central tail feathers largely black; a black mark from the base of the bill to around the front part of the eye; the chin whitish; the throat pale buff, changing to soft gray on the upper breast, which color in turn fades to white on the remaining underparts; a white bar across the middle of the open wing; the under wing coverts and axillaries black.

This is a much smaller bird than the preceding form. The wings are similarly long, but the tail is only slightly forked.

Family LARIDAE

CHLIDONIAS HYBRIDA SWINHOEI (Mathews)

Chinese Whiskered Tern

Hydrochelidon leucopareia swinhoei Mathews, The birds of Australia, vol. 2, 1912, p. 320 (Fuchow, Fukhien, China).

Delacour and Greenway have recorded (L'Oiseau et la Revue Française d'Ornithologie, 1940, p. 25) finding terns of this species on the Mae Khong near Ban Huai Sai in December 1938 and January 1939. The bird is not otherwise known from our provinces.

In nuptial dress this tern has the crown and nape black; the sides of the head below the eye white; the rest of the plumage gray, palest on the throat and darkest on the abdomen. In nonbreeding dress, it has the forecrown and entire underparts white; the hindcrown and nape blackish, streaked with white.

From our other terns it is best distinguished by its short, slightly forked tail and its red bill.

In the absence of suitable material, I can form no opinion on the validity of the various Oriental races of this tern recognized by Mathews. I follow Delacour and Greenway in calling our bird *swinhoei* but must point out that it may prove to be inseparable from *javanica* of Horsfield.

STERNA AURANTIA J. E. Gray

Indian River Tern

Sterna aurantia J. E. Gray, Illustrations of Indian zoology, vol. 1, No. 6, 1830–1832 [=1831], pl. 69, fig. 2 (no location given=India).

Sterna aurantia, Deignan, Journ. Siam Soc. Nat. Hist. Suppl., 1936, p. 169 (Chiang Rai).

An immature tern in the Raffles Museum, taken by a Thai collector at Chiang Mai in August 1936, is probably of this species and, if so, is the only example from the Mae Ping *above* the rapids. At Chiang Rai, on the Mae Kok, I observed at least eight individuals, May 6 and 7, 1936. Finally, it was found to be common on the Mae Khong near Chiang Saen Kao, where I took four specimens on January 8, 1937.

Our various terns have similar habits. They are seen in small flocks, resting on sand bars or beating back and forth above the water, uttering harsh cries and periodically plunging for fish. From gulls they are distinguishable by their more buoyant flight, due to the long wings and tail, and by their custom of keeping the pointed bill directed straight down.

The January birds from the Mae Khong, as well as two specimens from the Mae Ping near Rahaeng (December 27, 1935), are adults in full nuptial dress.

The breeding adult has the crown and nape black, this color reaching to below the eye and there edged by a streak of white; the upperparts silvery gray; the underparts very pale gray. Its nonbreeding plumage is much like that of the preceding species.

This is the largest of our northern terns; it has a very long, deeply forked tail and a stout, orange-yellow bill.

STERNA ACUTICAUDA J. E. Gray

BLACK-BELLIED TERN

Sterna acuticauda J. E. GRAY, Illustrations of Indian zoology, vol. 1, No. 6, 1830-1832 [=1831 ?], pl. 70, fig. 3 (Cawnpore, United Provinces, India).

In the collection at Washington is an example of this tern, taken by H. M. Smith on the Salwin near the Burmese village of Mae Hiak, January 13, 1933. I collected three specimens on the Mae Khong at Chiang Saen Kao, January 8 and 11, 1937, and another at Ban Mae Sai, January of the same year. The only record for its occurrence on the Mae Ping *above* the rapids is based upon a solitary individual seen by me at Ban Chang (about 12 km. north of Mae Rim), June 6, 1936.

All northern specimens examined have been in full nuptial plumage.

Dr. Smith has noted that his bird, a male, had the bill dull orange at the base, yellow at the tip; the feet and toes light red; the claws black.

The breeding adult has the crown and nape black; the upperparts silvery gray; the sides of the head below the eye and the throat white, this color changing to silvery gray on the upper breast, which color, in turn, changes to black on the remaining underparts. The nonbreeding dress is similar to that of our other terns.

This species somewhat resembles the whiskered tern, but may be distinguished by its long and deeply forked tail.

The present species has commonly been called *Sterna melanogaster* Temminck, 1827, with reference to the Nouveau recueil de planches coloriées d'oiseaux, vol. 5, livr. 72, 1827, pl. 434. Temminck's name, however, cannot be used inasmuch as Horsfield (Zoological researches in Java, No. 8, 1824, general catalog) has used *Sterna melanogaster* "T[emminck]" as a substitute name for *Sterna Javanica* Horsfield 1821, which=*Chlidonias hybrida javanica* (Horsfield).

STERNA ALBIFRONS SINENSIS Gmelin

CHINESE WHITE-FRONTED TERN

[*Sterna*] *sinensis* GMELIN, Systema naturae, vol. 1, pt. 2, 1789, p. 608 (China, *ex* Latham).

The only record for our area is based upon a specimen in the Royal Natural History Museum in Stockholm, taken by Eisenhofer and with no data other than "Nord Siam." If we assume that the locality is correct, this bird probably came from either the system of the Mae Yom or that of the Mae Wang. Since the species has been found not only along the coasts of Thailand but also on the Chao Phraya river, it is not at all unlikely that it should sometimes occur along the larger streams of our provinces.

A breeding male from southeastern Thailand had the bill yellow with black tip; the tongue and interior of the mouth yellow; the feet and toes yellow.

In nuptial dress this tern has the forehead white, this color extending back over the eye at the sides; the lores and the rest of the crown and nape black; the remaining upperparts silvery gray, becoming almost white on the upper tail coverts and tail; the underparts white. Its nonbreeding plumage is similar to that of other species.

This is much the smallest of our terns. The tail is relatively short but is deeply forked.

Order PSITTACIFORMES

Family PSITTACIDAE

PSITTACULA EUPATRIA SIAMENSIS (Boden Kloss)

THAI ROSE-RINGED PARAKEET

Palaeornis eupatria siamensis BODEN KLOSS, Journ. Nat. Hist. Soc. Siam, vol. 2, No. 3, 1917, pp. 219–220 (Lat Bua Khao, East Thailand).

Palaeornis indoburmanicus, GYLDENSTOLPE, Journ. Nat. Hist. Soc. Siam, 1915, p. 233 (listed).

Palacornis cupataria magnirostris, GYLDENSTOLPE, Kungl. Svenska Vet.-Akad. Handl., 1916, p. 118 (Khun Tan).

Palaeornis eupataria siamensis, GYLDENSTOLPE, Ibis, 1920, p. 591 (Khun Tan).

Psittacula eupatria indoburmanica, DEIGNAN, Journ. Siam Soc. Nat. Hist. Suppl., 1931, p. 160 (Chiang Mai); 1936, p. 86 (Chiang Mai).
Psittacula eupatria subsp., DE SCHAUENSEE, Proc. Acad. Nat. Sci. Philadelphia, 1934, p. 259 (Chiang Mai, Mae Taeng).
Psittacula eupatria siamensis, RILEY, U. S. Nat. Mus. Bull. 172, 1938, p. 118 (Chom Thong).

This largest of our parrots is so far recorded only from the lowlands of the Mae Ping basin, north to San Maha Phon (Mae Taeng) and south to Ban Sop Mae Chaem, east to Khun Tan and west to the foot of Doi Suthep; within this limited area I found it only irregularly present at any one locality and rarely with as many as 10 individuals in a flock. The species is frequently seen as a cage bird at Chiang Mai, and, if its restricted distribution be real and not due merely to lack of observers, I would suggest that its presence as a wild bird is perhaps attributable to human agency.

The rose-ringed parrot is found both in cultivated districts and in the dry deciduous forest, but its appearances seem always to be governed by the abundance of some species or other of fruit.

A specimen taken at Chiang Mai, December 5, had the testes greatly enlarged (14 by 20 mm.).

Adult males had the irides light yellow; the eyelids edged light orange; the orbital skin pale pinkish orange; the maxilla deep red, the mandible coral-red, both tipped horny yellow; the feet and toes dull yellow; the claws slate. De Schauensee notes that a bird from Chiang Mai had the feet gray.

The adult male is largely parrot green; it has the hindcrown more or less washed with blue; the throat and upper breast more or less washed with yellow; a pink collar across the nape, joined at each end to a narrow black line, which runs up the side of the throat to the base of the mandible; a conspicuous red patch on the shoulder; all the rectrices yellow beneath, the longer ones blue above on the apical two-thirds. The adult female and the immature lack the pink nuchal band and the black lines along the throat, and the latter has a much shorter tail.

Owing to the lack of suitable comparative material, I cannot say whether our birds show any approach toward *avensis* of Burma. My specimens *seem* to be inseparable from those of eastern Thailand, when we allow for considerable individual variation.

PSITTACULA ALEXANDRI FASCIATA (P. L. S. Müller)

INDIAN PINK-BREASTED PARAKEET

Psittacus fasciatus P. L. S. MÜLLER, Natursystems Supplements- und Register-Band, 1776, p. 74 (no locality given; Pondicherry designated as type locality by Stuart Baker, Fauna of British India, Birds, ed. 2, vol. 4, 1927, p. 210, error; type locality corrected to Arakan, by Ticehurst, Journ. Bombay Nat. Hist. Soc., vol. 36, 1933, p. 934).

Palaeornis fasciata, GYLDENSTOPLE, Kungl. Svenska Vet.-Akad. Handl., 1913, p. 60 (Den Chai); 1916, p. 119 (Khun Tan, Pha Kho); Journ. Nat. Hist. Soc. Siam, 1915, p. 233 (listed); Ibis, 1920, p. 591 ("Northern part of the country").

Palaeornis alexandri fasciata, DE SCHAUENSEE, Proc. Acad. Nat. Sci. Philadelphia, 1929, p. 571 (Chiang Rai).

Psittacula alexandri fasciata, DEIGNAN, Journ. Siam Soc. Nat. Hist. Suppl., 1931, p. 160 (Chiang Mai, Doi Suthep); 1936, p. 87 (Chiang Mai, Doi Suthep).—DE SCHAUENSEE, Proc. Acad. Nat. Sci. Philadelphia, 1934, p. 259 (Chiang Mai, Chiang Rai).—RILEY, U. S. Nat. Mus. Bull. 172, 1938, p. 120 (Doi Ang Ka, Sop Phung, Ban Nam Khian, Mae Khan).

This parrot is by far the most abundant of its family throughout the northern provinces, occurring irregularly in every town and village, in any type of vegetation, and, while chiefly a bird of the lowlands, ascending the mountains to at least 4,600 feet.

At Chiang Mai the raucous scream of the pink-breasted parrot may be heard overhead at any time of the year, but the species appears in greatest numbers when the mango is in fruit, at which season a flock composed of hundreds may descend upon a single tree. In other parts of our area even larger flocks settle in the ricefields just before harvest: De Schauensee mentions "flocks of well over a thousand birds," and I myself, at the end of December 1936, on a small rice plain to the south of Muang Fang, saw a flock that could not have had less than 10,000 individuals. Such swarms of birds must cause serious economic loss to the cultivator.

The breeding season covers a number of months. A male from Ban Muang Sum, December 24, had the gonads enlarged. In the dry forest just west of Ban Na Noi (Nan Province), April 1, I met a man who was engaged in removing young birds from the nest holes for a life of captivity.

There seems to be considerable color variation in this species at any age, which, combined with individual variation in the annual cycle, makes it difficult to interpret the sequence of plumages. Eleven specimens that are certainly juveniles were taken at various northern localities between February 1 and July 26. A male from Ban Nam Khian, April 22, is passing from the juvenal stage to what Ticehurst (Ibis, 1939, p. 20) calls "the young male in first winter," and a bird in rather worn "first winter" dress was taken at Ban Sop Mae Chaem, January 11. The female at this stage seems not to differ appreciably from the male, except perhaps in color of bill, and the specimens I have seen which correspond to Ticehurst's "female in first winter" are all *worn* birds. I am convinced that yet another stage, in which the rectrices are fully elongated, intervenes between the "first winter" and the adult plumages, but my material is insufficient to do more than indicate the probability. A series of late July from Wiang Pa Pao includes a number of fully adult birds that are molting from worn to fresh plumage.

De Schauensee notes that a male had the irides creamy yellow; the maxilla sealing-wax red, tipped yellow; the mandible blotchy dusky red; the feet and toes olive. The female differed in having the entire bill black. In museum specimens the mandible of the male usually appears blackish. The juvenile has the entire bill reddish orange.

The adult male has a narrow black frontal band reaching to the eyes; a broad black mustachial band from each side of the mandible; the rest of the head gray-violet; the remaining upperparts parrot green, becoming bright blue on the rectrices; a conspicuous golden-greenish area on the wing coverts, sometimes tinged with orange; the breast and upper abdomen pink, more or less washed with violet, changing to blue-green on the lower belly and to bright yellow-green elsewhere. The adult female differs chiefly in having the head gray-blue and the underparts of a rather deeper pink without violet wash. The juvenile is a generally green bird with the markings of the head dull brownish black.

PSITTACULA CYANOCEPHALA ROSA (Boddaert)

INDO-CHINESE BLOSSOM-HEADED PARAKEET

Psittacus rosa BODDAERT, Table des planches enluminéez d'histoire naturelle, 1783, p. 53 (Mahé, *ex* D'Aubenton, pl. 888, error; Chittagong designated as type locality by Whistler and Kinnear, Journ. Bombay Nat. Hist. Soc., vol. 37, 1935, p. 753).

Palaeornis rosa, GYLDENSTOLPE, Kungl. Svenska Vet.-Akad. Handl., 1913, p. 60 (Den Chai, Pak Pan); Journ. Nat. Hist. Soc. Siam, 1915, p. 233 (listed).

Palaeornis cyanocephalus rosa, GYLDENSTOLPE, Kungl. Svenska Vet.-Akad. Handl., 1916, p. 118 (Pha Kho); Ibis, 1920, p. 592 (Den Chai, Pak Pan, Pha Kho).

Psittacula cyanocephala rosa, DEIGNAN, Journ. Siam Soc. Nat. Hist. Suppl., 1931, p. 160 (Chiang Mai, error?); 1936, p. 86 (Chiang Mai, error?).

In 1931 and 1936 I recorded the occurrence of this parrot at Chiang Mai; since no specimen was taken and since I was at that time unfamiliar with the bird in life and since, moreover, it is a species not yet definitely known in our area from any locality west of the Khun Tan range, it seems best to withdraw the record until there is further evidence of its presence there. To the places where examples have been collected may be added Khun Tan, whence Eisenhofer sent to Stockholm six undated birds, including a juvenile, and Ban Mae Mo, where I took an adult male, August 18, 1936.

Gyldenstolpe found this species fairly common in the dry, deciduous forests of Phrae Province, but never in large flocks and usually associated with the pink-breasted parrot.

The adult male of this small species has the head rose-pink, strongly washed with violet-blue on crown and nape; a pair of black mustachial streaks connected to form a narrow nuchal collar; the upperparts parrot green, changing to bright blue on the central tail feathers, yellow on the others; a small maroon patch on the shoulder; the entire underparts bright yellow-green. The adult female differs chiefly in having the head soft gray-violet without any black markings.

PSITTACULA HIMALAYANA FINSCHII (Hume)

BURMESE SLATY-HEADED PARAKEET

Palaeornis Finschii HUME, Stray Feathers, vol. 2, 1874, pp. 509–510 (Kollidoo, Upper Salwin, Burma).

Palaeornis schisticeps, GYLDENSTOLPE, Journ. Nat. Hist. Soc. Siam, 1915, p. 233 (listed).

Palaeornis finschi, GYLDENSTOLPE, Journ. Nat. Hist. Soc. Siam, 1915, p. 233 (listed).

Palaeornis schisticeps finschii, GYLDENSTOLPE, Kungl. Svenska Vet.-Akad. Handl., 1916, p. 119 (Khun Tan, Pha Kho); Ibis, 1920, p. 592 (Khun Tan, Pha Kho).

Psittacula schisticeps finschi, DE SCHAUENSEE, Proc. Acad. Nat. Sci. Philadelphia, 1934, p. 259 (Doi Suthep, Doi Chiang Dao).

Psittacula himalayana finschi, DEIGNAN, Journ. Siam Soc. Nat. Hist. Suppl., 1931, p. 160 (Doi Suthep); 1936, p. 87 (Doi Suthep). — RILEY, U. S. Nat. Mus. Bull. 172, 1938, p. 119 (Phrae, Doi Buak Hua Chang, Mae Lang valley, Muang Pai, "Hang Nor Wu").

The slaty-headed parrot is probably generally distributed in the hilly districts of the North, although it is not yet recorded from Chiang Rai and Nan Provinces. Eisenhofer sent to Stockholm no less than 30 examples from Khun Tan. I collected it at Samoeng, Sala Mae Tha, Doi Mae Lai, and Doi Chiang Dao and have seen it at Ban Mae Klang. On Doi Suthep it has been found only three times, always at the large clearing near the Phrathat.

This bird is the commonest of its genus on the mountains, occurring irregularly and in small flocks in the more open mixed-deciduous forest, at cleared places, and along the wider trails, chiefly from 2,000 to 4,000 feet; when seen on the plains it is never at any great distance from the hills.

This is the sweet-voiced parakeet often seen fastened to wooden perches outside the huts of the various hill-peoples. The employment of these birds as decoys, tied to a bamboo frame near the village, is said frequently to bring about the capture of all the members of a wild flock at once. They seem to be kept for purely esthetic reasons.

A bird from Phrae, April 26, is in juvenal dress, with the whole head green. One from Doi Chiang Dao, November 19, and another from Samoeng, November 27, are acquiring gray feathers among the green of the head, have a longer tail, and a reddish maxilla. Finally, one from Sala Mae Tha, February 28, has the entire head light gray, washed with green on the crown, and the bill and tail as in the adult.

The adult male has the head slaty; a pair of black mustachial bands, sometimes joined to form a narrow nuchal collar; the slate of the head followed by a narrow band of blue-green and this, in turn, by an ill-defined band of yellow-green; the remaining upperparts parrot green; the longest tail feathers bright blue, changing to violet-yellow on the apical third, the remaining rectrices green, tipped bright yellow; a small maroon patch on the shoulder; the entire underparts light yellow-green; the under wing coverts and axillaries blue-green. The adult female differs only in lacking the maroon shoulder patch.

LORICULUS VERNALIS VERNALIS (Sparrman)

North Indian Lorikeet

Psittacus vernalis Sparrman, Museum Carlsonianum, fasc. 2, 1787, No. 29 and pl. (no locality given; Cachar designated as type locality by Stuart Baker, Journ. Bombay Nat. Hist. Soc., vol. 28, No. 2, 1922, p. 333).

Loriculus vernalis, Gyldenstolpe, Kungl. Svenska Vet.-Akad. Handl., 1913, p. 60 (Mae Raem, Den Chai); 1916, p. 119 (Pha Kho, Doi Pha Sakaeng, Khun Tan); Journ. Nat. Hist. Soc. Siam, 1915, p. 233 (listed); Ibis, 1920, p. 591 ("Throughout Siam proper").—de Schauensee, Proc. Acad. Nat. Sci. Philadelphia, 1928, p. 573 (Doi Suthep).

Loriculus vernalis vernalis, de Schauensee, Proc. Acad. Nat. Sci. Philadelphia, 1929, p. 571 (Chiang Saen, "Pa Tai—67 Klms. N. of Lampang").—Riley, U. S. Nat. Mus. Bull. 172, 1938, p. 122 (Ban Nam Khian).

Coryllis vernalis vernalis, Deignan, Journ. Siam Soc. Nat. Hist. Suppl., 1931, p. 161 (Doi Suthep); 1936, p. 87 (Doi Suthep, Chiang Mai).—de Schauensee, Proc. Acad. Nat. Sci. Philadelphia, 1934, p. 260 (Doi Chiang Dao).

The diminutive lorikeet occurs fairly commonly throughout our provinces, but since it is a bird of the wilder districts it is by no means conspicuous. It may be found in the more open evergreen, in the pines, in the dry deciduous jungle, and in bamboo, both on the plains and on the hills to at least 4,300 feet. In addition to the localities listed above, it is known from Ban Mae Wan, Doi Ang Ka, and Ban Mae Klang, whence I have specimens.

This is usually a difficult bird to observe, for the flocks are small and, in a leafy tree, by virtue of its color, it is almost invisible; I rarely became aware of its presence until it flew off with a characteristic twittering note. It is one of the many species that congregate in flowering trees and on Doi Suthep seemed always to be commoner when *Bombax* was in bloom.

An adult male had the irides white; the orbital skin light brown; the gular skin brownish yellow; the bill and cere orange, the maxilla more red-orange; the feet and toes brownish yellow; the claws light horn-brown.

This is by far our smallest parrot and our only one with a short tail. It has the upperparts parrot green, with the rump and upper tail coverts bright red; the underparts bright yellow-green, with a suffusion of blue on the lower throat; the undersurface of the remiges and rectrices bright blue.

Order COLUMBIFORMES

Family COLUMBIDAE

SPHENURUS APICAUDA APICAUDA (Blyth)

INDIAN PIN-TAILED GREEN PIGEON

Tr[*eron*] *apicauda* "Hodgson" BLYTH, Journ. Asiat. Soc. Bengal, vol. 14, pt. 2, 1845 [=1846], p. 854 ("South-eastern Himalayas and hill ranges of Assam—common at Darjeeling").

Sphenocercus apicauda, GYLDENSTOLPE, Kungl. Svenska Vet.-Akad. Handl., 1916, p. 151 (Khun Tan, Pang Hua Phong); Ibis, 1920, p. 740 (Khun Tan, Pang Hua Phong).—DEIGNAN, Journ. Siam Soc. Nat. Hist. Suppl., 1931, p. 166 (Doi Suthep).

Sphenocercus apicauda apicauda, CHASEN and BODEN KLOSS, Journ. Siam Soc. Nat. Hist. Suppl., 1932, p. 232 (Doi Suthep).

Sphenocercus apicaudus apicaudus, DE SCHAUENSEE, Proc. Acad. Nat. Sci. Philadelphia, 1934, p. 272 (Doi Chiang Dao).—DEIGNAN, Journ. Siam Soc. Nat. Hist. Suppl., 1936, p. 85 (Doi Suthep).

The Indian race of the pin-tailed pigeon is an uncommon resident in the evergreen forests above 4,000 feet on the high peaks of the western provinces. In addition to the localities listed above, it occurs on Doi Ang Ka, where I have seen it at 5,300 feet.

Nothing has been recorded of the habits of this bird in our districts. It is doubtless a frugivore that escapes notice by keeping to the tops of high trees, where it is well concealed by leaves.

De Schauensee has noted that a male had the irides salmon-pink with a blue inner ring; the orbital skin dull dark blue; the apical half of the bill pale blue, the basal half and adjacent skin very brilliant and intense light blue; the feet and toes brilliant scarlet; the claws whitish horn. One of Gyldenstolpe's specimens had the irides whitish red; the orbital skin pale blue; the bill green; the feet and toes pink.

The adult male has the head, neck, rump, and upper tail coverts bright yellow-green; the remaining upperparts bright olive-green, washed with gray on the upper back; the tail soft gray; the wing with a narrow pale yellow band separating the black apical half from the bright olive-green basal half; the underparts light yellow-green, washed on the breast with orange-pink; the under tail coverts dull chestnut. The female is similar but has the colors generally less bright and wholly lacks the orange wash on the breast.

This species is readily separable from all other northern fruit-pigeons by its tail: the two central feathers taper to a point and extend several inches beyond the next longest pair.

SPHENURUS APICAUDA LAOTIANUS Delacour

LAO PIN-TAILED GREEN PIGEON

Sphenurus apicauda laotianus DELACOUR, Bull. Brit. Orn. Club, vol. 47, 1926, pp. 10–11 (Chiang Khwang, Haut-Laos).

The Lao pin-tailed pigeon is known in Thailand only from Phu Kha in northeastern Nan Province, where I found it uncommon in dense evergreen from 4,500 feet to the summit.

While encamped on Phu Kha I seldom saw this pigeon but frequently heard its mellow, whistled notes as the flocks bedded down at nightfall. In the gathering darkness and amid the foliage of high trees the birds were extremely difficult to collect. A female shot on April 6, 1936, was lost in the undergrowth and, when found the next morning, was too much damaged by ants for preservation of the skin. Finally, on April 16, a single adult male was taken.

The bird of April 6 had the gonads enlarged and that of the 16th had them greatly enlarged. By the middle of the month the flocks had broken up into pairs and nest-building had doubtless begun.

The present race seems to differ from the preceding only in its rather paler coloration.

SPHENURUS SEIMUNDI SEIMUNDI (Robinson)

MALAYAN PIN-TAILED GREEN PIGEON

Sphenocercus seimundi ROBINSON, Bull. Brit. Orn. Club, vol. 25, 1910, pp. 98–99 (Semangko Pass, Selangor-Pahang border, Malaya).

The sole northern record for this rare fruit pigeon is based upon a male in my collection, taken at Doi San Huai Wai, a locality in the hills separating southern Phrae and Nan Provinces, June 4, 1936.

The tail of my specimen is in molt: one of the central pair of feathers has not yet emerged at all from its sheath, the other has not quite appeared from beneath the coverts.

The male of the present species is similar to that of *apicauda* but has all the green parts darker; the rectrices blackish, broadly tipped with soft gray; the bend of the wing maroon; the belly pure white; the under tail coverts yellow, marked at the base with olive-green. The female lacks the maroon at the bend of the wing and the orange-pink wash on the upper breast.

I use here a trinomial name but am somewhat doubtful of the validity of *modestus* (Annam), separated on the absence of a character that may well be connected merely with age of specimen. My bird is just possibly of an undescribed form, but for the present is best called *seimundi:* it has the uppermost part of the breast suffused with orange-pink, this color most marked at the sides, where it adjoins the gray band that crosses the upper back.

SPHENURUS SPHENURUS SPHENURUS (Vigors)

INDIAN WEDGE-TAILED GREEN PIGEON

Vinago sphenura VIGORS, Proc. Comm. Sci. Corr. Zool. Soc. London, pt. 1, 1830–1831 [=1832], p. 173 (Himalayas; type locality restricted to Simla-Almora district, by Ticehurst and Whistler, Ibis, 1924, p. 472).

Sphenocercus sphenurus, DEIGNAN, Journ. Siam Soc. Nat. Hist. Suppl., 1931, p. 166 (Doi Suthep).

Sphenocercus sphenurus sphenurus, DE SCHAUENSEE, Proc. Acad. Nat. Sci. Philadelphia, 1934, p. 272 (Doi Suthep, Doi Chiang Dao).—DEIGNAN, Journ. Siam Soc. Nat. Hist. Suppl., 1936, p. 85 (Doi Suthep).—RILEY, U. S. Nat. Mus. Bull. 172, 1938, p. 108 (Doi Langka).

The wedge-tailed pigeon, although rarely seen, is generally distributed in the evergreen forest between 3,000 and 5,000 feet, at least in the more western provinces. I have seen it at 3,000 feet on Doi Ang Ka in April 1931 and have a specimen from Ban San Pa Sak (northeast of Chiang Mai) taken on March 6, 1937. Fejos sent to Stockholm two females collected at Huai Mae Ta Man, March 26, 1938.

An adult male, shot from a small flock on Doi Suthep, November 22, 1931, had been gorging on a small, hard berry. All the rectrices of this bird were represented by short pinfeathers.

A male example had the irides with the inner ring light blue, the outer ring pink; the orbital skin plumbeous-blue; the bill with the apical third light blue, the rest a darker smalt blue; the feet and toes bright coral-red; the claws with the basal half pinkish horn, the rest dark horn-brown.

The male has the head and neck dark yellow-green, washed on the crown with rufous-orange; the upper back gray, this passing into maroon on the middle back, followed by dark olive-green on the lower back, rump, upper tail coverts, and tail; the lesser wing coverts (shoulder) maroon, the greater dark olive-green, the rest of the wing black; the underparts bright yellow-green, washed on the breast with orange-pink; the feathers of the thighs dark olive-green with pale yellow margins; the under tail coverts rufous-buff, the shorter ones with dull green centers. The female differs in lacking the orange on the crown and the maroon on the wings and back.

BUTRERON CAPELLEI MAGNIROSTRIS (Strickland)

MALAYAN LARGER THICK-BILLED GREEN PIGEON

Treron magnirostris STRICKLAND, Ann. Mag. Nat. Hist., vol. 14, 1844, p. 116, footnote (Malaya; type locality may be further restricted to Malacca, *ex* Cat. Strickland Coll. Birds, p. 556).

Butreron capellii, GYLDENSTOLPE, Kungl. Svenska Vet.-Akad. Handl., 1916, p. 153 (Khun Tan); Ibis, 1920, p. 739 (Khun Tan).

This fine pigeon finds a place in our list on the authority of Count Gyldenstolpe, who states (1916) that "Mr. E. Eisenhofer's native collector obtained a fine specimen at the neighbourhood of Koon Tan during my stay there in April 1914."

The fate of this important specimen is unknown. I failed to uncover it in Hannover, and there is no evidence in Stockholm to indicate that it ever formed part of the collection there. Since this is a Malaysian form that apparently scarcely ranges beyond Trang Province, its occurrence in northern Thailand is so extraordinary that I should consider the record erroneous had not Count Gyldenstolpe, in 1939, reaffirmed to me his belief in its correctness and shown, by reference to his early notes, that he had every reason to be certain of his identification.

It is to be hoped that sportsmen in our provinces will endeavor to rediscover the species, both to confirm the published report and to disclose whether an unnamed subspecies is resident in the northern hills.

The male has the upperparts grayish olive-green; the wings slate-gray, crossed by a narrow bright yellow bar; the breast bright golden-orange; the under tail coverts deep maroon; the remaining underparts light olive-green. The female has a greenish-yellow wash on the breast and the under tail coverts pale buff with dull brownish centers.

This is the largest of the treronine pigeons, with a notably heavy bill.

TRERON CURVIROSTRA NIPALENSIS (Hodgson)

INDIAN SMALLER THICK-BILLED GREEN PIGEON

Toria Nipalensis HODGSON, Asiatick Researches, vol. 19, 1836, p. 164, pl. 9 (Nepal).

Treron nepalensis, GYLDENSTOLPE, Kungl. Svenska Vet.-Akad. Handl., 1913, p. 65 (Ban Huai Hom); Journ. Nat. Hist. Soc. Siam, 1915, p. 234 (listed).

Treron nipalensis, GYLDENSTOLPE, Kungl. Svenska Vet.-Akad. Handl., 1916, p. 153 ("Meh Cha Di," Pha Kho, Pang Hua Phong, Khun Tan).

Treron curvirostra nipalensis, DEIGNAN, Journ. Siam Soc. Nat. Hist. Suppl., 1936, p. 85 (Chiang Mai).—RILEY, U. S. Nat. Mus. Bull. 172, 1938, p. 106 (Huai Mae Sae).

The smaller thick-billed pigeon is a common and widely distributed form but is not likely to occur throughout the year at any one locality, since the flocks wander extensively in search of food. In Hannover is a skin taken by Eisenhofer at Pha Hing, May 9, 1912. The same collector sent to Stockholm five undated specimens, including a juvenile, from Khun Tan. Fejos took a male at Doi Chiang Dao, April 15, 1938. Gyldenstolpe's examples from Ban Huai Hom were males, collected February 13 and 25, 1912. For Chiang Mai I have only two records: A couple of males bought alive in the market, October 30, 1931, and an immature female, taken May 16, 1935. I also have this species from the following places: Chiang Saen Kao, January 19, 1937; Ban Mai Tong Hong, May 2, 1936; about 5 km. south of

Muang Lae, April 21, 1936; Phu Het, June 10, 1936; and Ban Huai Oi, April 4 and 5, 1937.

In my experience, this is the commonest of all the northern green pigeons, although it may at some times and places be exceeded in numbers by the pompadoured pigeon. It is characteristically a species of the lowland evergreen forests but may appear in large flocks in more settled districts when there is an abundance of ripe figs.

Specimens of April 5 and 21 (Nan Province) had the gonads greatly enlarged.

Adult males had the irides with a blue inner, golden-orange outer ring; the orbital region verdigris green; the bill with the apical half cream, the basal half and rictus bright coral-red; the feet and toes deep rose-red; the claws horny white, tipped darker. My juvenile female had the irides with a gray inner, yellow-brown outer ring; the orbital skin and lores mixed blue and green, the eyelids edged green; the bill greenish white, dark horny brown near the tip, with the basal half and rictus red; the feet and toes old-rose; the claws horn.

The adult male has the crown gray; the hindneck grayish olive-green; the back and scapulars maroon; the remaining upperparts bright olive-green; the lesser wing coverts (shoulder) maroon, most of the others black edged with bright yellow; the quills black; the underparts bright olive-green, darker and mixed with white on the thighs; the under tail coverts deep rufous-buff. As with other green pigeons, the adult female differs in having all the maroon areas replaced by green; it has the under tail coverts pale buffy, barred with dark olive-green. The juvenile female has the under tail coverts almost white, the longer washed with buffy, the shorter washed with pale yellow and with indistinct olive-green central streaks.

TRERON POMPADORA PHAYREI (Blyth)

INDIAN POMPADOURED GREEN PIGEON

Osmotreron Phayrei BLYTH, Journ. Asiat. Soc. Bengal, vol. 31, 1862, p. 344 (Toungoo, Burma).

Osmotreron phayrei, GYLDENSTOLPE, Kungl. Svenska Vet.-Akad. Handl., 1913, p. 65 ("Vang Nun").

Osmotreron pompadora phayrei, GYLDENSTOLPE, Journ. Nat. Hist. Soc. Siam, 1915, p. 234 (listed); Kungl. Svenska Vet.-Akad. Handl., 1916, p. 154 (Pha Kho, Khun Tan).

Treron pompadora phayrei, GYLDENSTOLPE, Ibis, 1920, p. 739 ("Northern parts of the country").—DE SCHAUENSEE, Proc. Acad. Nat. Sci. Philadelphia, 1934, p. 271 (Mae Taeng).

This pigeon, like the preceding, is common and well distributed in the lowland evergreen of our provinces but is perhaps not so likely to appear in the less wild areas. It has never been found at Chiang Mai, doubtless because of the practically complete absence of evergreen on the plain. Eisenhofer sent to Hannover a male taken at Ban Huai

Hom, February 22, 1912. In Stockholm are two specimens collected by Fejos at Huai Mae Ta Man, March 24 and 26, 1938. I took it at Ban Tha Ko, August 5, 1935; at Ban Mai Tong Hong, May 2, 1936; at Phu Het, June 10, 1936; at Chiang Dao, March 21, 1937; and at Ban San Tha, March 30, 1937.

My specimen of May 2 had the gonads enlarged. A bird of June 10 is in rather worn juvenal plumage and another of August 5 is completing the postjuvenal molt.

Gyidenstolpe records that his examples had the irides pale crimson (males) or yellow (females); the bill plumbeous; the feet and toes purplish red. Others state, however, that this form has the bicolored iris characteristic of treronine pigeons.

The pompadoured pigeon is extraordinarily similar in plumage to the smaller thick-billed pigeon, but the latter may always be known by the bright red base of its much heavier bill.

The adult male has the upperparts, wings, and tail virtually identical with those of the corresponding sex of the preceding species; below it differs in having the general color more yellow-green, less olive-green, strongly washed on the throat with yellow, on the breast with orange-pink; the darker green of the thighs mixed with pale yellow as well as white; the under tail coverts dull chestnut. The adult female differs in plumage from the thickbill only in having the throat more yellow-green and the under tail coverts pale buffy with dark olive-green central streaks.

TRERON VERNANS GRISEICAPILLA Schlegel

MALAYAN PINK-NECKED GREEN PIGEON

[*Treron*] *griseicapilla* SCHLEGEL, Nederl, Tijdschr. Dierk., vol. 1, 1863, p. 71 (Sumatra and Bangka; type locality restricted to Sumatra by Oberholser, U. S. Nat. Mus. Bull. 159, 1932, p. 32; a male labeled "Côte S. O. de Sumatra" fixed as type specimen, by Junge, Temminckia, vol. 1, 1936, p. 6).

This pretty pigeon is known from the North by a single specimen in Stockholm: a female, without date, collected by Eisenhofer at Khun Tan. The next nearest locality for this southern form is Ban Dong, near Rahaeng (Journ. Siam Soc. Nat. Hist. Suppl., 1928, p. 155).

The adult male has the crown gray; the hindneck pinkish violet, this color continued as a broad band across the upper breast; the wing coverts, back, and rump olive-green, changing to brown on the upper tail coverts; the tail gray, with a broad subterminal band of black; the apical half of the wing black, separated from the olive-green basal half by a yellow band; the throat grayish green; the center of the lower breast, next to the violet band, deep orange; the remaining underparts bright olive-green, becoming bright yellow near the vent; the thighs dark olive-green mixed with bright yellow; the under tail coverts chestnut. The adult female is in general like other females of this group, but may be known by the upper tail coverts and tail, which are colored like those of the male.

The Thai orange-breasted green pigeon, *Treron bicincta praetermissa* Robinson and Boden Kloss, has not yet been recorded from our provinces but is almost certain to occur. The adult male differs from the pink-necked pigeon in having the crown and throat green; the nape and hindneck gray; the under tail coverts deep rufous-buff; the tail gray with a broad black band across the center, so that there is a broad, instead of very narrow, gray terminal band. The adult female is separable by having the nape gray and the tail pattern like that of the male.

TRERON PHOENICOPTERA VIRIDIFRONS Blyth

TENASSERIMESE YELLOW-FOOTED GREEN PIGEON

Tr[eron] viridifrons BLYTH, Journ. Asiat. Soc. Bengal, vol. 14, 1845 [=1846], pp. 849–850 (Tenasserim provinces; type specimen from Mergui, *fide* Sclater, Ibis, 1892, p. 86).

Crocopus viridifrons, GYLDENSTOLPE, Kungl. Svenska Vet.-Akad. Handl., 1913, p. 65 (Phrae).

Crocopus phoenicopterus viridifrons, GYLDENSTOLPE, Journ. Nat. Hist. Soc. Siam, 1915, p. 234 (listed); Ibis, 1920, p. 783 (Mae Yom river, Mae Rua).—DE SCHAUENSEE, Proc. Acad. Nat. Sci. Philadelphia, 1928, p. 575 (Chiang Mai).—DEIGNAN, Journ. Siam. Soc. Nat. Hist. Suppl., 1931, p. 166 (Chiang Mai); 1936, p. 85 (Chiang Mai).—RILEY, U. S. Nat. Mus. Bull. 172, 1938, p. 102 (Ban Nam Khian).

Sphenocercus pseudo-crocopus GYLDENSTOLPE, Orn. Monatsb., vol. 24, 1916, p. 29 (Pang Hua Phong, northern Thailand).

Sphenocercus pseudo-crocopus, GYLDENSTOLPE, Kungl. Svenska Vet.-Akad. Handl., 1916, p. 152 (Pang Hua Phong); Ibis, 1920, p. 470 (Pang Hua Phong).

Crocopus phaenicopterus viridifrons, GYLDENSTOLPE, Kungl. Svenska Vet.-Akad. Handl., 1916, p. 153 (Mae Rua).

Sphenurus pseudocrocopus, GYLDENSTOLPE, Ark. för Zool., 1926, p. 109 (Pang Hua Phong, Khun Tan).

Crocopus phoenicopterus annamensis, DE SCHAUENSEE, Proc. Acad. Nat. Sci. Philadelphia, 1934, p. 271 (Mae Taeng).

In Stockholm are six examples collected by Eisenhofer at Khun Tan, one of which, dated 1914, is the so-called *Sphenocercus pseudocrocopus*. At Chiang Mai I found this bird irregularly common during the rainy season, especially so during the month of September, and rarely present at other times. I also have taken it at Ban Mae Sun, Ban Sop Mae Chaem, Sala Mae Tha, Ban Pong Sanuk, Ban Pa Luat, Ban Mae Mo, Ban Mae Sariang, Ban Nong Mae La, Ban Tong Yang, and Muang Fang.

This species is less a bird of the forest than other fruit pigeons. It occurs rather in cultivated districts with scattered groves of tall trees, coming on occasion even into the larger towns and especially to the *bo* trees in temple precincts. Where fruit is abundant it eats to excess: I have shot examples so fat and so gorged with figs that they burst open upon striking the ground.

A series of 19 northern birds excellently illustrate the annual cycle. A specimen of December 21 is in perfect, unworn plumage. Birds of April 2 and 9 had the gonads enlarged. One of May 4 is most worn of all but has not yet begun to molt. Every example taken between July 10 and October 30 is molting.

An adult female had the irides with a bluish inner, pink outer ring; the bill bluish white, greenish at the base; the feet and toes bright yellow; the claws bluish white. De Schauensee records that a male had the irides white; the bill gray, darker at the base; the claws black.

The male has the forecrown olive-green, changing to deep gray on the hindcrown and nape; a brownish-olive band across the upper back, followed by a narrow band of ash gray; the remaining upperparts grayish olive, changing to gray on the rump and upper tail coverts; the tail golden olive-green, with the terminal third blackish; the wings with the apical half black, the basal half olive-green, a yellow cross bar, and a violet wash on the shoulder; the throat and breast olive-green, the latter deeper in color; the remaining underparts ashy gray, with the thighs and mesial area of the belly bright yellow; the under tail coverts deep chestnut, tipped and more or less barred with white. The female differs chiefly in having rather less violet on the shoulder.

T. p. annamensis, which I have been unable to examine, was described by Ogilvie-Grant as distinct from *phoenicoptera*, but I cannot learn how it differs, if at all, from *viridifrons*. Of the latter I have one worn April skin from Tenasserim, which agrees perfectly with a worn April bird from northern Thailand; both are quite different from my fresh specimens of December and January, which, to judge only from published descriptions, would all be *annamensis!* In this connection, it is interesting to find (Ibis, 1933, p. 485) that Lowe's birds from Tenasserim and western Thailand, in the virtually unworn dress of December, January, and February, are considered by Kinnear to be nearer *annamensis* than *viridifrons!*

My most worn skins differ from the freshest in having all the colors paler, the band on the upper back golden-olive instead of brownish olive, the mantle overlaid with a brownish tinge, the gray of the rump more olivaceous and less distinct from the upper back; in short, they appear to belong to a different race.

These birds also show considerable individual variation in the extent of green on the forecrown, of gray on the rump, and in the proportions of chestnut and white on the under tail coverts. One breeding female is unique in having the last almost wholly white, the longer with broad central streaks of slate mixed with chestnut, the shorter with broad bars of the same combination of colors.

Sphenocercus pseudo-crocopus, of which I have examined the type, is, in my opinion, quite certainly an example of the present form.

The absence of sinuation on the inner web of the third primary and the narrowness of the outer rectrices are both merely signs of immaturity in treronine pigeons; the color characters are all within the normal range of variation of the species. It is significant that Gyldenstolpe's specimen was shot on May 26, just after the breeding season, and that two of my birds which show the wing and tail characters of *pseudo-crocopus* are both in postjuvenal molt and just happen not yet to have lost the feathers in question.

DUCULA AENEA SYLVATICA (Tickell)

INDIAN GREEN IMPERIAL PIGEON

Columba sylvatica TICKELL, Journ. Asiat. Soc. Bengal, vol. 2, 1833, p. 581 (Borabham and Dholbham, India).

Carpophaga aenea, GYLDENSTOLPE, Kungl. Svenska Vet.-Akad. Handl., 1913, p. 66 ("Northern provinces").

Carpophaga aenea aenea, GYLDENSTOLPE, Journ. Nat. Hist. Soc. Siam, 1915, p. 234 (listed); Kungl. Svenska Vet.-Akad. Handl., 1916, p. 155 (Pang Hua Phong).

Muscadivora aenea sylvatica, GYLDENSTOLPE, Ibis, 1920, p. 740 ("Throughout the whole country").—DE SCHAUENSEE, Proc. Acad. Nat. Sci. Philadelphia, 1934, p. 272 (Chiang Rai).—DEIGNAN, Journ. Siam Soc. Nat. Hist. Suppl., 1936, p. 85 (Doi Suthep, error).

The green imperial pigeon is scarcely to be found outside of the districts with lowland evergreen forest, and while for this reason it is common and generally distributed in Chiang Rai and Nan, occurring even in the villages, it is only locally present in other provinces. In the immediate neighborhood of Chiang Mai it is unknown, and it seems not to occur nearer the city than at Ban Pong (a village south of Doi Suthep), where there is a small stand of tall evergreen; the market specimen recorded by me in 1936 possibly came from this place. Eisenhofer sent to Stockholm three examples from Khun Tan. I have it from Muang Fang, Ban Khana, and Muang Ngop.

A specimen from Ban Khana had the gonads enlarged, April 20; another from Ban Pong, February 15, had them slightly enlarged. An adult from Muang Fang, July 18, is nearing completion of the postnuptial molt.

A male had the irides deep red; the eyelids plumbeous, edged red; the cere purple-rose; the maxilla with the anterior half blue-white, the rest plumbeous; the mandible plumbeous, blue-white at the tip and edges of the commissure on the anterior half; the feet and toes purple-red.

The adult has the head, neck, and entire underparts soft gray, washed with pink; the remaining upperparts metallic green, glossed with copper, bronze, and deep blue; the under tail coverts deep chestnut.

DUCULA BADIA GRISEICAPILLA Walden

Burmese Mountain Imperial Pigeon

Ducula griseicapilla Walden, Ann. Mag. Nat. Hist., ser. 4, vol. 16, 1875, p. 228 (Karen Hills; type series from "the Cincona plantations about 16 miles east of Tonghoo," *fide* Wardlaw Ramsay, The Ornithological Works of Arthur, Ninth Marquis of Tweeddale, 1881, p. 416).

Ducula insignis griseicapilla, Gyldenstolpe, Journ. Nat. Hist. Soc. Siam, 1915, p. 234 (listed); Ibis, 1920, p. 741 ("Northern, North-western Siam").

Ducula badia griseicapilla, de Schauensee, Proc. Acad. Nat. Sci. Philadelphia, 1929, p. 580 (Doi Suthep); 1934, p 272 (Khun Tan, Doi Suthep, Doi Chiang Dao).—Deignan, Journ. Siam. Soc. Nat. Hist. Suppl., 1931, p. 166 (Doi Suthep); 1936, p. 85 (Doi Suthep).—Chasen and Boden Kloss, Journ. Siam Soc. Nat. Hist. Suppl., 1932, p. 232 (Doi Suthep).—Riley, U. S. Nat. Mus. Bull. 172, 1938, p. 109 (Doi Ang Ka, Khun Tan, Doi Langka, Doi Kiu Chong).

This handsome pigeon is very common on all the higher peaks of the North, occurring in the evergreen and rarely seen below 3,000 feet.

The mountain pigeon is the most numerous of its family in our highland forests, and its booming call, *ngum-ngum*, from which the Lao name is derived, carries far and can be heard constantly during the day. It is usually found in pairs, but an abundance of food may attract as many as a dozen to a single tree. It must range widely for suitable fruits: I have constantly noticed it flying high above the jungle at sunset, apparently headed for some habitual roosting place.

A specimen taken on Doi Ang Ka, April 30, had the ovaries enlarged. Birds of July 15 and 16 are beginning the postnuptial molt.

A breeding female had the irides with an ashy-white inner, gray outer ring; the bill dull purplish red, tipped violet-brown; the feet and toes dull purplish red; the soles pale brownish gray; the claws dark horny brown.

This species has the crown gray; the hindneck vinaceous-pink, deepening on the back and changing gradually to brownish slate on the wings and to slate on the rump and upper tail coverts; the tail slate at the base and gradually changing to black but with a broad brownish-slate terminal band; the throat whitish; the remaining underparts gray, washed with pink on the breast and sides of the neck; the under tail coverts pale buffy.

COLUMBA LIVIA INTERMEDIA Strickland

Indian Blue Rock Pigeon

Columba intermedia Strickland, Ann. Mag. Nat. Hist., vol. 13, 1844, p. 39 (India; type locality restricted to Calcutta, *apud* Peters).

Columba livia intermedia, Deignan, Journ. Siam Soc. Nat. Hist. Suppl., 1931, p. 167 (Chiang Mai); 1936, p. 85 (Chiang Mai).

The common rock pigeon is a common and well-known species of the towns and larger villages throughout the northern provinces.

I think there can be little doubt that our birds are feral descendants of introduced stock, which was perhaps brought in during the earliest days of Thai intercourse with India. The species is to a great extent associated with the monasteries, many of which have large cotes in their precincts. Since the birds are at liberty and must fend for themselves, they are often found feeding in the fields at some distance from home. In the open country the pigeon is wilder and warier than it is in the grounds of the monastery, where there is constant human activity.

In support of my opinion on the true status of this species in Thailand, two facts may have value as circumstantial evidence. First, while the truly wild rock pigeon in other parts of its range is characteristically a bird of cliffs and crags, especially in uninhabited areas, with us it is wholly unknown at such places, however suitable they seem to be; second, although all other pigeons and doves are constantly shot for food by the northern people, the rock pigeon is spared, being considered no more legitimate a target than the domestic fowl.

Since this bird is well known to everyone in Thailand, no detailed description will be given.

COLUMBA PULCHRICOLLIS Blyth

SLATE-COLORED WOOD PIGEON

C[olumba] pulchricollis "Hodgson" BLYTH, Journ. Asiat. Soc. Bengal, vol. 14, pt. 2, 1845 [=1846], pp. 866–867 ("The wooded region of the eastern Himalaya" =Nepal).

Columba pulchricollis, GREENWAY, Bull. Mus. Comp. Zool., vol. 87, 1940, p. 194 (Doi Ang Ka).

This large pigeon is known from Thailand by a single pair, collected March 29 and 30, 1937, at the summit of Doi Ang Ka, by the members of the Asiatic Primate Expedition. It may eventually be found at high altitudes on other northern peaks.

It has the head ashy gray; around the neck a buff collar, broader behind, where each feather has a partly exposed black base; below this collar, on the upper back and upper breast, another of glossy green and purple; the remaining upperparts slate, paler on the rump; the throat whitish; the remaining underparts ashy gray, on the abdomen washed with buff; the under tail coverts pale buff.

MACROPYGIA UNCHALL TUSALIA (Blyth)

INDIAN BARRED-TAILED CUCKOO DOVE

Columba (Macropygia) tusalia "Hodgson" BLYTH, Journ. Asiat. Soc. Bengal, vol. 12, 1843, pp. 936–937 (Darjiling).

Macropygia tusalia, GYLDENSTOLPE, Kungl. Svenska Vet.-Akad. Handl., 1916, p. 151 (Khun Tan).

Macropygia tusalia tusalia, GYLDENSTOLPE, Ibis, 1920, p. 742 (Khun Tan).

Macropygia unchall tusalia, DEIGNAN, Journ. Siam Soc. Nat. Hist. Suppl., 1931, p. 167 (Doi Suthep).—CHASEN and BODEN KLOSS, Journ. Siam Soc. Nat. Hist. Suppl., 1932, p. 233 (Doi Suthep).—DEIGNAN, Journ. Siam Soc. Nat. Hist. Suppl., 1936, p. 86 (Doi Suthep).—DE SCHAUENSEE, Proc. Acad. Nat. Sci. Philadelphia, 1934, p. 273 (Doi Chiang Dao).—RILEY, U. S. Nat. Mus. Bull. 172, 1938, p. 116 (Doi Ang Ka, Khun Tan, Doi Langka, Doi Hua Mot).

The larger species of cuckoo dove is generally distributed on the higher mountains, at least those of the more western provinces, dwelling in the heavy evergreen, chiefly above 3,500 feet, occasionally as low as 2,700 feet. It is, in my experience, a silent, retiring bird, occurring singly or in pairs, and rarely noticed before it flies out from the trees with noisy beating of wings.

The breeding season with us is rather indefinite, varying with the individual pair. Specimens with the gonads greatly enlarged were taken on Doi Suthep, February 24 and September 12; on Doi Ang Ka, September 1 (but a female taken there, September 3, had the ovaries quite inactive).

The period of molt shows corresponding irregularity. A female taken at Khun Tan, May 12, is in postnuptial molt. A bird from Doi Hua Mot, August 21, and another from Doi Ang Ka, December 7, are both in postjuvenal molt.

A breeding male had the irides with a white inner, violet-rose outer ring; the eyelids plumbeous; the orbital skin violet-red; the bill black; the feet and toes purplish red; the claws horn-brown. A breeding female had the irides with a pink inner, pale blue outer ring; the eyelids fleshy purple; the orbital skin plumbeous-gray; the bill slaty black; the feet, toes, and claws like those of the male. De Schauensee records that a male had the irides with a blue inner and a pink outer ring.

This is a slender, long-tailed pigeon. The adult male has the throat and forehead buff; the crown, nape, and upper back metallic green, violet, or a mixture of these colors; the remaining upperparts deep red-brown, broadly barred everywhere with black; the breast metallic violet, mixed with green, and more or less barred with black; the remaining underparts, including the under tail coverts, pale buff. The adult female is similar, but has the entire underparts deep buff, narrowly barred everywhere with blackish brown. A male and a female in postjuvenal molt resemble the adult female but differ in having the crown and center of the upper back blackish brown, narrowly barred with light rufous; the upper back and breast with little or no gloss; the bars of the underparts broader and blacker and extending to the chin; the ground color of the breast light rufous; the under tail coverts almost immaculate light rufous.

MACROPYGIA RUFICEPS ASSIMILIS Hume

BURMESE RUFOUS-HEADED CUCKOO DOVE

Macropygia assimilis HUME, Stray Feathers, vol. 2, 1874, pp. 441–442 ("Tenasserim hills north-east of Moulmein").

Macropygia ruficeps, GYLDENSTOLPE, Journ. Nat. Hist. Soc. Siam, 1915, p. 235 (listed).—WILLIAMSON, Journ. Nat. Hist. Soc. Siam, 1918, p. 32 (Muang Wang).

Macropygia ruficeps assimilis, GYLDENSTOLPE, Ibis, 1920, p. 742 (Khun Tan, Muang Wang).—DEIGNAN, Journ. Siam Soc. Nat. Hist. Suppl., 1931, p. 167 (Doi Suthep); 1936, p. 86 (Doi Suthep).—DE SCHAUENSEE, Proc. Acad. Nat. Sci. Philadelphia, 1934, p. 273 (Doi Suthep).—RILEY, U. S. Nat. Mus. Bull. 172, 1938, p. 117 (Khun Tan).

The small cuckoo dove is apparently rare in northern Thailand and so far is known only from the localities listed above. It seems to be confined to the mountain evergreen above 3,500 feet.

A specimen taken on Doi Suthep, September 10, had the gonads greatly enlarged.

Examples taken by me had the irides gray; the orbital region plumbeous-gray; the bill pinkish brown; the feet and toes brownish purple; the claws horny brown or brownish purple. De Schauensee records that a male had the irides white; the bill black; the feet and toes deep crimson.

The adult male has the crown rufous; an indistinct collar, beginning at the sides of the breast and crossing the hindneck, violet-brown glossed with violet and greenish; the outer rectrices bright red-brown with a broad subapical black bar; the remaining upperparts dark brown, the wing coverts, scapulars, and feathers of back and rump margined with bright red-brown; the entire underparts light rufous, paler on the throat, the feathers of the breast tipped with white or whitish and sometimes with partly exposed blackish bases. The adult female lacks iridescence on the neck and has the breast more mottled with black or blackish.

STREPTOPELIA ORIENTALIS AGRICOLA (Tickell)

BURMESE RUFOUS DOVE

C[olumba] Agricola TICKELL, Journ. Asiat. Soc. Bengal, vol. 2, 1833, p. 581 (Borabham and Dholbham, India).

"Pigeon at Xiengmai," SCHOMBURGK, Ibis, 1864, p. 250 (Chiang Mai).

"Pigeon from Xiengmai (*Siam*)," SALVADORI, Catalogue of the birds in the British Museum, vol. 21, 1893, p. 648.

Streptopelia turtur meena, GYLDENSTOLPE, Journ. Nat. Hist. Soc. Siam, 1915, p. 235 (listed); Kungl. Svenska Vet.-Akad. Handl., 1916, p. 149 (Khun Tan).

Streptopelia turtur agricola, GYLDENSTOLPE, Ibis, 1920, p. 742 (Khun Tan).

Streptopelia orientalis meena, DEIGNAN, Journ. Siam Soc. Nat. Hist. Suppl., 1931, p. 175 (Chiang Mai); 1936, p. 86 (Chiang Mai, Doi Suthep).—RILEY, U. S. Nat. Mus. Bull. 172, 1938, p. 116 (Chiang Dao, Mae Hong Son).

This turtle dove is decidedly uncommon and is perhaps locally migratory. At Chiang Mai I recorded it only in March, May, and August. In Stockholm are two undated specimens taken by Eisenhofer at Khun Tan, and a female collected by Fejos at Huai Mae Ta Man, March 25, 1938. Smith took a male at Mae Hong Son, January 7, and noted that it was "rare and wild." The same collector got two at Chiang Dao, February 1. I collected three at Doi Mae Kong Ka, October 17 and 18, and took a female at Ban Na Noi (Nan Province), April 2.

While the closely related spotted-necked dove abounds in cultivated districts, the rufous dove is largely confined to the dry, deciduous forest, only occasionally visiting the nearby fields. I sometimes saw it in the dry scrub on the lower slopes of Doi Suthep and suspected that a *Streptopelia* that occurred in the hill-forest at 3,800 feet might be this species, although I was never able to prove it. It is a shy pigeon and difficult to collect.

My specimen from Ban Na Noi had the ovaries slightly enlarged.

Smith records that his examples had the irides reddish brown; the bill, feet, and toes purple. According to the label, Fejos's bird in Stockholm had the "eye light green" (the orbital skin may be meant), and it should be remembered that Asiatic collectors do not always carefully distinguish between green and blue.

The adult has the crown vinaceous, suffused with gray; at each side of the neck a patch of black feathers with ashy-gray edges; the upper back dull brownish, each feather edged with dull rufous; the scapulars blackish, edged with bright rufous; the lower back and rump slaty gray; the rectrices blackish, all except the central pair broadly tipped with gray; the quills blackish; the upper wing coverts gray, those of the shoulder area blackish and edged with bright rufous; the underparts vinaceous, paler on the throat, and changing to soft gray on the flanks and under tail coverts.

Schomburgk's remarks on the unknown "Pigeon at Xiengmai" seem to be the earliest scientific record of any bird from our provinces. While it was surmised by Blyth (Ibis, 1867, p. 149) and Salvadori (*loc. cit.*) to be a form of *Columba pulchricollis*, I think that there can be no doubt that the present species is concerned.

STREPTOPELIA CHINENSIS TIGRINA (Temminck)

MALAYSIAN SPOTTED-NECKED DOVE

Columba Tigrina TEMMINCK, in Knip, Les pigeons, vol. 1, 1810, Les colombes, p. 94, pl. 43 (Timor, Batavia; type specimens from Java, *fide* Peters).

Streptopelia suratensis tigrina, GYLDENSTOLPE, Journ. Nat. Hist. Soc. Siam, 1915, p. 235 (listed); Kungl. Svenska Vet.-Akad. Handl., 1916, p. 149 (Ban Mae Na, Tha Chompu, Khun Tan, Doi Pha Sakaeng); Ibis, 1920, p. 742 ("Throughout the whole country").

Streptopelia chinensis tigrina, DE SCHAUENSEE, Proc. Acad. Nat. Sci. Philadelphia, 1929, p. 580 (Chiang Mai, Mae Rim); 1934, p. 273 (Doi Chiang Dao).—DEIGNAN, Journ. Siam Soc. Nat. Hist. Suppl., 1931, p. 167 (Chiang Mai); 1936, p. 85 (Chiang Mai).—RILEY, U. S. Nat. Mus. Bull. 172, 1938, p. 114 (Ban Nam Khian, Mae Hong Son, Mae Khan).

The *nok khao* abounds throughout the cultivated portions of all our provinces and is well known to everyone. It is chiefly a bird of the plains but is seen also on the mountains wherever the forest has been cleared: on Doi Ang Ka, I found it extremely common in the valley below Pha Mon, right up to the edge of the evergreen at 4,400 feet.

This dove is normally seen in pairs, perching in the bamboos or sedately walking on the ground at dry places, and even when large numbers occur together, as they do in the fields after harvest, the apparent flocks break up into twos when disturbed.

At Chiang Mai, although this species was more often the victim of gunners than any other and many were snared for the market, either by the use of bird lime or by traps baited with rice, it was, nevertheless, one of the commonest birds of the district.

A specimen taken May 27 had the gonads enlarged and another of January 29 had them greatly enlarged. It is probable that some pairs are breeding at any time of the year, for the nuptial flight display may be witnessed in the countryside almost daily: in this act, the bird flies up almost vertically from the top of a tree, then volplanes back to the same spot in a wide arc, with tail spread and wings stiffly outstretched.

The song, one of the most familiar sounds of early morning in the villages, where it is the favorite cage bird, may be represented as *co͝o-co͝o-co͞o′-o-o-o* or *c-co͞o′*, *c-c-co͞o′*, *co͞o*, with the accented notes higher.

A breeding female had the irides yellowish pink; the orbital region plumbeous; the bill black; the feet and toes violet-red; the soles pale brownish; the claws horny black.

This dove has the crown vinaceous, suffused with gray; a broad black collar beginning at the sides of the neck and crossing the nape, each feather bifurcate and with a white or brownish spot at each tip; the remaining upperparts dull brown, many of the feathers with narrow pale rufous edges; the outer tail feathers black with very broad white tips; the wing brown, with shoulder and some of the greater coverts ashy gray; the underparts vinaceous-pink, paler on the throat, becoming gray on the flanks, pale buff on the abdomen, and white on the under tail coverts.

STREPTOPELIA TRANQUEBARICA HUMILIS (Temminck)

INDO-CHINESE RED DOVE

Columba humilis TEMMINCK, Nouveau recueil de planches coloriées d'oiseaux, livr. 44, 1824, pl. 259 and text (Bengal, Luzón).

OEnopopelia tranquebarica humilis, GYLDENSTOLPE, Journ. Nat. Hist. Soc. Siam, 1915, p. 235 (listed) ; Kungl. Svenska Vet.-Akad. Handl., 1916, p. 150 (Khun Tan, Sop Tui) ; Ibis, 1920, p. 742 ("Throughout the country").—DE SCHAUENSEE, Proc. Acad. Nat. Sci. Philadelphia, 1928, p. 575 (Chiang Mai) ; 1929, p. 580 (Chiang Mai). — DEIGNAN, Journ. Siam Soc. Nat. Hist. Suppl., 1931, p. 167 (Chiang Mai) ; 1936, p. 86 (Chiang Mai).

It is probable that this little dove is common enough in all our provinces, but up to now it seems to be recorded only from Chiang Mai and Lampang. At Chiang Mai, while it was less numerous than the preceding species, it was nevertheless quite common on the plain, and was once (October 10, 1936) taken on Doi Suthep at 5,000 feet among pines; this example, a female, was perhaps a migrant from farther north.

The habits of the red dove at Chiang Mai differed little from those of the spotted-necked dove, although it was possibly more nearly confined to the immediate vicinity of the Mae Ping, where it haunted the giant bamboos and the banks of shingle or fed in the fields along the river.

Specimens of May 7 and 8 had the gonads enlarged and others of May 15 and June 3 had them greatly enlarged. I took a juvenile at Chiang Mai, May 16, 1935.

Gyldenstolpe records that his specimens had the irides brownish black; the bill black; the feet and toes blackish brown. My juvenile had the irides, bill, feet, toes, and claws brown.

The adult male has the head gray; a narrow black band beginning at the sides of the neck and crossing the nape; the upper back deep vinaceous-pink, becoming more vinaceous-red on the middle back, scapulars, and wing coverts; the lower back, rump, upper tail coverts, and tail slaty gray, the outer rectrices largely white; the underparts deep vinaceous-pink, albescent on the throat, becoming gray about the lower flanks and vent and white on the under tail coverts. The adult female resembles the male but has the vinaceous-red portions of the plumage replaced by dull grayish brown and the other colors much paler. The juvenile is similar to the adult female but lacks the black collar, has the vinaceous of crown and underparts replaced by dull grayish brown, and many of the feathers above and below edged with fulvous.

GEOPELIA STRIATA STRIATA (Linnaeus)

JAVANESE STRIATED GROUND DOVE

[*Columba*] *striata* LINNAEUS, Systema naturae, ed. 12, vol. 1, 1766, p. 282 ("in India orientali"; type locality restricted to Java, *apud* Stuart Baker).

Geopelia striata striata, DEIGNAN, Journ. Siam Soc. Nat. Hist. Suppl., 1931, p. 167 (Chiang Mai) ; 1936, p. 86 (Chiang Mai).

The striated ground dove is fairly common in an extensive grove of *mai kwao* (*Butea frondosa*) along the Mae Khao, near the point where it crosses the Choeng Doi road a few miles east of Chiang Mai, and I have also seen this species along the railway between Chiang Mai and Lamphun.

In 1936 (*loc. cit.*) I related as much as I knew of the history of this bird's introduction. I may repeat here that a few individuals were brought from Java by H. H. the late Chao Kaeo Nawarat na Chiang Mai, at the time of his visit to that island, and that they were set free east of the town near where the railway station now stands. In time the species may be recorded at any cultivated part of the great Chiang Mai plain, but it is not likely ever to cross the mountains into the neighboring provinces without human assistance.

A specimen taken on February 15 had the gonads greatly enlarged.

On June 28, 1930, I listened to a joint concert by what seemed to be a mated pair perched at the top of a tree. The song was a soft whistled *coo-d-coo-coo* or *coo-d-d-coo-coo* or *coo-d-d-coo-coo-coo*, the sound resembling that made by blowing into the mouth of a bottle.

A female had the irides pale gray; the orbital skin light blue; the bill plumbeous-blue, darker over the nares and becoming light blue at the base of the maxilla; the tarsi blue-white behind, the scutes in front dark brown, edged blue-white; the soles yellowish; the claws brownish horn.

This is the smallest of the northern pigeons; it is usually seen on the ground in pairs. The adult has the forecrown and throat ashy gray; the hindcrown light brown; the nape closely barred blackish brown and brownish white; the remaining upperparts light brown, with irregular bars formed by the narrow blackish tips of the feathers; the central rectrices light brown, the outer blackish brown with broad white tips; the sides of the breast closely barred black and white, changing to black and pale buff on the flanks; the center of the breast vinaceous-pink, changing to pale buffy on the abdomen and to white on the under tail coverts.

CHALCOPHAPS INDICA INDICA (Linnaeus)

INDIAN EMERALD DOVE

[*Columba*] *indica* LINNAEUS, Systema naturae, ed. 10, vol. 1, 1758, p. 164 ("in India orientali"; type locality restricted to Calcutta, Bengal, *apud* Stuart Baker).

Chalcophaps indica, GYLDENSTOLPE, Kungl. Svenska Vet.-Akad. Handl., 1913, p. 66 (Ban Huai Hom); 1916, p. 150 (Pha Kho, Khun Tan); Journ. Nat. Hist. Soc. Siam, 1915, p. 234 (listed).

Chalcophaps indica indica, GYLDENSTOLPE, Ibis, 1920, p. 741 ("Throughout the whole country").—DE SCHAUENSEE, Proc. Acad. Nat. Sci. Philadelphia, 1929, p. 580 (Chiang Saen); 1934, p. 272 (Doi Suthep, Doi Chiang Dao).—DEIGNAN, Journ. Siam Soc. Nat. Hist. Suppl., 1931, p. 166 (Doi Suthep); 1936, p. 85 (Doi Suthep).—RILEY, U. S. Nat. Mus. Bull. 172, 1938, p. 112 (Sop Phung, Mae Kong Ka valley).

The beautiful emerald dove is well distributed in our provinces but is virtually confined to moist evergreen forest or its immediate environs. Where the jungle is suitable it is a common resident anywhere from the plains to about 5,000 feet.

This pigeon spends much of its time on the ground in the dense cover along small streams and would seldom be noticed if it did not make a practice of feeding in pairs or small flocks on the forest trails. When startled, it rises with remarkable speed and either disappears at once around a bend of the track or perches for a moment upon some low branch and then vanishes into the undergrowth.

In southeastern Thailand I took specimens with greatly enlarged gonads April 29 and the species seems to breed with us at the same season, since Gyldenstolpe collected a male juvenile at Khun Tan, May 23, 1914.

De Schauensee records that a male had the irides dark brown; the bill coral-red, deep crimson at the base; the feet and toes purplish crimson, the tarsi livid white behind. Gyldenstolpe notes that his immature specimen had the bill black.

The adult male has the forehead and supercilia white; the crown and nape blue-gray; the upper back deep vinaceous-red, mixed with blue-gray; the middle back, scapulars, and most of the wing coverts deep metallic green, more or less glossed with copper and bronze; the shoulder coverts blue-gray, tipped with white; the lower back dull black, glossed with copper and crossed by two ashy-gray bars; the upper tail coverts slaty gray, edged blackish; the tail blackish; the underparts deep vinaceous-red, becoming paler and more grayish below the breast; the under tail coverts slaty gray; the under wing coverts rufous. The adult female has the forehead and supercilia gray; the crown and nape violet-brown; the upper back dull brown; the upper tail coverts deep brown, glossed with olive; some of the rectrices partly rufous; the underparts vinaceous-rufous, paler and more grayish below the breast; the other parts much as in the male.

Order CUCULIFORMES

Family CUCULIDAE

CLAMATOR COROMANDUS (Linnaeus)

RED-WINGED CRESTED CUCKOO

[*Cuculus*] *coromandus* LINNAEUS, Systema naturae, ed. 12, vol. 1, 1766, p. 171 (Coromandel).

Coccystes coromandus, GYLDENSTOLPE, Journ. Nat. Hist. Soc. Siam, 1915, p. 233 (listed); Kungl. Svenska Vet.-Akad. Handl., 1916, p. 101 (Khun Tan); Ibis, 1920, p. 592 ("Northern Siam").

Clamator coromandus, DEIGNAN, Journ. Siam Soc. Nat. Hist. Suppl., 1931, p. 159 (Chiang Mai); 1936, p. 88 (Chiang Mai).—RILEY, U. S. Nat. Mus. Bull. 172, 1938, p. 133 (Ban Nam Khian).

This handsome cuckoo occurs in the lowlands of northern Thailand as a rather common bird of passage in spring and autumn and as a very rare summer resident; it has never been recorded with us in winter. In the neighborhood of Chiang Mai the migration periods ran from February 9 (1929) to March 14 (1936) and from September 3 (1930) to November 16 (1929). Eisenhofer sent to Hannover two specimens from Pha Hing, taken April 23 and May 1, 1912; the same collector sent to Stockholm five undated examples, including one juvenile, from Khun Tan. The occasional presence of this species in summer is indicated by a juvenile brought to me at Chiang Mai, June 19, 1935, and by an adult observed at a village on the Mae Ping, near Mae Rim, July 27, 1935.

At Chiang Mai I saw only solitary individuals and always found them perched in giant bamboo or on a coconut palm in the immediate vicinity of houses or even in the heart of a village. In Nan Province, however, in the spring of 1936, I met with a loose flock in a wholly uninhabited area overgrown with bamboo. Attention is sometimes drawn to this cuckoo by its raucous scream, but in northern Thailand it is usually silent. Specimens I examined had fed entirely on caterpillars.

A bird from Chiang Mai, September 27, has not completed the postjuvenal molt: it still has the juvenal quills in wings and tail and a few brown feathers in the crown.

This immature example, a male, had the irides brown; the bill black, with the basal half of the mandible orange beneath; the rictus and interior of the mouth orange; the feet and toes plumbeous; the claws horny brown.

The adult has the head and conspicuous crest black glossed with steel blue; a narrow white nuchal collar; the wings rufous; the remaining upperparts black, glossed with steel green on scapulars and back, with steel blue on the tail; the throat and upper breast ferruginous, fading to ferruginous-white on the abdomen; the thighs smoky brown; the under tail coverts black, glossed with steel blue.

CUCULUS SPARVERIOIDES SPARVERIOIDES Vigors

INDIAN LARGE HAWK CUCKOO

Cuculus sparverioides VIGORS, Proc. Comm. Sci. Corr. Zool. Soc. London, 1830–1831 [= 1832], p. 173 (Himalayas; type locality restricted to Simla-Almora district, by Ticehurst and Whistler, Ibis, 1924, p. 471).

Hierococcyx sparverioides, GYLDENSTOLPE, Journ. Nat. Hist. Soc. Siam, 1915, p. 232 (listed); Kungl. Svenska Vet.-Akad. Handl., 1916, p. 102 (Khun Tan); Ibis, 1920, p. 593 (Khun Tan).—DEIGNAN, Journ. Siam Soc. Nat. Hist. Suppl., 1931, p. 159 (Doi Suthep).

Hierococcyx sparverioides sparverioides, CHASEN and BODEN KLOSS, Journ. Siam Soc. Nat. Hist. Suppl., 1932, p. 234 (Doi Suthep).—DEIGNAN, Journ. Siam Soc. Nat. Hist. Suppl., 1936, p. 87 (Doi Suthep).—DE SCHAUENSEE, Proc. Acad. Nat. Sci. Philadelphia, 1934, p. 257 (Doi Suthep).

The large hawk cuckoo is a common resident of the hills throughout our provinces; it is a bird of the more open forest, whether this be light evergreen, mixed-deciduous, or pine. In the neighborhood of Chiang Mai it is normally found only on Doi Suthep from 2,700 to 5,500 feet, but I have taken three wandering immature examples on the plain: one, December 14, 1935, and two, November 25, 1936. Young birds seem frequently to come into lowland districts; I collected one at Muang Fang, July 6, 1936, and another at Wiang Pa Pao, July 26, 1935. Eisenhofer sent to Stockholm three specimens, including a juvenile, from Khun Tan.

While any one of a number of our cuckoos might with reason be called a brain-fever bird, the name is properly applied to the present species, whose call is a shrill *brain-fever*, repeated again and again, each reiteration higher and louder than the preceding, until the bird can do no more and begins all over again. This is a characteristic sound of our mountain forests during the breeding season; on Doi Suthep it was heard on all sides, day and night, from February 6 (1937) to June 14 (1930). Despite the obvious commonness of the species, it is rarely observed, for it keeps to the tops of densely foliaged trees, where it remains motionless for long periods, and when not in song it will virtually never be seen.

I have taken juveniles on April 29 (Doi Ang Ka) and July 26 (Wiang Pa Pao). A bird of July 6 (Muang Fang) is molting from juvenal dress to what seems to be a subadult plumage; the latter is shown in a specimen of December 14 (Chiang Mai).

The very young example of April 29, a female, had the irides dull gray-brown; the edges of the eyelids yellow; the maxilla brownish black, with the culmen tinged olive at the base and the edges of the commissure dark brown on the apical half, yellow on the basal half; the mandible black at the extreme tip, then dull yellow, next olive, and near the base on either side slaty blue; the rictus and interior of the mouth bright yellow; the feet and toes bright yellow; the claws horny yellow.

This species, at any age, bears an extraordinary resemblance to an accipitrine hawk, both in shape and coloration. The adult has the crown and nape gray, this color changing gradually to brownish gray on the remaining upperparts and tail; the tail crossed by several broad blackish bands; the throat gray, mottled with white and rufous; the breast similar but with rufous the prevailing color; the remaining underparts closely barred with white and blackish brown and suffused with rufous; the under tail coverts white, more or less barred with blackish brown; the undersurface of the wings closely barred with white and dark brownish gray. The immature has the upper parts dark brown with indistinct light rufous bars and edgings; the underparts buffy, heavily streaked and spotted with blackish brown; the undersurface of the wings as in the adult.

CUCULUS FUGAX NISICOLOR Blyth

HODGSON'S FUGITIVE HAWK CUCKOO

C[uculus] nisicolor BLYTH, Journ. Asiat. Soc. Bengal, vol. 12, 1843, p. 943 (Nepal).

This small hawk cuckoo is known from northern Thailand by a single specimen: a juvenile male taken by me at Ban Hai Huai Som, Nan Province, June 15, 1936. The next nearest locality from which the bird is known is Tha Chang Tai, near Rahaeng, where Gairdner's collector took a juvenile male, July 15, 1924; this is the specimen recorded in the Journ. Siam Soc. Nat. Hist. Suppl., 1928, p. 168, and now deposited in Washington. Since both specimens came from localities under 1,000 feet above sea level, the species should be sought for in lowland areas of mixed-deciduous or open evergreen forest.

I have not seen the adult of this bird, which is said to have the upperparts slaty gray and the underparts largely rufous. The immature is a much smaller edition of the corresponding age of the preceding species. Both adult and immature have the tail tipped with rufous and barred black and brownish gray; the black band next to the rufous tip is much the broadest and the light band adjacent to it is much narrower than the others.

CUCULUS MICROPTERUS MICROPTERUS Gould

INDIAN SHORT-WINGED CUCKOO

Cuculus micropterus GOULD, Proc. Zool. Soc. London, 1837 [=1838], p. 137 (Himalayas; type locality restricted to Simla-Almora districts, *apud* Stuart Baker).

Cuculus micropterus, GYLDENSTOLPE, Journ. Nat. Hist. Soc. Siam, 1915, p. 232 (listed); Ibis, 1920, p. 593 ("Northern Siam").

Cuculus micropterus micropterus, DEIGNAN, Journ. Siam Soc. Nat. Hist. Suppl., 1931, p. 159 (Doi Suthep); 1936, p. 87 (Doi Suthep).

The short-winged cuckoo is, to judge from the ubiquity of its song, one of the commonest birds of the northern mountains, yet it is rarely seen and has been collected in our area only once or twice. During my entire stay in Thailand I took but one specimen: an adult male at 2,700 feet on Doi Suthep, May 17, 1936. I failed to find, either in Stockholm or in Hannover, Eisenhofer's example, upon which Gyldenstolpe based his published record (1915).

Like the large hawk cuckoo, this is a bird of the more open forest, both evergreen and pine. On Doi Suthep the song was heard from March 12 (1932) to June 7 (1930), both day and night, on all sides, from 2,700 feet to the summit. It is a melodious 4-note whistle, often repeated, which, to the people at Chiang Mai, says *Mister Queripel*, the name of a well-known resident. There is no evidence of the bird's occurrence outside the breeding season, but it is almost certainly present throughout the year.

The coloration of this cuckoo is much the same as that of the two following species, but it may always be distinguished in any plumage by having each tail feather with a broad black subterminal band and a white tip.

CUCULUS CANORUS BAKERI Hartert

Khasya Hills Common Cuckoo

Cuculus canorus bakeri Hartert, Vögel der paläarktischen Fauna, vol. 2, 1912, pp. 948–949 (Shillong, Khasya Hills, Assam).

The only example of this bird from our provinces is an immature female in the hepatic phase, taken by me on Doi Suthep at 3,000 feet, September 26, 1936. The specimen I recorded in 1931 and 1936 has proved to belong to another but very similar species and will be dealt with below.

The common cuckoo might be expected to occur in our districts with some frequency, for it appears to be numerous in April in the hills of Kengtung State, just beyond our borders; however, I have never heard the familiar call anywhere in Thailand.

This form is closely related to the cuckoo of Europe. The normal adult has the upperparts gray; the throat and breast ashy; the remaining underparts barred blackish brown and white. The hepatic phase of the female differs in having the entire upperparts barred rufous and blackish brown and the barring of the underparts extending to the chin.

The species should be distinguishable from its congeners by the absence of a black subterminal band from the tail and by its having the edge of the wing and the under wing coverts barred blackish brown and white.

My specimen can be matched in every particular by summer birds of comparable age, sex, and color phase from western Szechwan and northwestern Yunnan.

CUCULUS SATURATUS SATURATUS Blyth

Southern Saturated Cuckoo

C[uculus] saturatus "Hodgson" Blyth, Journ. Asiat. Soc. Bengal, vol. 12, 1843, p. 942 (no locality given; types from Nepal, *fide* Catalogue of the birds in the British Museum, vol. 19, 1891, p. 254).

Cuculus canorus, Deignan, Journ. Siam Soc. Nat. Hist. Suppl., 1931, p. 159 (Doi Suthep).

Cuculus canorus bakeri, Deignan, Journ. Siam Soc. Nat. Hist. Suppl., 1936, p. 87 (Doi Suthep).

An adult male, collected at 2,100 feet on Doi Suthep, March 7, 1931, and erroneously recorded by me as *Cuculus canorus*, is the only specimen known from the North.

The bird was found perched in a clump of bamboo at the edge of light mixed-deciduous forest; its stomach was filled with hairy caterpillars.

It had the irides orange-red; the eye ring yellow; the maxilla black; the mandible pale yellowish green, with black at the tip and yellow at the base beneath; the rictus bright yellow; the interior of the mouth bright orange; the feet and toes waxy yellow; the claws brownish horn.

This cuckoo is only with difficulty separated from the preceding species. It has the bars of the underparts rather broader and bolder; the edge of the wing white, unbarred but sometimes suffused with gray.

Any specimen of the genus taken in Thailand should be sent to a museum for expert identification, both because of the similarity of the various species and because of the probable occurrence of still unrecorded forms.

My example is now deposited in the collection of the Princeton Museum of Zoology. Charles H. Rogers has brought to my attention the true identity of the bird and writes me that the chord of the wing measures 182 mm., which clearly places it with the nominate race.

CACOMANTIS SONNERATII SONNERATII (Latham)

INDIAN BANDED CUCKOO

[*Cuculus*] *Sonneratii* LATHAM, Index ornithologicus, vol. 1, 1790, p. 215 (India; type locality restricted to North Cachar Hills, by Stuart Baker, Journ. Bombay Nat. Hist. Soc., vol. 28, 1922, p. 327; corrected to Bengal, by Ticehurst, *ibid.*, vol. 34, 1930, p. 470).

Penthoceryx sonnerati, GYLDENSTOLPE, Kungl. Svenska Vet.-Akad. Handl., 1916, p. 103 (Pha Hing).

Penthoceryx sonnerati sonnerati, GYLDENSTOLPE, Ibis, 1920, p. 593 ("Northern Siam").

Penthoceryx sonneratii sonneratii, DEIGNAN, Journ. Siam. Soc. Nat. Hist. Suppl., 1931, p. 159 (Chiang Mai, Doi Suthep); 1936, p. 88 (Chiang Mai, Doi Suthep).—RILEY, U. S. Nat. Mus. Bull. 172, 1938, p. 127 (Chiang Mai, Muang Pai).

The banded bay cuckoo is, in our provinces, an uncommon winter visitor and a very rare summer resident. At Chiang Mai I found it from October 31 (1936) to March 22 (1930), on the plain and on Doi Suthep to 4,600 feet. Gyldenstolpe's bird from Pha Hing was taken on April 11. I have winter examples from Ban Samoeng and Chom Thong and a specimen taken at Wiang Pa Pao, August 1. Two males recorded from Rahaeng by Chasen and Boden Kloss (Journ. Siam

Soc. Nat. Hist. Suppl., 1928, p. 168) were taken on May 6 and July 15, 1924, at Huai Mae Tha Khwae and Tha Chang Tai, respectively.

On the hills this bird occurs in deciduous forest and at the edge of light evergreen; in the cultivated lowlands it keeps to fruit gardens and copses. Like the following form, it loves to perch upon telephone wires, and I have frequently seen it along the line that runs up Doi Suthep to the Phrathat. Just before the species disappears in March there is a noticeable increase in numbers, as birds arrive from the South, and at this season I have occasionally heard the song, which may be described as that of the short-winged cuckoo in the voice of the plaintive cuckoo.

My specimens had the irides with a gray outer, dull brown inner ring (males) or wholly bright brown (females); the maxilla black; the mandible horny gray, tipped blackish; the rictus and interior of the mouth salmon; the feet and toes greenish slate; the soles yellow; the claws horny brown.

This species has the entire upperparts closely barred with blackish brown and rufous; the entire underparts white with fine, wavy bars of blackish brown.

CACOMANTIS MERULINUS QUERULUS Heine

Burmese Plaintive Cuckoo

Cacomantis querulus Heine, Journ. für Orn., vol. 11, 1863, p. 352. New name for *Polyphasia tenuirostris* "Gray" Jerdon, 1862 ("in Lower Bengal, and in all the countries to the East, as Assam, Sylhet, Burmah, and even so far as China"), not *Cuculus tenuirostris* Gray 1834, which=*Cuculus passerinus* Vahl 1797.

Cacomantis merulinus querulus, Gyldenstolpe, Journ. Nat. Hist. Soc. Siam, 1915, p. 232 (listed); Ibis, 1920, p. 593 ("Perhaps northern Siam").—de Schauensee, Proc. Acad. Nat. Sci. Philadelphia, 1928, p. 573 (Chiang Mai); 1929, p. 570 (Chiang Mai); 1934, p. 257 (Chiang Mai).—Deignan, Journ. Siam Soc. Nat. Hist. Suppl., 1931, p. 159 (Chiang Mai); 1936, p. 87 (Chiang Mai).—Riley, U. S. Nat. Mus. Bull. 172, 1938, p. 126 (Phrae).

The plantive cuckoo will probably be found at some time of the year anywhere in our provinces. An undated specimen in Stockholm was taken by Eisenhofer at Khun Tan. The bird from Phrae, recorded by Riley, was collected April 10. I have examples from Chom Thong, November 9, and Ban Bo Kaeo, April 3.

In 1936 I published some remarks on the status of the bird at Chiang Mai, which may be repeated here: "On 27 February (1930, 1931, 1932), it appears in numbers and thereafter can be heard singing everywhere in the lowlands until mid-June. During the rains its numbers decrease until by September it has become a rare bird; between September and the following February it is recorded only about once a month, except in November, when it seems to be completely absent. Immature birds are very seldom seen."

In the neighborhood of Chiang Mai the mournful call of this cuckoo is one of the most familiar sounds of the hot weather. Perching quietly for long periods in a roadside tree or upon a telephone wire, the bird utters again and again a clear, whistled song—five or six notes of the same pitch, followed by three or four much shorter notes in descending tones. It may be syllabified as *pik-pik-pik-pik-pik-pi-pe-pe-pe*.

The breeding season obviously embraces many months, for nestlings of the same age were brought to me at Chiang Mai on April 30 and August 8, 1935. Unfortunately, I have no information on the identity of the foster parents.

A male had the irides light brown; the bill brownish black with the basal half of the mandible brown; the rictus and interior of the mouth salmon-pink; the feet and toes yellowish brown; the soles bright yellow; the claws black. Immature birds of either sex had the irides gray; the bill horny flesh; the rictus yellow; the interior of the mouth orange; the feet and toes bright yellow; the claws horny brown.

The adult has the upperparts gray, more ashy on the head, more brownish on the scapulars and wings; the tail feathers blackish, tipped with white and barred with white near the edge of the inner web; the throat and upper breast ashy gray; the remaining underparts ferruginous. The immature has the upperparts light rufous, streaked on head and nape and barred elsewhere with blackish; the throat and upper breast light rufous, streaked with blackish, changing below to brownish white with indistinct, wavy blackish brown bars.

The immature might be confused with the banded cuckoo. The former is decidedly smaller, has the upperparts of a much paler rufous, is less clearly barred below, and has the entire undersurface of the tail distinctly and regularly barred.

CHALCITES MACULATUS (Gmelin)

EMERALD CUCKOO

[*Trogon*] *maculatus* GMELIN, Systema naturae, vol. 1, pt. 1, 1788, p. 404 (Ceylon; *vide* Whistler and Kinnear, Journ. Bombay Nat. Hist. Soc., vol. 37, 1934, pp. 521–522).

Chalcites maculatus maculatus, DE SCHAUENSEE, Proc. Acad. Nat. Sci. Philadelphia, 1929, p. 570 (Doi Suthep); 1934, p. 257 (Doi Chiang Dao).—DEIGNAN, Journ. Siam Soc. Nat. Hist. Suppl., 1931, p. 159 (Doi Suthep); 1936, p. 88 (Doi Suthep).

Chalcites maculatus, CHASEN and BODEN KLOSS, Journ. Siam Soc. Nat. Hist. Suppl., 1932, p. 234 (Doi Suthep).

The emerald cuckoo is apparently rare but is so small and conceals itself so well at the very tops of high trees that it may easily be commoner than it seems to be. On Doi Suthep, where it has been found only from December to February, it occurred at the edge of the evergreen between 4,600 and 5,500 feet, once at 2,300 feet. I have taken it on Phu Kha, April 9, 1936, and at Ban Hai Huai Som, June 18, 1936. In addition, I have of this genus a juvenile male from Muang Fang, July 10, 1936, and a juvenile female from Chiang Mai, November 27, 1936, which, in the absence of certainly identified comparative material, I place only provisionally with the present species.

The specimen from Phu Kha, which is not quite in full nuptial dress (retaining a few white bars on the throat), had the testes inactive. The bird from Hai Huai Som is completing a molt from the juvenal plumage to one like that described by Ticehurst (Ibis, 1939, pp. 15–16) as the dress of "the adult male in winter."

The Phu Kha example had the irides bright brown; the eye ring coral; the bill orange, tipped blackish; the tongue yellow; the feet and toes slate; the claws black.

The adult male has the throat, breast, and entire upperparts shining green, glossed on throat, breast, wings, and back with golden-bronze, on the quills with blue; the remaining underparts barred white and bronzed green. The adult female has the crown and nape rufous, changing to coppery green on the remaining upperparts; the outer rectrices rufous, marked with white and green; the entire underparts barred white and shining copper. The juvenile is entirely barred above with rufous and greenish brown, below with white and brown; it is perhaps indistinguishable from the juvenile of the violet cuckoo.

CHALCITES XANTHORHYNCHUS LIMBORGI (Tweeddale)

TENASSERIMESE VIOLET CUCKOO

Chrysococcyx limborgi TWEEDDALE, Proc. Zool. Soc. London, 1877, p. 366 ("under the Múlé-it range, east of Moulmain," Tenasserim).

The violet cuckoo must be extremely rare in northern Thailand and the only record for its occurrence is based upon two adult males shot by my collector from the top of a high tree near Ban Mae Wan (in the hilly country between Chiang Mai and Wiang Pa Pao), February 21, 1937.

The adult male has the throat, breast, and entire upperparts shining violet-purple; the remaining underparts barred white and violet, the latter color glossed with blue and green. The adult female has the crown and nape dull dark brown, changing to copper-brown glossed with greenish on the remaining upperparts; the underparts like those of the adult female emerald cuckoo.

The chords of the wings of my specimens measure 104.4 and 106.9 mm.; those of four adult males from Sumatra (assumed to represent true *xanthorhynchus*) range from 92.6 to 95.4 mm.

SURNICULUS LUGUBRIS DICRUROIDES (Hodgson)

INDIAN DRONGO CUCKOO

Pseudornis Dicruroides HODGSON, Journ. Asiat. Soc. Bengal, vol. 8, 1839, pp. 136–137 (Nepal).

Surniculus lugubris, GYLDENSTOLPE, Journ. Nat. Hist. Soc. Siam, 1915, p. 232 (listed).

Surniculus lugubris dicruroides, GYLDENSTOLPE, Kungl. Svenska Vet.-Akad. Handl., 1916, p. 102 (Ban Mae Na); Ibis, 1920, p. 592 ("Throughout the whole of Siam").—DEIGNAN, Journ. Siam Soc. Nat. Hist. Suppl., 1931, p. 159 (Doi Suthep); 1936, p. 88 (Chiang Mai, Doi Suthep).

This species seems to be merely a summer visitor to the North. At Chiang Mai and on Doi Suthep it has been found only from March to September. Gyldenstolpe's specimen from Ban Mae Na was taken June 24. Eisenhofer sent to Stockholm a bird from Pha Hing, May 11, and another, without date, from Khun Tan. I have it from Ban Tha Wang Luang, May 24; from Ban Huai Thae, June 12; and from Wiang Pa Pao, August 3.

I found the drongo cuckoo in open forest and in bamboo from the plains to about 4,000 feet. It is a tame species, often perching beside or above a trail and permitting close observation. The resemblance to the common bronzed drongo is so striking that, particularly within the drongo's range, the true identity of the cuckoo is probably often unrecognized. The latter's song sounds rather like that of the plaintive cuckoo but is in an ascending scale.

All my specimens are immature, with numerous white spots and with many unglossed blackish-brown feathers both above and below.

A male had the irides brown; the orbital skin gray; the bill black; the feet and toes slate; the claws black.

The adult is black with a steel-blue gloss, but it has the thighs (and usually a nuchal patch) pure white and the under tail coverts and the outermost rectrices narrowly banded with white. The immature is similar but is less glossed and has the head, nape, back, upper wing coverts and tail coverts, and entire underparts more or less profusely marked with small white dots.

EUDYNAMYS SCOLOPACEA CHINENSIS Cabanis and Heine

CHINESE KOEL

E[udynamis] chinensis CABANIS and HEINE, Museum Heineanum, Theil 4, Heft 1, 1862–1863 [=1864], p. 52, footnote (Canton, China).

Eudynamis honorata, GYLDENSTOLPE, Kungl. Svenska Vet.-Akad. Handl., 1913, p. 58 (Ban Huai Hom); Journ. Nat. Hist. Soc. Siam, 1915, p. 233 (listed).

Eudynamis orientalis malayana, GYLDENSTOLPE, Kungl. Svenska Vet.-Akad. Handl., 1916, p. 103 (Pang Hua Phong, Khun Tan); Ibis, 1920, p. 594 ("Throughout the whole country").

Eudynamis scolopaceus malayanus, DEIGNAN, Journ. Siam Soc. Nat. Hist. Suppl., 1931, p. 160 (Chiang Mai); 1936, p. 88 (Chiang Mai).

Judged from the number of birds heard during the hot weather, the koel is common and generally distributed in the northern districts, but it is seldom seen and still more rarely collected. Eisenhofer sent to Stockholm seven undated specimens from Khun Tan. Gyldenstolpe took it at Ban Huai Hom, February 25; at Khun Tan, May 4; and at Pang Hua Phong, May 8. I got an adult male at Ban Huai Muang, December 20, and an adult female at Ban Mae Mo, August 25.

From early March to the end of May the ringing *ko-el'*, *ko-el'* of this large cuckoo may be heard from tall *pa daeng* and the more open evergreen throughout the lowlands, but with the close of the period of song the bird virtually ceases to be recorded.

The *nok kawao* enters into northern legend and perhaps for this reason the species is prized as a cagebird in Chiang Mai and the villages.

An adult male had the irides brilliant red and the bill light olive-green. Gyldenstolpe notes that two females had the irides red; the bill greenish yellow; the feet and toes blackish gray.

The adult male is entirely black with a steel-blue gloss. The adult female has the upperparts dull dark brown, more or less glossed with greenish, the head, back, and wings spotted, the tail narrowly barred, with white or buffy; the underparts white or buffy, spotted on the throat and breast, barred elsewhere, with blackish brown.

All northern specimens are best placed with the Chinese race, with which they agree in wing length and size of bill and, in the case of the adult females, in coloration. The most northern Thai example of *malayana* I have examined is an adult male taken at Pak Nam Pho, April 8, 1924, and recorded by Chasen and Boden Kloss in Journ. Siam Soc. Nat. Hist. Suppl., 1928, pp. 168–169 (all other specimens there listed are, in my opinion, *chinensis*).

RHOPODYTES TRISTIS LONGICAUDATUS (Blyth)

TENASSERIMESE LARGE GREEN-BILLED MALKOHA

Phaenicophaeus longicaudatus BLYTH, Journ. Asiat. Soc. Bengal, vol. 10, 1841 [=1842], p. 923 (Tenasserim; type specimen "procured in the vicinity of Maulmain," *fide* Blyth, *ibid.*, p. 917).

Rhopodytes tristis hainanus [*partim*], GYLDENSTOLPE, Journ. Nat. Hist. Soc. Siam, 1915, p. 233 (listed); Kungl. Svenska Vet.-Akad. Handl., 1916, p. 104 (Khun Tan, Doi Pha Sakaeng).

Rhopodytes tristis longicaudatus [*partim*], GYLDENSTOLPE, Ibis, 1920, p. 595 ("Throughout the whole country").—RILEY, U. S. Nat. Mus. Bull. 172, 1938, p. 135 (Doi Langka).

Rhopodytes tristis longicaudatus, DE SCHAUENSEE, Proc. Acad. Nat. Sci. Philadelphia, 1929, p. 570 (Doi Suthep, Chiang Mai); 1934, p. 258 (Chiang Mai, Chiang Dao).—DEIGNAN, Journ. Siam Soc. Nat. Hist. Suppl., 1931, p. 160 (Doi Suthep, Chiang Mai).—CHASEN and BODEN KLOSS, Journ. Siam Soc. Nat. Hist. Suppl., 1932, p. 235 (Doi Suthep).—DEIGNAN, Journ. Siam Soc. Nat. Hist. Suppl., 1936, p. 89 (Doi Suthep, Chiang Mai).

The Tenasserimese race of the malkoha is apparently restricted in our provinces to the districts west of, and including, the Khun Tan range. At Chiang Mai it was common on the plain and in the more open evergreen of Doi Suthep from 2,000 to 3,500 feet, rarely to 4,500 feet. On Doi Ang Ka I found it both in the partially cleared valley under Pha Mon and in the evergreen to 5,000 feet. Eisenhofer sent to Stockholm 24 undated skins from Khun Tan.

This cuckoo seeks concealment in dense thickets and in liana-bound trees at the edge of the forest, making its way with remarkable agility through the interlaced stems. As it progresses lengthwise along a branch, with a long tail extending straight behind (but tending to droop slightly near the end), it markedly resembles a squirrel, and this similarity is honored in the vernacular name *nok bang hok.* The call is a low *cuck-cuck-cuck-cuck.*

I have no definite information on the breeding of this form, but the nesting season must be very protracted; an immature specimen from Chiang Mai, July 9, appears to be virtually equaeval with another from Chom Thong, November 3.

The July immature is very worn generally and is just beginning to acquire fresh rectrices; the November bird has completed the body molt but is still molting the quills of both tail and wings. The tail of this cuckoo becomes excessively abraded and in worn examples the white tips are often much reduced in size or entirely lost: an adult from Doi Langka, November 18, has obviously only recently molted but already shows signs of wear in the tail.

A Chiang Mai male had the irides brown; the orbital skin bright crimson; the bill apple green, red at the base of the maxilla; the rictus red; the feet and toes grayish olive; the claws slate. A female from the same locality had the irides crimson; the orbital skin lake red; the bill apple green, red at the base of the maxilla and about the nares; the feet plumbeous; the toes brownish plumbeous.

The malkoha has the head and back deep gray, changing to a glossy oil green on the wings and tail; the rectrices tipped white (very obvious from below); the underparts gray, deepening in shade toward the vent and more or less suffused with ochraceous on the throat and breast.

RHOPODYTES TRISTIS SALIENS Mayr

TONKINESE LARGE GREEN-BILLED MALKOHA

Rhopodytes tristis saliens MAYR, Ibis, 1938, pp. 306–307 (Chapa, Tongking).

Rhopodytes tristis hainanus [*partim*], GYLDENSTOLPE, Kungl. Svenska Vet.-Akad. Handl., 1913, p. 58 (Den Chai, Ban Huai Hom); 1916, p. 104 (Pha Kho); Journ. Nat. Hist. Soc. Siam, 1915, p. 233 (listed).

Rhopodytes tristis longicaudatus [*partim*], GYLDENSTOLPE, Ibis, 1920, p. 595 ("Throughout the whole country"). — RILEY, U. S. Nat. Mus. Bull. 172, 1938, p. 135 (Ban Nam Khian).

The range of the present subspecies in northern Thailand embraces all those districts not populated by *longicaudatus*. Eisenhofer, in 1912, took specimens at Ban Huai Hom, February 7 and 23, at Den Chai, February 14 (all in Hannover), and at Huai Pu, May 28 (in Stockholm). I have an example from Wiang Pa Pao and place provisionally under this name a very young bird from Muang Fang.

The Fang specimen, just out of the nest, is in postnatal molt; its coloration is practically identical with that of the adult. A bird from Doi Khrang, near Wiang Pa Pao, August 2, is in unworn juvenal dress; it differs from the adult only in having the rectrices rather narrower and more acuminate, the white tips smaller and less clearly defined from the adjacent black portion.

Specimens of this race are separable from examples of *longicaudatus* (of comparable age and state of wear) by having the white tips of the tail feathers of lesser size.

The birds here called *longicaudatus* have the white tip of the second outermost tail feather 23.9–28 mm. long and are, strictly speaking, *longicaudatus*>*saliens*; those here called *saliens* have the corresponding tip 20.7–22.3 mm. long and are really *saliens*>*longicaudatus*. See Mayr, Ibis, 1938, pp. 305–308.

CENTROPUS SINENSIS INTERMEDIUS (Hume)

BURMESE LARGER COUCAL

C[entrococcyx] intermedius HUME, Stray Feathers, vol. 1, 1873, p. 454 (Dhoon, Dacca, and Thayetmyo; type locality restricted to Thayetmyo, Upper Pegu, Burma, by Stresemann, Nov. Zool., vol. 20, 1913, p. 322).

Centropus sinensis, GYLDENSTOLPE, Kungl. Svenska Vet.-Akad. Handl., 1913, p. 59 (Pak Pan).

Centropus sinensis intermedius, GYLDENSTOLPE, Journ. Nat. Hist. Soc. Siam, 1915, p. 233 (listed); Kungl. Svenska Vet.-Akad. Handl., 1916, p. 103 (Khun Tan, Doi Pha Sakaeng); Ibis, 1920, p. 594 ("Everywhere in suitable localities").—DE SCHAUENSEE, Proc. Acad. Nat. Sci. Philadelphia, 1929, p. 571 (Chiang Mai, Chiang Rai); 1934, p. 258 (Chiang Mai).—DEIGNAN, Journ. Siam Soc. Nat. Hist. Suppl., 1931, p. 160 (Chiang Mai); 1936, p. 89 (Chiang Mai).

The crow-pheasant, or *nok kon put*, is one of the commonest lowland birds throughout our area. Eisenhofer sent to Stockholm a specimen from Pha Hing, May 1, 1912, and 19 undated examples (including four juveniles) from Khun Tan.

This large terrestrial cuckoo is a characteristic inhabitant of the bamboo, the second-growth jungle with its tangles of *Congea* and *Eupatorium*, and the brushy land around the ruins of old temples. Its size, long tail, and inclination to seek escape by running rather than by labored flight may cause it to be mistaken for a true pheasant. The song is a hollow-sounding *poot* repeated many times and rendered from the top of some bush or small tree, especially at evening.

Gyldenstolpe notes that his specimens had the irides red (adults) or grayish white (juveniles); the bill black (adults) or horn color (juveniles); the feet and toes black.

The adult has the wings, scapulars, and interscapular portion of the back red-brown; the rest of the plumage black, glossed with purple-blue on the head, nape, upper back, throat, and breast, and with more greenish blue elsewhere. The immature is similar but has the red-brown portions barred with black and the black portions barred with gray.

Yen (L'Oiseau et la Revue Française d'Ornithologie, 1933, pp. 618–620) has attempted to show that *intermedius* is inseparable from the nominate race, but his evidence is not convincing. He has compared examples of *sinensis* with numerous more or less intermediate specimens from Indochine but not with Burmese material. The long series from many localities measured by Stresemann (Nov. Zool., vol. 20, 1913, pp. 321–322) prove *intermedius* to be a recognizable form.

CENTROPUS BENGALENSIS BENGALENSIS (Gmelin)

INDIAN LESSER COUCAL

[*Cuculus*] *bengalensis* GMELIN, Systema naturae, vol. 1, pt. 1, 1788, p. 412 (Bengal).

Centropus bengalensis, GYLDENSTOLPE, Kungl. Svenska Vet.-Akad. Handl., 1913, p. 59 ("Vang Nun").

Centropus bengalensis bengalensis, GYLDENSTOLPE, Journ. Nat. Hist. Soc. Siam, 1915, p. 233 (listed); Ibis, 1920, p. 594 ("Northern Siam").

Centropus benghalensis benghalensis, DEIGNAN, Journ. Siam Soc. Nat. Hist. Suppl., 1931, p. 160 (Chiang Mai, Doi Suthep); 1936, p. 89 (Chiang Mai, Doi Suthep).

Although the small coucal is known to breed in the southern parts of Thailand, in the North it seems to be merely a winter visitor. At Chiang Mai it was fairly common from October 19 (1936) to April 2 (1931). In April 1931 I found it common on Doi Ang Ka, in the valley under Pha Mon. Eisenhofer sent to Stockholm two undated specimens from Khun Tan.

While the large coucal is restricted in range to the plains, the present form occurs also at suitable places to the summits of the mountains. The latter may be found in the same scrubby places as its congener but, in the lowlands, is seen oftenest in the tall grasses and sedges of marshy areas, on the hills in stands of lalang. The habits of the two species seem to be otherwise much the same. I have never heard the song of *bengalensis*, but it is said to resemble that of *intermedius*. A specimen taken by me had the stomach filled with beetles and grasshoppers.

An immature male had the irides pale, dull brown; the orbital region yellowish; the maxilla fleshy yellowish brown, the culmen darker and black at the base; the mandible fleshy; the feet and toes slaty; the soles gray; the claws horny black. The adult is said to have the irides red; the bill, feet, and toes black.

The full-plumaged adult will seldom be observed in our provinces; it is best described as a much smaller replica of adult *intermedius*. Most of our birds wear an immature dress, in which they have the upperparts red-brown, the feathers of head and back with conspicuous buffy-white shaft streaks; the tail dull, dark brown, glossed with greenish; the underparts buff, the feathers with paler shaft streaks; the flanks and under tail coverts darker and barred with blackish.

Order STRIGIFORMES

Family TYTONIDAE

TYTO ALBA STERTENS Hartert

INDIAN BARN OWL

Tyto alba stertens HARTERT, Nov. Zool., vol. 35, 1929, p. 98 (Silchar, Cachar).
Tyto alba javanica, DEIGNAN, Journ. Siam Soc. Nat. Hist. Suppl., 1931, p. 163 (Chiang Mai) ; 1936, p. 89 (Chiang Mai).—DE SCHAUENSEE, Proc. Acad. Nat. Sci. Philadelphia, 1934, p. 267 (Chiang Mai).

The barn owl is common in the city of Chiang Mai and its environs but is not yet known from any other locality in our provinces, although it may be expected to occur at least in the larger towns.

At Chiang Mai this owl was sometimes observed hiding in the crown of a coconut palm, but normally it concealed itself from the sun in some ruined pagoda. At nightfall it was often seen slowly flapping over the river or above such open places as the golf course and the parade ground. Its call, frequently uttered on the wing, has been described as a screech or scream but to my ears it more nearly resembles the sound made in tearing a piece of cloth; by the more superstitious of the townsfolk it is held to be an omen of death. Most of my specimens had the stomach empty, but one had been feeding upon small rodents.

An example of November 19, 1935, contained an oviduct egg; this is the only case known to me of any northern bird breeding in that month.

A female had the irides dark brown; the cere fleshy pink; the bill fleshy white; the interior of the mouth pink; the feet and toes gray-brown, the latter tipped dark brown; the bare patch behind the "knee" fleshy; the claws dark horn-brown.

This is a rather large owl which, in life, seems to be mostly white. It has a heart-shaped facial disk, which is white and outlined with yellowish brown; the upperparts mixed brownish gray and yellowish brown with many small whitish spots outlined with blackish brown; the tail yellowish brown, barred with blackish brown; the underparts varying from pure white to buff and more or less densely marked with blackish-brown dots.

I have not seen topotypical *stertens*, but all Thai specimens examined (Bangkok, Pak Chong, Chiang Mai) differ from a Javanese bird exactly as *stertens* is said by Hartert to do.

PHODILUS BADIUS BADIUS (Horsfield)

JAVANESE BAY OWL

Strix badia HORSFIELD, Trans. Linn. Soc. London, vol. 13, 1821, p. 139 (Java).
Photodilus badius, GYLDENSTOLPE, Kungl. Svenska Vet.-Akad. Handl., 1916, p. 122 (Khun Tan) ; Ibis, 1920, p. 754 (Khun Tan).
Phodilus badius saturatus, GREENWAY, Bull. Mus. Comp. Zool., 1940, p. 194 (Doi Nang Kaeo).

This beautiful owl seems to be very rare in Thailand, and the only northern specimens known to me are a female collected by Gyldenstolpe "in a dense valley among the Koon Tan mountains," September 17, 1914, and the male recorded by Greenway from Doi Nang Kaeo, 2,800 feet, April 12, 1937.

Gyldenstolpe notes that his bird had the irides blackish brown; the bill and toes pale gray.

The bay owl has the forehead, anterior portion of the crown, and the facial disk light vinaceous-pink; the upper parts rich chestnut, more or less marked with black and white dots, and with an ill-defined nuchal collar, the greater part of the scapulars, and some of the wing coverts golden-buff; the quills of wings and tail barred with black; the underparts light vinaceous-pink, more or less marked with black or blackish-chestnut dots, each feather with a golden-buff base, which shows through in places, especially on the breast and sides.

The specimen in Stockholm is intermediate in size (wing length: 215 mm.) between *badius* of Java and *saturatus* of Native Sikkim, but since it agrees perfectly with a Sumatran example in the coloration of the upperparts and is only very slightly paler below, I place it with the nominate race. The wing length of Greenway's skin, which I have not examined, measures 210 mm.

It will perhaps eventually be found advisable to employ a special name for the intermediate birds of Thailand, Burma, and Assam, but whether Oberholser's name *abbotti*, based upon a single unsexed specimen from so far south as the Province Wellesley, can be used for more northern examples, as has been done by Riley (1938), is open to question. The problem can be elucidated only by access to correctly sexed specimens from critical localities and by comparing measurements of skins of the *same* sex. The wing lengths published by Robinson (Bull. Brit. Orn. Club, vol. 47, 1927, p. 122) might have cast light upon it but have been rendered virtually useless by his complete failure to indicate the sexes of skins measured.

Family STRIGIDAE

OTUS SPILOCEPHALUS SIAMENSIS Robinson and Boden Kloss

THAI YELLOW-BILLED SCOPS OWL

Otus luciae siamensis ROBINSON and BODEN KLOSS, Journ. Federated Malay States Mus., vol. 10, 1922, p. 261 (Khao Nong, Ban Don, Peninsular Thailand).

Otus spilocephalus latouchi, GREENWAY, Bull. Mus. Comp. Zool., 1940, p. 193 (Doi Ang Ka).

An unsexed specimen in Stockholm, taken by Eisenhofer at Khun Tan in 1914, is the first example of this rare mountain owl known from the northern districts. It was collected again by the members of the Asiatic Primate Expedition at 4,300 feet on Doi Ang Ka, April 8, 1937.

It is a small, rufous horned owl, with beautiful, black-tipped, silvery-white drops on the scapulars. It has both the bill and the irides yellow.

When I examined the Stockholm bird in 1939, I had no comparative material at hand, and its true subspecific identity is highly uncertain. The fact is that no one really knows what forms of this owl occur in the Indo-Chinese countries. The putative races, *latouchi* and *siamensis*, were both described without reference to *spilocephalus* or to each other and seem never yet to have been compared in sufficiently good series to show whether they are recognizable subspecies.

Friedmann and Deignan, in the course of preparation of a paper on certain Asiatic members of the genus *Otus* (Journ. Washington Acad. Sci., vol. 29, 1939, pp. 287–291), succeeded in bringing together four skins of *spilocephalus*, five of *latouchi*, and one (paratype) of *siamensis* and were led to believe that *latouchi* is "only doubtfully distinct" from *spilocephalus*.

Even if *latouchi* be a valid form, it is not likely to occur in the western portions of Thailand and Lowe's record from Um Phang (Ibis, 1933, p. 483) is almost certainly erroneous. I suggest that northern Thai specimens will prove to be intermediate between a large northern race, *spilocephalus*, and a small southern one, *siamensis*, and rather nearer the latter.

OTUS SCOPS DISTANS Friedmann and Deignan

INDO-CHINESE COMMON SCOPS OWL

Otus senegalensis distans FRIEDMANN and DEIGNAN, Journ. Washington Acad. Sci., vol. 29, pp. 287–288 (Sala Mae Tha, Chiang Mai Province, North Thailand).

The only northern example of this owl, an adult female which is the type specimen, was discovered by my collectors near Sala Mae Tha, February 20, 1936. It was perched on the ground at midday in a deeply sunken road (perhaps a stream bed during the rains) heavily shaded by overarching bamboos. It was being set upon by a pack of village dogs and was easily captured by having a hat placed over it.

The present form (in the gray phase) has the upperparts brownish gray, beautifully mottled everywhere with black and white and washed in places with rufous; a conspicuous dark rufous band along the whole length of the forearm; the underparts white with heavy black streaks and wavy black cross bars. In the red phase it has the entire upperparts bright rufous, boldly streaked with black; the band along the forearm indicated by deeper rufous coloration; the underparts much as in the gray phase but with some of the black marks replaced by bright rufous. The irides are yellow. The first primary is equal to the eighth in length; the second falls between the fifth and sixth.

This owl resembles *stictonotus* but differs strikingly in having all its dark markings broader and more distinct, its colors richer and purer. In the gray phase of *distans* the ground color of the upperparts is brownish gray rather than grayish brown; the white markings are almost or wholly without buffy suffusion; there is much less vermiculation below. In the red phase the rufous is far brighter than in any similar specimen of *stictonotus* that I have seen. Finally, the red band along the forearm seems to be found only in examples of *distans*.

The U. S. National Museum has received two more skins of this form, collected by Dr. Joseph F. Rock in southern Annam, August and November 1939. One of them is in the red phase; the other is gray and agrees well with the birds of Thailand. The four known specimens are discussed by Delacour, Zoologica, vol. 26, No. 17, 1941, pp. 138–139.

OTUS SCOPS STICTONOTUS (Bowdler Sharpe)

CHINESE COMMON SCOPS OWL

Scops stictonotus BOWDLER SHARPE, Catalogue of the birds in the British Museum, vol. 2, 1875, pp. 54–56, pl. 3, fig. 2 (China).

Otus giu stictonotus, DE SCHAUENSEE, Proc. Acad. Nat. Sci. Philadelphia, 1928, p. 576 (Chiang Mai).

Otus sunia modestus [*partim*], DEIGNAN, Journ. Siam Soc. Nat. Hist. Suppl., 1931, p. 164 (Chiang Mai [*partim*]).

The Chinese race of the common scops owl appears to be a very rare winter visitor to the northern provinces. The only specimens yet known from our area are a male from Chiang Mai, March 16, 1928, and another from Doi Pha Hom Pok, 6,400 feet, February 15, 1938, both of which were taken by de Schauensee's collectors.

This small horned owl may be generally rufous, grayish brown, or somewhere between the two extremes. The feathers everywhere are finely and indistinctly vermiculated light and dark and most of them have indistinct, dark shaft streaks. The tarsi are feathered to the base of the toes; the third and fourth primaries are longest and the first falls between the sixth and the eighth in length.

The two northern birds are in the gray phase of plumage. They have been discussed by Friedmann and Deignan, Journn. Washington Acad. Sci., vol. 29, 1939, p. 288, and by Delacour, Zoologica, vol. 26, No. 17, 1941, p. 137.

OTUS ASIO CONDORENSIS Boden Kloss

INDO-CHINESE COLLARED SCOPS OWL

Otus bakkamoena condorensis BODEN KLOSS, Journ. Siam Soc. Nat. Hist. Suppl., vol. 8, No. 2, 1930, pp. 81–82 (Pulau Kondor, about 45 miles off the coast of Cochin-China).

Scops lempiji, GYLDENSTOLPE, Kungl. Svenska Vet.-Akad. Handl., 1913, p. 61 (Den Chai).

Scops baccamoena lempiji, GYLDENSTOLPE, Journ. Nat. Hist. Soc. Siam, 1915, p. 233 (listed).

Otus bakkamoena lettia, GYLDENSTOLPE, Kungl. Svenska Vet.-Akad. Handl., 1916, p. 120 (Pha Kho, Tha Chomphu, Khun Tan).—DE SCHAUENSEE, Proc. Acad. Nat. Sci. Philadelphia, 1934, p. 268 (Chiang Mai).—DEIGNAN, Journ. Siam Soc. Nat. Hist. Suppl., 1936, p. 89 (Chiang Mai).—RILEY, U. S. Nat. Mus. Bull. 172, 1938, p. 147 (Mae Khan, Khun Tan).

Scops bakkamoena lettia, GYLDENSTOLPE, Ibis, 1920, p. 752 (Den Chai, Pha Kho, Tha Chomphu, Khun Tan).

Otus sunia modestus [*partim*], DEIGNAN, Journ. Siam Soc. Nat. Hist. Suppl., 1931, p. 164 (Chiang Mai [*partim*]).

Otus sunia modestus, GREENWAY, Bull. Mus. Comp. Zool., 1940, p. 193 (Chiang Mai).

The collared scops owl is the only member of its genus that is common in our provinces. It occurs both in the lowlands and on the mountains: I have taken it at Chiang Mai, at Muang Chiang Dao, and on Doi Chiang Dao and have heard it calling at night on many of the higher hills.

At Chiang Mai its soft double hoot was a familiar nocturnal sound in the gardens of the town at any season, and the bird could easily be observed by flashing the beam of an electric torch into the tree whence the notes came. Despite its obvious commonness, I never once saw an individual in daylight and failed to discover where it roosted.

In the vicinity of Chiang Mai, de Schauensee took a specimen with an oviduct egg, February 2, and I collected a male with greatly enlarged testes, February 3. Other examples with the gonads enlarged were obtained there February 22 and May 7. In Stockholm are a juvenile from Chiang Mai, April 11 (Fejos), and another from Khun Tan, April 30 (Gyldenstolpe). The juvenile taken at Chiang Mai, April 29, and recorded by Greenway as *O. s. modestus* has been examined and proves to be of this species.

A male with greatly enlarged gonads had the irides golden-yellow; the eyelids edged fulvous; the cere dull brown; the maxilla greenish horn, with tip and edges of the commissure horn-color; the mandible horn, tipped greenish; the toes grayish flesh; the claws with the basal half light gray, otherwise horny brown. A female with inactive gonads had the irides rich brown; the bill horn; the toes light brown; the claws horn. Greenway's juvenile male had the irides yellow; the bill light gray; the toes blue-gray.

This is a rather larger bird than our other scops owls. In one phase it has the general coloration buffy brown, paler below, everywhere mottled and vermiculated with blackish, vivid buff, and buffy white; the forehead, superciliary region, outer portion of scapulars, and a broad but poorly defined nuchal collar vivid buff. Another phase has the general color grayish brown and the vivid buff replaced by brownish white.

The collared scops owls of Asia are, in my opinion, only subspecifically distinct from the North American forms grouped under the name *Otus asio*. As early as 1874 this was apparent to Robert Ridgway, who (*apud* Baird, Brewer, and Ridgway, A history of North American birds, vol. 3, pp. 55–56) discussed at some length the close resemblance between *Otus kennicottii* (Alaska) and *Otus semitorques* (Japan) and suggested the probability that "the latter is also a mere geographical form" of *O. asio*.

For an explanation of the use of the name *condorensis* for Thai birds, *cf.* Friedmann and Deignan, Journ. Washington Acad. Sci., vol. 29, 1939, pp. 289–291.

BUBO NIPALENSIS NIPALENSIS Hodgson

Nepalese Eagle Owl

[*Bubo*] *Nipalensis* Hodgson, Asiatic Researches, vol. 19, 1836, pp. 172–174 (Nepal).

Huhua nipalensis, Gyldenstolpe, Kungl. Svenska Vet.-Akad. Handl., 1916, p. 120 (Khun Tan); Ibis, 1920, p. 751 (Khun Tan).

Huhua nipalensis nipalensis, Greenway, Bull. Mus. Comp. Zool., 1940, p. 193 (Doi Ang Ka).

Gyldenstolpe obtained an example of this eagle owl at Khun Tan in 1914 and saw one other in the vicinity; he observes that "both these specimens occurred in a mixed pine and oak-forest at a fairly high altitude." The bird recorded by Greenway was taken on Doi Ang Ka at 4,300 feet, April 8, 1937.

This is a very large, horned species, with brown irides and yellow bill. It has the upperparts deep brown, most of the feathers edged or mottled with white or pale buff, especially on the wing coverts, scapulars, and lower back; the tail banded with buffy white and deep brown; the entire underparts white, suffused with buff, more or less barred with deep brown on throat and breast, boldly spotted elsewhere. The immature is said to have the entire plumage pale buff, paler on the head, barred everywhere with dark brown.

KETUPA ZEYLONENSIS ORIENTALIS Delacour

INDO-CHINESE BROWN FISH OWL

Ketupa ceylonensis orientalis DELACOUR, Bull. Brit. Orn. Club, vol. 47, 1926, p. 11 (Dakto, Annam).

Ketupa zeylonensis, GYLDENSTOLPE, Journ. Nat. Hist. Soc. Siam, 1915, p. 233 (listed).

Ketupa zeylonensis zeylonensis, GYLDENSTOLPE, Kungl. Svenska Vet.-Akad. Handl., 1916, p. 120 (Khun Tan); Ibis, 1920, p. 751 (Khun Tan).

Ketupa zeylonensis leschenaulti, DE SCHAUENSEE, Proc. Acad. Nat. Sci. Philadelphia, 1934, p. 268 (Muang Phrao). — DEIGNAN, Journ. Siam Soc. Nat. Hist. Suppl., 1936, p. 89 (Chiang Mai, San Kamphaeng).

The fish owl is rather generally distributed in the lowland forests of our provinces. In addition to the localities listed above, I have specimens from Muang Chiang Dao, Ban Pak Li, Ban Na Ko, and Ban Huai Ki.

This is the only large owl I have ever started in daylight in northern Thailand. It roosts at the top of some high tree, whether in the evergreen or in the taller deciduous jungle, but usually near a stream, and is extremely difficult either to observe or to collect.

It is frequently kept as a cage bird. One that was in my possession for several months thrived on live fish but never became at all tame, snapping its bill fiercely whenever I came to feed it.

A juvenile, taken at Ban Huai Ki, July 23, 1936, differs from the adult chiefly in having the upper wing coverts and the scapulars fulvous, each feather with a narrow blackish-brown streak the whole length of the shaft.

Two adult females had the irides bright golden-yellow; the eyelids edged dull olive outside, slate within; the cere olive-green; the maxilla with the apical half slate, the base and culmen greenish gray; the mandible greenish yellow or creamy yellow (the basal half slate in one specimen); the feet and toes dull brownish yellow; the claws gray at the base, otherwise slate.

This large, horned species has the upperparts generally fulvous-brown, paler on the head, each feather with a broad blackish-brown central streak and most feathers mottled with fulvous or fulvous-white; the tail barred with fulvous and deep brown, as are also the wing quills; the throat pure white; the remaining underparts light buffy brown, the feathers with narrow, indistinct, wavy cross bars of a deeper brown and with narrow blackish-brown shaft streaks.

If *orientalis* is really distinct from *leschenault* (which I have not seen), Delacour's name must be used for our birds, which agree closely with specimens from Hongkong, Laos, and Cochin-China.

GLAUCIDIUM BRODIEI BRODIEI (Burton)

INDIAN COLLARED PYGMY OWL

Noctua Brodiei BURTON, Proc. Zool. Soc. London, 1835 [=1836], p. 152 ("apud Montes Himalayenses"; type locality restricted to Simla, *apud* Stuart Baker).

Glaucidium brodiei, GYLDENSTOLPE, Journ. Nat. Hist. Soc. Siam, 1915, p. 233 (Khun Tan); Kungl. Svenska Vet.-Akad. Handl., 1916, p. 121 (Khun Tan, Pha Kho); Ibis, 1920, p. 754 (Khun Tan, Pha Kho).

Glaucidium brodiei tubiger, DE SCHAUENSEE, Proc. Acad. Nat. Sci. Philadelphia, 1929, p. 576 (Ban Chong, 10 km. south of the Kengtung border); 1934, p. 269 (Doi Suthep).—DEIGNAN, Journ. Siam Soc. Nat. Hist. Suppl., 1931, p. 164 (Doi Suthep); 1936, p. 90 (Doi Suthep).—CHASEN and BODEN KLOSS, Journ. Siam Soc. Nat. Hist. Suppl., 1932, p. 234 (Doi Suthep).—RILEY, U. S. Nat. Mus. Bull. 172, 1938, p. 151 (Khun Tan).

In Chiang Mai Province this diminutive owl is apparently confined to the mountains: on Doi Suthep it was common from the summit down to 3,500 feet, rare to 2,700 feet; on Doi Ang Ka it was heard constantly at 4,400 feet; on Khun Tan Smith took specimens only at 4,000 feet. In Nan and Chiang Rai Provinces, where the evergreen reaches the plains, it occurs also in the lowlands: De Schauensee collected one at Ban Chong in teak, and I have a specimen from Ban Hai Huai Som, at a still lower elevation.

On the western mountains it occurred at the edge of the evergreen, in the open forest of oak and chestnut, and even in the pinewoods. The bird must be extremely common, for its soft, whistled *toot′-too-toot-toot′* is heard day and night from all sides throughout the year. The sound is highly ventriloquial and can rarely be traced to the singer, although, when discovered, the latter may be perched, huddled against the trunk of a small tree, only a few feet from the observer. I have several times had my attention directed to the owl by the excitement of flocks of small passerine birds and again by its habit, when alarmed, of jerking the tail violently from side to side. One of my specimens had the stomach filled with grasshoppers.

A female had the irides golden-yellow; the eyelids edged brown; the cere and bill olive-green, the maxilla tipped yellow; the toes light green; the soles yellow; the claws black.

This species has the upperparts grayish brown or yellowish brown, on the head and nape barred and spotted, on the remaining portions (including the tail) barred, with grayish white or buff; across the upper back a buff collar, enclosing at either side a large black spot; the underparts white, sometimes suffused with cream, with a narrow brown gorget across the throat, brown and rufous bars at the sides of the breast, rufous spots and broad streaks down the flanks.

GLAUCIDIUM CUCULOIDES BRÜGELI (Parrot)

THAI BARRED PYGMY OWL

Athene cuculoides brügeli PARROT, Verh. Orn. Ges. Bayern, vol. 8, 1907, pp. 104–107 (Bangkok, error; type locality here corrected to Sam Khok district, halfway between Bangkok and Ayutthaya).

Glaucidium cuculoides, GYLDENSTOLPE, Kungl. Svenska Vet.-Akad. Handl., 1913, p. 61 (Ban Huai Hom, Den Chai, Pak Pan); 1916, p. 122 (Khun Tan, Ban Mae Na, Doi Pha Sakaeng, Pha Kho); Journ. Nat. Hist. Soc. Siam, 1915, p. 233 (listed); Ibis, 1920, p. 754 ("Throughout the whole country").—DE SCHAUENSEE, Proc. Acad. Nat. Sci. Philadelphia, 1928, p. 576 (Chiang Mai).

Glaucidium cuculoides cuculoides, DE SCHAUENSEE, Proc. Acad. Nat. Sci. Philadelphia, 1929, p. 576 (Chiang Mai, Doi Suthep).—DEIGNAN, Journ. Siam Soc. Nat. Hist. Suppl., 1931, p. 164 (Chiang Mai, Doi Suthep).

Glaucidium cuculoides rufescens, DE SCHAUENSEE, Proc. Acad. Nat. Sci. Philadelphia, 1929, p. 576 (Chiang Saen).

Glaucidium cuculoides brügeli, DE SCHAUENSEE, Proc. Acad. Nat. Sci. Philadelphia, 1934, p. 268 (Chiang Mai, Chiang Dao).—DEIGNAN, Journ. Siam Soc. Nat. Hist. Suppl., 1936, p. 90 (Chiang Mai, Doi Suthep).—RILEY, U. S. Nat. Mus. Bull. 172, 1938, p. 151 (Chiang Dao, Mae Khan, Mae Kong Ka valley).

The barred pygmy owl abounds throughout our provinces and has been taken by all collectors. Eisenhofer sent to Hannover a bird from Ban Huai Hom and another from Pak Pan, to Stockholm one from Pha Hing and 16 from Khun Tan. I have a long series from Mae Sariang, Thattafang, Ban Hong Tan, Muang Chiang Dao, Ban Wang Lung, Wiang Pa Pao, Ban Mae Mo, Chiang Mai, Chiang Saen Kao, Ban Pa Lao, Ban Mae Ka Huai Khian, Ban Tha Sala, Ban Ngao, Ban Hai Huai Som, and a locality about 50 km. east of Muang Phrayao. I have found it only at low altitudes but de Schauensee has taken it on Doi Suthep at 4,500 and 5,500 feet, where it must be quite rare.

This is perhaps our commonest species of owl and certainly, owing to its diurnal activity, the one oftenest seen. It occurs in the deciduous forest, in stands of teak, sometimes in bamboo, perching in such exposed situations as the ends of branches or the leafless tops of trees, and uttering its monotone, whistled trill without regard to human intruders. It is apparently untroubled by bright sunlight, although, like other birds, it is somewhat less active during the hottest hours of the day. Some of my specimens had the stomach filled with grasshoppers and beetles.

An example with the gonads enlarged was taken at Chiang Mai, March 3. A juvenile was collected at Ban Ngao, May 1, and others at Chiang Mai, May 1 and 6.

From living among and flying through the dry, leathery leaves of the deciduous trees, the feathers of head and nape become extraordinarily worn and decolorized; this process reaches its peak at the end of summer. Specimens taken at various places between August 3 and September 15 are molting the quills of wings and tail; one of October 13 is acquiring the new feathers of the crown, but not of the nape; a bird of October 26 has wholly completed the molt.

A male in breeding condition had the irides bright yellow; the cere olive-brown; the bill olive-green, tipped yellow; the toes greenish yellow; the claws horny gray with the apical half blackish.

This species is considerably larger than the preceding. It has the entire upperparts dark brown, barred with buff, fulvous, or white from forehead to tail tip; the underparts white, with a dark brown gorget across the throat (at the center extending to base of bill), dark brown bars at the sides of the breast, and broad rufous streaks on the flanks and belly.

There seems to be no significant size difference between the sexes. The wing lengths of thirteen adult *brügeli* (eastern and southeastern Thailand) vary from 134 to 147.2 mm.; of 18 northern specimens, from 138.5 to 152.5 mm.; of an unknown number of *rufescens* (*fide* Stuart Baker), from 141 to 162 mm. (the smallest measurements probably due to inclusion of birds better called *brügeli*). Our population is thus intermediate between the two races but, as is the case with other northern owls, is somewhat nearer the smaller, southern form.

I find no records for the occurrence of this species at Bangkok or in its immediate neighborhood.

NINOX SCUTULATA BURMANICA Hume

Burmese Brown Hawk Owl

N[*inox*] *burmanica* Hume, Stray Feathers, vol. 4, 1876, pp. 285–286 (Pegu and Tenasserim).

Ninox scutulata, Gyldenstolpe, Kungl. Svenska Vet.-Akad. Handl., 1913, p. 61 (Den Chai, "Vang Nun"); 1916, p. 121 (Pha Kho, Khun Tan, Ban Mae Na); Journ. Nat. Hist. Soc. Siam, 1915, p. 233 (listed).

Ninox scutulata burmanica, Gyldenstolpe, Ibis, 1920, p. 753 ("Northern . . . Siam").—Deignan, Journ. Siam Soc. Nat. Hist. Suppl., 1931, 164 (Chiang Mai); 1936, p. 90 (Chiang Mai).—de Schauensee, Proc. Acad. Nat. Sci. Philadelphia, 1934, p. 269 (Chiang Mai).—Riley, U. S. Nat. Mus. Bull. 172, 1938, p. 152 (Doi Langka).

The hawk owl is a rather uncommon resident throughout the northern provinces. Eisenhofer sent to Stockholm a female collected at Huai Pu, May 24, 1912, and two undated specimens from Khun Tan. I have taken it at Chiang Mai and at Ban Khana and have seen it in the forest west of Ban Na Noi (Nan Province).

This is a lowland species occurring both in mixed-deciduous jungle and in tall, dense trees near monasteries and villages. It is very inactive during the day, and for this reason I have never succeeded in identifying its notes. The stomach of one of my specimens contained a beetle.

A female from Chiang Mai, February 2, had the irides bright golden-yellow; the eyelids plumbeous; the cere dull olive-green; the maxilla slate, with culmen and extreme tip horn; the mandible slate, plumbeous beneath, tipped creamy white; the toes dull yellow; the claws slaty black, horny at the base. Another Chiang Mai female, October 4, differed in having the culmen and tip of the bill slaty green; the toes bright yellow.

This owl has the forehead white; the remaining upperparts uniform dark brown; the tail with blackish bars and a white tip; the scapulars and wing quills with white bars (more or less concealed); the feathers of throat and breast rufous-brown, fringed and barred with white; those of the remaining underparts white, broadly barred with rufous-brown.

The migratory northern race, *N. s. scutulata*, seems not to occur at all in our districts.

ATHENE BRAMA MAYRI Deignan

INDO-CHINESE SPOTTED OWL

Athene brama mayri DEIGNAN, Auk, vol. 58, 1941, p. 396 (Udon, East Thailand).

Athene brama pulchra, DEIGNAN, Journ. Siam Soc. Nat. Hist. Suppl., 1931, p. 164 (Chiang Mai); 1936, p. 90 (Chiang Mai).

Athene brama pulcra, DE SCHAUENSEE, Proc. Acad. Nat. Sci. Philadelphia, 1934, p. 268 (Chiang Mai, "Tung Sio").

This spotted owl has a remarkably broken distribution and in our area it is known only from the lowlands of a limited portion of the Mae Ping basin. Eisenhofer sent to Stockholm a single specimen from Khun Tan; I have taken it at Chiang Mai, Sala Mae Tha, and Ban Sop Mae Chaem. Its range with us is curiously similar to that of the rose-ringed parakeet.

It is a common species at Chiang Mai and, owing to its diurnal activity, one of the best known of our owls. It has a special fondness for the open groves of bamboo and *mai kwao* (*Butea*) in the environs of the outvillages but is also a resident of gardens throughout the city. It is the bird whose extraordinary cackling and scolding is heard about town bungalows in the cool of the afternoon; investigation of the noise may disclose a pair of small owls bobbing and bowing to each other in the most ludicrous fashion imaginable and wholly oblivious of the observer. My specimens had fed upon insects and, in one case, a small mammal.

A specimen taken December 12 had the gonads slightly enlarged, another of January 5 had them enlarged, and a third of January 20 had them greatly enlarged.

A bird of February 22 has the entire plumage very worn and bleached. Examples collected July 6 and August 13 are molting remiges and rectrices.

Adults had the irides golden-yellow; the eyelids edged slate; the cere dark olive, brownish gray, or olive-brown; the bill olive-green, yellowish at the tip; the toes brownish yellow or olive-yellow; the soles yellow; the claws black or slaty.

This species has the entire upperparts dark grayish brown, everywhere spotted or barred with white, more thickly on the upper back to form a broad, but not clearly defined, collar; the underparts white, with a dark brown band across the throat, and broad, irregular, dark brown bars on the lower breast, abdomen, and flanks.

The present race is distinguishable from *pulchra*, the form inhabiting southwestern Thailand, only by having the length of wing ranging from 152 to 163 mm., rather than from 138 to 152 mm.

STRIX LEPTOGRAMMICA NEWARENSIS (Hodgson)

Himalayan Brown Wood Owl

[*Ulula?*] *Newarensis* Hodgson, Asiatick Researches, vol. 19, 1836, pp. 168–170 (Nepal).

Strix leptogrammica newarensis, Chasen and Boden Kloss, Journ. Siam Soc. Nat. Hist. Suppl., 1932, p. 233 (Doi Suthep).—Deignan, Journ. Siam Soc. Nat. Hist. Suppl., 1936, p. 89 (Doi Suthep).

The brown wood owl has been recorded only from Doi Suthep. Aagaard took a female there at 4,600 feet in the spring of 1931; in September of the same year I heard and saw (with a torch) one at 5,500 feet but in the darkness was unable to collect it.

The song is composed of four deep, hollow-sounding hoots and is reminiscent of that of the Nearctic species, *Strix varia*.

This is a large species without horns. It has the facial region grayish or buffy, bordered blackish brown; the upperparts deep chocolate-brown, narrowly barred with white or light brown everywhere except on the head and nape, though rather less so on the shoulders and at the center of the back; the throat whitish; the remaining underparts buffy, narrowly and regularly barred everywhere with chocolate.

I have not been able to examine Aagaard's specimen, but it has been discussed by Chasen and Boden Kloss (*loc. cit.*), who state that "it is much less warmly coloured and paler below than *maingayi*." On the other hand, the wing length of 400 mm. is too short for the female of true *newarensis*. If it prove desirable to give nomenclatural recognition to the intermediate birds of northern Thailand, one of the several names already bestowed upon Indo-Chinese specimens will be available.

ASIO FLAMMEUS FLAMMEUS (Pontoppidan)

HOLARCTIC SHORT-EARED OWL

[*Strix*] *Flammea* PONTOPPIDAN, Den danske Atlas eller Konge-Riget Dannemark, vol. 1, 1763, p. 617, pl. 25 (Denmark).

Dr. Count Nils Gyldenstolpe has shown me in the museum at Stockholm two female specimens of this owl, taken at Chiang Mai, April 3, 1938, by Dr. P. Fejos, leader of the Swedish Film Industry Expedition. The species is otherwise unknown from our provinces.

This owl, which occurs on open plains and grassy areas, should be watched for on fallow ricefields during the cold weather and on the drying marshes, which spring up to grass and sedge after the rains.

The short-eared owl is a medium-sized, broad-winged species of peculiarly buoyant flight. It has the feathers of the upperparts buff with dark brown markings (or these colors reversed); the quills of wings and tail dark brown, barred with buff; an area around each eye blackish; the underparts buff, streaked with dark brown (more heavily on the breast). The horns are too small to be visible in the field.

Order CAPRIMULGIFORMES

Family PODARGIDAE

BATRACHOSTOMUS HODGSONI INDOCHINAE Stresemann

INDO-CHINESE FROGMOUTH

Batrachostomus hodgsoni indochinae STRESEMANN, Mitt. Zool. Mus. Berlin, vol. 22, 1937, pp. 320–321 (Dakto, Annam).

Batrachostomus hodgsoni indochinae, GREENWAY, Bull. Mus. Comp. Zool., 1940, p. 193 (Doi Ang Ka).

My collectors took an adult female at Doi Nang Kaeo, February 28, 1937, and the members of the Asiatic Primate Expedition an unsexed juvenile at 4,300 feet on Doi Ang Ka, April 17, 1937.

Frogmouths are confined to heavy evergreen forest. They somewhat resemble nightjars but have an enormously broad and swollen bill and a short, rounded wing. In the present form the male is mottled everywhere with blackish, brown, and white; the female has the plumage generally chestnut, with black-rimmed silvery-white drops on the scapulars and breast.

My specimen, of which both wing and tail measure 130 mm., is, strictly speaking, *indochinae*≷*hodgsoni*.

Family CAPRIMULGIDAE

EUROSTOPODUS MACROTIS CERVINICEPS (Gould)

INDO-CHINESE GREATER EARED NIGHTJAR

Lyncornis cerviniceps GOULD, Icones Avium, pt. 2 (Monograph of the Caprimulgidae, pt. 1), 1838, pl. 14 and text ("China or the adjacent islands," error; type locality corrected to Province of Trang, Peninsular Thailand, by Robinson and Boden Kloss, Journ. Nat. Hist. Soc. Siam, vol. 5, No. 2, 1923, p. 140).

Lyncornis cerviniceps, GYLDENSTOLPE, Journ. Nat. Hist. Soc. Siam, 1915, p. 232 (Khun Tan); Kungl. Svenska Vet.-Akad. Handl., 1916, p. 107 (Khun Tan).

The beautiful eared nightjar is fairly common, at least locally, in the lower hills of our provinces. Eisenhofer sent to Stockholm two undated specimens from Khun Tan. I took one at 3,000 feet on Doi Ang Ka, May 6, 1931; another at Ban San Tha, June 11, 1936; a third at Ban Mae Sariang, October 24, 1936.

The Ang Ka example was one of about 10 individuals hawking at dusk over a clearing in pine-forest. The stomach contained small moths and cicadas and the esophagus a large beetle.

Gyldenstolpe collected a subadult male at Khun Tan in May, 1914. My specimen of June 11 is molting both the remiges and the rectrices.

The bird from Doi Ang Ka, a female, had the irides dark brown; the bill brownish pink, with tip and apical half of the culmen brown; the interior of the mouth pink; the feet and toes fleshy brown; the soles fleshy; the claws horn-brown.

An adult male has the aigrettes and the crown generally gray-brown, the feathers finely vermiculated with blackish, some with a large black spot near the tip, those of the occiput black, narrowly tipped gray-brown; a nuchal collar rich buff; the remaining upperparts handsomely mottled and barred everywhere with gray-brown, buff, chestnut, and black; the throat crossed by a white band, which is connected with the nuchal collar; the remaining feathers of throat and breast blackish brown, narrowly tipped chestnut; the rest of the underparts banded buff and blackish brown, with black bases of the feathers showing through everywhere. An adult female is similar, but has the gray-brown portions of the plumage replaced by rich buff, the chestnut parts much more reddish.

The two types of coloration in this species seem to represent sexual dimorphism rather than mere dichromatism. Of five males before me, four are "gray" birds; of nine females, eight are "red." The two exceptional specimens may easily result from incorrect sexing by the Asiatic collectors.

CAPRIMULGUS INDICUS JOTAKA Temminck and Schlegel

JAPANESE JUNGLE NIGHTJAR

Caprimulgus jotaka TEMMINCK and SCHLEGEL, *in* Siebold, Fauna Japonica, Aves, 1850 [=1847], pp. 37–39, col. pl. 12, col. pl. 13 (Japan).

Caprimulgus indicus jotaka, RILEY, U. S. Nat. Mus. Bull. 172, 1938, p. 155 (Mae Khan).

Eisenhofer sent to Stockholm an undated specimen from Khun Tan, and Smith took one at Ban Mae Khan, February 8, 1932; the jungle nightjar is otherwise unknown from northern Thailand but probably occurs as a rare winter visitor throughout our provinces.

The adult male has the entire upperparts mottled blackish brown, brownish gray, and black, the last two colors especially prominent on the scapulars and innermost secondaries; a conspicuous white band across the four outermost primaries near their center; the *four* outer pairs of tail feathers with a broad, subterminal white band; a white throat patch; the breast closely barred blackish brown and gray; the remaining underparts buff with increasingly widely spaced blackish-brown bars. The adult female is similar but wholly lacks white markings in the wings and tail.

I have not examined the Stockholm bird and am not really certain that it belongs to the Japanese migratory race. The wing of the Washington specimen measures 192 mm.; the tail, 127 mm.; the distance between the tips of the first and fourth primaries, 17 mm. See Mayr, Ibis, 1938, pp. 310–312.

CAPRIMULGUS MACRURUS AMBIGUUS Hartert

TENASSERIMESE LONG-TAILED NIGHTJAR

C[aprimulgus] macrurus ambiguus HARTERT, Ibis, 1896, p. 373 ("Malay Peninsula, Burma, Assam, and the Eastern Himalayas"; type locality restricted to "the southern part of Tenasserim," by Boden Kloss, Ibis, 1918, p. 96).

Caprimulgus macrurus ambiguus, GYLDENSTOLPE, Kungl. Svenska Vet.-Akad. Handl., 1913, p. 57 (Mae Yom river near Phrae); Journ. Nat. Hist. Soc. Siam, 1915, p. 232 (listed).—DEIGNAN, Journ. Siam Soc. Nat. Hist. Suppl., 1936, p. 90 (Chiang Mai).

Caprimulgus macrurus albonotatus, GYLDENSTOLPE, Kungl. Svenska Vet.-Akad. Handl., 1916, p. 108 (Pha Kho); Ibis, 1920, p. 583 (Pha Kho, Mae Yom river).

Caprimulgus macrourus bimaculatus, DEIGNAN, Journ. Siam Soc. Nat. Hist. Suppl., 1931, p. 163 (Chiang Mai).—DE SCHAUENSEE, Proc. Acad. Nat. Sci. Philadelphia, 1934, p. 266 (Chiang Rai, Chiang Mai).

The long-tailed nightjar is a common permanent resident of the northern provinces, occurring chiefly on the plains, more rarely on the mountains to about 4,600 feet. Eisenhofer sent to Stockholm five undated specimens from Khun Tan; I have examples from Chiang Mai, Doi San Huai Wai, Doi Nang Kaeo, and Doi Chiang Dao.

This goatsucker rests during the day in much the same type of environment as *C. a. monticolus*, but I have never found the two species actually together. At Chiang Mai, the present form could always be seen at a place along the Mae Rim road, near Wat Phranon, where clumps of bushes alternate with small, open spaces of low grass. At night it occurs even in the town, if I am not wrong in attributing to it the hollow-sounding *tok-tok-tok-tok-tok*, which is a familiar nocturnal call there.

A bird from Doi Chiang Dao, 4,600 feet, March 19, had the testes greatly enlarged. Gyldenstolpe records (1916) that he found (either at Pha Kho or Pha Hing) two fresh eggs in a nest which was merely a slight depression in the ground, April 10, 1914. I took a juvenile at Doi San Huai Wai, June 4, and a subadult at Chiang Mai, July 16.

A male had the irides brown; the bill brown, tipped black; the feet and toes pinkish brown.

The adult male is rather like the corresponding sex of *C. i. jotaka* but has an indistinct dull rusty nuchal collar, conspicuous buff-edged black markings on the scapulars, and the *two* outer pairs of tail feathers with a broad, terminal white band. The adult female is similar and has the tail pattern of the male, but with the terminal bands sullied buff instead of white. The juvenile resembles the adult female but has the plumage very much paler throughout.

The wing lengths of six adult males from northern Thailand measure from 203 to 218 mm.; of two adult females, 198 and 198.5 mm.

CAPRIMULGUS ASIATICUS SIAMENSIS de Schauensee

Thai Little Nightjar

Caprimulgus asiaticus siamensis de Schauensee, Proc. Acad. Nat. Sci. Philadelphia, vol. 85, 1933 [=1934], p. 373 (Chiang Mai, North Thailand).

Caprimulgus asiaticus siamensis, de Schauensee, Proc. Acad. Nat. Sci. Philadelphia, 1934, p. 267 (Chiang Mai).—Deignan, Journ. Siam Soc. Nat. Hist. Suppl., 1936, p. 90 (Chiang Mai).

This small species is probably common throughout our provinces, although examples have been taken only at Chiang Mai and Chom Thong. I have heard its unmistakable call at Ban Huai Oi (Nan Province) in April.

In the neighborhood of Chiang Mai de Schauensee took numerous specimens flying above the parade ground at nightfall. I found it resting during the day on lightly shaded rocks and on the hard ground in the dry forest at the foot of Doi Suthep, but only up to 1,300 feet. The usual call is a distinctive *took-took-chuckeroo*, and I suspect that this bird is the author of the sharp *peenk* (like that of the American *Chordeiles minor*) sometimes heard before dawn at the base of Suthep. The stomach of one of my specimens was filled with beetles.

A male had the irides dark brown: the bill dull brown, tinged pink, with tip and culmen brownish black; the interior of the mouth pink; the feet and toes dull light brown; the claws black, with the pectinations horny white.

This is our smallest nightjar. The adult has the upperparts iron gray, finely vermiculated and streaked with dark brown, and with prominent buff-edged black streaks on crown and scapulars and a well-marked rufous-buff nuchal collar; a buff-washed white band across the four outermost primaries near their center; the *two* outer pairs of tail feathers black with broad white tips; a white patch on each side of the throat; the breast vermiculated iron gray and dark brown and more or less mottled with buff; the remaining underparts buff with narrow dark brown bars.

I have not examined recently collected *asiaticus* and am uncertain whether this species is subject to postmortem change of color. In the series I have seen, *siamensis* stands out clearly from *asiaticus* by its grayish, not brownish, mantle, and appears to be a quite valid form. *C. a siamensis* is apparently the race of all Thailand.

CAPRIMULGUS AFFINIS MONTICOLUS Franklin
INDIAN ALLIED NIGHTJAR

Caprimulgus monticolus FRANKLIN, Proc. Comm. Sci. Corr. Zool. Soc. London, pt. 1, 1830–1831 [=1831], p. 116 ("on the Ganges between Calcutta and Benares, and in the Vindhyian hills between the latter place and Gurrah Mundela, on the Nerbudda").

Caprimulgus monticola GYLDENSTOLPE, Journ. Nat. Hist. Soc. Siam, 1915, p. 232 (listed).

Caprimulgus monticolus, GYLDENSTOLPE, Ibis, 1920, p. 582 ("Northern parts").

Caprimulgus monticolus monticolus, DEIGNAN, Journ. Siam Soc. Nat. Hist. Suppl., 1931, p. 175 (Chiang Mai).

Caprimulgus monticolus burmanicus, DE SCHAUENSEE, Proc. Acad. Nat. Sci. Philadelphia, 1934, p. 267 (Chiang Mai).—DEIGNAN, Journ. Siam Soc. Nat. Hist. Suppl., 1936, p. 90 (Chiang Mai).

The allied nightjar is probably a rather common permanent resident throughout the northern lowlands, although the only records are from the more western provinces. Eisenhofer sent to Stockholm an undated female from Khun Tan; I have taken it at Chiang Mai, Chom Thong, and Ban Mae Sariang.

In the vicinity of Chiang Mai this species seemed to confine itself during the day to certain wastelands where cremations are performed; at such places lawnlike grassy areas are interspersed with low bushes and clumps of bamboo and the bird rests on the ground just where grass and thicket meet.

The only note I can with certainty associate with the present form is a low *chuck*, uttered when it is compelled to fly.

583136—45——13

My specimens had the irides dark brown; the edges of the eyelids fulvous; the bill light pinkish brown, with tip and apical half of culmen blackish brown, the edges of the commissure fleshy, the rictus fleshy white; the interior of the mouth pink; the feet and toes light pinkish brown; the claws blackish brown.

The adult male has the upperparts brownish gray or grayish brown, with a more or less distinct rufous-buff nuchal collar and bold, deep buff markings on the scapulars and innermost secondaries; the feathers of the back vermiculated with blackish but *without* distinct black streaks; a buff-washed white band across the four outermost primaries near their center; the *two* outer pairs of tail feathers entirely white except for a mottled brown area at the tip; a white throat patch; the breast colored like the back; the remaining underparts buff, narrowly barred with blackish brown, the bars disappearing posteriorly. The adult female lacks white markings in the wings and tail but may be recognized by its unstreaked back and general resemblance to the male.

Caprimulgus monticolus is, in my opinion, merely a continental representative of the Javanese *C. affinis*, to which it is linked by *C. griseatus* (Luzón), *C. mindanensis* (Mindanao), and *C. propinquus* (Celebes).

In the absence of comparative material, I can form no opinion on the validity of Stuart Baker's *burmanicus*, which Ticehurst (Ibis, 1939, p. 32) considers to be unrecognizable. In the event that it prove distinct, our birds must be known by Baker's name.

Order CHAETURIFORMES

Family CHAETURIDAE

COLLOCALIA INNOMINATA Hume

HUME'S GRAY-RUMPED SWIFTLET

Collocalia innominata HUME, Stray Feathers, vol. 1, 1873, pp. 294–297 (Andaman Islands; type specimen from Port Mouat, South Andaman, *fide* Hartert, Catalogue of the birds in the British Museum, vol. 16, 1892, p. 503).

Collocalia sp., DEIGNAN, Journ. Siam Soc. Nat. Hist. Suppl., 1931, p. 175 (Doi Suthep).

Collocalia innominata, ROGERS and DEIGNAN, Proc. Biol. Soc. Washington, 1934, p. 92 (Doi Ang Ka).

Collocalia fuciphaga innominata, DE SCHAUENSEE, Proc. Acad. Nat. Sci. Philadelphia, 1934, p. 266 (Doi Chiang Dao).—DEIGNAN, Journ. Siam Soc. Nat. Hist. Suppl., 1936, p. 91 (Doi Suthep).

The swiftlet is recorded only from a few of the higher peaks of Chiang Mai Province. I took three examples at 4,600 feet on Doi Ang Kà, April 20, 1931, but frequently saw it there as high as 5,500 feet. De Schauensee collected one at 4,600 feet on Doi Chiang Dao,

January 16, 1933, and I shot one at the same spot, March 19, 1937. On Doi Suthep it occurred irregularly throughout the year from 3,300 to 5,500 feet and was seen once or twice over the lowest slopes of the mountain.

This is a difficult bird to collect, owing to its small size, darting flight, and the forested or precipitous nature of its habitat; I was able to take specimens only on the few occasions which I happened to be on some treeless ridge or hilltop just as a loose flock passed by at a comparatively low altitude. On Doi Ang Ka it was often associated with *Apus a subfurcatus*, on Doi Chiang Dao and Doi Suthep with *Riparia c. sintaungensis*. Stomachs I examined were filled with minute insects.

My specimen of March 19 had the testes greatly enlarged, but the birds taken April 20 had the gonads quite inactive.

This swift has the irides dark brown; the bill black; the interior of the mouth dusky fleshy; the tarsi brownish pink; the toes dark brown; the claws black. De Schauensee records that his example had the feet and toes purplish.

The present species might be confused only with the palm swift of the lowlands; from the latter it may be known by its slightly greater size and by its having a noticeable gray band across the rump.

Dr. Ernst Mayr, who has made an intensive study of this difficult genus, kindly identified my specimens, in 1932 and again in 1939, as *innominata*.

For use of the names Chaeturiformes and Chaeturidae, see Brodkorb, Wilson Bull., 1940, p. 214.

CHAETURA GIGANTEA INDICA Hume

INDIAN BROWN-THROATED SPINE-TAILED SWIFT

Chaetura indica HUME, Stray Feathers, vol. 1, 1873, pp. 471–474 ("Andamans and various parts of Southern India").

Chaetura gigantea indica, GYLDENSTOLPE, Kungl. Svenska Vet.-Akad. Handl., 1913, p. 56 (Mae Raem); Ibis, 1920, p. 584 (Mae Raem, Pha Kho, Huai San Noi).

Chaetura sp., GYLDENSTOLPE, Kungl. Svenska Vet.-Akad. Handl., 1916, p. 106 (Huai San Noi, Pha Kho).

Hirundapus giganteus indicus, DEIGNAN, Journ. Siam Soc. Nat. Hist. Suppl., 1931, p. 163 (Doi Suthep); 1936, p. 91 (Doi Suthep).—RILEY, U. S. Nat. Mus. Bull. 172, 1938, p. 160 (Khun Tan).

This giant swift is a rather common winter visitor throughout our provinces. On Doi Suthep it was normally seen only above the highest ridges (5,500 feet) but at least once (January 2, 1937) was found with *Apus p. cooki* as low as 2,800 feet. Gyldenstolpe twice saw it flying up and down small lowland streams at dusk. I myself observed great numbers of migrating birds flying just above the leafless trees on the low hills west of Ban Na Noi (Nan Province), April 1, 1937. The extreme dates for its stay on Doi Suthep are September 26 (1936) and April 2 (1931).

Probably no bird in the world surpasses the present species in speed of flight, which doubtless on occasion exceeds 100 miles an hour. To appreciate its velocity one must have braced oneself against the wind on some treeless, knife-edged ridge, where the mountain falls away on either hand into an abyss, and heard the swish of wings as an individual hurtled by, just skimming the rocks and, apparently intentionally, almost grazing the observer, then curving in a wide arc far beyond and returning to repeat the spectacular performance. Throughout the daylight hours, however strong the gale, it is the very incarnation of tireless flight.

The spinetail has a conspicuous patch on the lores pure white; the head, nape, wings, and tail black, highly glossed with greenish blue; the back brown; the underparts brown, paler on chin and throat, and slightly glossed with green on the upper breast; the under tail coverts pure white with black shafts, the white continued as a narrow line along the lower flanks above the thighs.

APUS PACIFICUS COOKI (Harington)

BURMESE WHITE-RUMPED SWIFT

Cypselus pacificus cooki HARINGTON, Bull. Brit. Orn. Club, vol. 31, 1913, p. 57 (caves of the Gokteik Gorge, Hsipaw State, Northern Shan States).

Micropus pacificus cooki, DE SCHAUENSEE, Proc. Acad. Nat. Sci. Philadelphia, 1934, p. 266 (Doi Chiang Dao).

The white-rumped swift occurs with us only rarely, but it has been observed in some numbers on several occasions. De Schauensee found it common on Doi Chiang Dao, where he took a female at 4,500 feet, January 19, 1933. It was numerous at a place near Ban Hua Fai, on the track from Muang Fang to Muang Hang, December 27, 1936, and I collected a male there. Finally, a flock of these birds appeared on Doi Suthep at 2,800 feet, January 2, 1937, and I succeeded in shooting two females.

De Schauensee notes that his specimen had the irides dark brown; the bill, feet, toes, and claws black.

This rather large species has the entire upperparts, except for a narrow white rump band, black, more or less glossed with greenish; the throat white with narrow black shaft streaks, not clearly defined from the remaining underparts, which are black, with each feather broadly tipped white so as to give a barred appearance.

Of the swifts now known from our provinces, this species can be confused only with the smaller house swift, which is unbarred beneath. There is a possibility, however, that the northern white-rumped swift, *A. p. pacificus*, will also occur with us in winter; from the present form it is chiefly distinguished by its browner, less glossed, upperparts and much broader white rump band.

APUS AFFINIS SUBFURCATUS (Blyth)

MALAYAN HOUSE SWIFT

Cypselus subfurcatus BLYTH, Journ. Asiat. Soc. Bengal, vol. 18, 1849, pp. 807–809 ("Malay Peninsula," *fide* Sclater, Ibis, 1892, p. 83; type locality usually restricted to Pinang Island, one of the localities mentioned by Blyth).

Micropus affinis subfurcatus, DEIGNAN, Journ. Siam Soc. Nat. Hist. Suppl., 1931, p. 163 (Chiang Mai); 1936, p. 91 (Chiang Mai, ? Doi Suthep, Doi Ang Ka).

Above a small pond near Chiang Mai, August 10, 1929, I observed, in company with palm swifts, between 15 and 25 white-rumped birds, which were probably, but not certainly, of this species. The swifts seen at the summit of Doi Suthep, May 11 and 12, 1935, and recorded by me in 1936 under this name may well have belonged to the preceding form, which had not yet been taken on that mountain. The house swift, however, was found to be common between 4,000 and 5,500 feet on Doi Ang Ka in the spring of 1931, and on May 2 no less than 8 specimens, breeding adults and unfledged young, were brought to me by Karens.

I was informed that the birds were breeding in considerable numbers on a precipice near the White Karen village called Ban Nong Lom. The nestlings were obtained by shooting buckshot at the face of the cliff to break off fragments of rock to which nests were attached. These nests were not seen by me but were described as having the shape of a shallow cup. Some of the nests held eggs, which were shattered by the fall.

My specimens of all ages had the irides dark brown; the eyelids plumbeous; the bill black; the interior of the mouth pink; the tarsi fleshy in front, white behind; the toes with the basal half fleshy, the rest dark brown; the soles white; the claws blackish brown.

The house swift is black with the chin and throat and a conspicuous rump band white. From the preceding species it may perhaps be recognizable by its lesser size and its only slightly forked tail.

CYPSIURUS PARVUS INFUMATUS (Sclater)

MALAYSIAN PALM SWIFT

Cypselus infumatus SCLATER, Proc. Zool. Soc. London, 1865, p. 602 (Banjermassin, southwest Borneo).

Tachornis batasinensis infumatus, DE SCHAUENSEE, Proc. Acad. Nat. Sci. Philadelphia, 1929, p. 575 (Chiang Mai).

Cypsiurus batassiensis infumatus, DEIGNAN, Journ. Siam Soc. Nat. Hist. Suppl., 1931, p. 163 (Chiang Mai); 1936, p. 91 (Chiang Mai).—RILEY, U. S. Nat. Mus. Bull. 172, 1938, p. 159 (Ban Nam Khian).

Tachornis batassiensis infumatus, DE SCHAUENSEE, Proc. Acad. Nat. Sci. Philadelphia, 1934, p. 266 ("North Siam").

The palm swift is a common bird of towns and villages throughout the northern lowlands, wherever the vegetation is suitable for its requirements. I have specimens from Chiang Mai, Ban Mae Klang, and Sala Mae Tha.

The occurrence of this species is wholly dependent upon the presence of palms of the genera *Cocos*, *Borassus*, and *Areca*, and, accordingly, it is found in our provinces only in close proximity to human habitation. The bands of small, slim swifts, darting through the palm groves with constant chattering, are familiar to all residents of Thailand.

At Ban Nam Khian, April 21, Smith found a nest with two eggs fastened to a frond of *Areca*. I never discovered a nest at Chiang Mai but took specimens there with enlarged gonads, June 7 and July 2.

A male had the irides brown; the bill black; the interior of the mouth pinkish; the feet, toes, and claws brownish black.

This is a small, dark-colored swift with forked tail. It has the entire upperparts grayish black, the underparts brownish gray.

Family HEMIPROCNIDAE

HEMIPROCNE LONGIPENNIS CORONATA (Tickell)

INDIAN CRESTED TREE SWIFT

Hirundo Coronata TICKELL, Journ. Asiat. Soc. Bengal, vol. 2, 1833, p. 580 (Borabham and Dholbham, India).

Hemiprocne coronata, GYLDENSTOLPE, Kungl. Svenska Vet.-Akad. Handl., 1916, p. 107 (Ban Mae Na, Doi Pha Sakaeng, Khun Tan); Ibis, 1920, p. 584 ("Northern and north-western Siam").—DE SCHAUENSEE, Proc. Acad. Nat. Sci. Philadelphia, 1929, p. 575 (Chiang Mai).—DEIGNAN, Journ. Siam Soc. Nat. Hist. Suppl., 1931, p. 163 (Chiang Mai, Doi Suthep); 1936, p. 91 (Chiang Mai, Doi Suthep).—RILEY, U. S. Nat. Mus. Bull. 172, 1938, p. 157 (Ban Mae Klang, Mae Khan, Khun Tan, Mae Hong Son).

Though the tree swift is a common resident of the plains and lower hills in the more western provinces, it is not yet recorded from any locality east of Ban Mae Mo (Lampang Province). Eisenhofer sent to Stockholm a single undated example from Khun Tan. I have taken it at Chiang Mai, Sala Mae Tha, Ban Sop Mae Chaem, and Ban Mae Mo and have occasionally seen it on Doi Suthep to 3,300 feet.

At Chiang Mai I often saw tree swifts hawking over the river and the bazaar in company with *Cypsiurus*, but the species was commoner in the countryside, especially near some tall, dead tree standing isolated in the fields, upon which, between flights, the birds rested, usually huddled closely together, in a curiously erect position. While flying, the bird keeps its deeply forked tail folded and then resembles a small, slim parakeet; this likeness is increased by its low, screaming notes.

A male taken on September 1 at Ban Mae Mo is completing the postnatal molt.

Gyldenstolpe and de Schauensee note that their specimens had the irides dark brown; the bill black; the feet and toes dark reddish brown or dusky lake.

The adult male has the plumage generally soft blue-gray, with the lores black, the chin, upper throat, sides of lower throat, and the ear coverts soft chestnut. The adult female differs in having the chestnut replaced by blue-gray.

Order TROGONIFORMES

Family TROGONIDAE

HARPACTES ERYTHROCEPHALUS ERYTHROCEPHALUS (Gould)

BURMESE RED-HEADED TROGON

Trogon erythrocephalus GOULD, Proc. Zool. Soc. London, 1834, p. 25 (Rangoon, Burma).

Harpactes erythrocephalus, GYLDENSTOLPE, Journ. Nat. Hist. Soc. Siam, 1915, p. 232 (listed).

Pyrotrogon erythrocephalus, GYLDENSTOLPE, Kungl. Svenska Vet.-Akad. Handl., 1916, p. 105 (Doi Pha Sakaeng, Khun Tan).

Pyrotrogon erythrocephalus erythrocephalus [*partim*], GYLDENSTOLPE, Ibis, 1920, p. 606 ("Northern Siam" [*partim*]).

Pyrotrogon erythrocephalus subsp., DE SCHAUENSEE, Proc. Acad. Nat. Sci. Philadelphia, 1929, p. 574 (Doi Suthep).

Harpactes erythrocephalus intermedius, CHASEN and BODEN KLOSS, Journ. Siam Soc. Nat. Hist. Suppl., 1932, p. 234 (Doi Suthep).

Harpactes erythrocephalus erythrocephalus, DEIGNAN, Journ. Siam Soc. Nat. Hist. Suppl., 1931, p. 163 (Doi Suthep); 1936, p. 92 (Doi Suthep).—DE SCHAUENSEE, Proc. Acad. Nat. Sci. Philadelphia, 1934, p. 264 (Doi Suthep, Doi Chiang Dao).

Harpactes erythrocephalus erythrocephalus [*partim*], RILEY, U. S. Nat. Mus. Bull. 172, 1938, p. 163 (Doi Ang Ka, Doi Suthep, Doi Khun Tan, Doi Hua Mot).

The Burmese form of the red-headed trogon is a common resident of the mountain evergreen from 2,500 to 5,500 feet, but probably it reaches its eastern limit of range on the higher peaks of the Khun Tan chain. Eisenhofer sent to Stockholm two males and a female, taken in 1914 at Khun Tan. I have specimens from Doi Suthep, Doi Ang Ka, and an unknown locality between Chiang Mai and Wiang Pa Pao.

This trogon is a silent bird, occurring, singly or in pairs, in damp, dark forest and especially in cool ravines. Here it perches quietly upon some low branch, its back to the observer, and one's first intimation of its presence is often a bright crimson flash as it crosses the trail to vanish again in the foliage beyond.

I took a male, just out of the nest, on Doi Ang Ka, April 8; since members of the Trogonidae are well known to have an extraordinarily thin skin, it is worth mentioning that this specimen's skin was no more delicate than that of any other bird of equal size.

An example of July 22, sexed as a male, is like the adult female but has the black-barred buffy secondaries and pointed rectrices of immaturity. A male of August 28 has almost wholly assumed the red head an dbreast of the adult but shows its you in wings and tail. A male of October 21 retains only one of the immature secondaries but has some brown feathers among the crimson of head and breast and the rectrices pointed. Males of December 15 and February 21 have lost all marks of the juvenal dress except the acuminate tail feathers.

An adult female, collected on May 10, is acquiring one new central rectrix, but the loss of the old feather may have been due to accident. Adults that are clearly in molt were taken on August 23 and September 1 and 5.

De Schauensee's specimens had the irides reddish brown; the orbital skin violet; the bill violet, with the entire culmen and the edges of the commissure on the basal half black; the rictus purplish red; the feet and toes fleshy pink; the soles yellow. Gyldenstolpe states that his females had the irides plain brown, while the males had them pale brown, reddish brown, or (in one case) bright red, and that both sexes had the bill black with the base blue, the feet and toes pale gray.

My nestling male had the irides gray with a narrow, dark outer ring; the orbital skin flesh color; the bill black, white at the tip, fleshy at the base; the rictus and interior of the mouth fleshy; the feet and toes flesh color; the claws horn-brown, tipped fleshy.

The adult male has the head, neck, throat, and breast deep crimson; an indistinct, narrow white crescent across the lower breast; the remaining underparts brighter and lighter crimson; the primaries black; the secondaries and upper wing coverts finely vermiculated black and white; the central pair of tail feathers chestnut, narrowly tipped with black; the next two pairs black, with some chestnut; the others black with white outer webs and broad white tips; the remaining upperparts golden-brown, more ferruginous on the rump and upper tail coverts. The adult female has the head, neck, throat, and breast colored like the back and the rest of the plumage similar to that of the male. Adults of either sex have the rectrices square-tipped and slightly flaring near the end.

HARPACTES ERYTHROCEPHALUS ANNAMENSIS (Robinson and Boden Kloss)

Annamese Red-headed Trogon

Pyrotrogon erythrocephalus annamensis Robinson and Boden Kloss, Ibis, 1919, pp. 424–425 (Dran, South Annam).

Harpactes erythrocephalus, Gyldenstolpe, Kungl. Svenska Vet.-Akad. Handl., 1913, p. 57 (Mae Raem river).

Pyrotrogon erythrocephalus erythrocephalus [*partim*], GYLDENSTOLPE, Ibis, 1920, p. 606 ("Northern Siam" [*partim*]).

A red-headed trogon, which may for the present be placed with this form, is of rare occurrence in the lowland evergreen forests of the more eastern provinces. Gyldenstolpe saw three examples near the Mae Raem and collected one of them, a female, March 11, 1912.

H. e. annamensis was described after comparison with Malayan birds, believed by the authors to represent *erythrocephalus* but subsequently (and quite properly) separated by Riley as *chaseni*. From true *erythrocephalus*, *annamensis* differs only in having the upper wing coverts distinctly banded, rather than vermiculated, and the black element present in much greater proportion.

The birds dwelling east of the Khun Tan range are neither *erythrocephalus* nor *annamensis* but represent an intermediate population, which will probably be given subspecific status in the future. It is interesting to find that males from Doi Khun Tan belong with *erythrocephalus* while females from the same mountain agree with examples from farther east.

HARPACTES ORESKIOS STELLAE Deignan

STELLA'S ORANGE-BREASTED TROGON

Harpactes oreskios stellae DEIGNAN, Auk, vol. 58, 1941, pp. 396–397 (Muang Chiang Dao, North Thailand).

Harpactes oreskios, GYLDENSTOLPE, Kungl. Svenska Vet.-Akad. Handl., 1913, p. 57 (Ban Huai Hom); Journ. Nat. Hist. Soc. Siam, 1915, p. 232 (listed).

Pyrotrogon oreskios, GYLDENSTOLPE, Kungl. Svenska Vet.-Akad. Handl., 1916, p. 105 (Khun Tan, Pha Hing, Pha Kho).

Pyrotrogon oreskios uniformis, GYLDENSTOLPE, Ibis, 1920, p. 606 ("Throughout Siam").—DE SCHAUENSEE, Proc. Acad. Nat. Sci. Philadelphia, 1929, p. 575 (Doi Suthep).

Harpactes oreskios uniformis, DEIGNAN, Journ. Siam Soc. Nat. Hist. Suppl., 1931, p. 163 (Doi Suthep); 1936, p. 92 (Doi Suthep).—DE SCHAUENSEE, Proc. Acad. Nat. Sci. Philadelphia, 1934, p. 265 (Doi Suthep).—RILEY, U. S. Nat. Mus. Bull. 172, 1938, p. 167 (Chiang Dao, Khun Tan).

The orange-breasted trogon occurs rather commonly throughout our provinces, inhabiting the evergreen and mixed-deciduous forest from the plains to about 5,500 feet (but seldom found above 3,500 feet).

Its habits are much like those of the red-headed species, and, like its congener, it usually perches with its back turned toward a source of potential danger, so that it is often overlooked, although near at hand, until it flies a short distance with a sudden burst of color. Gyldenstolpe observes (1916) that "it has a smacking note which is fairly loud and may be heard some distance."

The same author found the species breeding near Pha Kho, March 11, 1914: two eggs had been laid in an open hole of a decayed tree, in which there was no trace of nest-building material. I took an example in postnuptial molt at Doi San Pa Bong, June 2.

An adult male had the irides dark brown; the orbital skin bright smalt blue; the bill duller smalt blue, with the culmen blackish; the feet and toes plumbeous; the soles dusky flesh; the claws horn.

The male has the head, neck, and upper breast olive-green, strongly suffused with yellow on the throat and upper breast; the remaining upperparts chestnut-brown; the primaries and outer secondaries black, narrowly edged with white along the outer web; the inner secondaries and the coverts black, narrowly and regularly barred with white; the central pair of rectrices chestnut-brown, narrowly tipped with black; the next two pairs all black; the other pairs black, broadly tipped with white; the remaining underparts bright yellow, strongly suffused with red-orange on the lower breast and sides of the abdomen. The female differs in having the head, neck, and upper breast dull brownish olive; the back dull olivaceous-brown, changing to rufous on the rump and upper tail coverts; the upper wing coverts and inner secondaries barred with rufous-buff instead of white; the underparts yellow with only a slight suffusion of orange on the breast.

Order CORACIIFORMES

Family ALCEDINIDAE

ALCEDO ATTHIS BENGALENSIS Gmelin

INDIAN COMMON KINGFISHER

[*Alcedo*] *bengalensis* GMELIN, Systema naturae, vol. 1, pt. 1, 1788, p. 450 (Bengal).

Alcedo ispida bengalensis, GYLDENSTOLPE, Journ. Nat. Hist. Soc. Siam, 1915, p. 231 (listed); Kungl. Svenska Vet.-Akad. Handl., 1916, p. 115 (Mae Rua, Chiang Saen); Ibis, 1920, p. 589 ("Throughout the whole country").—DE SCHAUENSEE, Proc. Acad. Nat. Sci. Philadelphia, 1928, p. 572 (Chiang Mai).

Alcedo atthis bengalensis, DE SCHAUENSEE, Proc. Acad. Nat. Sci. Philadelphia, 1929, p. 573 (Chiang Mai); 1934, p. 261 (Chiang Saen).—DEIGNAN, Journ. Siam Soc. Nat. Hist. Suppl., 1931, p. 162 (Chiang Mai); 1936, pp. 92, 133 (Chiang Mai, Mae Ping river north of the Gorges).

The *nok katen noi* is one of the commonest and most familiar birds of the northern lowlands. Eisenhofer sent to Hannover one taken at Pha Hing, April 26, 1912, and to Stockholm 12 from Khun Tan. I have 19 specimens from localities in all parts of our area, including Mae Sariang, the base of Doi Mae Kong Ka, Ban Bo Sali, Ban Thung Ma Num, Chom Thong, Sala Mae Tha, Ban Na Noi (Chiang Mai Province), Bang Hong Khaeo, Muang Pong, and Ban Nam Puat (French Laos). At Chiang Mai it completely disappeared during the driest months (early April to early June) and then seemed to be absent also from other localities in the western districts, although at the same season I found it common enough in Nan and Chiang Rai Provinces.

On the plains this little bird may be seen at any body of water, from the greatest river to the muddiest ditch. It is usually in pairs, which take possession of some likely spot and, day after day, use the same stones and bushes from which to dive upon their prey of insects and tiny fishes. Flight is very rapid and accompanied by a characteristic sharp, shrill *chee-chee-chee-chee.*

I have no information on the actual breeding season, but examples in plumage that shows them to be young of the year have been taken between August 27 and November 11. A female of the latter date has scattered ferruginous feathers appearing among the ashy brown of the breast.

An adult male had the irides dark brown; the bill black; the interior of the mouth orange; the feet and toes coral-red; the claws dark brown. An immature female had the irides dark brown; the maxilla blackish; the mandible reddish, with tip and extreme base blackish; the rictus orange; the feet and toes dark red; the soles coral-red; the claws dark horny brown.

The adult has the head and nape narrowly barred with blackish and shining blue; the back, rump, and upper tail coverts shining turquoise blue; the remaining upperparts deep blue or greenish blue, most of the wing coverts tipped with a spot of shining blue; the lores and ear coverts ferruginous, the latter followed by a broad white streak; a broad streak from the base of the bill deep blue or greenish blue; the chin and throat white; the remaining underparts ferruginous. The immature is similar but has the ferruginous replaced by ashy brown, with the abdomen albescent.

ALCEDO MENINTING COLTARTI Stuart Baker

ASSAMESE DEEP-BLUE KINGFISHER

Alcedo meninting coltarti STUART BAKER, Bull. Brit. Orn. Club, vol. 39, 1919, p. 39 (Sadiya, Lakhimpur, Assam).

A female *Alcedo*, taken by my collectors near Chiang Mai, August 3, 1936, appeared to me to be of this form but was so badly shot about the head and back that I could not feel sure it was not an aberrant example of the preceding species. Fortunately, they succeeded in collecting, at the same spot, August 7, a second female, which removed all doubt of the bird's identity. Although, in describing *coltarti*, Stuart Baker stated that it ranged through "North and Central Siam," I believe that this is the first record of its actual occurrence anywhere in Thailand.

My specimens were taken on the left bank of the Mae Ping, near Ko Klang, at a place where a small watercourse, heavily shaded by bamboos, enters the main stream.

The second example, which seems to be subadult, had the irides brown; the bill black with extreme tip horn and the base of the mandible reddish; the rictus coral-red; the feet coral-red; the toes with the basal half light orange, the rest horn.

The adult differs from the common kingfisher in having the ear coverts deep blue; the scapulars black; the dark blue portions of the plumage deeper in shade, the light blue more brilliant; the underparts of a more intense ferruginous. The immature has the ear coverts deep ferruginous but is otherwise similar to the adult.

I have not seen topotypical *coltarti* but feel certain that these birds are correctly placed. From an example of *rufigastra* (Andaman Islands) they differ only in having the bars of the *nape* deep purplish blue, the spots of the upper wing coverts smaller and more numerous.

CEYX ERITHACUS ERITHACUS (Linnaeus)

INDIAN THREE-TOED KINGFISHER

[*Alcedo*] *erithaca* LINNAEUS, Systema naturae, ed. 10, vol. 1, 1758, p. 115 (Bengal).

Ceyx tridactylus, GYLDENSTOLPE, Journ. Nat. Hist. Soc. Siam, 1915, p. 231 (listed=Den Chai, *fide* Williamson, *ibid.*, 1917, p. 333).

Ceyx tridactyla, GYLDENSTOLPE, Kungl. Svenska Vet.-Akad. Handl., 1916, p. 115 ("Northern Siam"); Ibis, 1920, p. 588 ("Throughout Siam").

The lovely three-toed kingfisher is uncommon and local in the lowland evergreen forest of the provinces east of the Khun Tan range. In Stockholm is a female, taken by Eisenhofer at Pha Hing, April 30, 1912; this is probably the bird listed by Gyldenstolpe in 1915. I have specimens from Ban Thap Man, Ban Huai Som, Ban Huai Ki, Muang Fang, and Ban Don Chai (in French Laos, just north of Nan Province), and have seen a pair between Ban Nong Lom and Muang Phan, at the head of the Mae Wang basin.

On clear jungle brooks and rivulets, densely shaded by palms and tree ferns, this brilliant and diminutive species is at home. It takes up residence at some tiny pool, where it conceals itself in the overhanging vegetation; when alarmed it darts from bush to bush before one along the stream until, reaching the boundary of its selected territory, it suddenly turns off among the trees to circle back to its original perch.

An immature example was taken at Muang Fang, July 5, 1936.

The adult has a spot or streak at the center of the forehead black glossed with deep blue; a white streak behind the ear coverts, bordered above by a streak of deep blue; the upper back and scapulars deep blue; the wings black glossed with deep blue; the remaining upperparts orange-rufous glossed, especially on the tail coverts, with violet; the underparts yellow, albescent on the chin and throat, elsewhere, especially on the breast and under tail coverts and under wing coverts, suffused with orange. The immature differs chiefly in having indistinct dark edgings to the feathers at the base of the bill and at the sides of the breast; the chin and throat white and clearly defined from the remaining underparts, which are brownish orange, albescent at the center of the abdomen.

CERYLE RUDIS LEUCOMELANURA Reichenbach

INDIAN LESSER PIED KINGFISHER

C[eryle] leucomelanura REICHENBACH, Icones ad synopsin avium, continuatio No. viii, Alcedineae, 1851, p. 21, col. pl. ccccix b, No. 3488 (Ceylon).

Ceryle rudis leucomelanura, GYLDENSTOLPE, Kungl. Svenska Vet.-Akad. Handl., 1916, p. 144 (Chiang Rai); Ibis, 1920, p. 590 ("Northern . . . Siam"). —DE SCHAUENSEE, Proc. Acad. Nat. Sci. Philadelphia, 1929, p. 573 (Chiang Mai, Chiang Rai). —DEIGNAN, Journ. Siam Soc. Nat. Hist. Suppl., 1931, p. 161 (Chiang Mai); 1936, pp. 92, 133 (Chiang Mai, Mae Ping river above the Rapids).

The smaller pied kingfisher is now known only from the systems of the Mae Ping and the Mae Khong, in both of which it is very common; it will doubtless be found to occur at one season or another on all our major streams.

The species is locally migratory in northern Thailand and, since it feeds wholly on aquatic life, its movements are governed, at least in part, by the recurrent periods of rainfall and drought. At Chiang Mai it appeared with the first rains late in May and was common until the end of September. For no obvious reason it was extremely rare or absent during the two following months, for which the only records are: one, October 13, 1936; one, November 25, 1936. From December to the end of March it was more common than at any other time, but during the driest season, April and most of May, it was never seen.

This kingfisher is sometimes found over the great marshes but is characteristically a bird of the rivers, particularly where they are broad and the water flows smoothly. It flies at some distance above the stream, with bill pointed downward, occasionally uttering a shrill *peet-weet*, *peet-weet*, *peet-weet*, which curiously resembles the call of the common sandpiper. Upon sighting some tiny fish or crustacean, the bird pulls up short and, with wings beating rapidly, hovers like a kestrel, before plunging headlong into the water.

An adult female had the irides brown; the bill black; the feet, toes, and claws dull black; the soles brownish gray.

The male has the entire upperparts barred and spotted with black and white; the underparts white, the lower throat, breast, and flanks heavily spotted with black, the spots on the breast larger and run together to form two conspicuous gorgets. The female differs chiefly in having only one gorget (often broken at the middle).

CERYLE LUGUBRIS GUTTULATA Stejneger

INDIAN GREATER PIED KINGFISHER

Ceryle guttulata STEJNEGER, Proc. U. S. Nat. Mus., vol. 15, 1892, pp. 294–295. New name for *Alcedo guttatus* Vigors 1831 (Himalayas; type locality restricted to Cachar, by Stuart Baker, Journ. Bombay Nat. Hist. Soc., vol. 28, 1922, p. 314; corrected to Simla-Almora district, by Ticehurst and Whistler, Ibis, 1924, p. 471), not *Alcedo guttata* Boddaert, 1783.

Megaceryle lugubris guttulata, RILEY, U. S. Nat. Mus. Bull. 172, 1938, p. 169 (Mae Kong Ka valley, Thattafang).

Ceryle lugubris scutulata, GREENWAY, Bull. Mus. Comp. Zool., 1940, p. 193 (Doi Ang Ka).

The greater pied kingfisher is found only along the broadest of mountain streams, in uninhabited districts west of the Khun Tan range. Since there are few torrents of suitable size in our provinces, the bird is local in distribution and nowhere common. It has been collected on the Mae Klang (Doi Ang Ka) as high as 4,300 feet. I have a specimen from Doi Mae Kong Ka (in the hills between Mae Sariang and the Salwin) and have seen a pair on a rushing stream in the hills southwest of Wiang Pa Pao and another on the Mae Mao (at the foot of Doi Pha Hom Pok).

This species is usually seen at rest on some branch that overhangs the stream or perched upon a rock rising from the midst of the turbulent water. In flight it utters a harsh, rattling sound much like the call of the American *C. alcyon*.

Greenway records that three nestlings were collected by the members of the Asiatic Primate Expedition at 4,300 feet on Doi Ang Ka, April 14, 1937.

The male has the upper half of the head and the conspicuous crest black spotted with white; a broad white nuchal collar connected with a white band on each side of the head from the base of the bill; the remaining upperparts slaty gray, barred everywhere with white; the underparts white, but with a line of black streaks at either side of the throat and neck connected with a broad breast band formed by black and dull rufous spots, and with black bars at the sides of the abdomen and on some of the under tail coverts. The female differs in having the axillaries and under wing coverts pale rufous.

This and the preceding species are our only crested kingfishers.

RAMPHALCYON CAPENSIS BURMANICA (Bowdler Sharpe)

BURMESE STORK-BILLED KINGFISHER

Pelargopsis burmanica BOWDLER SHARPE, Proc. Zool. Soc. London, 1870, pp. 67–68 ("Tavoy, Tenasserim Provinces . . . Burma . . . Siam . . . Andaman Islands"; type specimen from Toungoo, *fide* Bowdler Sharpe, Catalogue of the birds in the British Museum, vol. 17, 1892, p. 105).

Pelargopsis gurial burmanica, GYLDENSTOLPE, Kungl. Svenska Vet.-Akad. Handl., 1913, p. 54 (Den Chai); 1916, p. 114 (Chiang Rai, Pha Kho, Pak Ta); Journ. Nat Hist. Soc. Siam, 1915, p. 231 (listed); Ibis, 1920, p. 590 ("Siam proper").

Ramphalcyon capensis burmanica, DEIGNAN, Journ. Siam Soc. Nat. Hist. Suppl., 1931, p. 162 (Chiang Mai); 1936, pp. 92, 133 (Chiang Mai, Mae Ping river north of the Rapids).—RILEY, U. S. Nat. Mus. Bull. 172, 1938, p. 174 (Mae Khan).

Eisenhofer sent to Hannover a male taken at Pang Pui, April 21, 1912, and to Stockholm an unsexed, undated specimen from Khun Tan. I took examples at Chiang Mai, Ban Mae Klang, Ban Sop Mae Chaem, Ban Mae Wan, and at the foot of Doi Mae Kong Ka. In April and May, 1931, I observed it on Doi Ang Ka to 2,000 feet. In the neighborhood of Chiang Mai it was wholly absent during the driest season (March 25–June 29), uncommon and local during the rest of the year.

Gyldenstolpe took a specimen in dry forest (Den Chai, February 15, 1912), but I have observed this large and heavy kingfisher only in the immediate vicinity of water, whether this be a bamboo-shaded lagoon, a rushing stream of the lower hills, or a broad and placid river. It requires considerable depth of water and a favorite perch from which to plunge upon its prey is a branch which shades an undercut riverbank. It is a shy species and avoids exposed positions, and it would be more often overlooked were it not for the loud, harsh cries that it utters when startled.

Gyldenstolpe notes that one of his specimens had the irides brown; the bill red, tipped dusky brown; the feet and toes brick red.

This is a large kingfisher with a massive bill. It has the upper half of the head brownish gray; a broad nuchal collar and the entire underparts ochraceous; the center of the back, the rump, and some of the upper tail coverts shining turquoise blue; the remaining upperparts deep blue.

HALCYON COROMANDA COROMANDA (Latham)

INDIAN RUFOUS KINGFISHER

[*Alcedo*] *coromanda* LATHAM, Index ornithologicus, vol. 1, 1790, p. 252 ("in Coromandela," *ex* Sonnerat; *vide* Whistler and Kinnear, Journ. Bombay Nat. Hist. Soc., vol. 37, 1935, p. 763).

Callialcyon lilacina, GYLDENSTOLPE, Journ. Nat. Hist. Soc. Siam, 1915, p. 231 (listed).

Halcyon coromanda coromanda, GYLDENSTOLPE, Kungl. Svenska Vet.-Akad. Handl., 1916, p. 116 (Khun Tan); Ibis, 1920, p. 588 (Khun Tan).

Eisenhofer sent to Stockholm an undated male from Khun Tan and Gyldenstolpe, at the same locality, took a female, April 28, 1914; the bird is otherwise unknown from the northern provinces, where it is probably very rare.

Gyldenstolpe observes that it is a shy and retiring species, haunting creeks and small rivers, the banks of which are densely overgrown with evergreen forest or scrub.

The female had the irides brown; the bill, feet, and toes brick red.

The adult has the center of the lower back and rump opalescent white, tinged with pale blue; the remaining upperparts chestnut-rufous, everywhere more or less glossed with violet; the underparts light orange-rufous, more or less albescent on chin, throat, and center of abdomen.

HALCYON SMYRNENSIS PERPULCHRA von Madarász

MALAYAN WHITE-BREASTED KINGFISHER

Halcyon perpulchra VON MADARÁSZ, Ann. Hist.-Nat. Mus. Nat. Hungarici, vol. 2, 1904, pp. 85–86 (Singapore Island).

Halcyon smyrnensis fusca, GYLDENSTOLPE, Journ. Nat. Hist. Soc. Siam, 1915, p. 231 (listed); Ibis, 1920, p. 589 ("Throughout the whole country").—DE SCHAUENSEE, Proc. Acad. Nat Sci. Philadelphia, 1928, p. 572 (Chiang Mai); 1929, p. 573 (Chiang Mai); 1934, p. 262 (Chiang Mai).—DEIGNAN, Journ. Siam Soc. Nat. Hist. Suppl., 1931, p. 162 (Chiang Mai); 1936, pp. 92, 133 (Chiang Mai, Mae Ping river north of the Gorges).—RILEY, U. S. Nat. Mus. Bull. 172, 1938, p. 176 (Mae Suya valley).

With the exception of *Alcedo a. bengalensis*, this is the commonest and most generally distributed kingfisher of our area; specimens have been taken at numerous localities in Mae Hong Son, Chiang Mai, Chiang Rai, and Nan, and the bird is certain to occur in the remaining provinces. On Doi Suthep it follows the larger streams up the slopes for only a few hundred feet, but on Doi Ang Ka it is found as high as 4,400 feet in the deforested valley below Pha Mon. At Chiang Mai it was the only member of its family observed in every month of the year, but its numbers were much decreased in April and May.

This species is almost as common in the more open *pa daeng* and over dry fields as it is in the neighborhood of water, and it is constantly to be seen perched upon fences and telegraph poles beside the public ways. The loud, cackling call is a familiar sound in the environs of our towns; it is usually delivered while the bird rests upon a dead branch near the top of some high tree, but I have also heard it uttered by individuals in flight at a great altitude.

I have a very young juvenile from Phu Het, June 8, and Eisenhofer took a similar bird at Khun Tan, June 10. Older juveniles have been collected at Chiang Mai, July 6 and August 10.

My most worn example was taken August 13, while the one in freshest plumage was collected January 21. All specimens shot between September 26 and November 5 are in molt.

Nonbreeding adults had the irides brown; the bill deep red, purplish brown at the tip and along the edges of the maxilla; the interior of the mouth orange; the tarsi brownish red in front, coral-red behind; the toes brownish red; the soles coral-red; the claws black.

The adult has the crown, nape, and sides of the head chocolate-brown; the lesser wing coverts chocolate-brown, the median ones black; the rest of the wing blue or greenish blue, with a white bar visible when the wing is outspread; the center of the back, the rump, and the upper tail coverts shining blue; the remaining upperparts blue or greenish blue; the chin, throat, center of breast and upper abdomen white; the remaining underparts chocolate-brown. The immature is similar but has very narrow dark edgings to the white feathers of the breast.

Whistler and Kinnear have shown (Journ. Bombay Nat. Hist. Soc., vol. 37, 1935, pp. 761–762) that the name *fusca* must be restricted to the birds of Ceylon and the western side of the Madras Presidency in the rain-area from Coorg to Cape Comorin. They believe that the white-breasted kingfishers of all other parts of India, Burma, and the countries farther east, although alike in color, may be divisible on size into a northern and a southern race. For such races, the names *fokiensis* (Fuhkien) and *perpulchra* (Singapore) are respectively available, but so great is the variation in size in any given locality that it seems improbable that both forms can be maintained. In any case, northern Thai birds, with wing length 117–120 mm., cannot be separated from a Malayan series with wing length 115–122 mm. (one specimen from Singapore, 117 mm.).

HALCYON PILEATA (Boddaert)

BLACK-CAPPED KINGFISHER

Alcedo pileata BODDAERT, Table des planches enluminéez d'histoire naturelle, 1783, p. 41 (China, *ex* D'Aubenton, pl. 673).

Halcyon pileata, GYLDENSTOLPE, Kungl. Svenska Vet.-Akad. Handl., 1913, p. 55 (Mae Raem river); Journ. Nat. Hist. Soc. Siam, 1915, p. 231 (listed); Ibis, 1920, p. 589 ("Throughout Siam").

The black-capped kingfisher, so common and familiar a bird in Bangkok, is, in the northern provinces, a rare and local species. Eisenhofer sent to Hannover a specimen taken at Pha Hing, April 26, 1912, and to Stockholm seven collected in 1914 at Khun Tan. Gyldenstolpe took a single example on the Mae Raem, March 11, 1912. At Chiang Mai I have seen it only twice, October 8 and 23, 1936; the bird of the latter date was collected. I have also found it on the Mae Ping below Muang Chiang Dao, on a stream between Chiang Mai and Wiang Pa Pao, and in the Mae Yom basin a few miles northwest of Ban Rong Kwang.

In the North, this beautiful bird avoids the haunts of man and may be expected to occur only in the wildest places. With the exception

583136—45——14

of the two wandering individuals recorded from Chiang Mai, I have observed it only along swift, clear streams that flowed through gorges or dense forest. It is shy and difficult to collect.

One of my specimens had the irides brown; the bill, feet, and toes coral-red; the claws black.

The adult has the crown, nape, and sides of the head black; a broad collar on the hindneck white or buffy white; the remaining upperparts deep shining blue, brighter on the lower back and rump; the basal half of the wing black, the rest deep shining blue with a white band across the primaries; the chin and throat white, changing gradually to rufous-buff on the remaining underparts (including the under wing coverts). The immature is similar but has very narrow dark edgings to the feathers of the breast.

LACEDO PULCHELLA AMABILIS (Hume)

BURMESE BANDED KINGFISHER

Carcineutes amabilis HUME, Stray Feathers, vol. 1, 1873, pp. 474–475 ("the eastern Pegu Hills in the latitude of Thayetmyo").

Carcineutes pulchellus, GYLDENSTOLPE, Journ. Nat. Hist. Soc. Siam, 1915, p. 231 (listed); Kungl. Svenska Vet.-Akad. Handl., 1916, p. 115 (Pha Kho, Huai Pu); Ibis, 1920, p. 588 ("Throughout the whole country").

Lacedo pulchellus amabilis, DE SCHAUENSEE, Proc. Acad. Nat. Sci. Philadelphia, 1934, p. 262 (Doi Suthep).—DEIGNAN, Journ. Siam Soc. Nat. Hist. Suppl., 1936, p. 93 (Doi Suthep).

In the North, the banded kingfisher is an uncommon but generally distributed species. At Huai Pu, Eisenhofer took one female, May 22, 1912 (Stockholm), another May 31, 1912 (Hannover); at Khun Tan, an adult female, June 9, 1913, and four others without dates, including two juvenile males (Stockholm). On Doi Suthep, where it has been taken a number of times, it is found between 2,000 and 3,800 feet. I collected an adult male at Ban Muang Sum, December 25, 1936; this is probably the most northern locality at which the species has been taken, but it occurs also in Kengtung State, where I have once seen it.

Gyldenstolpe's specimens were shot in thick bamboo jungle, at some distance from running water, and the bird observed by me in Kengtung was in a similar situation. The example from Ban Muang Sum was on a low hill covered with dry, open pine forest. On Doi Suthep it lived in dense evergreen or mixed evergreen and bamboo and, while never far from some stream on that well-watered mountain, was obviously a dry-land species. My specimens had fed upon grasshoppers and other insects and, in one case, a lizard.

Three males had the irides gray; the eyelids pale orange, edged coral-red; the bill and interior of the mouth coral-red; the feet and toes dull yellow; the claws dark brown. A female differed only in having the irides brownish gray; the feet and toes dull brownish yellow.

The male has the forepart of the crown and the sides of head and neck rufous-chestnut, this color sometimes continued as a narrow band across the nape; the rest of the crown and nape bright shining violet-blue, with black and white bases of the feathers showing through here and there; the remaining upperparts barred black, white, and turquoise blue; the underparts white, more or less deeply suffused with pale rufous on the breast, upper abdomen, and flanks. The female differs in having the entire upperparts barred black and rufous; the entire underparts white, with narrow V-shaped black bars on the feathers of breast and flanks.

While *amabilis* cannot be distinguished from *pulchella* by color characters, the two forms can unquestionably be separated by the difference in their respective tail lengths, as has been pointed out by de Schauensee (1934). In the material before me, the tails of 9 specimens from localities south of the Isthmus of Kra measure 63–72 mm.; of 11 from more northern districts, 73–83 mm. (The type specimens of *amabilis* have the tail lengths 83.82 and 76.20 mm.)

Peguan birds are said to have the feet and toes "greenish-brown" (Oates) or "dull pale green" (Hume and Davison); specimens from Thailand and Malaya have these parts dull yellow or ochraceous. If the two populations consistently differ in this particular, a new name must be found for the birds of Thailand north of the Isthmus.

Family MEROPIDAE

MEROPS SUPERCILIOSUS PHILIPPINUS Linnaeus

Malaysian Brown-breasted Bee-eater

[*Merops*] *philippinus* Linnaeus, Systema naturae, ed. 12, vol. 1, 1766, *errata* [omitted from p. 183] ("in Philippinis").

Merops superciliosus philippinus, Gyldenstolpe, Kungl. Svenska Vet.-Akad. Handl., 1916, p. 110 (Chiang Rai).

Merops superciliosus javanicus, Deignan, Journ. Siam Soc. Nat. Hist. Suppl., 1931, p. 161 (Chiang Mai); 1936, p. 93 (Chiang Mai).

In Stockholm are two specimens collected by Gyldenstolpe at Chiang Rai, August 1 and 2, 1914, and another taken by Eisenhofer at Khun Tan sometime during the same year. At Chiang Mai this bird was locally common between March 5 (1931) and September 5 (1930) and wholly absent at other seasons; it probably occurs nowhere in our provinces during the cold weather.

Upon its first arrival at Chiang Mai, the brown-breasted bee-eater may be seen in small, loose bands at the few places in the ricefields that retain water, resting between flights upon the bunds or neighboring clumps of bamboo. Somewhat later it is found along the river above the city in the vicinity of high earthen banks, where, I suspect, it might be discovered breeding in April and May. From July to September it is common on the great marshes between Chiang Mai and Lamphun. Its notes and manner of feeding are much like those of the following species.

A nonbreeding adult male, taken June 27, had the irides crimson; the bill black; the feet and toes purplish brown; the claws black.

This is a comparatively large bee-eater, with much elongated and narrowed central rectrices. It has the upper parts green, in certain lights glossed with copper, changing to bright blue on the secondaries, scapulars, rump, upper tail coverts, and tail; a black bar through the eye, bordered below by a streak of light blue; the chin and upper throat yellow; the lower throat and uppermost breast rufous-chestnut, gradually changing to copper-glossed green on the lower breast and abdomen, which color in turn passes into light blue on the under tail coverts; the under wing coverts buff.

MEROPS ORIENTALIS BIRMANUS Neumann

BURMESE GREEN BEE-EATER

Merops viridis birmanus NEUMANN, Orn. Monatsb., vol. 18, 1910, p. 80 (Myingyan, Upper Burma).

Merops orientalis birmanus, GYLDENSTOLPE, Kungl. Svenska Vet.-Akad. Handl. 1913, p. 52 (Den Chai); 1916, p. 110 (Khun Tan); Journ. Nat. Hist. Soc. Siam, 1915, p. 231 (listed).—DE SCHAUENSEE, Proc. Acad. Nat. Sci. Philadelphia, 1929, p. 571 (Chiang Mai); 1934, p. 260 (Chiang Mai, Doi Chiang Dao).—DEIGNAN, Journ. Siam Soc. Nat. Hist. Suppl., 1931, p. 161 (Chiang Mai); 1936, p. 93 (Chiang Mai, Doi Suthep).—RILEY, U. S. Nat. Mus. Bull. 172, 1938, p. 180 (Chom Thong, Ban Mae Klang, Chiang Dao).—GREENWAY, Bull. Mus. Comp. Zool., 1940, p. 192 (Chiang Mai, Chiang Dao).

Merops lamark birmanus, GYLDENSTOLPE, Ibis, 1920, p. 587 (Den Chai, Khun Tan).

This small bee-eater is one of the commonest birds of the lowlands in all parts of our provinces; as a straggler it occurs rarely in open country at higher altitudes: De Schauensee took specimens at 4,000 feet on Doi Chiang Dao (January), and I recorded it once at the summit of Doi Suthep (February), although, on the latter mountain at least, it was found normally only to 1,800 feet along the telephone wires.

Every resident of Thailand must be familiar with this beautiful little bird, which may be seen almost anywhere in open, cultivated country, perching on wires and fences along the highways, on the bunds of the ricefields, and even upon the net posts of the tennis court in one's garden. It is a sociable species, and great numbers sometimes congregate at a suitable feeding ground, such as a pond or stream. When a passing insect is sighted, a bird will leave its perch and, after a few wing beats and a snap of the bill, glide in a wide circle back to the same resting place, all the while uttering a musical, trilling note.

De Schauensee has remarked (1929) that he found this species numerous at Chiang Mai in December but practically absent in March and April. With the advance of the dry season it restricts itself more and more to the river shores and other wet areas, but the true reason for its apparent rarity in April and May is the fact that virtually the whole of the local population is then gregariously breeding in holes in the high banks of the Mae Ping some miles above Chiang Mai. In June and July, when the fields are again filled with water, bee-eaters occur everywhere. Late in October and early in November the species is sometimes extraordinarily abundant on the marshes, owing to the temporary presence of enormous flocks of what are probably true migrants from farther north; I have no record of a corresponding return movement during the dry months of spring.

Perhaps because of underground nesting, the plumage, especially the elongated central rectrices and the feathers of crown and nape, becomes excessively worn and bleached; the green portions tend to become verditer blue, the rufous pale brownish. Examples taken in July and August are in molt.

I find no mention in literature of the not infrequent occurrence of yellow-throated birds in the summer months. This variation seems to be rather common among juveniles but is seen also in certain very worn adults.

Mature birds of either sex had the irides crimson; the bill black; the feet and toes purplish brown, slaty brown, or brownish black; the claws black. A juvenile had the irides brown; the bill black; the feet flesh color; the toes gray; the soles whitish; the claws slaty black.

The adult in fresh plumage has the upperparts bright green, in certain lights glossed with copper, this latter color very strong on crown and nape; the concealed portions of the remiges rufous (very conspicuous in flight); a black line through the eye, edged below by a streak of verditer blue; a narrow black gorget between the throat and breast; the underparts otherwise copper-glossed green, bluer on the throat, paler on the belly and under tail coverts, the light rufous bases of the feathers showing through in places, especially on the flanks. The immature is similar but is duller everywhere and lacks the elongated central rectrices.

MEROPS LESCHENAULTI LESCHENAULTI Vieillot

INDIAN BAY-HEADED BEE-EATER

Merops Leschenaulti VIEILLOT, Nouveau dictionnaire d'histoire naturelle, nouv. éd., vol. 14, 1817, pp. 17–18 (Java, *ex* Levaillant, error; type locality corrected to Ceylon, by Whistler and Kinnear, Journ. Bombay Nat. Hist. Soc., vol. 37, 1935, p. 758).

Melittophagus swinhoii, GYLDENSTOLPE, Kungl. Svenska Vet.-Akad. Handl., 1913, p. 53 (Mae Yom river near Phrae).

Melittophagus swinhoei, GYLDENSTOLPE, Journ. Nat. Hist. Soc. Siam, 1915, p. 231 (listed).

Melittophagus leschenaulti swinhoei, GYLDENSTOLPE, Kungl. Svenska Vet.-Akad. Handl., 1916, p. 110 (Mae Rua, Ban Mae Na); Ibis, 1920, p. 587 ("Throughout the whole country").

Melittophagus erythrocephalus erythrocephalus, DEIGNAN, Journ. Siam Soc. Nat. Hist. Suppl., 1931, p. 161 (Doi Suthep).—CHASEN and BODEN KLOSS, Journ. Siam Soc. Nat. Hist. Suppl. 1932, p. 234 (Doi Suthep).—DE SCHAUENSEE, Proc. Acad. Nat. Sci. Philadelphia, 1934, p. 261 (Doi Suthep).—RILEY, U. S. Nat. Mus. Bull. 172, 1938, p. 183 (Mae Sariang).

Merops leschenaulti leschenaulti, DEIGNAN, Journ. Siam Soc. Nat. Hist. Suppl., 1936, p. 93 (Doi Suthep).

The bay-headed bee-eater has been found in all parts of the northern provinces. Eisenhofer sent to Stockholm three undated specimens from Khun Tan. The example recorded without definite locality by Gyldenstolpe in 1916 was taken at Pak Pan. I have it from Thattafang, near Chiang Mai, Ban Pha Khwang, and Muang Fang.

In 1936 (*loc. cit.*) I commented on the curious status of the present form in the Chiang Mai district in the following words: "This species has the most limited range of any bird of regular occurrence here. Two or three pairs occur at 5,500 feet from 28 February (1933) to 10 May (1930), breeding at this place in April. During their stay they confine themselves to an open space a few hundred feet long and less than one hundred wide, bordered by evergreen jungle, which they do not enter. A single specimen taken at 4,600 feet in the spring of 1931 (Aagaard) constitutes the only exceptional record." To these remarks may now be added that I found the bird rather common between San Sai Luang and Ban Pa Muat, March 7, 1936, and saw a single individual in the same neighborhood, March 19 of the same year. Finally, I met with one or two at 2,000 feet on Doi Suthep, October 10, 1936.

This bee-eater is not likely to be seen in cultivated and densely inhabited areas; it prefers broken country clothed with open deciduous forest and, perhaps for this reason, seems to be more common in Nan Province than elsewhere, at least during the spring months. Its favorite perch is on a dead branch at the top of some high tree, but otherwise its behavior is much like that of the preceding forms.

This small species never has the central rectrices elongated. The adult has the crown, sides of head, nape, and upper back chestnut-rufous; the center of the lower back and the rump pale blue, more greenish on the upper tail coverts; the remaining upperparts deep green; the chin and throat pale yellow, separated from the breast by a chestnut-rufous gorget, edged below first by black, then by yellow; the remaining underparts pale green, more bluish on the abdomen and under tail coverts; the under wing coverts and undersurface of the remiges light rufous. The green portions of the plumage have the coppery gloss characteristic of the group. An immature male from Muang Fang (July 20) differs in having all the colors rather paler and the rufous of the upperparts restricted to the head and nape but heavily washed with deep green on the forehead and the center of the crown.

NYCTIORNIS ATHERTONI (Jardine and Selby)

BLUE-BEARDED BEE-EATER

Merops Athertoni JARDINE and SELBY, Illustrations of ornithology, ser. 1, vol. 2, pt. 4, 1828, pl. 58 and text (India; type locality restricted to Cachar, by Stuart Baker, Journ. Bombay Nat. Hist. Soc., vol. 28, 1922, p. 314; corrected to Bangalore, Mysore, South India, by Kinnear, Ibis, 1925, p. 751).

Nyctiornis athertoni, GYLDENSTOLPE, Kungl. Svenska Vet.-Akad. Handl., 1913, p. 53 (Ban Huai Hom); 1916, p. 111 (Doi Pha Sakaeng, Khun Tan); Journ. Nat. Hist. Soc. Siam, 1915, p. 231 (listed); Ibis, 1920, p. 588 ("Throughout Siam proper").—DE SCHAUENSEE, Proc. Acad. Nat. Sci. Philadelphia, 1929, p. 572 (Doi Suthep).

Alcemerops athertoni, DEIGNAN, Journ. Siam Soc. Nat. Hist. Suppl., 1931, p. 161 (Doi Suthep, Chiang Mai); 1936, p. 93 (Doi Suthep, Chiang Mai).—DE SCHAUENSEE, Proc. Acad. Nat. Sci. Philadelphia, 1934, p. 261 (Doi Suthep, Doi Chiang Dao).—RILEY, U. S. Nat. Mus. Bull. 172, 1938, p. 184 (Doi Hua Mot, Doi Khun Tan, "Doi Phra Chao" [= Doi Saket ?]).

This huge bee-eater is rather uncommon but generally distributed in the North. At Pha Hing Eisenhofer took a female, May 1, 1912 (Hannover), and a male, May 11 (Stockholm), and at Khun Tan five undated specimens (Stockholm). I have it from Doi San Pa Bong, Doi Suthep, Doi Chiang Dao, Ban Samoeng, and Thattafang, and found it common on Doi Ang Ka at 4,400 feet. Its presence anywhere seems to be governed by the development of tall and fairly open forest; thus, in one district it will be seen only on the mountains, but in another where there is lowland evergreen it will occur at quite low altitudes. In the vicinity of Chiang Mai I found it normally only on Doi Suthep from 2,800 to 5,500 feet, but recorded it several times between June 25 and August 1 on the plain; such wandering individuals may have been birds of the year.

The blue-bearded bee-eater is a more sluggish species than the smaller members of its family, and as it perches motionless on a branch at the top of some high tree it might be more often overlooked if it were not for its hoarse, croaking calls. The song is composed of a series of notes that sound like the syllable *kuk;* it begins slowly but finishes with a rapid rattling *kuk-kuk-kuk-kuk-kuk*, during which the bird points its bill at the sky and erects the elongated feathers of the throat. The stomachs of my specimens contained only Hymenoptera.

Breeding probably takes place during the hot weather; I have an example from Doi San Pa Bong, June 2, which, in its short bill, seems to be a bird of the year. All adults taken between August 6 and October 23 are in molt.

A male had the irides bright brown; the maxilla slaty black, the commissure edged transparent whitish at the base; the mandible slaty black, pale plumbeous on the basal half; the feet and toes olive-green, tinged purple; the claws purplish slate.

This is a huge bee-eater with the central rectrices not prolonged beyond the others. It has the entire upperparts bright green (with the usual coppery gloss), sometimes tinged with verditer blue on the crown; the sides of the head, throat, and neck bright green; the center of the throat shining light blue, mixed with darker blue, these feathers elongated and covering the center of the breast; the remaining underparts buffy yellow, heavily streaked with green; the undersurface of the wings and tail unmarked buffy yellow.

Family CORACIIDAE

CORACIAS BENGHALENSIS AFFINIS McClelland

Indo-Chinese Black-billed Roller

Coracias affinis McClelland, Proc. Zool. Soc. London, pt. 7, 1839 [=1840], p. 164 (Assam).

Coracias affinis, Gyldenstolpe, Kungl. Svenska Vet.-Akad. Handl., 1913, p. 51 (Pak Pan, "Vang Nun"); 1916, p. 117 (Khun Tan); Journ. Nat. Hist. Soc. Siam, 1915, p. 230 (listed); Ibis, 1920, p. 585 ("Throughout the whole country").—Riley, U. S. Nat. Mus. Bull. 172, 1938, p. 186 (Ban Nam Khian).

Coracias bengalensis affinis, de Schauensee, Proc. Acad. Nat. Sci. Philadelphia, 1929, p. 571 (15 km. north of Chiang Saen).

Coracias benghalensis affinis, Deignan, Journ. Siam Soc. Nat. Hist. Suppl., 1931, p. 161 (Chiang Mai); 1936, p. 94 (Chiang Mai).—de Schauensee, Proc. Acad. Nat. Sci. Philadelphia, 1934, p. 260 (Chiang Mai).

The black-billed roller is very common in settled districts throughout the northern lowlands. Eisenhofer sent to Stockholm eleven undated specimens from Khun Tan; to Hannover, examples from Pak Pan, Huai Pu, and Pha Hing, collected February 18, June 4, and May 12, 1912. I have taken it at Chiang Mai, Chom Thong, Wiang Pa Pao, and Ban Na Noi (Nan Province) and have observed it at numerous other localities.

The "blue jay" is a familiar species of the cultivated areas and the more open deciduous forest. It is often seen along traveled roads, perching upon low branches, fence posts, and telegraph wires, whence, with a gorgeous flashing of blue wings and tail, it sails into the air after passing prey or swoops to seize it on the ground. It is usually solitary or in pairs, but I have more than once seen a number gathered together at the edge of a jungle grass fire, catching insects as they escaped the flames. One stomach I examined contained a large mantis and several small beetles.

During the breeding season (April and May) this species disappeared from its usual haunts about Chiang Mai, and I recorded it there only once in the month of May, although in June it again became as common as ever. I have a specimen from Na Noi, May 25, still in postnatal molt, and an older juvenile from Wiang Pa Pao, July 26.

An adult male, taken October 7, had the irides brown; the lores and orbital region dull yellow; the bill black; the feet and toes dull brownish yellow; the claws black. An adult female of August 11 had the irides brown; the eyelids edged with orange-yellow; the orbital skin dull yellow; the bill black; the interior of the mouth sulphur yellow, tinged greenish; the feet and toes yellowish brown; the claws black.

This roller has the crown blue-green; the nape, scapulars, and upper back dull brownish green; the lower back, rump, and upper tail coverts verditer blue, more or less washed with purple; the central rectrices dull bluish green, the others verditer blue with purplish-blue bases; the shoulder purplish blue, the rest of the wing verditer blue, crossed by a broad band of purplish blue; the sides of the head, the throat, breast, and upper abdomen violet-washed brown, the feathers of the throat with narrow, shining violet-blue central streaks; the remaining underparts verditer blue; the under wing coverts purplish blue.

EURYSTOMUS ORIENTALIS DEIGNANI Ripley

LAO RED-BILLED ROLLER

Eurystomus orientalis deignani RIPLEY, Proc. Biol. Soc. Washington, vol. 55, 1942, pp. 171–172 (Muang Ngop, Nan Province, North Thailand).

Eurystomus orientalis calonyx, GYLDENSTOLPE, Journ. Nat. Hist. Soc. Siam, 1915, p. 230 (listed); Kungl. Svenska Vet.-Akad. Handl., 1916, p. 118 (Pha Kho).

Eurystomus orientalis orientalis [*partim*], GYLDENSTOLPE, Ibis, 1920, p. 585 ("Throughout the whole country" [*partim*]).

Eurystomus orientalis calonyx [*partim*], GYLDENSTOLPE, Ibis, 1920, p. 585 (Pha Kho.)

East of the Khun Tan range the red-billed roller is a common and conspicuous bird of the wilder districts. Eisenhofer took a male at Huai Pu, June 5, 1912 (Hannover) and seven examples at Khun Tan in 1914 (Stockholm). I have specimens from Wiang Pa Pao, Ban Huai Som, and Muang Ngop and have found it everywhere along the highway between Rong Kwang and Bun Yun. West of the Khun Tan range it is rare and of uncertain status: on the lower slopes of

Doi Suthep I have twice in March observed pairs of birds which were probably of this species but were at too great a distance for satisfactory identification; I saw a pair at Bang Choeng Doi, April 1, 1929, and another at Ban Mae Klang, early in April 1931; finally, Fejos sent to Stockholm a pair taken at the foot of Doi Chiang Dao, April 16, 1938. It is probable that some of these records should be listed under *E. o. abundus*, a form not yet definitely known from our area.

This roller inhabits the hot, dry *pa daeng* of the lower hills and burnt-over districts where tall, dead trees rise above the usurping scrub. Here the birds (always in pairs) rest quietly high above the ground, occasionally flying out to snatch some passing insect, but then returning to the same perch. During the breeding season, however, they become much more active; in the month of April may be witnessed a beautiful aerial courtship, in the course of which the pair rise high into the sky and swoop and circle about each other, all the while uttering a grunting *ugh-ugh-ugh*.

A female with enlarged gonads was taken at Ban Huai Som, March 30, and a juvenile at Wiang Pa Pao, July 25.

Adults collected by Gyldenstolpe had the irides brown; the bill brick red, the maxilla tipped black; the feet and toes pale coral red. My juvenile specimen had the bill black.

Against the sky this bird appears black with a red bill and a silvery circular patch in the outspread wing. The adult has the head and nape blackish brown, changing gradually to the dark bluish green of the remaining upperparts; the tail black, more or less suffused, especially beneath, with purplish blue; the wing with a large area of light blue near the center and the apical third black; the throat purplish blue, the feathers with narrow, shining violet-blue central streaks; the remaining underparts bluish green. The juvenile is similar but has the throat colored like the rest of the underparts and the feathers of the breast narrowly edged paler.

Family UPUPIDAE

UPUPA EPOPS SATURATA Lönnberg

MONGOLIAN HOOPOE

Upupa epops saturata LÖNNBERG, Ark. för Zool., vol. 5, No. 9, 1909, pp. 29–30 (Kyakhta, Buryat Mongol Republic, U.S.S.R.).

The northern race of the hoopoe seems to be a very rare winter visitor to Thailand, and the only record for our provinces is based upon a female acquired by me from a small boy at Chiang Mai, November 9, 1936. The bird was so badly mutilated that only the head and neck were suitable for preservation, but these are fortunately the parts that show the main subspecific characters.

The present form is distinguished from our resident hoopoe by having the general color more earthy brown, much less suffused with rufous above and vinaceous below, and by having the longer posterior feathers of the crest subterminally marked with white.

UPUPA EPOPS LONGIROSTRIS Jerdon

BURMESE HOOPOE

U[pupa] longirostris JERDON, Birds of India, vol. 1, 1862, p. 393 (Burma; type locality restricted to Rangoon, by Stuart Baker, Fauna of British India, Birds, ed. 2, vol. 4, 1927, p. 312).

Upupa epops indica, GYLDENSTOLPE, Kungl. Svenska Vet.-Akad. Handl., 1913, p. 56 (Den Chai, Pak Pan); Journ. Nat. Hist. Soc. Siam, 1915, p. 232 (listed).

Upupa epops longirostris, GYLDENSTOLPE, Kungl. Svenska Vet.-Akad. Handl., 1916, p. 111 (Khun Tan); Ibis, 1920, p. 585 ("Throughout the whole country").—DE SCHAUENSEE, Proc. Acad. Nat. Sci. Philadelphia, 1929, p. 574 (Chiang Rai, Chiang Mai, Doi Suthep); 1934, p. 264 (Doi Chiang Dao, Doi Suthep, Chiang Mai).—DEIGNAN, Journ. Siam Soc. Nat. Hist. Suppl., 1931, p. 162 (Chiang Mai, Doi Suthep); 1936, p. 94 (Chiang Mai, Doi Suthep).—RILEY, U. S. Nat. Mus. Bull. 172, 1938, p. 189 (Chiang Dao, Muang Pai, Mae Hong Son).

The Burmese hoopoe is a locally common permanent resident throughout the North. Eisenhofer sent to Hannover a female taken at Den Chai, February 10, 1912, and to Stockholm eight undated specimens from Khun Tan. In addition to localities listed above, I have it from Doi Ang Ka, Ban Mae Klang, Chom Thong, Doi Langka, Wiang Pa Pao, Muang Fang, Ban Mae Mao, and Chiang Saen Kao. It is chiefly a bird of the plains but is found also on the mountains at suitable places: On Doi Ang Ka it occurs at 4,200 feet (breeding); on Doi Chiang Dao it has been collected at 4,700 and 5,000 feet; for Doi Suthep there are three records at 2,000, 2,600, and 4,500 feet (stragglers).

The wastelands devoted to cremations and the shrub-grown grassy slopes about the ruined *phrachedi* dotting the fields are the favorite haunts of the hoopoe, just as they are of the allied nightjar (*C. a. monticolus*), and at such places the two species are usually found together. The hoopoe may also be seen in parklike glades of the deciduous forest and frequently on the lawns of town gardens. When flushed it travels only a short distance, with low and dipping flight, to drop again to the ground behind some nearby bush. Ordinarily the beautiful crest is kept folded and makes a continuous arc with the long, curved bill, out at the moment of alighting and when the bird is alarmed it is expanded like a fan, as it is also during delivery of the song—an accelerated rendition of the syllable *hoop*, from which the English name is derived. Stomachs I examined contained only insects.

A male taken at Chiang Mai, February 25, had the gonads slightly enlarged. I saw very young birds on Doi Ang Ka, April 29, 1931, and at Chiang Mai, April 29, 1935, and have juveniles from Muang Fang, July 20, and Wiang Pa Pao, August 4.

Adults had the irides dark brown; the eyelids plumbeous; the bill black, bluish plumbeous or fleshy plumbeous at the base of mandible; the feet and toes plumbeous, the soles tinged yellowish; the claws dark plumbeous or horny black. A juvenile male had the irides dull brownish gray; the eyelids dark plumbeous; the bill black, dusky flesh at the base of the mandible; the rictus dead white; the interior of the mouth fleshy violet; the feet and toes dark slaty; the claws brownish black.

This is a broad-winged, short-legged, rather elongated bird with a thin, sickle-shaped bill and a large, flabelliform crest. It has the head, black-tipped crest feathers, and nape light rufous; the upper back earthy brown, suffused with rufous; the middle back, scapulars, and wings broadly banded black and buffy white; the rump pure white; the tail black, with a narrow white cross bar at the middle when folded, a white inverted V when spread; the throat, breast, and upper abdomen rufous-vinaceous; the remaining underparts white, with long black streaks on the flanks and lower belly; the under wing coverts rufous-vinaceous.

Family BUCEROTIDAE

DICHOCEROS BICORNIS CAVATUS (Shaw)

INDIAN CONCAVE-CASQUED HORNBILL

Buceros cavatus SHAW, General zoology, vol. 8, pt. 1, 1812, pp. 18–19 ("supposed to be a native of the Philippine isles," error; type locality corrected to India, by Stuart Baker, Fauna of British India, Birds, ed. 2, vol. 7, 1930, p. 356; here restricted to Travancore).

Dichoceros bicornis, GYLDENSTOLPE, Kungl. Svenska Vet.-Akad. Handl., 1913, p. 55 (Ban Huai Hom, Khao Phlung); 1916, p. 112 (Pha Kho, Khun Tan); Journ. Nat. Hist. Soc. Siam, 1915, p. 231 (listed); Ibis, 1920, p. 586 ("Throughout the whole country").—DE SCHAUENSEE, Proc. Acad. Nat. Sci. Philadelphia, 1928, p. 572 (Doi Suthep); 1929, p. 574 (Doi Suthep); 1934, p. 263 (Khun Tan, Doi Suthep).—DEIGNAN, Journ. Siam Soc. Nat. Hist. Suppl., 1931, p. 162 (Doi Suthep); 1936, p. 94 (Chiang Mai, Doi Suthep).

The giant hornbill is a common resident of primeval evergreen forest in every part of our area, from the plains to about 5,500 feet. The earliest northern specimen is a female in Hannover, taken by Eisenhofer in 1910 "between Utaradit & N. Lampang." To Stockholm the same collector sent three undated skins from Khun Tan, and Fejos a female from Doi Chiang Dao, April 19, 1938. On Doi Suthep it occurred at all seasons in the heavy jungle between 3,300 and 4,600 feet, less commonly up to 5,000 feet. The only record of its visiting the Chiang Mai plain, where the vegetation is unsuitable, is September 16, 1935, when one was collected from a small flock feeding on ripe figs, but I have several times observed parties flying over the city so high as to be almost invisible to the naked eye.

This great bird is well known to the northern people and is the subject of many superstitions, some of which I recounted in 1931. The belief that the killing of one of a pair will cause the death of the other is quite true during the breeding season, when the female is walled up in the nesting hole and wholly dependent upon the male for food.

From some mountain summit one may often hear the loud barking calls of this species, especially toward evening, and looking down the slopes see a pair or small flock traveling above the forest-canopy with alternate sailing and flapping of wings. Each downward beat is accompanied by a chuffing sound (like that of a steam locomotive getting under way), which carries for an immense distance.

At about 5,000 feet on Doi Ang Ka in April I discovered a pair breeding in a gigantic tree; the cavity was perhaps 75 feet above the ground. A juvenile was taken at Doi Mon Khwam Long, July 18. An adult male of September 16 is molting remiges and rectrices.

Just at the base and on top of the central pair of tail feathers is a large, exposed gland, densely covered with short, gray-brown pilose feathers. From this gland exudes a bright yellow oil, with which, in living adults, the bill, foreneck, and central wing bar (but not the other white portions of the plumage) are liberally stained. I have myself seen a bird rub its bill against the gland and then smear the oil along the outspread wing. In death the brilliant color soon fades to buff or wholly disappears.

An adult male had the irides red; the orbital skin black; the casque deep yellow, orange on top, black behind and on the sides near the front; the basal three-fourths of the culmen black; the maxilla yellow, red at the tip, black at the extreme base; the mandible white, black at the base; the interior of the mouth black, orange near the tip; the feet and toes olive-slate; the soles brown; the claws slate.

A juvenile male with the casque represented merely by a soft swelling had the irides brown; the lower eyelid livid flesh; the upper eyelid and the orbital skin dark slate; the bare skin of the throat livid purple; the culmen red-orange, lighter at the tip; an ill-defined sagittate mark from the nares with its point on the culmen slaty brown, blacker in the narial region, this mark edged orange-red below; between the culmen and the nares a whitish area; the maxilla otherwise with the apical half bright yellow, then whitish, and the basal fifth blackish, the edges of the commissure blackish on the basal two-thirds; the mandible with the tip light orange, otherwise light gray-green, more plumbeous toward the base, a streak running lengthwise below bright orange, the edges of the commissure orange, paler toward the base and with the basal fifth black; the interior of the mouth gray-green, with an orange median ridge on both floor and roof; the bare skin behind the tibiae with the upper half pink, the lower half greenish blue; the tarsi green behind, greenish yellow in front; the toes blackish brown; the soles light brown; the claws black.

This is an enormous bird with a large, heavy, curved bill (surmounted in the adult by a broad bifid casque), broad wings, and a relatively long tail. It has the face and throat black; the neck all white; the back and scapulars black; the upper tail coverts and tail white, the latter with a broad black subterminal band; the wings black with a broad white band near the center and another along the hinder edge; the breast and upper abdomen black; the remaining underparts white. As has been mentioned above, some of the white areas are stained bright yellow in life.

Specimens from Sumatra, Malaya, and all Thailand show a gradual increase in length of wing from south to north, and I believe that subspecies based upon size of nonmolting *adults* may properly be recognized.

Only Hume (Stray Feathers, vol. 4, 1876, pp. 384–387) seems to have brought together examples from South India, the Himalayas, and Malaysia, and, while he placed all under one name, he clearly indicated that Himalayan birds are largest, Malayan smallest, and those of Travancore intermediate. Specimens from Thailand north of the Isthmus are likewise intermediate and must be called by whatever name is applied to the population of Travancore.

I accept Sumatra as type locality of the nominate race (see Chasen, Handlist of Malaysian Birds, 1935, p. 105, footnote). This leaves *cavatus* of Shaw as the earliest available name for a non-Malaysian subspecies, with type locality by designation "India," here further restricted to Travancore, as the part of its Indian range most likely to be the provenance of a specimen taken before 1812. This makes the name *cavatus* certainly applicable to the intermediates of Travancore and Thailand and leaves *homrai* of Hodgson for the Himalayan population, if they be considered large enough to justify recognition of yet a third race.

ANTHRACOCEROS CORONATUS LEUCOGASTER (Blyth)

TENASSERIMESE PIED HORNBILL

B[uceros] leucogaster BLYTH, Journ. Asiat. Soc. Bengal, vol. 10, 1841 [=1842], p. 922 (Tenasserim; type specimen "procured in the the vicinity of Maulmain," *fide* Blyth, *ibid.*, p. 917).

Anthracoceros albirostris, GYLDENSTOLPE, Kungl. Svenska Vet.-Akad. Handl., 1913, p. 55 (Ban Huai Hom, Mae Raem and Mae Song rivers); 1916, p. 112 (Pha Kho, Pang Hua Phong, Khun Tan); Journ. Nat. Hist. Soc. Siam, 1915, p. 232 (listed); Ibis, 1920, p. 586 ("Throughout the country").

Hydrocissa malabarica leucogastra, DEIGNAN, Journ. Siam Soc. Nat. Hist. Suppl., 1931, p. 162 (Doi Suthep); 1936, p. 94 (Chiang Mai, Doi Suthep).

Hydrocissa malabarica leucogaster, DE SCHAUENSEE, Proc. Acad. Nat. Sci. Philadelphia, 1934, p. 263 (Khun Tan, Doi Suthep).

The pied hornbill is rather common throughout the North, occurring in tall lowland evergreen and sometimes in quite open forest or even in extensive bamboo brakes. It is a bird of low elevations, seldom ascending the hills as high as 2,200 feet. In the dry jungle on the lower slopes of Doi Suthep I found it uncommon and present only from November to February, but it could usually be observed in the evergreen forest near Ban Pong, at the southern base of the mountain. In addition to the localities listed above, it is known from Huai Pu, where Eisenhofer took a male, May 22, 1912 (Hannover), and from Doi Ang Ka, where I found it from the vicinity of Ban Mae Klang up to 2,000 feet.

This small species is usually seen in flocks that travel rapidly from tree to tree, crossing open spaces one or two birds at a time. It flies, like the larger hornbills, with alternate flapping and sailing but, unlike them, with silent wings; on the other hand, it is a highly vocal bird, constantly uttering shrill cries, *cack-cack-cack-cack*, from which the vernacular name is derived.

The breeding season in our provinces is not certainly known, but I took a very young example, still in postnatal molt, at Ban Hai Huai Som, June 17. A female collected at Muang Fang, July 22, is in molt.

De Schauensee records that a female had the irides light brown; the orbital skin and the naked area at the base of the mandible bluish white; the bill ivory and black; the feet, toes, and claws black. Gyldenstolpe states that an adult had the feet and toes greenish yellow. In dried skins I find that the adult male has the entire bill ivory except for a broad, black transverse bar across the apical half of the casque; the adult female has the entire apical half of the casque and the apical half of the culmen black and the extreme base of the mandible black, preceded by a patch of dark red.

This genus has the casque long and high, sharp-edged and projecting in front. The adult of the present species has the chin, throat, neck, upper breast, and entire upperparts black, more or less highly glossed with green; the primaries (except the two outermost pairs) and the outer secondaries broadly tipped with white, so that the outspread wing is conspicuously margined behind with a white band; the rectrices (except the central pair) with the apical third white.

Judged from material I have seen, birds from more northern and eastern Indo-Chinese localities and also from Arakan have the innermost secondaries so long as wholly to conceal the longest primaries in the folded wing, while more southern examples have them much shorter than the longest primaries. I have not enough specimens to decide whether this difference is to be explained by individual or by geographical variation.

ACEROS UNDULATUS TICEHURSTI (Deignan)

NORTHERN WAVED HORNBILL

Rhyticeros undulatus ticehursti DEIGNAN, Auk, vol. 58, 1941, p. 397 (Huai Oi, 14 km. north of Ban Pak Li, Nan Province, North Thailand).

Rhytidoceros subruficollis, GYLDENSTOLPE, Kungl. Svenska Vet.-Akad. Handl., 1913, p. 56 (Mae Raem) ; Ibis, 1920, p. 587 (Mae Raem).

Rhytidoceros undulatus, GYLDENSTOLPE, Journ. Nat. Hist. Soc. Siam, 1915, p. 232 (listed) ; Kungl. Svenska Vet.-Akad. Handl., 1916, p. 113 (Pha Hing) ; Ibis, 1920, p. 587 (Pha Hing).

Rhyticeros sp., DE SCHAUENSEE, Proc. Acad. Nat. Sci. Philadelphia, 1934, p. 263 (Chiang Rai, Chiang Saen).

Rhyticeros undulatus, DEIGNAN, Journ. Siam Soc. Nat. Hist. Suppl., 1936, p. 94 (Doi Suthep).

The waved hornbill is a bird of the tall evergreen, from the plains to 5,500 feet. In the provinces east of the Khun Tan range it is common wherever the jungle is suitable; farther west it seems to be very rare. With the exception of an example mentioned by me in 1936, said to have been bred on Doi Suthep, my only record for that mountain was made November 7, 1936, when at least three (a male and two females) were observed at 5,500 feet, and, later in the same day, a flock of four (possibly the same individuals) were seen flying over the forest far below the summit.

This species, like *Dichoceros b. cavatus*, is usually found in small flocks, flying above the trees with noisy wing beats and gathering in some numbers wherever ripe fruit is plentiful. On Phu Kha, where it was the commonest of its family, what appeared to be always the same flock flew daily, early in the evening, over my camp, presumably resorting regularly to a particular roosting tree.

An old female, which lived for several months on a perch in my garden at Chiang Mai, began at dawn to utter loud, hoarse, double roars, with gular skin inflated and the head raised and lowered, and continued her cries until she was fed. Although she was blind in both eyes (probably from having been too much exposed to bright sunlight while in the possession of a preceding owner), any fruit given her was at once tossed into the air and swallowed as it fell into the gaping bill; I do not recall any occasion on which the object fell to the ground. Water was frequently proffered her, but she was never seen to accept it, apparently finding sufficient moisture in the juices of fruits.

A male from Ban Hai Hua Som, June 18, is in postnuptial molt.

The female referred to above had the irides with a broad, vermilion outer ring and a narrow, yellow inner ring; the orbital skin dull red; the bill and casque old ivory, dull olive at the extreme base, with the hollows of the corrugations stained dark brown; the gular skin bright blue, with a transverse black band, interrupted in the center; the skin of the neck, beneath the feathers, purple-blue; the naked skin under the wings bluish slate; the bare skin inside the tibiae and on the sides of the abdomen livid plumbeous; the naked skin around the vent plumbeous-blue; the feet and toes slaty gray, tinged olive; the soles dull brownish; the claws dark brown, with the apical half black and the underside horny white. The adult male differs chiefly in having the gular skin bright orange-yellow.

In the present form the casque is reduced to a low, corrugated outgrowth on the basal half of the culmen, and there are still lower ridges on the sides of both maxilla and mandible at the base. The male has the forehead shining, deep purple-chestnut, this color continuing as a narrow line down the center of the crown and broadening posteriorly to include the whole of the bushy crest; the feathers of the rest of the head and the whole foreneck shining buffy white; the tail white; the rest of the plumage black, glossed with steel green. The female differs in having the entire plumage black, except for the white tail.

I have found no example of *Rhyticeros subruficollis* from our area in either Hannover or Stockholm and feel certain that Gyldenstolpe's records for that bird are based upon sight misidentifications of *ticehursti*, although, in his "List of the Birds of Siam" (1920), he states that he "obtained it at the Meh Lem River in northern Siam."

ACEROS NIPALENSIS (Hodgson)

Rufous-necked Hornbill

Buceros Nipalensis Hodgson, Asiatic Researches, vol. 18, pt. 1, 1833, pp. 178–186, fig. 1, 2 (Nepal).

Aceros nepalensis, de Schauensee, Proc. Acad. Nat. Sci. Philadelphia, 1929, p. 573 (Doi Suthep); 1934, p. 263 (Doi Suthep).

Aceros nipalensis, Deignan, Journ. Siam Soc. Nat. Hist. Suppl., 1931, p. 162 (Doi Suthep); 1936, p. 95 (Doi Suthep).—Riley, U. S. Nat. Mus. Bull. 172, 1938, p. 195 (Doi Langka).

The rufous-necked hornbill is known in our provinces only from some of the higher peaks of the districts west of the Khun Tan range, where it is a not rare but seldom observed resident of the heaviest evergreen. I found it common on Doi Ang Ka at 6,000 feet and fairly so on Doi Suthep from 3,300 to 5,500 feet. Smith took one from a party of seven or eight on Doi Langka.

I have always seen this species in pairs or small flocks, usually in the tops of lofty trees, but once feeding upon fruit fallen to the ground. Its ordinary note is a loud croak, and in flight the wings produce a sound like that made by our other large hornbills.

I took a male with enlarged gonads on Doi Suthep at 3,300 feet, January 22. Smith's female from Doi Langka, April 29, is molting the central rectrices.

De Schauensee records that an adult male had the irides garnet; the orbital region bright light blue; the bill creamy white, with the basal half of the mandible more olive-green; the grooves at the base of the maxilla black, anteriorly gray; the bare skin behind the mandible dark blue, followed by a flesh-colored area; the gular skin almost covered by an inverted heart of bright brick red, edged posteriorly by deep blue, which is joined in a narrow line to the blue behind the mandible; a narrow brick-red line between the blue behind the heart and the feathered portion of the foreneck; the feet, toes, and claws black. An adult female differed chiefly in having the orbital region rather duller; a dusky blue-black patch at the side of the throat where the male had flesh color; the whole throat brick red except for a small deep blue triangle posteriorly.

This is a medium-sized species that never develops a casque. The adult male has the head, neck, and breast bright rufous, changing to deep chestnut on the belly and under tail coverts; the rest of the plumage green-glossed black, but with the tips of the longest primaries and the apical half of the graduated tail feathers white. Smith's female (a bird with only one groove developed on the maxilla) differs in having the rufous of head, neck, and breast duller and much sullied with blackish.

Indo-Chinese examples should be critically compared with topotypical material. The former may prove to be separable by lesser dimensions.

PTILOLAEMUS TICKELLI AUSTENI (Jerdon)

WHITE-THROATED BROWN HORNBILL

Anorhinus austeni JERDON, Ibis, 1872, p. 6 (no locality given; type specimen from Asalu, North Cachar hills, *fide* Ogilvie Grant, Catalogue of the birds in the British Museum, vol. 17, 1892, p. 393).

Anorrhinus austeni, GYLDENSTOLPE, Kungl. Svenska Vet.-Akad. Handl., 1916, p. 113 (Khun Tan); Ibis, 1920, p. 586 (Khun Tan).

Ptilolaemus tickelli tickelli, DE SCHAUENSEE, Proc. Acad. Nat. Sci. Philadelphia, 1934, p. 264 (Doi Suthep).—DEIGNAN, Journ. Siam Soc. Nat. Hist. Suppl., 1936, p. 95 (Doi Suthep).

The little brown hornbill seems to be a bird of considerable rarity on the higher hills of the western provinces. Gyldenstolpe shot a female from a small flock at Khun Tan, June 4, 1914; de Schauensee took a male at 3,500 feet on Doi Suthep, February 22, 1933; I found a pair on Doi Chiang Dao, about 5,000 feet, December 8, 1936, and collected the female. In addition to these specimens, I examined in Stockholm three undated birds (an adult male and two juveniles) taken by Eisenhofer at Khun Tan.

This species, usually seen in small flocks, acts much like *Anthracoceros*. De Schauensee's specimen was found at the edge of the evergreen; those observed by me, whether on Doi Chiang Dao or in Keng-tung State (where it is a not uncommon form), were in open forest of oak and pine. The call is a nasal *ank-ank-ank.*

Gyldenstolpe records that his female had the irides brown; the orbital skin blue; the bill dirty yellow; the feet and toes brownish gray.

In this genus the casque is small, low, and laterally compressed. The adult male of the present form has the upperparts dark gray-brown, the feathers of crown and hindneck with grayish-white shaft streaks; the primaries blackish, glossed with green, edged with buffy on the outer web near the center and more or less broadly tipped with white; the rectrices broadly tipped white (the central pair, however, usually uniformly gray-brown); the throat and foreneck white, more or less suffused with pale rufous; the remaining underparts pale rufous. My female specimen differs in having the underparts brownish gray, a litle paler on the throat and foreneck, slightly suffused everywhere with pale rufous; the central rectrices uniform gray-brown, the remainder (with the exception of the third pair) indistinctly and irregularly tipped with white and pale brownish (*vide infra*).

The adult female described above is in beautiful, unworn dress except for the third pair of rectrices; these are frayed and discolored and clearly have been retained from a precedent plumage. The interesting thing about them is that, quite unlike the newer feathers, they are broadly and distinctly tipped with pure white. This may indicate that the tail patterns thought to be diagnostic of *austeni* and *tickelli* are really age characters, a fact that would explain the numerous exceptional examples found in either population.

P. t. indochinensis (North Annam), described from a unique male, is, in my opinion, only doubtfully distinct from *austeni.*

Order PICIFORMES

Family CAPITONIDAE

MEGALAIMA VIRENS VIRENS (Boddaert)

CHINESE GIANT BARBET

Bucco virens BODDAERT, Table des planches enluminéez d'histoire naturelle, 1783, p. 53 (China, *ex* D'Aubenton, pl. 871).

Megalaema virens, GYLDENSTOLPE, Journ. Nat. Hist. Soc. Siam, 1915, p. 230 (listed); Kungl. Svenska Vet.-Akad. Handl., 1916, p. 97 (Khun Tan, Doi Pha Sakaeng); Ibis, 1920, p. 596 ("Northern and northwestern Siam").

Megalaima virens virens, DE SCHAUENSEE, Proc. Acad. Nat. Sci. Philadelphia, 1929, p. 568 (Doi Suthep); 1934, p. 253 (Doi Suthep, Doi Chiang Dao, Khun Tan).—DEIGNAN, Journ. Siam Soc. Nat. Hist. Suppl., 1931, p. 158 (Doi Suthep); 1936, p. 95 (Doi Suthep).—RILEY, U. S. Nat. Mus. Bull. 172, 1938, p. 198 (Khun Tan, Doi Langka, Doi Hua Mot).

Megalaema virens virens, CHASEN and BODEN KLOSS, Journ. Siam Soc. Nat. Hist. Suppl., 1932, p. 235 (Doi Suthep).

The giant barbet occurs in dense evergreen forest throughout the northern provinces but is commonest in the mountainous districts west of (and including) the Khun Tan chain and on the high hills of northwestern Nan (Phu Kha); between these areas I have recorded it only from Muang Phayao, but it will doubtless be found wherever the jungle is suitable. Its altitudinal range is largely governed by the distribution of such jungle: on Doi Ang Ka it is very common from 4,500 to 8,400 feet; on Doi Suthep, from 2,700 to 5,500 feet; on Doi Pha Hom Pok, from the lowest foothills to at least 6,000 feet.

This barbet's loud, querulent *pre-e-o, pre-e-o, pre-e-o* can be heard on the northern mountains from morning till night, but the singer, concealed in the foliage of some forest giant, is seldom seen. It will be most easily observed in the vicinity of fruiting trees, where it often gathers in considerable numbers. Perched against the sky it looks like a blackish bird with large, light-colored bill; in the air it may be known by its rather labored, dipping flight and the noisy rattling of its wings.

I have a long series of well-grown juveniles, collected between August 13 and October 23. All adults taken between August 28 and October 21 are in molt.

An adult female had the irides bright brown; the bill bright chrome yellow on the basal half, otherwise pale green; the anterior half of the culmen slaty, becoming almost black at the tip; the feet and toes olive-green; the claws slaty black.

The giant barbet has the whole head and neck deep blue, sometimes with a sort of nuchal collar formed by light-colored shaft streaks; the upper back and the shoulders green suffused with chestnut; the remaining upperparts chiefly deep grass green; the upper breast blackish brown; the under tail coverts bright red; the rest of the underparts heavily streaked with cream, yellow, bright green, and greenish blue (the last color restricted to the center of the lower breast and upper belly).

CYANOPS LINEATA HODGSONI (Bonaparte)

NEPALESE LINEATED BARBET

Megalaimus [*sic*] *hogdsoni* [*sic*] BONAPARTE, Conspectus generum avium, vol. 1, 1850, p. 144 (Nepal).

Therciceryx [*sic*] *lineatus hodgsoni*, GYLDENSTOLPE, Kungl. Svenska Vet.-Akad. Handl., 1913, p. 50 (Den Chai, Pak Pan); 1916, p. 100 (Khun Tan, Doi Pha Sakaeng).

Thereiceryx lineata hodgsoni, GYLDENSTOLPE, Journ. Nat. Hist. Soc. Siam, 1915, p. 230 (listed).

Thereiceryx lineatus hodgsoni, GYLDENSTOLPE, Ibis, 1920, p. 597 ("Northern Siam").—DE SCHAUENSEE, Proc. Acad. Nat. Sci. Philadelphia, 1928, p. 574 (Doi Suthep).

Thereiceryx lineatus intermedius, DE SCHAUENSEE, Proc. Acad. Nat. Sci. Philadelphia, 1929, p. 568 (Doi Suthep, Chiang Rai) ; 1934, p. 254 (Mae Taeng, Khun Tan, Doi Suthep).—DEIGNAN, Journ. Siam Soc. Nat. Hist. Suppl., 1931, p. 158 (Doi Suthep, Chiang Mai) ; 1936, p. 95 (Doi Suthep, Chiang Mai).—RILEY, U. S. Nat. Mus. Bull. 172, 1938, p. 199 (Mae Hong Son, Mae Lang valley, Mae Suya valley, Thattafang, Doi Ang Ka, Lampang, "Doi Phra Chao" [=Doi Saket?], Nan, Ban Nam Khian).

The lineated barbet abounds in the dry, deciduous forest of all the northern provinces; it occurs chiefly on the plains but ascends the hills to the altitudinal limit of this type of vegetation, on Doi Ang Ka reaching about 2,500 feet, on Doi Suthep, 2,700 feet. So general is its distribution that it has been recorded by every collector from virtually all localities where work has been done.

This is the green bird with brownish head and breast and light-colored bill that, perched at the top of a leafless tree, calls *bang-kok*, *bang-kok*, *bang-kok*, at regular intervals all through the heat of the day. While really an inhabitant of the *pa daeng*, a wandering individual may appear at times in a village garden and I have once or twice heard it even in the center of Chiang Mai. All stomachs I examined contained wild fruit.

Breeding seems to take place throughout the hot weather. An example with enlarged gonads was collected March 7 and several juveniles wearing heel pads were taken in August. From May 27 to October 19 all adults examined are in molt. Owing to the leathery foliage among which the species lives, the plumage becomes very frayed and bleached and the color differences between fresh and worn birds are striking.

A male in breeding condition had the irides violet-red; the eyelids and orbital region deep yellow; the bill pale creamy flesh, with the extreme tip and the edges of the commissure horny gray, the extreme base of the maxilla deep yellow; the feet and toes chrome yellow; the claws dark horn-brown.

This species in unworn dress has the entire head, neck, breast, and upper abdomen buffy gray, each feather (except on the throat) broadly edged with deep brown, so that these parts appear heavily streaked light and dark; the remaining upperparts bright, deep green, with pale shaft streaks on the upper back; the remaining underparts bright yellow-green, somewhat streaked with deeper green; the under surface of the tail blue-green. Through fading and wear the dark edgings of the feathers of head and breast become paler or even wholly disappear, so that these parts are more or less uniformly colored.

CYANOPS FAIOSTRICTA (Temminck)

GREEN-EARED BARBET

Bucco faiostrictus TEMMINCK, *in* Temminck and Laugier, Nouveau recueil de planches coloriées d'oiseaux, livr. 88, 1831, pl. 527 and text (Cochin-China).

Thereiceryx phaeostricta saigonensis, GYLDENSTOLPE, Journ. Nat. Hist. Soc. Siam, 1915, p. 230 (listed).

Therciceryx phaeostricta, GYLDENSTOLPE, Kungl. Svenska Vet.-Akad. Handl., 1916, p. 99 (Khun Tan, Doi Pha Sakaeng).

Thereiceryx faiostricta faiostricta, GYLDENSTOLPE, Ibis, 1920, p. 597 ("Northern and north-western Siam").

Thereiceryx faiostrictus faiostrictus, DE SCHAUENSEE, Proc. Acad. Nat. Sci. Philadelphia, 1934, p. 254 (Khun Tan). — RILEY, U. S. Nat. Mus. Bull. 172, 1938, p. 201 (Khun Tan, "Doi Phra Chao" [=Doi Saket?]).

The green-eared barbet, a common bird whose distribution may serve as an indication of the geographical limits of the Indo-Chinese Province, occurs throughout the more eastern districts but reaches the absolute periphery of its range at the western foot of the Khun Tan chain. In addition to the localities listed above, I have it from Ban Huai Tak, Wiang Pa Pao, Phu Het, Doi San Huai, Doi Lom, and Doi Up Fa (Laos).

Wherever this species is found, the related lineated barbet occurs even more commonly in the same forests. The notes and habits of the two forms seem to be much the same.

I took specimens with enlarged gonads April 24 and May 13, juveniles with heel pads from June 4 to September 10. All adults collected between June 13 and October 23 are in molt.

Gyldenstolpe's northern examples had the irides brown or reddish brown; the bill horn color, plumbeous at the base; the feet and toes olive-green.

This barbet, in fresh plumage, has the feathers of the crown and sides of the neck blackish brown, edged brownish gray to give a streaky appearance; the remaining upperparts bright, deep green; the lores, ear coverts, and a very narrow supercilium bright yellow-green; the throat, neck, and upper breast creamy white, each feather with a deep brown shaft streak; at each side of the lower neck a small red spot, edged with orange; the remaining underparts light green, most of the feathers with green-washed brown shaft streaks; the under surface of the tail bluish green. In worn plumage the striation above and below becomes much less distinct.

CYANOPS FRANKLINII RAMSAYI (Walden)

BURMESE GOLDEN-THROATED BARBET

Megalaema Ramsayi WALDEN, Ann. Mag. Nat. Hist., ser. 4, vol. 15, 1875, p. 400 (Karen-ni).

Cyanops ramsayi, GYLDENSTOLPE, Kungl. Svenska Vet.-Akad. Handl., 1916, p. 99 (Doi Pha Sakaeng).

Cyanops franklini ramsayi, GYLDENSTOLPE, Ibis, 1920, p. 598 (Doi Pha Sakaeng).—DE SCHAUENSEE, Proc. Acad. Nat. Sci. Philadelphia, 1928, p. 574 (Doi Suthep); 1929, p. 569 (Doi Suthep).—CHASEN and BODEN KLOSS, Journ. Siam Soc. Nat. Hist. Suppl., 1932, p. 235 (Doi Suthep).—RILEY, U. S. Nat. Mus. Bull. 172, 1938, p. 205 (Doi Ang Ka, Doi Suthep, Doi Langka, Doi Hua Mot).

Cyanops franklinii ramsayi, DEIGNAN, Journ. Siam Soc. Nat. Hist. Suppl., 1931, p. 158 (Doi Suthep); 1936, p. 95 (Doi Suthep).—DE SCHAUENSEE, Proc. Acad. Nat. Sci. Philadelphia, 1934, p. 255 (Doi Suthep).

In Thailand the Burmese race of the golden-throated barbet is virtually confined to the evergreen above 4,500 feet on a limited number of the higher peaks of Chiang Mai Province. Occasionally an individual will be found at a fruiting tree as low as 2,500 feet, and Gyldenstolpe's unique specimen from Pha Sakaeng was doubtless such a wandering bird; normally, however, *ramsayi* avoids competition with the closely related blue-throated barbet by keeping to higher altitudes. The localities here listed are the only ones in our area from which the species is yet known. Its complete absence from Doi Khun Tan and Doi Chiang Dao may readily be explained by the insufficient elevation of the first, by the lack of suitable forest above 4,500 feet on the second; both mountains are strongholds of *C. a. davisoni*.

On Doi Ang Ka and Doi Suthep this barbet is abundant, and its monotone *tookarook-took* is heard from every side throughout the day. Stomachs examined contained only fruits of various types, both hard and soft.

Breeding seems to be confined to the later portion of the rainy season: birds with the gonads slightly enlarged were taken September 2 and 4, juveniles from August 23 to October 25. All adults collected between October 19 and November 6 are in molt.

This species has the irides orange-brown, with a narrow whitish outer ring; the orbital region slaty gray; the maxilla slaty black, plumbeous-white at the corners of the mouth; the mandible plumbeous, tipped slaty black; the feet and toes plumbeous-olive; the soles yellow; the claws blackish brown, dark plumbeous at the extreme base.

The adult has the forehead and occiput red, the center of the crown golden-yellow; a supercilium gray, streaked with black, posteriorly broadening and becoming all black; the remaining upperparts bright, deep green, brighter on the nape, the shoulder and edge of the wing washed with deep blue; the chin and upper throat golden-yellow with an indistinct orange spot on either side at the base of the bill; the sides of the head and the lower throat silvery gray; the remaining underparts yellow-green; the under surface of the tail blue-green.

CYANOPS ASIATICA DAVISONI (Hume)

TENASSERIMESE BLUE-THROATED BARBET

Megalaima Davisoni HUME, Stray Feathers, vol. 5, 1877, pp. 108–109 ("Tenasserim Central Hills . . . at Meetan and other lower localities").

Cyanops davisoni, GYLDENSTOLPE, Journ. Nat. Hist. Soc. Siam, 1915, p. 230 (listed); Kungl. Svenska Vet.-Akad. Handl., 1916, p. 98 (Khun Tan, Doi Pha Sakaeng, Nong Bia).

Cyanops asiatica, GYLDENSTOLPE, Kungl. Svenska Vet.-Akad. Handl., 1916, p. 98 (Doi Pha Sakaeng, "Doi Vieng Par" [= Doi Chom Hot?], Khun Tan).

Cyanops asiatica asiatica, GYLDENSTOLPE, Ibis, 1920, p. 597 (Khun Tan, Doi Pha Sakaeng, "Doi Vieng Par" [=Doi Chom Hot?]).—GREENWAY, Bull. Mus. Comp. Zool., 1940, p. 192 (Chiang Dao, Doi Nang Kaeo, Doi Ang Ka).

Cyanops asiatica davisoni, GYLDENSTOLPE, Ibis, 1920, p. 597 ("North-western Siam").—DE SCHAUENSEE, Proc. Acad. Nat. Sci. Philadelphia, 1929, p. 569 (Chiang Rai, Chiang Saen); 1934, p. 255 (Khun Tan, Doi Chiang Dao).—DEIGNAN, Journ. Siam Soc. Nat. Hist. Suppl., 1931, p. 158 (Doi Suthep); 1936, p. 95 (Doi Suthep).—RILEY, U. S. Nat. Mus. Bull. 172, 1938, p. 204 (Khun Tan, Doi Hua Mot).

The blue-throated barbet is found in the evergreen of all the northern provinces from the plains to about 4,000 feet, less commonly to 4,600 feet, above which elevation it is replaced by the preceding species. In the vicinity of Chiang Mai, where lowland evergreen is absent, the bird is restricted to Doi Suthep between 2,700 and 4,600 feet; on Doi Ang Ka, where the evergreen below 4,600 feet has been largely destroyed by the hill tribes, it is rare and local.

While descending the northern mountains amidst the ubiquitous chorus of barbet music, one can scarcely be certain at what moment he is hearing the last individual of the golden-throated species, the first of the blue-throated. The songs of the two are to my ear not definitely distinguishable, but that of the former seems to have four notes, that of the latter only three—*tookarook, tookarook, tookarook.*

Reproduction takes place during the spring months. A male with greatly enlarged gonads was taken March 7 on Doi Suthep at 3,300 feet; at about 4,500 feet on Phu Kha, during the first half of April, a pair had young in a hole, some 20 feet above ground, in the side of a broken-off tree. Juveniles have been secured in August at several localities. All adults collected between August 19 and October 17 are in molt.

A breeding male had the irides dull orange-brown; the eyelids edged orange; the orbital skin greenish brown; the maxilla with the basal half greenish cream, the apical half black; the mandible greenish cream, tipped blackish; the feet and toes slaty green; the claws dull black.

The birds of our area have a conspicuous red frontal patch, followed by a very narrow bar of golden-bronze, then by a much broader bar of blue or black or (most commonly) a mixture of the two colors; a streak of black bordering the posterior crown on either side; the remaining upperparts bright, deep green; the supercilia, sides of the head, the throat, and foreneck cerulean blue; a patch at each side of the lower neck and (sometimes) a minute speck at either side of the upper throat at the base of the mandible red; the remaining underparts yellow-green; the under surface of the tail blue-green.

The blue-throated barbets of northern Thailand lie between *asiatica* and *davisoni.* In a series of 24 birds before me, two are separable from Indian specimens of *asiatica* only by the rather paler color of the throat (like that of *davisoni*), two others are indistinguishable from a topotype of *davisoni;* the remainder have the blue of the throat as in *davisoni* but show every degree of intergradation between the black and blue vertical bars which respectively characterize the northern and southern races. In almost every case the bar is as narrow as in *asiatica*, with corresponding increase in the extent of the red frontal patch. In view of their instability and the intermediate nature of the characters, I feel that, at least for the present, our population should be left unnamed.

CYANOPS AUSTRALIS INVISA Deignan

Northern Thai Blue-eared Barbet

Cyanops australis invisa Deignan, Auk, vol. 58, 1941, pp. 397–398 (Pang Makham Phong, at the foot of Doi Pha Sakaeng, North Thailand).

Cyanops cyanotis, Gyldenstolpe, Kungl. Svenska Vet.-Akad. Handl., 1913, p. 51 (Ban Huai Hom, Khao Phlung); Journ. Nat. Hist. Soc. Siam, 1915, p. 230 (listed).

Mesobucco duvaugli cyanotis, Gyldenstolpe, Kungl. Svenska Vet.-Akad. Handl., 1916, p. 100 (Khun Tan).

Cyanops duvaucelii cyanotis, Gyldenstolpe, Ibis, 1920, p. 598 ("Siam, north of the Peninsula").

Mesobucco duvauceli cyanotis, de Schauensee, Proc. Acad. Nat. Sci. Philadelphia, 1929, p. 570 (Chiang Mai, error [=Chiang Saen Kao], Doi Suthep); 1934, p. 256 (Khun Tan).

Cyanops duvaucellii cyanotis, Deignan, Journ. Siam Soc. Nat. Hist. Suppl., 1931, p. 159 (Doi Suthep); 1936, p. 95 (Doi Suthep).

Mezobucco duvaucelii cyanotis, Riley, U. S. Nat. Mus. Bull. 172, 1938, p. 207 (Khun Tan, Doi Langka).

The blue-cheeked barbet is an inhabitant of the evergreen from the plains to about 5,500 feet; I found it very common, especially at low elevations, in the districts east of, and including, the Khun Tan range and rare on the mountains of the more western provinces.

Its small size, green coloration, ventriloquial voice, and custom of perching at the very top of a high tree combine to render this bird one of the most difficult to observe or collect; its presence, however, may always be known by the endlessly repeated double note, *too-rook*, *too-rook*, *too-rook*.

An example with the gonads greatly enlarged was taken at Muang Ngop, April 23, and a wholly green juvenile at Ban Hai Huai Som, June 17. Smith collected a number of specimens in postjuvenal and postnuptial molt at Khun Tan, between August 29 and September 10.

De Schauensee states (1929) that a male had the bill black, grayish at the rictus; the feet and toes olive.

The adult male has the forehead and forecrown black (sometimes flecked with blue), followed by an equally broad, blue vertical band, which changes to bright, deep green on the nape and remaining upperparts; a short malar streak scarlet, more or less mixed with yellow and bordered below by a black mustachial streak; the ear coverts blue, edged above and below by crimson streaks; the chin and throat blue, the feathers with black bases which show through on the lower throat to form a more or less distinct, irregular plastron; the remaining underparts yellow-green, sometimes with a narrow, indistinct reddish gorget edging the blue of the lower throat; the under surface of the tail blue-green. The adult female seems always to have the black of forehead and forecrown strongly overlaid with blue. The juvenile has the entire plumage green, slightly more bluish green on the throat and sides of the head.

XANTHOLAEMA HAEMACEPHALA INDICA (Latham)

INDIAN COPPERSMITH

[*Bucco*] *indicus* LATHAM, Index ornithologicus, vol. 1, 1790, p. 205 (India; type locality restricted to Calcutta, by Stuart Baker, Journ. Bombay Nat. Hist. Soc., vol. 28, 1921, p. 105).

Xantholaema haematocephala, GYLDENSTOLPE, Kungl. Svenska Vet.-Akad. Handl., 1913, p. 51 (Phrae); 1916, p. 101 (Pha Kho, Pang Hua Phong, Khun Tan); Journ. Nat. Hist. Soc. Siam, 1915, p. 230 (listed).

Xantholaema haemacephala indica, GYLDENSTOLPE, Ibis, 1920, p. 598 ("Throughout the whole country").—DE SCHAUENSEE, Proc. Acad. Nat. Sci. Philadelphia, 1929, p. 569 (Chiang Mai); 1934, p. 256 (Chiang Mai, "Tung Sio," Chiang Rai).—DEIGNAN, Journ. Siam Soc. Nat. Hist. Suppl., 1931, p. 159 (Chiang Mai); 1936, p. 95 (Chiang Mai).—RILEY, U. S. Nat. Mus. Bull. 172, 1938, p. 209 (Mae Lang valley, Mae Hong Son, Nan).

This little barbet, which is strictly confined to the lowlands, is very common throughout the area.

The *nok pok* may be found at times in the dry, deciduous forest or in the more open evergreen but is always more numerous in cultivated country and especially so in the gardens and orchards of towns and villages, where its monotonous *poke-poke-poke* or *wock-wock-wock* is a familiar sound from the mango and tamarind trees during the heat of the day. The voice is with difficulty traced to the small green singer concealed in the foliage; if the bird be perched upon an exposed limb it will be seen that the head is constantly turned from side to side, so that the metallic notes seem to come from all directions at once.

It feeds upon fruits and the species may be observed in great numbers where there is an abundance of ripe figs.

A bird of February 19 had the gonads greatly enlarged and juveniles have been taken between April 15 and July 10. An adult collected September 16 is just completing the molt.

Two females had the irides dark brown; the eyelids edged purplish slate; the orbital skin dull crimson; the bill dull black, the mandible fleshy beneath at the base; the feet and toes coral red; the claws dull red.

The adult has the front half of the crown shining crimson, separated by a narrow black bar from the slaty green of the hind crown; the remaining upperparts deep green, suffused with bronze on the back and wings; a short supercilium and a patch below the eye bright yellow; the side of the head otherwise black; the throat bright yellow; a shining crimson gorget on the upper breast, broadly bordered below with golden-yellow; the remaining underparts cream, everywhere boldly streaked with deep green. The immature may be known at any stage by its streaked underparts.

Family PICIDAE

PICUS ERYTHROPYGIUS NIGRIGENIS (Hume)

Western Red-rumped Green Woodpecker

Gecinus nigrigenis Hume, Proc. Asiat. Soc. Bengal, No. 5, 1874, p. 106 (no locality given; type specimen from "Pakchan Creek," Tenasserim, *fide* Hargitt, Catalogue of the birds in the British Museum, vol. 18, 1890, p. 68).

Gecinus nigrigenis, Gyldenstolpe, Kungl. Svenska Vet.-Akad. Handl., 1913, p. 47 (Den Chai, valley of the Mae Yom river, Pak Pan); 1916, p. 88 (Pha Kho, Khun Tan); Journ. Nat. Hist. Soc. Siam, 1915, p. 229 (listed).

Picus erythropygius nigrigenis, Gyldenstolpe, Ibis, 1920, p. 599 ("Northern Siam").—Deignan, Journ. Siam Soc. Nat. Hist. Suppl., 1931, p. 157 (Chiang Mai, Doi Suthep); 1936, p. 96 (Chiang Mai, Doi Suthep).—de Schauensee, Proc. Acad. Nat. Sci. Philadelphia, 1934, p. 249 (Chiang Mai, Mae Taeng).—Riley, U. S. Nat. Mus. Bull. 172, 1938, p. 215 (Mae Sariang, Mae Hong Son, Huai Salop, Mae Kong Ka valley, Muang Pai, Mae Khan, Doi Ang Ka, "Doi Phra Chao" [=Doi Saket?], Ban Nam Khian).

Picus erythropygus nigrigenis, de Schauensee, Proc. Acad. Nat. Sci. Philidelphia, 1929, p. 566 (Chiang Mai, Pang La).

The red-rumped green woodpecker is a very common bird of the dry, deciduous forest almost everywhere, although, in the Mae Khong drainage, it has so far been found only at Muang Fang. It is necessarily a lowland form but ascends the hills to the limit of suitable vegetation, on Doi Suthep reaching 2,700 feet.

This woodpecker is one of the several species of unrelated birds which, in pairs, commonly accompany the loose flocks of white-crested laughing-thrushes through the *pa daeng*. When frightened, it flies before one from tree to tree, concealing itself behind the trunks, all the while uttering a remarkably loud, ringing call. Its main food is termites, in pursuit of which it may often be observed on rotting stumps, logs, or even on the ground.

I have no definite information on the breeding season but have a series of eight juveniles collected between June 8 and August 24. Molting adults have been taken from August 28 to November 9.

Adult specimens had the irides lemon-yellow; the orbital skin slate; the bill dark horny brown (horny black in the dried skin); the feet and toes dull olive-green; the claws slate.

The male has the center of the crown shining red; the rest of the crown, the sides of the head, and the nape black; the rump and lower back deep scarlet; the remaining upperparts bright golden olive-green; the remiges and rectrices black, the former with broken white bars on the basal half; the throat, foreneck, and sides of the lower neck bright yellow, changing to greenish yellow on the breast, which color, in turn, changes to whitish on the remaining underparts; the feathers of the lower breast, abdomen, flanks, and under tail coverts marked with dull brownish V-shaped bars, which give a scaly appearance to these parts. The female differs only in lacking the red crown patch. Juveniles may always be recognized by their having the tips of the primaries narrowly edged with white on the outer web.

PICUS VITTATUS EISENHOFERI Gyldenstolpe

Thai Plain-breasted Scaly-bellied Green Woodpecker

Picus vittatus eisenhoferi Gyldenstolpe, Orn. Monatsb., vol. 24, 1916, p. 28 (Pha Hing, northern Thailand).

Gecinus striolatus, Gyldenstolpe, Journ. Nat. Hist. Soc. Siam, 1915, p. 229 (listed).

Picus striolatus, Gyldenstolpe, Ibis, 1920, p. 599 ("Northern Siam").

Picus vittatus eisenhoferi, Gyldenstolpe, Kungl. Svenska Vet.-Akad. Handl., 1916, p. 88 (Pha Hing); Ibis, 1920, p. 598 ("The whole of Siam").—de Schauensee, Proc. Acad. Nat. Sci. Philadelphia, 1929, p. 566 (Chiang Rai); 1934, p. 248 (Chiang Mai).—Deignan, Journ. Siam Soc. Nat. Hist. Suppl., 1931, p. 156 (Chiang Mai); 1936, p. 96 (Chiang Mai, Doi Suthep).—Riley, U. S. Nat. Mus. Bull. 172, 1938, p. 210 (Nan).

In the North, the present species seems to be a rather uncommon but well-distributed form. Eisenhofer sent to Stockholm a male taken at Huai Pu, May 28, 1912, and another collected at Khun Tan in 1914. I have examples from Chiang Mai, Chiang Rai, and Nan Provinces.

Gyldenstolpe's type specimen was taken in "fairly dense evergreen forest," but it is probable that bamboo was growing in the neighborhood, for this woodpecker is partial to that type of growth beyond all others. Near Chiang Mai is occurred chiefly in the extensive brakes at the foot of Doi Suthep, less commonly in the deciduous forest of the lower slopes to 2,000 feet, very rarely in town gardens. In Nan Province it was frequently observed in clumps of giant bamboo along roads and even in the heart of villages. This is a shy bird that probably often escapes notice among the canes, and little is known of its habits in our area.

In Nan Province I took specimens with the gonads greatly enlarged, April 1 and 8, and a juvenile, June 8.

Adults had the irides red or brown; the orbital skin slaty or plumbeous; the maxilla brownish black or dark brown; the mandible horny yellow, olive at the base, brownish black or dark brown at the tip; the feet and toes slaty green or dull olive; the claws horny gray or horn.

The male has the crown and nape shining red; the remaining upperparts bright golden olive-green with the rump and lower back bright greenish yellow; the remiges and rectrices black, the former with broken, narrow white bars; a supercilium and a broad malar streak black mixed with white; the sides of the head otherwise gray; the chin, throat, foreneck, and breast immaculate buffy yellow or greenish yellow, much brighter on the sides of the lower neck; the remaining underparts buffy white or greenish white, each feather marked with deep olive V-shaped bars, which give a scaly appearance. The female differs in having the crown and nape black. The juvenile has the tips of the primaries narrowly margined with white on the outer webs and the underparts almost uniform in color.

This form apparently was described from a unique example, correctly recorded in the original description as a female collected by Gyldenstolpe at Pha Hing, April 9, 1914. In the same author's "Types of Birds in the Royal Natural History Museum in Stockholm" (Ark. för Zool., vol. 19A, No. 1, 1926, p. 74), *two* specimens are listed, the first of which is a male taken by Eisenhofer at Khun Tan in 1914. I have examined this alleged cotype in Stockholm and found it both cataloged and labeled as "Typ," but since it was presumably not part of an original series and first found mention in print ten years after the formal description of the Pha Hing female, I cannot imagine what standing as a type can be claimed for the Khun Tan specimen. Inasmuch as the birds to east and west of the Khun Tan chain may in future require subspecific division, it is important that confusion not arise in connection with the true type locality of *eisenhoferi*.

In 1915 Gyldenstolpe added *Picus xanthopygaeus* to the northern avifauna under the name *Picus striolatus;* no data were given, but the example was said to be among the birds sent by Eisenhofer to Hannover. This collection, made between February 7 and June 27, 1912, is now divided between the museums in Hannover and Stockholm. Search in both places failed to discover the bird, and I feel certain that the record is due to misidentification of a skin of *Picus vittatus eisenhoferi*, collected by Eisenhofer at Huai Pu, May 28, 1912, and now deposited in Stockholm. If my surmise be correct, Gyldenstolpe's repetition of the record in 1920 can be explained only as an oversight. Up to now the species is not definitely known nearer our area than Mae Tha Khwae in the Rahaeng district, whence it has been recorded by Chasen and Boden Kloss as *Picus viridanus viridanus* (Journ. Siam Soc. Nat. Hist. Suppl., 1928, p. 170), later corrected to *P. myrmecophoneus* (*ibid.*, 1932, p. 235).

PICUS CANUS HESSEI Gyldenstolpe

THAI BLACK-NAPED GREEN WOODPECKER

Picus canus hessei GYLDENSTOLPE, Orn. Monatsb., vol. 24, 1916, pp. 28–29 (Pha Kho and Den Chai, northern Thailand).

Picus canus occipitalis, GYLDENSTOLPE, Kungl. Svenska Vet.-Akad. Handl., 1913, p. 47 (Den Chai, Mae Raem, "Vang Nun"); Journ. Nat. Hist. Soc. Siam, 1915, p. 229 (listed).

Picus canus hessei, GYLDENSTOLPE, Kungl. Svenska Vet.-Akad. Handl., 1916, p. 89 (Khun Tan, Pha Kho, Pang Hua Phong, Den Chai); Ibis, 1920, p. 599 ("Northern parts of the country").—DEIGNAN, Journ. Siam Soc. Nat. Hist. Suppl., 1931, p. 156 (Doi Suthep, Chiang Mai); 1936, p. 96 (Doi Suthep, Chiang Mai).—RILEY, U. S. Nat. Mus. Bull. 172, 1938, p. 214 (Chiang Dao, Mae Lang valley, Huai Mae Sae).

The black-naped green woodpecker is uncommon but generally distributed throughout the northern provinces at low elevations. Eisenhofer sent to Hannover an undated female from "Siam" and a male taken at Den Chai, February 10, 1912; to Stockholm, two females collected at Khun Tan in 1913. I have examples from Doi Suthep, Ban Muang Sum, and Ban Huai Ki.

Gyldenstolpe reported (1913) not only that this was one of the commonest woodpeckers in the dry forests of Phrae Province but also that it was "very abundant" at Den Chai, Mae Raem, and "Vang Nun." I never succeeded in finding it even common anywhere in our area and suggest that at least half of the birds observed by Gyldenstolpe were of the nearly related form, *P. v. eisenhoferi*, a species of precisely similar habits and habitat and at that period still unknown to him. In the neighborhood of Chiang Mai *hessei* was uncommon in bamboo and deciduous forest at the foot and on the lower slopes of Doi Suthep, rare in semideciduous jungle as high as 3,200 feet. My specimen from Ban Muang Sum was collected in pine-forest on one of the low hills at the base of Doi Pha Hom Pok. Where *eisenhoferi* occurs we may expect to find *hessei* also; in fact, so close is the agreement in habits and preferred environment between these two that their mutual uncommonness may well be explicable by the competition between two closely allied species (with nearly identical survival requirements) for possession of a single ecological niche.

My entire series of six northern specimens were, by chance, taken between November 7 and March 28; at this season all are in fresh, clean plumage and have the gonads quite inactive.

The male has the forehead and forecrown shining red; the supercilium, hindcrown, and center of the nape black, more or less mixed with gray; the sides of the head uniform gray, edged below by a narrow, black streak; the remaining upperparts bright olive-green, with the rump and lower back bright yellowish green and the exposed portions of the wings strongly washed with bronze; the remiges and rectrices blackish, the former with small white spots at the margin of the outer vane, the latter more or less washed with bronze and indistinctly barred with grayish toward the base; the throat green-washed gray, changing gradually to a uniform olive-green on the remaining underparts. The female resembles the male but has the entire crown black, streaked with gray.

P. c. hessei is distinguishable from the following race only by its rather larger bill, the length of which (in adults) normally exceeds 40 mm.

PICUS CANUS GYLDENSTOLPEI Stuart Baker

ASSAMESE BLACK-NAPED GREEN WOODPECKER

Picus canus gyldenstolpei STUART BAKER, Bull. Brit. Orn. Club, vol. 39, 1918, p. 19 (Sadiya, Lakhimpur, Assam).

This more northern form of the black-naped woodpecker is apparently a very rare winter visitor to northern Thailand: the only record is based upon an adult male taken by me on Doi Suthep at 4,500 feet, November 7, 1936.

In favor of my conclusion that this specimen, with bill only 36 mm. in length, was truly an extralimital wanderer rather than an abnormally small-billed example of the resident form, the following points of evidence may be adduced:

1. In a series of 29 adults (including 14 females) of *hessei* from all parts of Thailand, not one has the bill measuring less than 40 mm.

2. My bird was solitary and was shot along a narrow track through dense evergreen at 4,500 feet; thus, not only was it in a type of forest always, in my experience, avoided by *hessei*, but it represents the sole record for the species on Doi Suthep above 3,200 feet (at which elevation it is exceptional) and was taken 1,300 feet higher than the species has otherwise ever been observed in Thailand.

3. The example of *gyldenstolpei* is molting the two outermost pairs of remiges and the central pair of rectrices; an adult male of *hessei* (with bill measuring 43.5 mm.) collected on the same day and on the same mountain, but at only 2,500 feet, has entirely completed the molt.

If an example of *gyldenstolpei* can appear in winter well within the range of *hessei*, it seems likely that a similar tendency to wander may be shown by occasional individuals of other northern subspecies; such stragglers could easily be responsible for the apparent instability of many of the races discussed by Greenway in his valuable study of winter-taken specimens (Auk, 1940, pp. 550–560).

PICUS CHLOROLOPHUS BURMAE R. Meinertzhagen

BURMESE LESSER YELLOW-NAPED WOODPECKER

Picus chorolophus burmae R. MEINERTZHAGEN, Bull. Brit. Orn. Club, vol. 44, 1924, pp. 54–55 (Pegu Town, Pegu, Burma).

Brachylophus chlorolophus chlorolophus [*partim*], GYLDENSTOLPE, Kungl. Svenska Vet.-Akad. Handl., 1916, p. 90 (Doi Pha Sakaeng).

Brachylophus chlorolophus chlorolophoides [*partim*], GYLDENSTOLPE, Ibis, 1920, p. 599 ("Various localities in Siam").

Picus chlorophus [*sic*] *chlorophoides* [*sic*], DE SCHAUENSEE, Proc. Acad. Nat. Sci. Philadelphia, 1929, p. 567 ([Doi Suthep], Chiang Saen).

Picus chlorolophus chlorophoides [*sic*], DEIGNAN, Journ. Siam Soc. Nat. Hist. Suppl., 1931, p. 156 (Doi Suthep).

Picus chlorolophus chlorolophoides, CHASEN and BODEN KLOSS, Journ. Siam Soc. Nat. Hist. Suppl., 1932, p. 235 (Doi Suthep).—DEIGNAN, Journ. Siam Soc. Nat. Hist. Suppl., 1936, p. 96 (Doi Suthep).—DE SCHAUENSEE, Proc. Acad. Nat. Sci. Philadelphia, 1934, p. 248 (Doi Suthep, Doi Chiang Dao).

Cirropicus chlorolophus chlorolophoides [*partim*], RILEY, U. S. Nat. Mus. Bull. 172, 1938, p. 216 (Mae Khan, Huai Salop).

This race of the lesser yellow-naped woodpecker is at present known in our area only from the Thanon Thong Chai range and from Chiang Saen, but it may confidently be expected to occur also in Mae Hong Son Province and throughout Chiang Rai.

The bird is almost confined to hilly districts, where both de Schauensee and I found it only in evergreen forest. On Doi Suthep it was very common from 3,500 to 4,500 feet, slightly less so down to 2,400 and up to 5,500 feet; on Doi Ang Ka it was equally common in clumps of trees in the semicleared valley below Pha Mon (4,000–4,500 feet) and in the dense evergreen but was not observed above 5,000 feet. It probably occurs at low elevations wherever the evergreen reaches the plains, as at Doi Pha Sakaeng and Chiang Saen.

This is a very striking species along shaded forest tracks, flying before one (usually in pairs) from tree to tree and attracting attention by the shining gold of its erected nuchal crest. Stomachs I examined contained only ants.

An adult male had the irides crimson; the maxilla yellow with the culmen blackish slate; the mandible bright yellow, tipped blackish slate; the feet and toes olive; the claws horny plumbeous.

The coloration of this bird not only varies a great deal individually, but, as is the case with other woodpeckers, may be much altered by bleaching, wear, and stains. Males in fresh plumage have the front and a long supercilium deep crimson; the crown deep olive-green, with few or many of the feathers tipped deep crimson; a broad nuchal crest deep golden-yellow; the remaining upperparts bright olive-green, strongly suffused with golden, especially on the back, rump, and upper tail coverts; the rectrices black; the inner primaries and outer secondaries with the outer web largely chestnut-red, the inner web black with white spots near the edge; a narrow white streak below the eye from the base of the bill to below the ear coverts; a broad crimson malar stripe; the throat and breast brownish olive, with white bases of the feathers showing through on the throat; the remaining underparts closely banded whitish and dull brownish. Females differ in having the crimson on the head restricted to the sides of the hind-crown.

Subspecific differences in the populations of northern Thailand are discussed under the following forms.

PICUS CHLOROLOPHUS CHLOROLOPHOIDES (Gyldenstolpe)

KHUN TAN LESSER YELLOW-NAPED WOODPECKER

Brachylophus chlorolophoides, GLYDENSTOLPE, Orn. Monatsb., vol. 24, 1916, p. 29 (Khun Tan, North Thailand).

Brachylophus chlorolophoides, GLYDENSTOLPE, Kungl. Svenska Vet.-Akad. Handl., 1916, p. 90 (Khun Tan).

Brachylophus chlorolophus chlorolophoides [*partim*], GYLDENSTOLPE, Ibis, 1920, p. 599 (Khun Tan).

Cirropicus chlorolophus chlorolophoides [*partim*], RILEY, U. S. Nat. Mus. Bull. 172, 1938, p. 216 (Doi Hua Mot, Doi Langka, Khun Tan).

The present form is confined to the forests of the Khun Tan range, occurring from Doi Khun Tan in the South to the Nang Kaeo-Langka-Hua Mot complex of mountains in the North.

Nothing is recorded of this bird's habits, which are doubtless precisely like those of *burmae*. Dr. Smith has noted that some of his specimens were taken at 4,000 feet. All examples collected between August 23 and October 17 are in molt.

The Khun Tan subspecies is separable from *burmae* and *laotianus* on average differences, which can be seen only by careful study of extensive series.

In Washington are 16 absolute topotypes of *chlorolophoides*, taken throughout the year, which show that Gyldenstolpe has unfortunately bestowed his name upon an unstable population, more or less exactly intermediate between *burmae and laotianus*. Of the series, one specimen is indistinguishable from true *laotianus*, several others from *burmae*, and the remainder fall somewhere between the two, varying in the degree of golden suffusion in the yellow of the crest and the green of the back. This intermediate character o f the Khun Tan population is confirmed by geography, for on Doi Suthep (about 32 miles northwest of Doi Khun Tan) we find only *burmae*, while at Ban Mae Mo (about 32 miles east-southeast of Doi Khun Tan) only *laotionus occurs.*

Because of the possibility of perfectly matching specimens of *laotianus* and *burmae* with certain examples from Khun Tan, both names have been synonymized by authors with *chlorolophoides.* The employment of a single designation for the quite distinct forms of Pegu and Laos leads to nullification of the real purpose of nomenclature, and it seems advisable to recognize both a western and an eastern race; the unstable intermediates of the Khun Tan chain, while not deserving of subspecific separation, may conveniently be known by Gyldenstolpe's name, since it is already available for them.

PICUS CHLOROLOPHUS LAOTIANUS Delacour

LAO LESSER YELLOW-NAPED WOODPECKER

Picus chlorolophus laotianus DELACOUR, Bull. Brit. Orn. Club, vol. 47, 1926, p. 12 (Chiang Khwang, Laos).

Picus chlorolophus chlorolophus [*partim*], GYLDENSTOLPE, Kungl. Svenska Vet.-Akad. Handl., 1913, p. 47 (Pak Pan, Den Chai).

Picus chlorolophus chlorolophus, GYLDENSTOLPE, Journ. Nat. Hist. Soc. Siam, 1915, p. 229 (listed).

Brachylophus chlorolophus chlorolophus [*partim*], GYLDENSTOLPE, Kungl. Svenska Vet.-Akad. Handl., 1916, p. 90 (Pang Hua Phong, Pha Kho).

Brachylophus chlorolophus chlorolophoides [*partim*], GYLDENSTOLPE, Ibis, 1920, p. 599 ("Various localities in Siam").

Cirropicus chlorolophus chlorolophoides [*partim*], RILEY, U. S. Nat. Mus. Bull. 172, 1938, p. 216 (Ban Nam Khian).

The present race is widespread in those portions of our area lying east of the Khun Tan hills and south of Chiang Rai Province; at Ban Mae Mo it occurs only 32 miles from the type locality of *chlorolophoides.*

I found this bird common in the evergreen on Phu Kha at 4,500 feet, but otherwise it has been collected only at low elevations, whether in evergreen or in deciduous forest. Gyldenstolpe considered it fairly common in the dry jungles at Pak Pan and Den Chai, and I observed it at Mae Mo in a similar environment.

P. c. laotianus differs from *burmae* in the more or less complete absence of golden suffusion from the plumage of the upperparts, with the result that the crest is lemon yellow, the back a duller and purer olive-green.

PICUS FLAVINUCHA LYLEI (Boden Kloss)

THAI GREATER YELLOW-NAPED WOODPECKER

Chrysophlegma flavinucha lylei BODEN KLOSS, Ibis, 1918, pp. 110–111 (Ko Lak [=Prachuap Khirikhan], southwestern Thailand).

Chrysophlegma flavinucha, GYLDENSTOLPE, Kungl. Svenska Vet.-Akad. Handl., 1916, p. 92 (Khun Tan, Doi Pha Sakaeng).—DEIGNAN, Journ. Siam Soc. Nat. Hist. Suppl., 1931, p. 157 (Doi Suthep).

Chrysophlegma flavinucha flavinucha [*partim*], GYLDENSTOLPE, Ibis, 1920, p. 601 ("Northern and north-western Siam").

Chrysophlegma flavinucha lylei, CHASEN and BODEN KLOSS, Journ. Siam Soc. Nat. Hist. Suppl., 1932, p. 235 (Doi Suthep).—DEIGNAN, Journ. Siam Soc. Nat. Hist. Suppl., 1936, p. 96 (Doi Suthep).—DE SCHAUENSEE, Proc. Acad. Nat. Sci. Philadelphia, 1934, p. 249 (Doi Suthep, Mae Taeng, Doi Chiang Dao).—RILEY, U. S. Nat. Mus. Bull. 172, 1938, p. 220 (Sop Phung, Khun Tan, Doi Hua Mot).

This more western race of the greater yellow-naped woodpecker is fairly common in the hilly districts east to (and including) the Khun Tan range and is probably the form of all Chiang Rai Province. In Stockholm are four males and two females collected by Eisenhofer at Khun Tan in 1914. I have taken specimens at Muang Fang, Samoeng, Doi Suthep, and Doi Ang Ka.

This woodpecker is largely restricted to the evergreen, occurring in such forest on Doi Suthep from 2,700 to 5,500 feet, on Doi Ang Ka from 4,400 to 4,900 feet or higher. At Muang Fang, however, it was found in lowland evergreen at 1,400 feet and at Mae Taeng was taken by de Schauensee in lowland deciduous jungle. It agrees in habits with *Picus chlorolophus burmae* but is perhaps a rather shier bird. The stomach of a specimen from Doi Ang Ka contained ants, ant pupae, and a small green tree frog.

Breeding probably takes place during the spring months. A bird of July 18 is exceedingly worn and bleached, and all examples obtained between September 6 and November 21 are in molt.

I have noted that an adult male had the irides crimson; the orbital skin plumbeous; the bill pale plumbeous, tinged horny yellow at the tip, much darker at the base of the mandible; the feet and toes plumbeous; the claws horny plumbeous. Specimens taken by de Schauensee differed in having the irides pinkish white.

The adult male has the crown and sides of the head dark olive-green, the former more or less strongly suffused with rufous-maroon; a broad nuchal crest golden-yellow or orange-yellow; the remaining upperparts bright shining olive-green; the rectrices black; the remiges black, broadly banded with rufous; the chin and throat clear lemon yellow; the feathers of the foreneck pure white, tipped and often centered with brownish black to give a streaky appearance, the streaked area frequently invading the center of the throat; the remaining underparts olive-gray, darker on the breast. The adult female differs in having the yellow of the chin and throat replaced by rufous-brown and the streaked area of the foreneck extending up the center of the throat almost to the chin.

The male of *lylei* (type specimen in Washington) differs from the corresponding sex of *flavinucha* in the decidedly paler yellow of its chin and throat, the lesser suffusion of orange in the nuchal crest, the tendency of the black streaking to invade the center of the throat, and (apparently) in its shorter wing length; the two agree in having the dark streaks of the foreneck almost black and the apical third or half of the maxilla pale-colored (at least in the dried skin). The birds of northwestern Thailand have, in most cases, the characters of *lylei* but certain individuals show approach to *flavinucha* in having a rather longer wing and a deepening of the colors of throat and crest. I have been unable to compare females of the two forms.

PICUS FLAVINUCHA ARCHON, new name

LAO GREATER YELLOW-NAPED WOODPECKER

Chrysophlegma flavinucha, GYLDENSTOLPE, Kungl. Svenska Vet.-Akad. Handl., 1913, p. 48 (Den Chai, Pak Pan); Journ. Nat. Hist. Soc. Siam, 1915, p. 229 (listed).

Chrysophlegma flavinucha flavinucha [*partim*], GYLDENSTOLPE, Ibis, 1920, p. 601 ("Northern and north-western Siam").

Chrysophlegma flavinucha annamensis [*sic*] DELACOUR and JABOUILLE, Bull. Brit. Orn. Club, vol. 48, 1928, p. 130 (Khebon, North Annam), not *Picus chlorolophus annamensis* R. Meinertzhagen 1924.

The present subspecies probably has in our provinces a distribution identical with that of *Picus chlorolophus laotianus*. Specimens taken by Eisenhofer at Huai Pu, May 20 and 29, 1912, are in the museums at Hannover and Stockholm; I have examples from Ban Bo Thong, Ban Pha Lai, and Phu Kha.

The Phu Kha bird was found in the evergreen at about 4,500 feet but otherwise this form is known only from the dry, deciduous forests of the lowlands. Gyldenstolpe considered it very common in such jungle at Den Chai and Pak Pan.

This race cannot be distinguished in the field from *lylei;* direct comparison in the hand shows the dark streaks of the foreneck to be deep brown rather than brownish black.

P. f. archon is a poorly defined form. From *pierrei* and the birds of eastern Thailand usually placed under that name, it is at once separable by its having the apical third or half of the maxilla pale-colored in the dried skin. From *lylei* it seems to differ only in having the dark streaks of the foreneck deep brown, not brownish black, a distinction particularly well marked in the female specimens before me.

GECINULUS VIRIDIS VIRIDIS Blyth

BURMESE GREEN BAMBOO WOODPECKER

Gecinulus viridis BLYTH, Journ. Asiat. Soc. Bengal, vol. 31, 1862, p. 341 (Toungoo, Burma).

Gecinulus viridis, GYLDENSTOLPE, Journ. Nat. Hist. Soc. Siam, 1915, p. 229 (listed); Kungl. Svenska Vet.-Akad. Handl., 1916, p. 92 (Doi Pha Sakaeng, Khun Tan).

Gecinulus grantia viridis, GYLDENSTOLPE, Ibis, 1920, p. 601 ("Northern and northwestern Siam").

Gecinulus viridis viridis, DE SCHAUENSEE, Proc. Acad. Nat. Sci. Philadelphia, 1934, p. 249 (Doi Chiang Dao).—RILEY, U. S. Nat. Mus. Bull. 172, 1938, p. 222 ("Doi Phra Chao" [=Doi Saket ?]).

In addition to the localities listed above, this bird has been found by me at Ban Mae Mo and Ban Samoeng. It will probably be recorded eventually from all the northern provinces but, in the lowlands of Chiang Rai, may just possibly be replaced by the allied *Gecinulus grantia indochinensis*.

In our districts this species is very local, occurring only in extensive brakes of tall bamboo, from the low hills (Mae Mo) to 4,000 feet (Doi Chiang Dao), and not observed at all in many places that appear to be eminently suitable. Gyldenstolpe, who took a number of specimens at Khun Tan and Doi Pha Sakaeng, considered it "very abundant," but, with the exception of Eisenhofer (who sent to Stockholm three males from Khun Tan), no later collector has found it at either locality. The few examples observed by me were quietly climbing the bamboo canes, feeding upon ants.

An adult female had the irides red; the orbital skin olive-gray above the eye, plumbeous below; the bill blue-white, plumbeous at the base of the mandible; the feet and toes clear olive-green; the claws light plumbeous.

The adult male has the crown and short nuchal crest crimson, the feathers with dull olive-golden bases, the sides of the head and the longer, posterior feathers of the crest bright olive-golden; the remaining upperparts deep golden-olive, more or less suffused with crimson on the rump and upper tail coverts; the rectrices blackish; the remiges blackish with round white spots on the inner web; the underparts deep olive-green, paler on the throat. The adult female differs in having the crown and crest bright olive-golden, the longer, posterior feathers of the latter sometimes more or less suffused with crimson.

BLYTHIPICUS PYRRHOTIS PYRRHOTIS (Hodgson)

INDIAN BAY WOODPECKER

[*Picus*] *Pyrrhotis* HODGSON, Journ. Asiat. Soc. Bengal, vol. 6, 1837, p. 108 (Nepal).

Pyrrhopicus pyrrhotis, GYLDENSTOLPE, Kungl. Svenska Vet.-Akad. Handl., 1916, p. 93 (Doi Pha Sakaeng); Ibis, 1920, p. 602 (Doi Pha Sakaeng).

Blythipicus pyrrhotis pyrrhotis, DEIGNAN, Journ. Siam Soc. Nat. Hist. Suppl., 1931, p. 157 (Doi Suthep); 1936, p. 96 (Doi Suthep).—DE SCHAUENSEE, Proc. Acad. Nat. Sci. Philadelphia, 1934, p. 251 (Doi Chiang Dao).—RILEY, U. S. Nat. Mus. Bull. 172, 1938, p. 226 (Doi Suthep, Doi Langka, Khun Tan, Huai Mae Lao).

Blythipicus pyrrhotis annamensis, GREENWAY, Bull. Mus. Comp. Zool., 1940, p. 192 (Doi Nang Kaeo).

The bay woodpecker is a local and rather uncommon form in our provinces. On Doi Suthep, where it has been recorded only five times, it occurred in the heaviest evergreen from 3,300 to 5,500 feet; on Doi Khun Tan, at 4,000 feet; on Doi Chiang Dao, from 2,000 to 4,000 feet; on Doi Nang Kaeo, at 2,800 feet; on Doi Ang Ka, where it is one of the commonest members of its family, from 4,400 to 5,500 feet. In addition to the localities listed above, I have it from Samoeng, Ban Mae Ho, and Ban Hai Huai Som (at the last place in lowland evergreen).

I found this bird, singly or in pairs, haunting the dense evergreen forest, sometimes appearing at its edge or along a trail or even entering an adjacent bamboo brake. It spends much of its time on the ground or upon fallen trees whence, when frightened, it flies with an astonishingly loud and harsh cackling call to hide on the farther side of the trunk of some nearby tree or stump. One of my specimens had fed upon berries, but the stomachs of two others contained beetle larvae of enormous size.

The species seems to breed earlier in the year than our other woodpeckers: birds in juvenal dress have been collected between the middle of January and the middle of July.

The adult has the irides chestnut (male), dull red (female, *fide* de Schauensee), or brownish orange (female); the orbital region slaty; the bill yellow, the maxilla tinged green at the base between the nares, the mandible paler and tinged green at the base; the feet and toes brownish black or olive-slate; the claws olive-slate, brownish black, or horn. Immature males had the irides pale olive-brown or dark brown; the bill bright yellow, tinged greenish at the base, or wholly pale yellow; the feet, toes, and claws dark brown or horny slate.

The adult male has the forehead pale fulvous-brown, deepening to dull brown on the crown; a broad crimson band from the sides of the neck across the nape (where it is less distinct); the remaining upperparts (including the wings and tail) rufous, conspicuously barred with black, the bars sometimes obsolescent on the back, where there may be more or less maroon suffusion; the chin and throat pale fulvous-brown, changing gradually to the deep chocolate-brown of the remaining underparts (often suffused with maroon on the breast). The adult female differs chiefly in wholly lacking the scarlet nuchal band. Immature birds have the feathers of the crown and sides of the head dull blackish with broad fulvous shaft streaks; the underparts blackish or blackish brown, indistinctly and narrowly barred with rufous.

Greenway (*loc. cit.*) seems to have confused the characters of *annamensis* and *pyrrhotis*. All examples from our provinces (including Nan) are definitely of the Indian race.

MICROPTERNUS BRACHYURUS PHAIOCEPS Blyth

BURMESE RUFOUS WOODPECKER

P[icus] (*M[icropternus]*) *phaioceps* BLYTH, Journ. Asiat. Soc. Bengal, vol. 14, 1845, p. 195 ("India proper extending eastwards to Tipperah and Arracan"; co-types, *fide* Robinson and Boden Kloss, Journ. Nat. Hist. Soc. Siam, vol. 5, 1923, p. 183, the specimens "from the vicinity of Calcutta" listed by Blyth, Catalogue of the birds in the Museum Asiatic Society, 1849, p. 60).

Micropternus phaioceps phaioceps, GYLDENSTOLPE, Kungl. Svenska Vet.-Akad. Handl., 1913, p. 48 (Den Chai, Pak Pan); 1916, p. 94 (Doi Pha Sakaeng, Khun Tan).

Micropternus phaeoceps phaeoceps, GYLDENSTOLPE, Journ. Nat. Hist. Soc. Siam, 1915, p. 230 (listed).

Micropternus brachyurus burmanicus, GYLDENSTOLPE, Ibis, 1920, p. 603 ("Northern, north-western . . . Siam").

Micropternus brachyurus phaeoceps, DEIGNAN, Journ. Siam Soc. Nat. Hist. Suppl., 1931, p. 157 (Chiang Mai).—RILEY, U. S. Nat. Mus. Bull. 172, 1938, p. 230 (Doi Langka).

Micropternus brachyurus phaioceps, DE SCHAUENSEE, Proc. Acad. Nat. Sci. Philadelphia, 1934, p. 251 (Chiang Mai, "Tung Sio," Chiang Dao).—DEIGNAN, Journ. Siam Soc. Nat. Hist. Suppl., 1936, p. 97 (Chiang Mai).

The rufous woodpecker occurs rather commonly in suitable lowland jungle throughout our area.

This species is usually seen in pairs in bamboo brakes and dry, scrubby forest, often traveling with the noisy mixed flocks of *Garrulax*, *Dissemurus*, *Crypsirina*, etc. It not only seems to feed wholly upon ants but even breeds in holes bored into occupied ant nests; perhaps because of this association both plumage and flesh of this woodpecker possess a scent, at once sweet and musty, stronger than that of any other of its family known to me.

Adult female specimens had the irides brown; the bill black, slate-gray at the base of the mandible; the feet and toes dull brown or slaty; the claws horny slate.

The adult male has the feathers just under the eye, from the lores to the anterior ear coverts, tipped crimson; the crown and sides of the head ochraceous; the remaining upperparts rufous, narrowly barred everywhere (including the wings and tail) with black; the underparts rufous, the feathers of the throat conspicuously edged with ochraceous to give a streaked appearance, those of the breast almost unmarked, the remainder with narrow black bars which are obsolescent on the center of the abdomen. The adult female differs only in lacking the crimson tips to the feathers below the eye.

MEIGLYPTES JUGULARIS Blyth

BLACK-AND-BUFF WOODPECKER

P[*icus*] (*M*[*eiglyptes*]) *jugularis* BLYTH, Journ. Asiat. Soc. Bengal, vol. 14, 1845, p. 195 (Arakan).

Miglyptes jugularis, GYLDENSTOLPE, Journ. Nat. Hist. Soc. Siam, 1915, p. 230 (listed); Kungl. Svenska Vet.-Akad. Handl., 1916, p. 94 (Pha Kho, Khun Tan, Pang Hua Phong).

Meiglyptes jugularis, GYLDENSTOLPE, Ibis, 1920, p. 603 (Pha Kho, Khun Tan, Pang Hua Phong).—RILEY, U. S. Nat. Mus. Bull. 172, 1938, p. 229 ("Doi Phra Chao" [=Doi Saket ?]).

The black-and-buff woodpecker seems to be a rather uncommon resident of the more eastern lowlands. Eisenhofer sent to Hannover two males from Pha Hing (April 29 and May 11, 1912) and to Stockholm a female from the same place (April 25, 1912). I have examples from a number of localities in Nan Province and a single specimen from Sala Mae Tha (at the western foot of the Khun Tan range). It has not yet been found anywhere between Sala Mae Tha and the Burmese bank of the Salwin.

Gyldenstolpe (1916) states that he met with this species in old clearings or open forests, never in thick jungle. My specimens were found in similar locations; where the lowland evergreen was very dense, the birds were seen only along the broader trails.

Molting adults were taken June 6 and August 6.

Gyldenstolpe's examples had the irides brown; the bill black; the feet and toes olive-green.

The adult male has the top and sides of the head black, narrowly barred with buff, becoming uniform black on the crest; a broad buffy-white collar on the back and sides of the neck; the scapulars, back, upper tail coverts, and tail black; the rump buffy white; the remiges black with small buffy-white spots on either web that become broad buffy-white bars on the innermost secondaries; most of the upper wing coverts buffy white, forming a broad, conspicuous wing stripe; the feathers of the throat buff, narrowly barred with black; a short, dull crimson mustachial streak on each side of the head from the base of the mandible; the under wing coverts buffy white; the remaining underparts black. The adult female differs from the male only in lacking the red mustachial streaks.

The buffy tinge which appears on both the black and the white portions of this bird's plumage varies greatly individually and seems to be caused by stain.

DRYOBATES HYPERYTHRUS HYPERYTHRUS (Vigors)

BURMESE RUFOUS-BELLIED PIED WOODPECKER

Picus hyperythrus VIGORS, Proc. Comm. Sci. Corr. Zool. Soc. London, pt. 1, 1830–1831 [=1831], p. 23 ("Himalayan Mountains"; type locality restricted to Nepal, by Hartert, Vögel der paläarktischen Fauna, vol. 2, 1912, p. 925).

Hypopicus hyperythrus, WILLIAMSON, Journ. Nat. Hist. Soc. Siam, 1916, p. 61 (Ban Mae Mo).—GYLDENSTOLPE, Ibis, 1920, p. 602 (Ban Mae Mo).
Hypopicus hyperythrus hyperythrus, RILEY, U. S. Nat. Mus. Bull. 172, 1938, p. 223 (Huai Salop).

For many years this rare woodpecker was known from Thailand only by Williamson's old record. In 1936 I sent my men to Ban Mae Mo especially to make a search for it and on the last day of a week's stay, September 2, an adult male was seen and collected. Curiously enough, just eight days later, I myself shot a second adult male a few miles south of Ban Mae Ten, a village in the upper Mae Yom basin. However, unknown to me, Smith had obtained a specimen (adult male) at Huai Salop, January 3, 1933.

It is a bird of low elevations, inhabiting parklike *pa daeng*, where the trees are widely spaced and fairly tall. I found it a shy, solitary form, most easily discoverable by its call—the notes of a *Dryobates* but the voice of a *Dinopium*.

My two September specimens are in molt.

Smith records that his example had the maxilla black; the mandible horn; the feet and toes green.

The adult male has the forehead, lores, chin, and sides of the head to the eye gray; the crown and nape shining crimson; the remaining upperparts boldly barred black and white, except for the shoulders, upper tail coverts, and central rectrices, which are uniform black; the region of the vent and the under tail coverts rose-red or crimson; the remaining underparts unmarked rufous. The adult female differs only in having the crown and nape black, thickly spotted with white. Juveniles of either sex have the crown like that of the adult female, except that the anterior portion is spotted with crimson instead of white; the underparts (except for the pink under tail coverts) rufous-gray or pale rufous, everywhere barred with blackish.

Thai examples agree well with a series from the eastern Himalayas.

Ticehurst and Whistler have set aside Hartert's restriction of the type locality for the nominate race and rechristened the population of the eastern Himalayas *sikkimensis* (Ibis, 1924, p. 473). Since *some* forms in the original collection clearly did not come from the western Himalayas; since Gould's plate, founded upon Vigors's type, does indeed seem to represent an eastern bird; and since Hartert, the first reviser, designated a not improbable type locality, to refuse to accept his conclusions seems highhanded and unwarrantable.

DRYOBATES CATHPHARIUS TENEBROSUS Rothschild

YUNNANESE CRIMSON-BREASTED PIED WOODPECKER

Dryobates cathpharius tenebrosus ROTHSCHILD, Nov. Zool., vol. 33, 1926, p. 240 (Shweli-Salwin divide, Yunnan).
Dryobates cathparius perneyi, DE SCHAUENSEE, Proc. Acad. Nat. Sci. Philadelphia, 1938, p. 30 (Doi Pha Hom Pok).

This species has been found in Thailand only by de Schauensee's collectors, who took a single male at 6,000 feet on Doi Pha Hom Pok, sometime in February 1938.

I have no material of this form at hand. An adult male of the closely related *D. c. pernyii* has the forecrown black, the rest of the crown and the nape crimson; the back, scapulars, rump, upper tail coverts, and central rectrices unmarked black; the outer rectrices black, barred with fulvous-white; the wings black, barred and spotted with white on the apical two-thirds, the coverts of the innermost secondaries almost wholly white; the ear coverts and sides of the neck fulvous-white; the throat and sides of the breast black; the center of the breast deep crimson; the remaining underparts deep fulvous, heavily streaked with black; the under tail coverts buff, broadly edged with crimson. The adult female differs chiefly in lacking crimson on the head.

DRYOBATES ATRATUS (Blyth)

STRIPED-BREASTED PIED WOODPECKER

P[icus] atratus BLYTH, Journ. Asiat. Soc. Bengal, vol. 18, 1849, pp. 803–804 ("Tenasserim provinces").

Dryobates atratus, DE SCHAUENSEE, Proc. Acad. Nat. Sci. Philadelphia, 1929, p. 567 (Doi Suthep) ; 1934, p. 250 (Doi Chiang Dao, Doi Suthep).—DEIGNAN, Journ. Siam Soc. Nat. Hist. Suppl., 1931, p. 157 (Doi Suthep).—CHASEN and BODEN KLOSS, Journ. Siam Soc. Nat. Hist. Suppl., 1932, p. 236 (Doi Suthep.)—DEIGNAN, Journ. Siam Soc. Nat. Hist. Suppl., 1936, p. 96 (Doi Suthep).—RILEY, U. S. Nat. Mus. Bull. 172, 1938, p. 223 (Khun Tan, Doi Suthep, Doi Langka, Doi Hua Mot).

The striped-breasted woodpecker is common on all the northern mountains that exceed 4,000 feet in elevation (including Phu Kha), ranging from that altitude to at least 5,500 feet. On Doi Khun Tan, where it was not found by Eisenhofer and Gyldenstolpe, Smith took numerous examples between 3,000 and 4,000 feet (the summit) and one as low as 2,000 feet.

On Doi Ang Ka this bird occurred in solitary small trees standing on lalang-covered hillsides; elsewhere I found it also in the open forests of oak or pine and among the stunted trees that clothe the mountain ridges. Its call is the shrill, descending whinny characteristic of the small dryobatines.

A specimen taken on January 11 had the gonads enlarged. Juveniles have been collected between February 17 (just out of the nest) and September 4 (a female with only one red feather still in the crown).

De Schauensee records that a male had the irides chestnut; the maxilla dark gray; the mandible light pearl gray; the feet, toes, and claws gray. Females taken by me had the irides brown; the orbital skin slaty; the bill horny olive, darker on the culmen and paler below, or wholly slaty, or plumbeous with the culmen slaty; the feet, toes, and claws slaty olive, or the feet and toes plumbeous and the claws slaty.

The adult male has the crown and nape crimson; the uppermost back, the rump, upper tail coverts, and the two central pairs of rectrices usually unmarked black; the remaining upperparts, including the wings and outer rectrices, black, barred and spotted with white; the sides of the head gray, changing to white on the sides of the neck, some of the feathers behind the eye with black shaft streaks; a black streak, broadening posteriorly, from the base of the mandible; the chin and throat whitish; the remaining underparts gray, more or less strongly suffused with fulvous, boldly streaked, especially on the breast, with black; the under tail coverts crimson. The adult female differs in lacking crimson on the crown. Immature birds of either sex have the feathers of the crown tipped with crimson.

DRYOBATES MACEI LONGIPENNIS (Hesse)

THAI SPOTTED-BREASTED PIED WOODPECKER

Dendrocopos analis longipennis HESSE, Orn. Monatsb., vol. 20, 1912, p. 82 (Bangkok, Thailand).

Dryobates analis longipennis, DE SCHAUENSEE, Proc. Acad. Nat. Sci. Philadelphia, 1929, p. 567 (Chiang Mai); 1934, p. 250 (Chiang Mai).—DEIGNAN, Journ. Siam Soc. Nat. Hist. Suppl., 1931, p. 157 (Chiang Mai); 1936, p. 96 (Chiang Mai).

No member of the Thai avifauna has a more curiously discontinuous distribution than the present species, until now recorded only from Ban Hua Mak, Bangkok, Mae Klong, Ko Lak, and the vicinity of Chiang Mai.

At Chiang Mai this woodpecker, like the spotted owl (*Athene brama mayri*) and the white-winged starling (*Sturnia malabarica nemoricola*), is closely associated with the open groves of *mai kwao* (*Butea frondosa*) and, while fairly common, is local and confined to the neighborhood of lowland villages to the same extent as the tree. The reason for this relationship, which seems not to obtain elsewhere, is obscure and worthy of investigation. A male with enlarged gonads, shot in a *mai kwao*, February 9, 1929, had fed upon the larvae of a beetle.

Examples of either sex had the irides brown; the orbital skin slaty; the bill slaty, paler toward the base; the feet and toes plumbeous; the claws slaty.

An adult male from Chiang Mai has the crown crimson; the nape black; the remaining upperparts, including the upper tail coverts, wings, and tail, black barred with white; the sides of the head fulvous-white; a black streak, broadening posteriorly, from the base of the mandible; the remaining underparts pale fulvous, marked on the breast with elongated black spots, on the abdomen with faint brownish streaks, and on the sides with indistinct blackish-brown bars; the under tail coverts light crimson, indistinctly barred and spotted with blackish brown. The adult female differs in having the entire crown black. Immatures of either sex have the feathers of the crown black, tipped with crimson.

Ticehurst has adduced reasons (Ibis, 1939, p. 5) for considering *atratus* conspecific with *macei*, but the arguments advanced by him may with equal propriety be employed to show that the lowland *macei* should be coupled with the similarly lowland *longipennis*. It is significant that Chiang Mai specimens differ from topotypical *longipennis* in having the underparts a deeper fulvous, the spots on the breast smaller and less numerous, the streaks on the belly almost absent, the under tail coverts more crimson than pink—in all these characters approximating *macei*. To the objection that *macei* has the upper tail coverts and central rectrices unmarked black while *longipennis* has them barred with white, I need only point out that the same variation is exhibited among the races of *Dryobates canicapillus* (*cf. semicoronatus* and *canicapillus*).

DRYOBATES CANICAPILLUS CANICAPILLUS (Blyth)

BURMESE GRAY-CROWNED PIED WOODPECKER

P[icus] canicapillus BLYTH, Journ. Asiat. Soc. Bengal, vol. 14, 1845, p. 197 (Arakan; type specimen from Ramree Island, *fide* Robinson and Boden Kloss, Journ. Nat. Hist. Soc. Siam, vol. 5, 1923, p. 177).

Iyngipicus canicapillus, GYLDENSTOLPE, Kungl. Svenska Vet.-Akad. Handl., 1913, p. 48 (Den Chai, Pak Pan); 1916, p. 93 (Khun Tan, Pang Hua Phong, Pha Hing, Doi Pha Sakaeng); Journ. Nat. Hist. Soc. Siam, 1915, p. 230 (listed); Ibis, 1920, p. 602 ("Northern Siam").—DE SCHAUENSEE, Proc. Acad. Nat. Sci. Philadelphia, 1928, p. 575 (Doi Suthep).

Yungipicus hardwickii canicapillus, DE SCHAUENSEE, Proc. Acad. Nat. Sci. Philadelphia, 1929, p. 567 (Doi Suthep).

Yungipicus nanus canicapillus, DEIGNAN, Journ. Siam Soc. Nat. Hist. Suppl., 1931, p. 157 (Chiang Mai, Doi Suthep).—RILEY, U. S. Nat. Mus. Bull. 172, 1938, p. 224 (Doi Ang Ka, Mae Khan, Doi Suthep, "Doi Phra Chao" [=Doi Saket?], Khun Tan).

Dryobates hardwickii canicapillus, CHASEN and BODEN KLOSS, Journ. Siam Soc. Nat. Hist. Suppl., 1932, p. 236 (Doi Suthep).—DEIGNAN, Journ. Siam Soc. Nat. Hist. Suppl., 1936, p. 96 (Chiang Mai, Doi Suthep).

Dryobates nanus canicapillus, DE SCHAUENSEE, Proc. Acad. Nat. Sci. Philadelphia, 1934, p. 250 (Doi Suthep, Doi Chiang Dao, Khun Tan).

D[ryobates] n[anus] canicapillus, DEIGNAN, Journ. Siam Soc. Nat. Hist. Suppl., 1938, p. 123 ("Me Hong Son, Chiengmai, and Lampang provinces").

D[ryobates] n[anus] pumilus [*partim*], DEIGNAN, Journ. Siam Soc. Nat. Hist. Suppl., 1938, p. 123 ("Nan province").

The pygmy woodpecker is a common resident of the dry, deciduous forests of all our provinces, from the plains to about 2,700 feet. On

Doi Suthep I sometimes saw it in the open hill-forest between 3,300 and 4,600 feet, and on Doi Ang Ka it occurred in pines at 4,000 feet.

This bird, which may readily be distinguished from others of the genus by its small size, seems not to differ from them in notes and habits.

A well-grown juvenile was taken at Phu Het, June 13. Adults collected between August 2 and 28 are in molt.

Gyldenstolpe notes that his specimens had the irides gray, yellowish white, or brown; the bill bluish black; the feet and toes yellowish green.

The adult male has the crown ashy gray; the sides of the crown from above the eye, the nape, and the uppermost back black; at each side of the occiput a narrow streak of scarlet; the remaining upperparts black, barred and spotted with white; the sides of the neck from the eye white, bordered below by a broad streak, anteriorly brown, posteriorly black; the remaining underparts gray, more or less suffused with fulvous and everywhere streaked with blackish. The adult female differs only in lacking scarlet on the head.

Ticehurst has shown (Journ. Bombay Nat. Hist. Soc., 1940, p. 592) that my restoration of Hargitt's name *pumilus* for a supposedly browner Indo-Chinese population cannot stand. In the meantime de Schauensee has named the bird of eastern Thailand *delacouri* (Proc. Acad. Nat. Sci. Philadelphia, 1938, pp. 109–111). When only *fresh-plumaged* specimens (September to December) are compared, the alleged differences between *canicapillus* and *delacouri* are not very obvious, but in series they seem to be indeed separable.

It is possible that the birds of Nan Province should be called *delacouri*, but my material (females taken from April to June) does not permit me to decide this point.

HEMICIRCUS CANENTE CANENTE (Lesson)

BURMESE HEART-SPOTTED WOODPECKER

Picus Canente LESSON, Centurie Zoologique, 1830 [=*ante* May, 1832], pp. 215–216, pl. 73 (Pegu).

Hemicercus canente, GYLDENSTOLPE, Kungl. Svenska Vet.-Akad. Handl., 1913, p. 50 (Ban Huai Hom, Pak Pan); 1916, p. 96 (Tha Chomphu, Pha Kho); Journ. Nat. Hist. Soc. Siam, 1915, p. 230 (listed); Ibis, 1920, p. 605 ("Throughout northern Siam").

Hemicercus canente canente, DE SCHAUENSEE, Proc. Acad. Nat. Sci. Philadelphia, 1929, pp. 567, 568 (Chiang Saen, Chiang Rai).

The heart-spotted woodpecker is sparsely distributed across the lowlands of the more eastern provinces; its known range in our area does not extend beyond Tha Chomphu and Ban Mae Dok Daeng Nai, localities at the western foot of the Khun Tan chain.

It has been found in heavy evergreen, in deciduous forest, and in bamboo brakes. Gyldenstolpe notes that he saw it only on the lower portions of the trees and that, when alarmed, it would freeze against a branch and remain motionless for a long period; this habit may account for the paucity of records.

Birds of this genus have a patch of bristly feathers in the middle of the back smeared with a sweet-smelling, sticky glandular secretion which, in the dried skin, loses both its odor and viscidity. The purpose of this substance is still unknown, but it is, I feel sure, the origin of the buffy or greenish-yellow color with which the plumage is usually suffused and which, when the specimen is newly killed, can be washed off on damp cotton, as I discovered in cleaning bloodstains from the feathers.

De Schauensee records that his examples had the irides yellowish white (male) or sandy brown (female); the bill black; the feet and toes greenish black. Gyldenstolpe's birds of either sex had the irides dark brown.

This is a small species with tail so short as not to extend beyond the wings. The male has the upper half of the head and the crest black, the front and forecrown minutely speckled with whitish; the upper back white; the scapulars and the middle of the back black; the rump white; the upper tail coverts and the tail black; the primaries, outer secondaries, and outer wing coverts black; the shoulder white; the inner coverts and inner secondaries white with conspicuous cordiform black bars at or near the tip; the chin, throat, and sides of the neck white; the under wing coverts white; the remaining underparts blackish, deepening toward the under tail coverts. The female differs only in having the front and crown white.

N. B.—I have given descriptions of ideal specimens; the fact is that the plumage (except the most recently grown feathers in molting birds) is always more or less strongly stained, the white portions becoming buffy, the black (especially on the breast), olivaceous.

DINOPIUM JAVANENSE INTERMEDIUM (Blyth)

Burmese Three-toed Golden-backed Woodpecker

P[*icus*] (*T*[*iga*]) *intermedius* Blyth, Journ. Asiat. Soc. Bengal, vol. 14, 1845, p. 193 (Nepal, error; "Blyth's type was from north Arrakan," *fide* Stuart Baker, Ibis, 1919, p. 208; type locality restricted to Ramree Island, by Robinson and Boden Kloss, Journ. Nat. Hist. Soc. Siam, vol. 5, 1923, p. 187).

Tiga javanensis, Gyldenstolpe, Kungl. Svenska Vet.-Akad. Handl., 1913, p. 49 (Den Chai); Journ. Nat. Hist. Soc. Siam, 1915, p. 230 (listed).

Tiga javanensis intermedia, Gyldenstolpe, Kungl. Svenska Vet.-Akad. Handl., 1916, p. 95 (Pak Mae Ta, Pha Kho, Khun Tan, Tha Chomphu); Ibis, 1920, p. 604 ("Throughout the whole of Siam proper").

Dinopium javanense intermedium, de Schauensee, Proc. Acad. Nat. Sci. Philadelphia, 1929, p. 567 (Chiang Saen).—Deignan, Journ. Siam Soc. Nat. Hist. Suppl., 1931, p. 157 (Chiang Mai, Doi Suthep); 1936, p. 97 (Chiang Mai, Doi Suthep).—Riley, U. S. Nat. Mus. Bull. 172, 1938, p. 233 ("Doi Phra

Chao" [=Doi Saket ?], Doi Ang Ka, Chom Thong, Mae Hong Son, Thattafang, Ban Nam Khian).

Dinopium javanensis intermedia, DE SCHAUENSEE, Proc. Acad. Nat. Sci. Philadelphia, 1934, p. 253 ("Tung Sio").

The three-toed golden-backed woodpecker is a fairly common species of the dry, deciduous forests, from the plains to about 2,000 feet. It has been recorded from all parts of our area.

I found this form, usually in pairs, in open woodlands, feeding upon ants low down on the trunks of trees or on stumps. Its presence is soon made known by its loud, shrill, nasal cries but it is quick to take alarm and, in my experience, difficult to observe.

A subadult male was collected at Muang Fang, July 23, and adults in molt at various localities between August 2 and November 9.

De Schauensee records that a male had the irides chestnut; the maxilla black; the mandible black, with the basal half slaty blue; the feet and toes pale slaty blue. I have noted that a female had the irides brown; the orbital skin slate; the maxilla dull black, plumbeous-blue at the corners of the mouth; the mandible slate, with the basal half plumbeous-blue; the feet and toes dull olive-green; the claws dark slate.

The adult male has the crown and long nuchal crest crimson; the uppermost back black; the upper back, scapulars, wing coverts, and outer webs of the secondaries golden-yellow, suffused with olive and sometimes more or less washed with crimson; the lower back and rump crimson; the upper tail coverts and the tail black; the primaries black with large white spots on the inner web; the sides of the head and neck and the entire underparts fulvous-white, with a broad black streak from behind the eye, a broad black streak at either side of the throat and neck from the base of the mandible, and a broken narrow black streak down the center of the throat and foreneck; the feathers of the remaining underparts edged with black, most broadly on the breast, to give a scaly appearance. The adult female differs in having the crown and crest black, each feather with a white guttate streak near the tip.

For distinctions between the two golden-backed woodpeckers of our provinces, see under the following form.

CHRYSOCOLAPTES LUCIDUS GUTTACRISTATUS (Tickell)

BURMESE FOUR-TOED GOLDEN-BACKED WOODPECKER

Picus Guttacristatus TICKELL, Journ. Asiat. Soc. Bengal, vol. 2, 1833, pp. 578–579 (Borabham and Dholbham).

Chrysocolaptes guttacristatus indo-malayicus, GYLDENSTOLPE, Kungl, Svenska Vet.-Akad. Handl., 1913, p. 49, (Pak Pan, Ban Huai Hom, Den Chai); Journ. Nat. Hist. Soc. Siam, 1915, p. 230 (listed).

Chrysocolaptes guttacristatus guttacristatus, GYLDENSTOLPE, Kungl. Svenska Vet.-Akad. Handl., 1916, p. 95 (Pha Kho, Khun Tan); Ibis, 1920, p. 605

("Northern Siam").—DE SCHAUENSEE, Proc. Acad. Nat. Sci. Philadelphia, 1928, p. 575 (Doi Suthep); 1934, p. 252 (Mae Taeng, Khun Tan, Doi Suthep).—DEIGNAN, Journ. Siam Soc. Nat. Hist. Suppl., 1931, p. 157 (Chiang Mai, Doi Suthep); 1936, p. 97 (Chiang Mai, Doi Suthep).

Chrysocolaptes strictus guttacristatus, CHASEN and BODEN KLOSS, Journ. Siam Soc. Nat. Hist. Suppl., 1932, p. 235 (Doi Suthep).—RILEY, U. S. Nat. Mus. Bull. 172, 1938, p. 235 ("Doi Phra Chao" [=Doi Saket?], Thattafang, Mae Hong Son).

This species, like the preceding one, is a fairly common bird in the wooded districts of all our provinces, occurring not only in deciduous forest but also in the evergreen and ascending the hills at least to 5,500 feet.

Not only are the two golden-backed woodpeckers strikingly similar in appearance but they agree in voice and habits and may even, on occasion, be observed on the same tree trunk.

Smith took a juvenile male on the Burmese bank of the Salwin, January 28. I collected molting adults at a number of localities between April 21 and August 15.

Gyldenstolpe records that his specimens had the irides yellowish red; the bill slate; the feet and toes olive-green.

The golden-backed woodpeckers are superficially so much alike that it is scarcely necessary to give a detailed description of the present form. The four-toed species differs, *inter alia*, in the following characters: it is a distinctly larger bird, with a much longer, more robust bill; at each side of the throat, from the base of the mandible, it has *two* narrow black lines, which fuse posteriorly into one; the female has a *round* white spot near the tip of each feather of crown and crest.

DRYOCOPUS JAVENSIS FEDDENI (Blyth)

BURMESE GREAT BLACK WOODPECKER

Mulleripicus Feddeni "Blanford" BLYTH, Journ. Asiat. Soc. Bengal, vol. 32, 1863, p. 75 (Pegu; *in epist.*, *ibid.*, vol. 31, 1862, p. 195, Blanford writes: "Of *Mulleripicus Heddeni* [*sic, nomen nudum* here] I believe that I obtained one specimen at Thayetmyo, and subsequently I again shot it S. of Bassein").

Thriponax javensis, GYLDENSTOLPE, Kungl. Svenska Vet.-Akad. Handl., 1913, p. 50 (Den Chai).

Thriponax javensis feddeni, GYLDENSTOLPE, Journ. Nat. Hist. Soc. Siam, 1915, p. 230 (listed); Kungl. Svenska Vet.-Akad. Handl., 1916, p. 96 (Huai San, Khun Tan).

Thriponax javanensis feddeni, GYLDENSTOLPE, Ibis, 1920, p. 605 ("Throughout northern Siam").—DE SCHAUENSEE, Proc. Acad. Nat. Sci. Philadelphia, 1938, p. 575 (Doi Suthep).

Macropicus crawfurdi crawfurdi, DEIGNAN, Journ. Siam Soc. Nat. Hist. Suppl., 1931, p. 158 (Doi Suthep); 1936, p. 97 (Doi Suthep).—DE SCHAUENSEE, Proc. Acad. Nat. Sci. Philadelphia, 1934, p. 253 (Mae Taeng).

Macropicus feddeni, RILEY, U. S. Nat. Mus. Bull. 172, 1938, p. 242 (Doi Ang Ka, Ban Nam Khian).

This fine bird, while not common, is found throughout the northern provinces, occurring in the dry, deciduous forest from the plains to about 2,000 feet and, on Doi Suthep, rarely in the open hill-forest at 4,600 feet.

Gyldenstolpe found it in parties of from four to six birds but I have myself never recorded more than two together, although it is quite likely to be travelling with mixed flocks of unrelated forms, such as *Garrulax*, *Crypsirina*, *Garrulus*, etc. It is frequently seen on stumps and disproportionately small trees and I have scarcely ever observed it more than six feet above the ground; it is, nevertheless, one of the most difficult woodpeckers to collect, for it keeps just beyond gunshot range and seeks concealment behind the tree trunks. Its hammering is slow and deliberate and loud in direct proportion to the bird's size.

Definite breeding dates for our area are unknown but I took a juvenile female at Muang Lae, April 21, 1936.

Adult examples had the irides creamy-yellow; the orbital skin slate; the bill slate, with the extreme tip and base of the mandible plumbeous; the feet, toes, and claws plumbeous.

The adult male has the crown and nuchal crest bright crimson; the lower back, rump, basal half of the quills on the inner web, and the extreme tip of the primaries white; the remaining upperparts black; the orbital region and anterior portion of the ear coverts black; a broad, short mustachial streak, at each side of the throat, bright crimson; the chin, throat, foreneck, and posterior ear coverts white, heavily streaked with black; the breast and under tail coverts black; the remaining underparts white, usually suffused with a buffy stain. The adult female differs in lacking the red mustachial streaks and in having the front and forecrown black.

MÜLLERIPICUS PULVERULENTUS HARTERTI Hesse

NORTHERN GREAT GRAY WOODPECKER

Mülleripicus pulverulentus harterti HESSE, Orn. Monatsb., vol. 19, 1911, p. 182 (Assam; type specimen from Pya, Upper Chindwin, *fide* Hesse, Mitt. Zool. Mus. Berlin, vol. 6, 1912, p. 232).

Mülleripicus pulverulentus harterti, GYLDENSTOLPE, Kungl. Svenska Vet.-Akad. Handl., 1913, p. 50 (Ban Huai Hom); Journ. Nat. Hist. Soc. Siam, 1915, p. 230 (listed); Kungl. Svenska Vet.-Akad. Handl., 1916, p. 96 (Doi Pha Sakaeng, Khun Tan); Ibis, 1920, p. 605 ("Throughout northern and north-western Siam").—DE SCHAUENSEE, Proc. Acad. Nat. Sci. Philadelphia, 1934, p. 252 (Mae Taeng).—DEIGNAN, Journ. Siam Soc. Nat. Hist. Suppl., 1936, p. 97 (Doi Suthep).—RILEY, U. S. Nat. Mus. Bull. 172, 1938, p. 240 (Mae Khan, "Doi Phra Chao" [=Doi Saket?]).

The largest Thai woodpecker is uncommon but generally distributed in well-wooded districts of the North, occurring in lowland evergreen, in deciduous forest from the plains to the altitudinal limit of this type of vegetation, and, at least on Doi Ang Ka, in tall pines from

3,000 to 3,500 feet. The irregular appearances of the bird on Doi Suthep (2,200 to 2,900 feet) suggest that the species is more or less of a wanderer when breeding.

Where some decaying giant tree stands at the edge of a jungle clearing, one may meet with a party (as many as five or six) of these huge woodpeckers. Certainly they cannot be overlooked, for they follow one another from tree to tree with rattling wings and a constant harsh screaming of the syllable *woik*. When seen flying high above the forest, they appear to be dark, crowlike birds with a light-colored patch on the nape (an optical illusion due to the remarkably constricted neck). Specimens taken by me had fed upon ants and termites.

An adult male had the irides dark brown; the eyelids and orbital skin slaty; the maxilla bone-white, with the culmen and tip slaty black; the mandible with the tip slaty black and the base plumbeous, otherwise bone-white; the interior of the mouth slaty; the feet and toes plumbeous; the claws horny slate. An immature male had the irides gray-blue; the orbital skin slaty; the maxilla blue-gray, with the culmen slaty, the tip and the edges of the commissure dead white; the mandible blue-gray; the feet and toes gray-blue; the claws dark slate. Gyldenstolpe notes that a male had the feet and toes dark olive-green.

The male has a broad patch of bright crimson on each side of the head below the eye; the chin, throat, and foreneck vivid buffy yellow, more or less suffused with rose, especially on the foreneck; the rest of the plumage ashy slate-gray, the scalelike feathers of the head and nape tipped with silvery gray, the feathers of the underparts similarly (though less distinctly) tipped. The female differs in lacking the crimson malar markings and the rosy tinge on the throat and foreneck.

PICUMNUS INNOMINATUS MALAYORUM Hartert

MALAYAN SPECKLED PICULET

Picumnus innominatus malayorum HARTERT, Vögel der paläarktischen Fauna, vol. 2, 1912, p. 937 (Gunong Ijau, Perak, Malay Peninsula).

Picumnus innominatus malayorum, GYLDENSTOLPE, Kungl. Svenska Vet.-Akad. Handl., 1916, p. 97 (Khun Tan); Ibis, 1920, p. 605 (Khun Tan).

Vivia innominata malayorum, DEIGNAN, Journ. Siam Soc. Nat. Hist. Suppl., 1931, p. 158 (Doi Suthep).—CHASEN and BODEN KLOSS, Journ. Siam Soc. Nat. Hist. Suppl., 1932, p. 236 (Doi Suthep).—DEIGNAN, Journ. Siam Soc. Nat. Hist. Suppl., 1936, p. 97 (Doi Suthep).—DE SCHAUENSEE, Proc. Acad. Nat. Sci. Philadelphia, 1934, p. 253 (Doi Suthep, Doi Chiang Dao).—RILEY, U. S. Nat. Mus. Bull. 172, 1938, p. 243 (Doi Langka, Doi Hua Mot).

The speckled piculet has so far been recorded only from the higher peaks of the Thanon Thong Chai and Khun Tan ranges. On Doi Ang Ka I found it common in the evergreen from 4,400 to 5,500 feet; on Doi Suthep, from 2,700 to 4,600 feet, occasionally down to 2,200 feet in ravines; on Doi Chiang Dao, de Schauensee took it at 4,600 feet.

This little bird, in all its actions, is like the larger woodpeckers. I have seen it feeding on the trunks of saplings and on the stems of bamboo and exploring the apical twigs of the lower branches of the trees. For drumming purposes it seeks a hollow limb or dry bamboo, by means of which it can produce a sound as loud as that of a much larger species.

A male taken by me had the irides brown; the bill slaty; the feet and toes plumbeous.

The adult male has the forecrown orange, each feather with an exposed black base; the hindcrown and nape grayish olive, changing to deep olive-ochre on the remaining upperparts; the rectrices black, the central pair with the inner web white, the others with a broad, diagonal, subterminal white bar; a white line, broadening posteriorly, from above the eye to the nape; a second from the base of the bill down the side of the neck; the area between the two lines dark brown; the remaining underparts pale yellow (whiter on the throat and upper breast), boldly marked with black spots, which gradually change to bars on the lower flanks. The adult female differs only in having the entire crown grayish olive.

SASIA OCHRACEA QUERULIVOX Stuart Baker

Hill Tipperah White-browed Rufous Piculet

Sasia ochracea querulivox Stuart Baker, Bull. Brit. Orn. Club, vol. 47, 1926, p. 43 (Tipperah Hills, Eastern Bengal).

Sasia ochracea reichenoui, Gyldenstolpe, Kungl. Svenska Vet.-Akad. Handl., 1916, p. 97 (Doi Pha Sakaeng); Ibis, 1920, p. 606 (Doi Pha Sakaeng).—de Schauensee, Proc. Acad. Nat. Sci. Philadelphia, 1929, p. 568 (Chiang Rai, Chiang Saen).—Deignan, Journ. Siam Soc. Nat. Hist. Suppl., 1931, p. 158 (Chiang Mai); 1936, p. 97 (Chiang Mai).—Riley, U. S. Nat. Mus. Bull. 172, 1938, p. 243 (Chiang Dao).

This piculet is uncommon and local in the lowland districts of Chiang Rai, Phrae, and Nan Provinces (Muang Fang, Wiang Pa Pao, Chiang Rai, Chiang Saen, Ban Pha Khwang, Ban Huai Ki), very rare on the plains (Chiang Dao, Chiang Mai) and mountains (Doi Chiang Dao, Doi Ang Ka) of Chiang Mai Province. The only record for Chiang Mai Town is a solitary individual seen in a dense clump of giant bamboo, July 2, 1930.

The predilection of the rufous piculet for extensive brakes of bamboo may account for its broken distribution. The only example observed on Doi Ang Ka, however, was climbing about on a reedlike grass in a clearing amid wild bananas at about 5,000 feet.

My specimens had the irides bright crimson; the orbital skin deep crimson or crimson-lake; the maxilla plumbeous or slaty; the mandible horn or plumbeous, darker at the tip; the feet and toes orange (duller in the female); the soles yellow; the claws horn-brown.

The adult male has the forehead golden-yellow, changing to dull olive-green on the crown; the nape dull rufous; the scapulars, back, and rump rufous, more or less suffused with olive-green; the upper tail coverts and tail black; the wing coverts and the exposed portion of the quills olive-green, changing to olivaceous-rufous on the innermost secondaries; a white stripe from above the eye to the end of the ear coverts; the entire underparts rufous, suffused with golden-yellow on the abdomen. The adult female differs in having the forehead dull rufous and in lacking the golden suffusion on the underparts.

Among the specimens before me, I find four recognizable races of this piculet: (1) a distinctly green-backed population from Tongking (Chapa, Chora), which are probably *kinneari;* (2) a deeply colored rufous-backed population from Sikkim, Assam (north of the Brahmaputra), Upper Burma (Mansum, Pyepat, Bhamo), which must be considered *ochracea;* (3) a much paler and rather smaller population from North Cachar, Pegu, North and East Thailand, which, for the present, I call *querulivox;* (4) a population from South Tenasserim and Peninsular Thailand, which agree in color with *querulivox* but differ from it in the more robust bill and from all others of the genus in having the orbital skin blackish or slaty instead of red and which, for the present, I take to be *reichenowi.*

The original description of *reichenowi* is so incomplete that, without examination of the type or at least of topotypes, it is impossible to say that the population of Thayetchoung (type locality) are not small-billed, red-orbited birds, in which case *querulivox* (1926) would become merely a synonym of *reichenowi* (1911) and the more southern examples with slaty orbits would be left without a name.

JYNX TORQUILLA CHINENSIS Hesse

CHINESE WRYNECK

Iynx torquilla chinensis HESSE, Orn. Monatsb., vol. 19, 1911, p. 181 (China; type specimen from Peking, *fide* Hesse, Mitteil. Zool. Mus. Berlin, vol. 6, 1912, p. 143).

Iynx torquilla, GYLDENSTOLPE, Journ. Nat. Hist. Soc. Siam, 1915, p. 230 (listed); Ibis, 1920, p. 606 (Khun Tan).

Iynx torquilla japonica, DE SCHAUENSEE, Proc. Acad. Nat. Sci. Philadelphia, 1929, p. 568 (Chiang Rai).

Jynx torquilla japonica, DEIGNAN, Journ. Siam Soc. Nat. Hist. Suppl., 1931, p. 158 (Chiang Mai); 1936, p. 97 (Chiang Mai).

The wryneck, as a winter visitor, doubtless occurs throughout our area. Eisenhofer sent to Stockholm one unsexed, undated specimen from Khun Tan. I have examples from Chiang Mai, Chom Thong, and Mae Sariang. The extreme dates at Chiang Mai, where it was rather common, are September 18 (1936) and March 14 (1931).

This aberrant woodpecker haunts the wastelands where cremations are performed, burnt-over areas, the borders of scrubby jungle, and roadsides. I usually found it gathering ants on the ground, whence it would fly silently to some nearby tree or fence post and wait for the interruption to pass so that it might resume its feeding.

A male had the irides light brown; the orbital skin plumbeous; the maxilla fleshy horn; the mandible plumbeous-horn; the feet and toes light olive-green; the claws horn. A female had the irides dull gray-brown; the bill horn; the feet and toes light horny olive; the claws horn.

The wryneck has the upperparts grayish, finely vermiculated with gray-brown and pale rufous, marked from the nape to the center of the back with broad black streaks and elsewhere with numerous black streaks and bars, gray and pale rufous spots; the primaries barred black and pale rufous; a deep brown band behind the eye and a narrow black streak below the ear coverts; the underparts rufous-buff, deepest on throat and upper breast, marked with narrow black or blackish-brown cross bars, which break up into small sagittate spots on the albescent abdomen.

Order PASSERIFORMES

Family EURYLAIMIDAE

PSARISOMUS DALHOUSIAE DALHOUSIAE (Jameson)

INDIAN LONG-TAILED BROADBILL

[*Eurylaimus*] *Dalhousiae* JAMESON, Edinburgh New Philos. Journ., vol. 18, [not before] April 1835, pp. 389–390 ("Northern India"; type specimen from "Himalayas, 10,000 feet," *fide* Stenhouse, Nov. Zool., vol. 35, 1930, p. 272).

Eurylaimus Dalhousiae "Wilson" ROYLE, Illustrations of the botany and other branches of the natural history of the Himalayan Mountains and of the flora of Cashmere, vol. 1, No. 6, 1839 [=April 1835], pl. 7, fig. 2 (no locality given; figured specimen from "Mussooree, at 6,500 feet of elevation," *fide* Royle, *ibid.*, Suppl. No., 1840, p. lxxviii, where name is corrected to *Eurylaimus Dalhousiae* "Jameson").

Psarisomus dalhousiae, GYLDENSTOLPE, Kungl. Svenska Vet.-Akad. Handl., 1916, p. 86 ("Meh Nja Min" [between Muang Fang and Chiang Rai]).—DEIGNAN, Journ. Siam Soc. Nat. Hist. Suppl., 1931, p. 156 (Doi Suthep).

Psarisomus dalhousiae dalhousiae, GYLDENSTOLPE, Journ. Nat. Hist. Soc. Siam, 1915, p. 229 (Pha Hing); Ibis, 1920, p. 581 ("Northern Siam").—CHASEN and BODEN KLOSS, Journ. Siam Soc. Nat. Hist. Suppl., 1932, p. 236 (Doi Suthep.)—DEIGNAN, Journ. Siam Soc. Nat. Hist. Suppl., 1936, p. 98 (Doi Suthep.)—DE SCHAUENSEE, Proc. Acad. Nat. Sci. Philadelphia, 1934, p. 246 (Doi Suthep).—RILEY, U. S. Nat. Mus. Bull. 172, 1938, p. 252 (Khun Tan, Doi Hua Mot, Doi Langka).

The long-tailed broadbill is an uncommon or rare resident of dense, well-watered evergreen, at whatever elevation, probably throughout our area. During a six weeks' stay on Doi Ang Ka I saw only three, between 4,500 and 5,300 feet; on Doi Suthep it was rare from 3,300 to 4,600 feet; on Phu Kha, a single pair was found at 4,300 feet. On the other hand, it has been taken at feeble altitudes by Fejos (lower slopes of Doi Chiang Dao), by Eisenhofer (Pha Hing), and by my collectors (Bang Pang An), and I have observed it on Doi Mon Khwam Long at about 2,500 feet in mixed-deciduous forest and bamboo (although not far from heavy evergreen).

In deep ravines where, shaded by ginger-lilies and tree ferns and overarched by liana-bound trees, some tiny brook falls down the mountainside among tumbled rocks, this beautiful species travels about in small parties, the members of which explore the branches and climb the creepers in parrotlike fashion, all the while keeping up a conversation of shrill whistles and chattering notes. Specimens whose stomachs I examined had fed only upon insects.

In April and May, when the flocks break up into pairs for breeding, it becomes a much shier bird. On Doi Ang Ka, April 7, 1931, in a tract of comparatively open evergreen, I observed a couple beginning to add the pendent tail to an otherwise completed nest; this nest, a remarkably bulky pyriform structure of closely woven vegetable material, with the entrance hole on the side near the base, was suspended by a length of vine from the end of a branch, about 10 feet from the ground and almost overhanging a small brook.

On Doi Khun Tan, Smith took four examples in various stages of the postjuvenal molt between August 24 and October 25 and two adults in the postnuptial molt, August 26 and September 2.

An adult male (April 29) had the irides with a violet-pink inner ring, smalt-blue outer ring; the eyelids with the inner surface blue, edged greenish yellow, the outer surface of the upper yellowish green, of the lower greenish yellow; the maxilla green, tipped light blue, with a patch on each side near the base dark blue, the corners of the mouth greenish blue, the edges of the commissure violet-gray; the mandible with two orange patches separated by a narrow greenish-yellow strip and otherwise edged by green, the tip and corners of the mouth light blue; the interior of the mouth light blue; the tarsi yellowish olive; the toes dull olive; the claws horny violet. An adult female (April 10) had the irides with a pink inner ring, pinkish-gray outer ring; the upper eyelid with the inner surface bright blue, edged grass green, the outer surface olive-green; the lower eyelid with the inner surface fleshy, edged blue, the outer surface yellow; the maxilla yellowish green, with the tip, anterior half of the culmen, and a patch on each side at the base sky blue, the edges of the commissure violet-gray; the mandible with two pinkish-orange patches separated by greenish yellow and otherwise surrounded by bright green, the tip and corners of the mouth sky blue; the interior of the mouth sky blue; the tarsi dull olive-green; the toes plumbeous-olive; the claws horny brown, fleshy gray at the base.

The adult has a small frontal area, the lores, and the orbital region yellowish green; a large patch on the crown bright blue; a smaller, elongate patch on either side of the occiput yellow, more or less suffused with green or blue; the rest of the crown, the nape, the ear coverts, and the sides of the neck black; the chin and throat bright yellow, this color produced as a collar behind the black but broken on the nape by a narrow patch of bright blue; the yellow of throat and collar posteriorly edged with silvery white, which, in turn, on the upper breast is edged with sky blue; the entire back, upper tail coverts, scapulars, exposed portion of the secondaries, and the upper wing coverts bright, deep green; the primaries with the basal half of the outer web shining turquoise blue changing to deep green on the apical half, the inner web black with a large white area near the base; the rectrices with the upper surface bright, deep blue, the lower surface black; the remaining underparts bright emerald green, sometimes suffused with sky blue. Juveniles differ from adults in having the blue and black portions of the head replaced by bright, deep green and in having the yellow of the throat and collar strongly tinged with green.

Jameson's description of this bird was communicated to the Wernerian Natural History Society on January 24, 1835, but it did not appear in print before the following April. The title page of Royle's work is dated 1839, but the *part* in which the bird is named and figured came out in April 1835. It is thus quite possible that Royle unwittingly acquired the right to be credited with the name and that the original reference must stand as given above. Until this has been proved, however, it seems advisable to consider Jameson the first describer, as Royle sincerely believed to be the case.

Chasen and Boden Kloss (*loc. cit.*) have restricted the type locality of the nominate race to Nepal, but it can probably be shown that Lady Dalhousie's specimen, the type of Jameson's name, came from the western Himalayas.

SERILOPHUS LUNATUS LUNATUS (Gould)

BURMESE SILVER-BREASTED BROADBILL

Eurylaimus lunatus GOULD, Proc. Zool. Soc. London, 1833 [=1834], pp. 133–134 (Rangoon, Burma).

Serilophus lunatus lunatus [*partim*], DE SCHAUENSEE, Proc. Acad. Nat. Sci. Philadelphia, 1929, p. 565 (Doi Suthep).

Serilophus lunatus lunatus, DEIGNAN, Journ. Siam Soc. Nat. Hist. Suppl., 1931, p. 156 (Doi Suthep); 1936, p. 98 (Doi Suthep).—RILEY, U. S. Nat. Mus. Bull. 172, 1938, p. 250 (Khun Tan, Doi Hua Mot).

Serilophus lunatus elizabethae, SMITH, Journ. Siam Soc. Nat. Hist. Suppl., 1934, p. 328 (Khun Tan.)

Serilophus lunatus stolidus, DE SCHAUENSEE, Proc. Acad. Nat. Sci. Philadelphia, 1934, p. 246 (Doi Chiang Dao).

The Burmese race of the silver-breasted broadbill is a rare resident of the evergreen forests of the western provinces, reaching its eastern periphery of range on the hills of the Khun Tan chain. On Doi Suthep it occurred from 2,700 to 5,300 feet and on Doi Chiang Dao from 4,000 to 4,600 feet, but I took it at quite low elevations at Ban Muang Sum and Wiang Khae, where the evergreen reaches the plains.

This broadbill moves in loose bands of as many as 20 individuals through the dense jungle, feeding in the bushes and lower branches of trees with the usual loud whistles and chatter of its family and showing so little fear of man that a flock may be largely collected without causing alarm to the survivors.

I have taken immatures in postjuvenal molt between August 13 and September 2 and adults in postnuptial molt between August 13 and December 25.

Adults had the irides dark brown; the eyelids edged light green; the orbital skin greenish yellow; the bill light blue with the edges of the commissure blue-white, the base, rictus, and narial region orange-yellow (the yellow portions separated from the light blue by slaty blue); the interior of the bill light blue, of the throat orange-yellow; the skin of the chin and throat orange-yellow; the tarsi yellowish olive; the toes olive-slate, each scute edged with orange; the claws blue-white, slaty blue on the basal half at the sides.

The male has the forehead ashy gray, this color changing through ashy brown on the crown, nape, and back, and chestnut-rufous on the rump, to chestnut on the upper tail coverts; the rectrices black, the outer pairs with broad white tips; the upper wing coverts black; the primaries and outer secondaries blue with a broad black area near or at the tip and a white spot on the inner web near the base; the innermost secondaries light chestnut-rufous; a broad black supercilium from above the lores to the nape; the sides of the head ashy brown; the throat and breast ashy gray, fading to white on the abdomen and under tail coverts; the thighs black. The female differs in having a gorget of shining silvery white across the upper breast and sides of the neck behind the ear coverts.

SERILOPHUS LUNATUS ELISABETHAE La Touche

YUNNANESE SILVER-BREASTED BROADBILL

Serilophus lunatus elisabethae LA TOUCHE, Bull. Brit. Orn. Club, vol. 42, 1921, p. 14 (Hokow, southeastern Yunnan).

Serilophus lunatus, GYLDENSTOLPE, Kungl. Svenska Vet.-Akad. Handl., 1913, p. 46 (Ban Huai Hom).

Serilophus lunatus lunatus, GYLDENSTOLPE, Journ. Nat. Hist. Soc. Siam, 1915, p. 229 (Khao Phlung); Ibis, 1920, p. 581 (Khao Phlung, Ban Huai Hom),

Serilophus lunatus lunatus [*partim*], DE SCHAUENSEE, Proc. Acad. Nat. Sci. Philadelphia, 1929, p. 565 (Chiang Saen).

The eastern form of the silver-breasted broadbill seems to be generally distributed, even though rare, in those parts of the North not inhabited by the preceding race. In addition to the localities listed above, it is known from Pha Hing, where Eisenhofer took specimens on May 7 and 8, 1912 (Hannover).

This subspecies apparently occurs as a usual thing at low altitudes but otherwise does not differ in habits from *lunatus*. De Schauensee notes that, at Chiang Saen, he watched a flock flycatching from the upper branches of bushes.

From *lunatus*, *elisabethae* differs only in having the chestnut-rufous of the rump and the chestnut of the upper tail coverts rather deeper in tone.

EURYLAIMUS JAVANICUS PALLIDUS Chasen

THAI BANDED BROADBILL

Eurylaimus javanicus pallidus CHASEN, Bull. Raffles Mus., No. 10, 1935, pp. 43–44 (Khao Nong, Ban Don, Peninsular Thailand).

Eurylaemus javanicus, GYLDENSTOLPE, Journ. Nat. Hist. Soc. Siam, 1915, p. 229 (listed); Kungl. Svenska Vet.-Akad. Handl., 1916, p. 86 (Khun Tan, Pha Hing); Ibis, 1920, p. 581 (Khun Tan, Pha Hing).

The banded broadbill is a bird of extreme rarity in northern Thailand, and I never succeeded in finding it anywhere within our limits. Eisenhofer sent to Stockholm four undated specimens (one male, three females) from Khun Tan and two males, taken April 23 and 28, 1912, from Pha Hing. Gyldenstolpe shot a pair from a small flock at Khun Tan, May 24, 1914. In the Raffles Museum (Singapore) is a male taken by a Thai collector at the foot of Doi Chiang Dao, March 16, 1937. The species should be sought for in districts with extensive lowland evergreen.

The adult male has the head and neck deep vinaceous-red; the back and scapulars black, boldly streaked with yellow; the upper tail coverts black, broadly tipped with yellow; the rectrices black, the outer pairs with a broad subterminal spot or band of buffy white; the primaries black with a yellowish-white spot on the inner web near the base; the secondaries black with a yellow spot on the outer web near the center; the upper wing coverts black; the under wing coverts yellow; the throat vinaceous-red washed with silvery gray; across the upper breast a narrow black gorget, followed by an indistinct broader band of deep silvery gray; the remaining underparts vinaceous-red, changing to vinaceous-yellow on the under tail coverts; the thighs black. The adult female differs from the male only in lacking the black gorget.

CORYDON SUMATRANUS LAOENSIS de Schauensee

THAI DUSKY BROADBILL

Corydon sumatranus laoensis DE SCHAUENSEE, Proc. Acad. Nat. Sci. Philadelphia, vol. 80, 1928 [=1929], p. 555 ("The Siamese Lao"; type specimen from Doi Suthep, *fide* de Schauensee, *ibid.*, p. 571).

Corydon sumatranus, GYLDENSTOLPE, Journ. Nat. Hist. Soc. Siam, 1915, p. 229 (Khun Tan): Kungl. Svenska Vet.-Akad. Handl., 1916, p. 87 (Pha Kho, Khun Tan); Ibis, 1920, p. 582 (Pha Hing, Khun Tan).

Corydon sumatranus laoensis, DE SCHAUENSEE, Proc. Acad. Nat. Sci. Philadelphia, 1928, p. 571 (Doi Suthep).—RILEY, U. S. Nat. Mus. Bull. 172, 1938, p. 247 (Doi Ang Ka, Khun Tan, Huai Salop, Thattafang).

Corydon sumatranus sumatranus, DE SCHAUENSEE, Proc. Acad. Nat. Sci. Philadelphia, 1929, p. 565 (Chiang Saen).

Corydon corydon laoensis, DE SCHAUENSEE, Proc. Acad. Nat. Sci. Philadelphia, 1934, p. 245 (Doi Chiang Dao).—DEIGNAN, Journ. Siam Soc. Nat. Hist. Suppl., 1931, p. 156 (Doi Suthep); 1936, p. 98 (Doi Suthep).

The dusky broadbill is fairly common in the unsettled districts of all the northern provinces from the plains to a maximum elevation of 3,300 feet. On Doi Suthep (the type locality) it is distinctly rare, and I recorded it there only twice: Two at 2,500 feet, October 10, 1936, and two at 3,300 feet, January 23, 1937.

This large species haunts, in fearless flocks of as many as 20 individuals, both the more open evergreen and the mixed-deciduous forest, and behaves much as other members of its family. Gyldenstolpe observes (1916) that the clear whistling note is given only during flight from tree to tree, the carrying croaking note while the bird is at rest.

I took a male with enlarged gonads at Ban Huai Ki, March 28, 1937. De Schauensee, speaking of his original series (taken March 17, 1928), says: "We saw about ten of these birds, all apparently engaged in building the same nest. They were going in and out of a hole in the side. The nest was collected but was unfortunately not completed." Eight adults taken by me between May 24 and December 8 are in postnuptial molt.

My specimens had the irides dark brown; the orbital region rose; the bill rose, the tip and the edges of the commissure plumbeous-blue; the feet, toes, and claws brownish black.

The adult has the throat and upper breast fulvous-white, each feather narrowly margined with deeper fulvous; each primary with a broad band of white near the center; the rectrices (except the two central pairs) crossed by a diagonal, subterminal white bar; a flame-colored patch at the center of the back (usually concealed in life); the rest of the plumage black, faintly suffused with oily green, especially on the underparts, rump, and upper tail coverts.

De Schauensee believed (1929) that the birds of Doi Suthep differed subspecifically from other northern examples in their whiter throat and upper breast. The long series of northern skins before me (taken throughout the year) show that the pale color is seasonal (January 23 to July 20) and wholly due to wear.

Peninsular Thai specimens are variably intermediate between *sumatranus* and *laoensis*, which makes it difficult to decide where a line should be drawn between the two forms. The Indo-Chinese countries farther north, however, are inhabited by a comparatively uniform population, for which de Schauensee's name must be used.

Family PITTIDAE

PITTA CYANEA CYANEA Blyth

BURMESE BLUE PITTA

P[itta] cyanea BLYTH, Journ. Asiat. Soc. Bengal, vol. 12, 1843, p. 1008 (Arakan).

Pitta cyanea, GYLDENSTOLPE, Journ. Nat. Hist. Soc. Siam, 1915, p. 172 (listed); Kungl. Svenska Vet.-Akad. Handl., 1916, p. 84 (Khun Tan); Ibis, 1920, p. 580 (Khun Tan).

Pitta cyanea cyanea, DEIGNAN, Journ. Siam Soc. Nat. Hist. Suppl., 1931, p. 175 (Doi Suthep); 1936, p. 98 (Doi Suthep).—DE SCHAUENSEE, Proc. Acad. Nat. Sci. Philadelphia, 1934, p. 245 (Doi Suthep).—RILEY, U. S. Nat. Mus. Bull. 172, 1938, p. 257 (Khun Tan).

The blue pitta seems to be a rather rare and local permanent resident of the mountain evergreen in the Thanon Thong Chai and Khun Tan ranges, comparatively common only at Doi Khun Tan. On Doi Suthep I found it from 3,500 to 5,000 feet and on Doi Chiang Dao at similar elevations. From the eastern portion of our area the species is known only by an example taken by me in lowland evergreen at Ban Huai Ki (in the border hills between Phrae and Nan Provinces); the specimen is tentatively placed with the Burmese form, although it may just possibly represent an undescribed race.

I found this species, usually by accident, on the ground in the densest cover imaginable: Swampy glades thickly covered with ginger-lilies, or moist groves of thorny palm-scrub. It usually sought escape by running and *jumping* through the vegetation like a small mammal, less often by flying to some low branch where it stopped to survey the intruder.

I have no reason to believe that this bird is at all migratory in our provinces, where it has been recorded at all seasons. Smith took a juvenile on Doi Khun Tan, August 24.

Adult specimens had the irides dark brown; the eye ring slate; the bill black; the rictus and interior of the mouth dusky flesh; the feet, toes, and claws fleshy plumbeous; the soles yellowish white.

The adult male has a broad black median streak from the forehead to the nape; the remainder of the forehead and forecrown ochraceous changing gradually to scarlet on the posterior crown and the nape; the remaining upperparts blue; the primaries black, each with a large white area near the base; a broad black streak from the base of the bill, through the eye, down the side of the neck; the throat white (sometimes streaked with blackish), bordered on either side by a broad black mustachial streak; the remaining underparts shining pale blue (often suffused with pale yellow on the breast, with vinaceous-pink on the belly), closely marked with bold black spots and bars (less so on the center of the abdomen and the vent, which tend to be immaculate white). The adult female differs from the male chiefly in having the upperparts dull brownish, suffused with pale blue, changing gradually to pure blue on the rump, upper tail coverts, and tail.

PITTA SORDIDA CUCULLATA Hartlaub

INDO-CHINESE GREEN-BREASTED PITTA

Pitta cucullata HARTLAUB, Rev. Zool., vol. 6, 1843, p. 65 (Malacca).

This gorgeous bird is known from northern Thailand by a single adult male, collected by my men in an extensive bamboo-brake on Phu Het (Nan Province), June 11, 1936.

It has the forehead and crown to the nape chestnut-brown; the lores, chin, throat, sides of head, and a collar across the nape black; the mantle shining bottle green; the upper tail coverts shining turquoise blue; the rectrices black, narrowly tipped with blue; the closed wing paler bottle green but with a large, conspicuous turquoise-blue area on the shoulder and the primaries black, crossed by a broad white subapical band; an irregular area at the center of the upper abdomen black; the center of the lower abdomen, the region of the vent, and the under tail coverts scarlet-crimson; the under wing coverts and axillaries black; the remaining underparts shining light green, more or less strongly washed with blue.

PITTA BRACHYURA MOLUCCENSIS (P. L. S. Müller)

INDO-CHINESE BUFF-BREASTED PITTA

Turdus Moluccensis P. L. S. MÜLLER, Natursystems Supplements- und Registerband, 1776, p. 144 ("in den moluccischen Inseln," *ex* d'Aubenton, pl. 257, error; type locality corrected to Tenasserim, by Stuart Baker, Journ. Bombay Nat. Hist. Soc., vol. 28, 1921, p. 92).

Pitta cyanoptera, GYLDENSTOLPE, Journ. Nat. Hist. Soc. Siam, 1915, p. 172 (listed); Kungl. Svenska Vet.-Akad. Handl., 1916, p. 85 (Ban Mae Na, Pha Hing); Ibis, 1920, p. 580 ("Northern Siam").

Eisenhofer sent to Stockholm a male of this species, taken at Huai Pu, May 24, 1912, and an unsexed, undated example from Khun Tan; Gyldenstolpe collected one male at Pha Hing, May 9, and a second at Ban Mae Na, June 24, 1914. It was not recorded again from our provinces until, in 1936, I traced an unfamiliar song to this bird, with the result that, between April 27 and July 14, I was able to collect no less than ten specimens. At least during the season of song, it appears to be common and generally distributed in all districts with lowland evergreen and mixed-deciduous forest. My series came from every part of Nan and Chiang Rai Provinces, but Gyldenstolpe's second specimen was found at the foot of Doi Chiang Dao and I have myself heard one singing about halfway between Muang Chiang Dao and Chiang Mai.

The loud, clear, double whistle of the buff-breasted pitta, once learned, is unmistakable and in Nan and Chiang Rai I heard it constantly from the edge of the forest and in adjacent semi-cleared areas invaded by bamboo, *Eupatorium*, etc. The song, usually delivered from the top of a tree, is somewhat ventriloquial, and the singer, despite its brilliant coloration, is by no means easy to pick out from the surrounding foliage.

In some parts of its range the present species is certainly migratory. The fact that all northern records have been made during the breeding season cannot be used to show that this is the case with us also, but merely indicates that most specimens have owed their death to their song—a conclusion supported by the additional fact that, of the 14 northern examples now known, ten are males, two are unsexed, and two are females found in proximity to singing males.

Gyldenstolpe notes that a male had the irides dark brown; the bill black; the feet and toes yellowish white.

Adults have a black median streak, broadening posteriorly, from the forehead to the nape; the rest of the crown buffy brown; on either side of the head a broad black band from the base of the bill, through the eye, to the nape (where the two join to form a nuchal collar); the back, scapulars, and inner secondaries deep green; the upper wing coverts, rump, and upper tail coverts shining malachite blue; the rectrices black, tipped with dull blue; the primaries white with broad black bases and tips, the outer secondaries black with the outer web largely dull blue; the throat white; the center of the abdomen, the vent, and the under tail coverts crimson; the under wing coverts black; the remaining underparts bright buff.

For those who are unconvinced of the applicability of Müller's name, *cyanoptera* of Temminck is available. It is true that Müller described his *Turdus Moluccensis* as "eine grüne Merle mit einem *blauen* Kopfe" (italics mine), but reference to d'Aubenton's plate shows that "blauen" is a mere misprint for "braunen."

PITTA OATESI OATESI (Hume)

Burmese Rufous-naped Pitta

Hydrornis Oatesi Hume, Stray Feathers, vol. 1, 1873, pp. 477–478 (Eastern Pegu Hills).

Pitta oatesi, Gyldenstolpe, Journ. Nat. Hist. Soc. Siam, 1915, p. 172 (listed).

Pitta nipalensis oatesi, Williamson, Journ. Nat. Hist. Soc. Siam, 1918, p. 24 (Muang Wang).

Hydrornis oatesi, GYLDENSTOLPE, Ibis, 1920, p. 580 (Khun Tan, Muang Wang).
Pitta oatesi oatesi, DE SCHAUENSEE, Proc. Acad. Nat. Sci. Philadelphia, 1934, p. 244 (Doi Chiang Dao, Doi Suthep).—DEIGNAN, Journ. Siam Soc. Nat. Hist. Suppl., 1935, p. 64 (Doi Ang Ka); 1936, p. 98 (Doi Suthep).—RILEY, U. S. Nat. Mus. Bull. 172, 1938, p. 255 (Doi Langka, Khun Tan).

This large pitta has been found only at the various localities listed above, living in the densest evergreen from 3,000 to 5,400 feet.

On moonlit nights, upon the higher northern peaks, can be heard a melodious *bong-bong*, nearly always answered at once by a similar call at a lower pitch. This lovely sound is, by the hill-people everywhere, attributed to the *pet bong* (which seems to mean "bong duck" but may be merely a combination of onomatopoeic syllables), described as a green bird which lives along small brooks in the forest. The identity of the singer was ascertained only when the Karens on Doi Ang Ka brought me a snared example of the present species and identified it as the mysterious *pet bong.*

So heavy is the undergrowth amid which it lives that the bird is almost never observed and, if seen, will probably be mistaken for a small mammal as it jumps and scuttles through the vegetation; only by the nocturnal calls can its numbers be estimated.

I have collected specimens with enlarged gonads on Doi Ang Ka, April 7, 1931, and September 4, 1935. Williamson's juvenile, "a very young bird," was taken in September 1917.

A breeding male had the irides brown; the maxilla dark wood brown with the tip and edges of the commissure horny; the mandible dark wood brown, orange-horny below and becoming a true light orange at the base; the rictus and interior of the mouth salmon-pink; the feet and toes light orange; the soles bright orange; the claws orange-white.

The adult male has the whole head and nape rufous, usually with a more or less distinct black band behind the eye and above the ear coverts; the remaining upperparts dull, dark green, often more or less strongly suffused with blue on the rump; the chin and throat fulvous, more or less suffused with pale pink; the remaining underparts rufous, becoming deep buff posteriorly (the breast sometimes suffused with pink). The adult female differs in having the green upperparts more or less suffused with rufous; the underparts deep fulvous, with black bases and bars on the feathers of the lower foreneck showing through.

ANTHOCINCLA PHAYREI PHAYREI Blyth

BURMESE EARED PITTA

A[nthocincla] Phayrei BLYTH, Journ. Asiat. Soc. Bengal, vol. 31, 1862, p. 343 (Toungoo, Burma).

Anthocincla phayrei, GYLDENSTOLPE, Journ. Nat. Hist. Soc. Siam, 1915, p. 172 (listed); Kungl. Svenska Vet.-Akad. Handl., 1916, p. 84 (Pha Kho, Khun Tan).

Anthocincla phayrii, GYLDENSTOLPE, Ibis, 1920, p. 579 (Pha Kho, Khun Tan).

Anthocincla phayrei phayrei, DE SCHAUENSEE, Proc. Acad. Nat. Sci. Philadelphia, 1934, p. 244 (Khun Tan).

The eared pitta has been collected only eight times in our provinces. In addition to the three specimens recorded by Gyldenstolpe and the one taken by de Schauensee, there are in Stockholm two undated females from Khun Tan and one male from Pha Hing, May 7, 1912 (Eisenhofer), and in Washington a male from Phu Kha, 5,000 feet, April 11, 1936 (Deignan).

Beyond the fact that it dwells upon the ground in dense evergreen forest, nothing is known of the bird's habits in the northern districts.

Gyldenstolpe records that one of his specimens had the irides brown; the bill black; the feet and toes pale brown. De Schauensee's female had the irides light brown; the bill horny brown; the feet, toes, and claws flesh.

The adult male has, along each side of the crown, a broad, black-barred, light brown supercilium from the base of the maxilla to the nape, the feathers becoming white posteriorly and lengthened to form pointed aigrettes; the sides of the head, the center of the crown, and the entire nape black (the ear coverts streaked with light brown); the upper wing coverts with deep buff tips and black subterminal bands; the primaries blackish brown with a large area of buff at the base; the remaining upperparts deep rufous-brown; the throat buffy white, bordered on each side by an ill-defined mustachial streak formed by narrow black tips to the feathers; the under tail coverts buffy rose; the remaining underparts deep rufous-buff, more or less spotted and barred with black on the breast and sides of the body. The adult female differs in having the black of the head and nape replaced by deep brown; the underparts fulvous, more heavily marked with black; the under tail coverts paler and duller, more buffy than pink.

Northern birds become slightly deeper in color from west to east but all must be called *phayrei.* The population of eastern Thailand is almost exactly intermediate between *phayrei* and *obscura.*

Family ALAUDIDAE

MIRAFRA ASSAMICA SUBSESSOR Deignan

LAO COLLARED BUSH LARK

Mirafra assamica subsessor DEIGNAN, Zoologica, vol. 26, pt. 3, 1941, p. 241 (Chiang Mai, North Thailand).

Mirafra microptera, GYLDENSTOLPE, Journ. Nat. Hist. Soc. Siam, 1915, p. 171 (listed); Kungl. Svenska Vet.-Akad. Handl., 1916, p. 30 (Khun Tan, Sop Tui); Ibis, 1920, p. 459 ("Throughout northern Siam").

Mirafra assamica, DEIGNAN, Journ. Siam Soc. Nat. Hist. Suppl., 1931, p. 154 (Chiang Mai).

Mirafra assamica marionae [*partim*], DE SCHAUENSEE, Proc. Acad. Nat. Sci. Philadelphia, 1934, p. 239 (Chiang Mai).—RILEY, U. S. Nat. Mus. Bull. 172, 1938, p. 262 (Chiang Mai).

Mirafra assamica marionae, DEIGNAN, Journ. Siam Soc. Nat. Hist. Suppl., 1936, p. 98 (Chiang Mai).

Despite Gyldenstolpe's assertion (1920) that this lark is "very common . . . throughout northern Siam," it is, in fact, definitely known only from the basins of the Mae Ping and the Mae Wang (if, indeed, the birds of Lampang Province are of the same race as those of Chiang Mai).

On the Chiang Mai plain it is a common inhabitant of dry places with short grass and light bush-cover, such as may be found along roadsides and about ruined *phrachedi;* after the harvest it occurs also among the rice stubbles, often in small flocks or family parties. When surprised, even in so exposed a situation as the middle of a highway, it has a characteristic habit of first running, then squatting and drawing in the head; upon one's closer approach it takes off with feeble flight to drop headlong into denser cover in the manner of a hemipode. The song, which is pretty but weak, may be given from a fence post or the top of a bush but is frequently delivered in the course of a special flight, in which the bird leaves its perch, ascends a little way into the air, and, after suspending itself for a few seconds by fluttering, sails to the ground on outspread wings. The stomach of one of my specimens contained grass seeds and ants.

Examples with the gonads enlarged were taken on May 22 and 31, but a bird in postnatal molt (just out of the nest) was collected as early as May 6. Specimens in postjuvenal molt were shot on July 13 and August 13, while adults in postnuptial molt were got between August 15 and November 24.

Adults had the irides bright, light brown or dark brown; the maxilla blackish brown or horny brown, with the edges of the commissure pale horny or pale fleshy; the mandible pale fleshy, sometimes with the apical half horny white; the rictus fleshy pink; the feet and toes yellowish flesh or fleshy yellow; the claws fleshy or horny brown.

The adult has the feathers of the upperparts blackish brown, broadly edged on the crown with sandy buff, on the nape with buffy white (to form a more or less distinct collar), on the mantle with ashy brown; the wings blackish brown, the primaries and outer secondaries broadly margined along both inner and outer web with rufous (conspicuous in flight), the inner secondaries and the coverts broadly edged with rufous-buff or sandy buff; the abbreviated tail blackish brown, each feather very narrowly edged with sandy buff; an indistinct buffy-white supercilium; the ear coverts rufous-buff, tipped with blackish brown; the chin and throat buffy white (some of the feathers with minute blackish-brown tips), this color continued up behind the ear coverts to connect with the nuchal collar; the remaining underparts pale buff, the feathers of the breast with broad black central streaks to form a conspicuous gorget. The juvenile resembles the adult but differs chiefly in having all the feathers of the upperparts with narrow rufous-buff tips and those of the breast with rounded spots rather than streaks.

Family HIRUNDINIDAE

HIRUNDO RUSTICA GUTTURALIS Scopoli

WHITE-BELLIED HOUSE SWALLOW

Hirundo (*gutturalis*) SCOPOLI, Deliciae florae et faunae insubricae, pt. 2, 1786, p. 96 ("In nova Guiana," error; type specimen from Antigua, Panay, Philippine Islands, *fide* Hartert, Vögel der paläarktischen Fauna, vol. 1, 1910, p. 803).

Hirundo rustica gutturalis, DE SCHAUENSEE, Proc. Acad. Nat. Sci. Philadelphia, 1929, p. 561 (Chiang Saen).—DEIGNAN, Journ. Siam Soc. Nat. Hist. Suppl., 1931, p. 153 (Chiang Mai); 1936, p. 99 (Chiang Mai).

Six males from Chiang Saen (de Schauensee) and two males and a female from Chiang Mai (Deignan) seem to be the only examples yet taken in our area; it is, nevertheless, a very common bird of the northern lowlands during two-thirds of the year. At Chiang Mai it appeared in numbers between July 13 (1935) and July 21 (1929, 1930) and thereafter was irregularly common on the plain until the following spring (latest date: March 29, 1929). I have found it along the Nan river, however, as late as April 9 and took a specimen as far south as Chanthaburi, May 5, 1937.

In season the common swallow can usually be seen tirelessly flying above such open country as ricefields and marshes, frequently in company with others of its family. Unlike the red-rumped swallow, the present form rests and roosts among the reeds rather than on telegraph wires.

Examples of either sex had the irides dark brown; the bill black; the feet and toes dark brown; the soles horny brown; the claws brownish black.

The adult has the forehead chestnut; the remaining upperparts glossy steel blue; each of the rectrices (except the central pair) with a diagonal white mark on the inner web near the center; the throat chestnut; a steel blue gorget across the upper breast, more or less broken at the center by encroaching chestnut; the rest of the underparts white, more or less suffused with creamy rufous. The immature differs in having the upperparts less glossy, the gorget unglossed brown.

Hirundo rustica tytleri, in which the entire underparts are chestnut, should be watched for among the flocks of *gutturalis*. An atypical bird (*tytleri*> *gutturalis*) was collected by me at Ban Pha Tao (on the Nan river just south of our area), April 10, 1937.

HIRUNDO SMITHII FILIFERA Stephens

INDIAN WIRE-TAILED SWALLOW

Hi[rundo]? filifera STEPHENS, *in* Shaw's "General Zoology," vol. 13, pt. 2, 1826, pp. 78–79 (India, *ex* Latham).

Hirundo smithii filifera, DEIGNAN, Journ. Siam Soc. Nat. Hist. Suppl., 1936, p. 99 (Chiang Mai).—RILEY, U. S. Nat. Mus. Bull. 172, 1938, p. 267 (Salwin river).

The status of the wire-tailed swallow is uncertain: It has been recorded only during the cold weather but will doubtless eventually be found to breed on precipices along the larger rivers. At Chiang Mai, between January 28 and February 14, 1936, one to four individuals were constantly seen over a small marsh with large flocks of common and red-rumped swallows, and one was collected January 30. A second specimen was taken above the Salwin at Thattafang, October 13, 1936. The species should be looked for also along the Mae Khong between Chiang Saen and Chiang Khong.

In December 1935 I found this bird very common in the gorges of the Mae Ping (just south of our limits), sailing over the river and resting upon the large sand bars, in actions and notes resembling the preceding form.

My specimens had the irides brown; the bill black; the feet and toes brownish black; the claws black.

The wiretail differs from the house swallow in having the entire crown chestnut; the "wires" of the outermost tail feathers much more filiform; the entire underparts immaculate white. Only the last character is ordinarily noticeable in the field.

HIRUNDO STRIOLATA SUBSTRIOLATA (Hume)

KHASYA HILLS STRIATED SWALLOW

L[illia] substriolata HUME, Stray Feathers, vol. 5, 1877, pp. 264–265 (Cachar).

Hirundo daurica nepalensis, DE SCHAUENSEE, Proc. Acad. Nat. Sci. Philadelphia, 1929, p. 561 (Chiang Mai, Chiang Rai).

Hirundo daurica nipalensis [*partim*], DEIGNAN, Journ. Siam Soc. Nat. Hist. Suppl., 1931, p. 153 (Chiang Mai [*partim*], Doi Suthep [*partim*]); 1936, p. 99 (Chiang Mai [*partim*], Doi Suthep [*partim*]).

Hirundo daurica nipalensis, RILEY, U. S. Nat. Mus. Bull. 172, 1938, p. 267 (Doi Ang Ka).

Striated swallows are irregularly common between October 8 (1936) and July 24 (1930) in the valleys of the Mae Khong and the Mae

Ping (south to the northern entrance of the Gorges) and on the mountains to 5,500 feet. Mayr has shown (Ibis, 1941, pp. 367–370) that at least two races, separable only in fresh adult plumage, occur in our area and, of 12 such specimens examined by him, 9 collected between November 12 and January 6 (Chiang Rai, Chiang Mai, Chom Thong) belonged to the present form. I place here also (with reservations) immature examples taken between November 12 and February 10 at Chiang Mai, Chom Thong, Ban Sop Mae Chaem, Ban Mae Klang, and on Doi Ang Ka at 3,500 feet. It is probable that *substriolata* is merely a winter visitor and that all striated swallows seen late in spring and during summer are of the following (presumably resident) race.

This species, as seen in our provinces, differs from other swallows chiefly in its habit of roosting in great numbers on telegraph lines, rather than among the reeds.

Two adults from Chom Thong, November 12, are molting remiges and rectrices. Immatures taken between November 12 and December 7 are molting the body feathers.

Specimens collected by de Schauensee (1929) had the irides brown; the bill black; the feet and toes horny brown.

The adult has the upperparts, except for a conspicuous chestnut-rufous rump band, steel blue; a narrow superciliary line and the sides of the neck chestnut-rufous; the entire underparts (except for the black longer under tail coverts) white, suffused with salmon-buff and everywhere heavily streaked with black. The immature differs in having the upperparts unglossed brown and the chestnut-rufous areas paler.

Mayr observes (*loc. cit.*, p. 369): "Birds from North Siam are slightly more narrowly streaked below and have longer tails . . . They are best included with *substriolata* until more material of the latter is known."

HIRUNDO STRIOLATA STANFORDI Mayr

UPPER BURMESE STRIATED SWALLOW

Hirundo striolata stanfordi MAYR, Ibis, 1941, p. 367 (Tamu, Myitkyina district, Upper Burma).

Hirundo striolata, WILLIAMSON, Journ. Nat. Hist. Soc. Siam, 1918, p. 23 (Chiang Mai).

Chelidon daurica striolata, GYLDENSTOLPE, Ibis, 1920, p. 579 (Chiang Rai, error [= Chiang Mai]).

Hirundo daurica nipalensis [*partim*], DEIGNAN, Journ. Siam Soc. Nat. Hist. Suppl., 1931, p. 153 (Chiang Mai [*partim*], Doi Suthep [*partim*]); 1936, p. 99 (Chiang Mai [*partim*], Doi Suthep [*partim*]).

Hirundo daurica striolata, DE SCHAUENSEE, Proc. Acad. Nat. Sci. Philadelphia, 1934, p. 237 (Doi Chiang Dao).—DEIGNAN, Journ. Siam Soc. Nat. Hist. Suppl., 1936, p. 99 (Chiang Mai).

From the fact that an example from Muang Ngoi, Laos, June 10, was found by Mayr to be nearest *stanfordi*, it may for the present be assumed that summer birds from our area are also of that race, and I place here, accordingly, the female taken in June 1917 at Chiang Mai by Williamson. Mayr, in describing *stanfordi*, records two specimens from Doi Chiang Dao, December 14, and a third from Chiang Mai, November 11.

The bird of November 11 is molting remiges and rectrices.

This form differs from the last in its larger size (wing length 128–136 mm., against 120–124 mm.); its deeper chestnut-rufous rump band; its broader streaking below; the presence of a large, glossy black spot on the lower flanks where the feathers of rump and thighs meet.

DELICHON URBICA WHITELEYI (Swinhoe)

East Siberian House Martin

C[helidon] whiteleyi Swinhoe, Proc. Zool. Soc. London, 1862 [=1863], p. 320 (Peking, China).

Delichon urbica cashmeriensis [*partim*], Deignan, Journ. Siam Soc. Nat. Hist. Suppl., 1931, p. 153 (Chiang Mai [*partim*]).

Delichon urbica whiteleyi, Rogers and Deignan, Proc. Biol. Soc. Washington, 1934, p. 91 (Chiang Mai).

Delichon urbica whiteleyi [*partim*], Deignan, Journ. Siam Soc. Nat. Hist. Suppl., 1936, p. 98 (Chiang Mai [*partim*]).

I have twice taken the Siberian house martin on the Chiang Mai plain: An immature male, March 20, 1931, and an adult male, January 23, 1937.

House martins of one kind or another are irregularly common in flocks at Chiang Mai from November 23 (1929) to March 20 (1931). Since they are usually seen high in the sky and have never been found roosting, too few specimens have been collected to give any true idea of the status of the various forms present.

My immature bird had the irides dark brown; the bill black; the feet and toes (beneath the feathers) pale fleshy; the claws brown.

The genus *Delichon* is an extraordinarily difficult group of small swallows having the tail somewhat forked and the feet and toes densely clothed with white feathers. The present form has the rump and upper tail coverts (*including the longest ones*) white; the remaining upperparts steel blue; the entire underparts white; the under wing coverts gray-brown, barred with dark brown and white in the region of the carpal and carpometacarpal joints.

DELICHON DASYPUS DASYPUS (Bonaparte)

Japanese House Martin

[*Chelidon*] *dasypus* "Temm." Bonaparte, Conspectus generum avium, vol. 1, 1850, p. 343 (Borneo, *ex* Temminck).

Delichon urbica cashmeriensis [*partim*], Deignan, Journ. Siam Soc. Nat. Hist. Suppl. 1931, p. 153 (Chiang Mai [*partim*]).

Delichon urbica whiteleyi [*partim*], Deignan, Journ. Siam Soc. Nat. Hist. Suppl., 1936, p. 98 (Chiang Mai [*partim*]).

An immature female taken by me at Chiang Mai, January 30, 1937, with the wing measuring 108 mm. in length, seems to be referable to the Japanese race. I place under this name also the two long-winged females recorded (1938) by Riley from Sichon (Peninsular Thailand).

From *whiteleyi*, *dasypus* differs in having the longest upper tail coverts black; the white underparts suffused, especially on the breast, with gray-brown; the longer under tail coverts with more or less well-marked gray-brown centers.

The Chiang Mai bird differs from any other I have examined in having the long, black upper tail coverts narrowly edged with white near the tip; this is possibly a mark of immaturity.

DELICHON DASYPUS CASHMERIENSIS (Gould)

KASHMIRI HOUSE MARTIN

Chelidon Cashmeriensis GOULD, Proc. Zool. Soc. London, 1858, p. 356 (Kashmir).

Delichon urbica cashmeriensis, DE SCHAUENSEE, Proc. Acad. Nat. Sci. Philadelphia, 1929, p. 560 (Doi Suthep).

Delichon urbica cashmeriensis [*partim*], DEIGNAN, Journ. Siam Soc. Nat. Hist. Suppl., 1931, p. 153 (Doi Suthep).

Delichon urbica nigrimentalis, CHASEN and BODEN KLOSS, Journ. Siam Soc. Nat. Hist. Suppl., 1932, p. 238 (Doi Suthep).—DEIGNAN, Journ. Siam Soc. Nat. Hist. Suppl., 1936, p. 98 (Doi Suthep).

De Schauensee has (in my opinion, correctly) identified as *cashmeriensis* a male (wing length of 100 mm.) and a female (wing length of only 94 mm., but with primaries in molt!), taken on Doi Suthep at 5,500 feet, December 11 and 30, 1928. Chasen and Boden Kloss have recorded (as *nigrimentalis*) a male collected by Aagaard at 4,600 feet in the spring of 1931.

House martins are irregularly common over Doi Suthep (4,600 to 5,500 feet) from November 15 (1930) to April 2 (1931) and were numerous at 5,500 feet, May 11 and 12, 1935. On Doi Ang Ka I observed a large flock at 6,500 feet in April 1931. The difficulties of collecting these swallows in the hills are even greater than in the lowlands, and it is quite impossible to know how many forms occur.

The Kashmiri house martin differs from *whiteleyi* in the same characters as *dasypus;* from the latter it is separable by its lesser size.

The winter visitors to the hills of northern Thailand probably come from the mountains of southwestern China, where there seems to be a population intermediate between *cashmeriensis* and *nigrimentalis* (if the latter be valid), varying greatly in size and occasionally showing a dark chin spot, but on the whole nearer *cashmeriensis*. The specimen recorded by Chasen and Boden Kloss (*loc. cit.*) is quite likely an example of this unstable population rather than of true *nigrimentalis* (whose winter quarters are still unknown); since they lacked comparative material and have failed to give measurements of their bird, I cannot accept the identification with any confidence.

RIPARIA CONCOLOR SINTAUNGENSIS (Stuart Baker)

EASTERN DUSKY CRAG MARTIN

Krimnochelidon concolor sintaungensis STUART BAKER, Bull. Brit. Orn. Club, vol. 54, 1933, p. 24 (Sintaung, Southern Shan States).

Krimnochelidon concolor, RILEY, Journ. Siam Soc. Nat. Hist. Suppl., 1933, p. 155 (Doi Langka).

Krimnochelidon concolor sitaungensis, DE SCHAUENSEE, Proc. Acad. Nat. Sci. Philadelphia, 1934, p. 237 (Doi Chiang Dao, Doi Suthep).—DEIGNAN, Journ. Siam Soc. Nat. Hist. Suppl., 1936, p. 99 (Doi Suthep, Doi Chiang Dao).

Krimnochelidon concolor sintaugensis, RILEY, U. S. Nat. Mus. Bull. 172, 1938, p. 264 (Doi Langka, Doi Hua Mot).

The crag martin has been found within our provinces only on the mountains listed above, on all of which it seems to occur commonly but irregularly throughout the year, from 4,600 to 5,500 feet.

Above the summit of Doi Suthep, as well as on Doi Chiang Dao, this swallow was usually seen in company with the gray-rumped swiftlet.

The dusky crag martin has the entire plumage dark grayish brown (paler below), the feathers of the chin, throat, and upper breast broadly margined with pale rufous; each of the rectrices, except the central and outermost pairs, with a large white spot on the inner web.

The white spots on the tail feathers will be sufficient to distinguish the present species from any swift that may occur with it.

RIPARIA RIPARIA IJIMAE (Lönnberg)

JAPANESE GORGETED SAND MARTIN

Clivicola riparia ijimae LÖNNBERG, Journ. Coll. Sci. Imp. Univ. Tokyo, vol. 23, art. 14, 1908, pp. 38–39 (Sakhalin Island).

An unsexed, worn, and badly mutilated specimen, shot by me at Ban Na Noi (Nan Province), April 2, 1937, is the sole example of the species yet known from Thailand.

This bird, the only one of its kind observed at Na Noi, was associated with a migrating flock of house swallows, sailing above the small river (tributary to the Mae Nan) that flows just east of the town. At Ban Pha Tao, however, a few miles south of our limits, on April 10, numerous others were seen (but could not be collected) with a great flock of *Hirundo rustica* subspp. over an area of broad sand bars. It appears then that the Japanese sand martin is by no means a rare visitor, at least to the basin of the Mae Nan.

The present form has the entire upperparts gray-brown; the underparts white, except for a broad gray-brown breast band.

RIPARIA PALUDICOLA CHINENSIS (J. E. Gray)

CHINESE BROWN-THROATED SAND MARTIN

Hirundo chinensis J. E. GRAY, *in* Hardwicke, Illustrations of Indian zoology, vol. 1, pt. 2, 1830–1832 [=1830], pl. 35, fig. 3 (no locality given=China).

Riparia paludicola chinensis, GYLDENSTOLPE, Kungl. Svenska Vet.-Akad. Handl., 1916, p. 83 (Chiang Rai); Ibis, 1920, p. 579 (Chiang Rai).—DE SCHAUENSEE, Proc. Acad. Nat. Sci. Philadelphia, 1929, p. 560 (Chiang Rai, Chiang Saen Kao).

Riparia chinensis chinensis, RILEY, U. S. Nat. Mus. Bull. 172, 1938, p. 264 (Hang Tum Kai, Mae Hiak [localities on the Salwin]).

This diminutive swallow is, at least locally, very common on the Salwin, the Mae Kok (Chiang Rai), and the Mae Khong but has never been found elsewhere in our provinces (although it occurs in small numbers on the Mae Ping *below* the Gorges).

Gyldenstolpe has noted (1916) that the flocks rest on the sand bars, often crowding the branches of the scattered bushes growing in such places.

Specimens taken by Smith, January 15, 1933, on the bank of the Salwin, were captured at night in holes, which may indicate that breeding was in progress at that time.

This species has the upperparts gray-brown, distinctly paler on the rump and upper tail coverts; the entire throat and breast pale gray-brown, changing to white on the remaining underparts.

Family CAMPEPHAGIDAE

PERICROCOTUS SPECIOSUS ELEGANS (McClelland)

BURMESE SCARLET MINIVET

Phoenicornis elegans MCCLELLAND, Proc. Zool. Soc. London, 1839 [=1840], pp. 156–157 (Assam).

Pericrocotus fraterculus, GYLDENSTOLPE, Kungl. Svenska Vet.-Akad. Handl., 1913, p. 33 (Pak Pan); 1916, p. 72 (Pha Kho, Khun Tan, Pang Hua Phong, Doi Pha Sakaeng); Journ. Nat. Hist. Soc. Siam, 1915, p. 168 (listed).

Pericrocotus speciosus fraterculus, GYLDENSTOLPE, Ibis, 1920, p. 571 ("Throughout northern Siam").—DE SCHAUENSEE, Proc. Acad. Nat. Sci. Philadelphia, 1928, p. 569 (Doi Suthep); 1929, p. 550 (Doi Suthep, Chiang Saen).

Pericrocotus speciosus speciosus, DE SCHAUENSEE, Proc. Acad. Nat. Sci. Philadelphia, 1929, p. 550 (Doi Suthep).

Pericrocotus flammeus speciosus, DEIGNAN, Journ. Siam Soc. Nat. Hist. Suppl., 1931, p. 146 (Doi Suthep).

Pericrocotus flammeus bakeri, CHASEN and BODEN KLOSS, Journ. Siam Soc. Nat. Hist. Suppl., 1932, p. 241 (Doi Suthep).

Pericrocotus flammeus elegans, DE SCHAUENSEE, Proc. Acad. Nat. Sci. Philadelphia, 1934, p. 222 (Doi Suthep, Khun Tan, Doi Chiang Dao).—RILEY, U. S. Nat. Mus. Bull. 172, 1938, p. 267 (Doi Hua Mot, Doi Langka, "Doi Phra Chao" [=Doi Saket ?], Doi Buak Hua Chang, Ban Nam Khian, Khun Tan, Chiang Dao, Doi Suthep).—GREENWAY, Bull. Mus. Comp. Zool., 1940, p. 186 (Doi Suthep, Doi Saket, Chiang Dao, Doi Nang Kaeo, Doi Ang Ka).

Pericrocotus flammeus fraterculus, DEIGNAN, Journ. Siam Soc. Nat. Hist. Suppl., 1936, p. 100 (Doi Suthep).

This large minivet is a very common permanent resident of the more open evergreen and the mixed-deciduous forest in every part of our area, from the plains to about 5,500 feet.

The various Thai species of this group have very similar habits. When not breeding they are found in loose bands of 20 or more individuals, which move restlessly through the jungle, from the top of one high tree to the next, all the while keeping up an endless conversation of melodious chatter and snatches of song.

The molts and plumages of the minivets seem to be poorly understood and some quite recent authors have erroneously stated that color change occurs in these birds *without* molt. In northern Thailand, breeding takes place in April and May (Doi Angka, April 18). Birds of the year wear a barred juvenal plumage during the following summer. This is lost by a partial postjuvenal molt (August 29–November 21); some males pass directly into the orange first-nuptial dress but the majority assume a first-winter plumage resembling the habit of the adult female but distinguishable by the orange suffusion on front, throat, and breast, and the orange tinge in the retained juvenal remiges and rectrices (first-winter females are recognizable from adults only by the juvenal remiges and rectrices). In spring (February 18–April 19) there is a partial prenuptial molt: The yellow body feathers of the male are replaced by orange; the female is scarcely to be known from old birds of the same sex. During the following summer and autumn there is a complete postnuptial molt by which the male assumes the scarlet and black plumage of the old adult. I have taken old adults in postnuptial molt from June 13 to November 22.

My specimens had the irides brown; the bill feet, toes, and claws black.

The adult male has the entire head, throat, neck, scapulars, and upper half of the back glossy blue-black; the lower back, rump, and upper tail coverts bright scarlet; the rectrices bright scarlet, the central pair with the entire inner web and the base of the outer web black (rarely with both webs all scarlet or all black); the wing quills with the basal half bright scarlet, the apical half black, the *inner secondaries* also with a conspicuous, elongate scarlet spot along the outer web near the tip; the thighs dark gray; the remaining underparts bright scarlet. The adult female has the lores gray; the forehead, forecrown, and sides of the head deep yellow, changing to olive-washed gray on the posterior crown, scapulars, and upper half of the back; the lower back, rump, and upper tail coverts deep yellow or olivaceous-yellow; the central pair of rectrices wholly black, the others deep yellow with an outwardly decreasing amount of black; the wings as in the male but with deep yellow in place of scarlet; the thighs dark gray; the remaining underparts bright yellow.

PERICROCOTUS BREVIROSTRIS (Vigors)

SHORT-BILLED MINIVET

Muscipeta brevirostris VIGORS, Proc. Comm. Sci. Corr. Zool. Soc. London, pt. 1, 1830–1831 [=1831], p. 43 (Himalayas; "[type specimen] probably [from] Sikkim foothills," *fide* Mayr, Ibis, 1940, p. 720).

Percrocotus [*sic*] *brevirostris neglectus*, CHASEN and BODEN KLOSS, Journ. Siam Soc. Nat. Hist. Suppl., 1932, p. 241 (Doi Suthep).

Pericrocotus brevirostris neglectus [*partim*], DE SCHAUENSEE, Proc. Acad. Nat. Sci. Philadelphia, 1934, p. 224 (Doi Suthep).

Pericrocotus brevirostris neglectus, DEIGNAN, Journ. Siam Soc. Nat. Hist. Suppl., 1936, p. 100 (Doi Suthep).

The short-billed minivet has so far been found in Thailand only on Doi Ang Ka and Doi Suthep, between 4,000 and 5,500 feet. It may be expected to occur on all the higher peaks of the western provinces.

Within its altitudinal range this species occurs in the same places as the preceding bird, from which it is only with difficulty separable in the field.

I have no notes on the breeding season or the sequence of plumages in the young. Adults in postnuptial molt have been taken between July 14 and October 26.

My specimens had the irides dark brown; the bill, feet, toes, and claws black.

The adult male differs from the adult male of the scarlet minivet in its lesser size; in having the red portions of the plumage scarlet-crimson rather than scarlet; in having the central rectrices black with (in fresh plumage) a very narrow red edging along the outer web on the apical half; in lacking the elongate spot on the inner secondaries. The adult female differs from the adult female of the scarlet minivet in its lesser size and in lacking the elongate spot on the inner secondaries.

PERICROCOTUS ETHOLOGUS CRYPTUS Mayr

THAI FLAME-COLORED MINIVET

Pericrocotus ethologus cryptus MAYR, Ibis, 1940, p. 719 (Doi Pha Hom Pok, North Thailand).

Pericrocotus brevirostris, WILLIAMSON, Journ. Nat. Hist. Soc. Siam, 1918, p. 20 (Doi Nga Chang).—GYLDENSTOLPE, Ibis, 1920, p. 571 (Doi Nga Chang).

Pericrocotus brevirostris affinis [*partim*], DE SCHAUENSEE, Proc. Acad. Nat. Sci. Philadelphia, 1929, p. 551 (Doi Suthep).

Pericrocotus brevirostris affinis, DEIGNAN, Journ. Siam Soc. Nat. Hist. Suppl., 1931, p. 146 (Doi Suthep); 1936, p. 100 (Doi Suthep).—DE SCHAUENSEE, Proc. Acad. Nat. Sci. Philadelphia, 1934, p. 224 (Doi Suthep).—RILEY, U. S. Nat. Mus. Bull. 172, 1938, p. 269 (Khun Tan).

Peircrocotus [*sic*] *brevirostris affinis*, CHASEN and BODEN KLOSS, Journ. Siam Soc. Nat. Hist. Suppl., 1932, p. 242 (Doi Suthep).

Pericrocotus brevirostris neglectus [*partim*], DE SCHAUENSEE, Proc. Acad. Nat. Sci. Philadelphia, 1934, p. 224 (Doi Chiang Dao).

The flame-colored minivet has been collected only on the mountains listed above, but it should be looked for on other high peaks in the more western districts. The normal range seems to be the evergreen from 4,000 to 4,600 feet, although it has been found during the cold weather in the dry, deciduous forest at the very foot of Doi Suthep (about 1,000 feet).

Here again nothing is recorded of the breeding season or of the sequence of plumages. An adult pair from Doi Suthep, July 16, are in postnuptial molt. Two red males from Doi Khun Tan, February 13 and 27, are undergoing molt of the feathers of head and throat. I have been unable to find evidence of a first-nuptial dress, different from that of older birds, in either *P. brevirostris* or *P. e. cryptus*.

The present form is separated from *brevirostris* by a number of characters that, if the two did not breed together over a large area, would be considered of merely subspecific value. The adult male of *cryptus* is distinguished from the adult male of the short-billed minivet by having the red portions of the plumage a rather less intense scarlet-crimson, the black portions (especially the throat) less glossed; a narrow whitish or pink margin to the outer web of the first primary; the red on the inner secondaries continued to the tip as a narrow margin along the outer web. The adult female of *cryptus* is separated from that of *brevirostris* by having the yellow on the head restricted to a narrow frontal band, as well as by a number of other minor differences.

Pericrocotus solaris ripponi, described from the Southern Shan States by Stuart Baker (Fauna of British India, Birds, ed. 2, vol. 2, 1924, p. 327), may prove to be an earlier naming of this race.

PERICROCOTUS ETHOLOGUS ETHOLOGUS Bangs and Phillips

CHINESE FLAME-COLORED MINIVET

Pericrocotus brevirostris ethologus BANGS and PHILLIPS, Bull. Mus. Comp. Zool., vol. 58, 1914, pp. 282–283 (Hsien Shan, Hupeh, China).

Pericrocotus solaris solaris [*partim*], RILEY, U. S. Nat. Mus. Bull. 172, 1938, p. 270 (Doi Langka [*partim*]).

This minivet is known as a Thai bird only through two female specimens: One collected by Smith at Doi Langka, November 18, 1930; the other taken by me at Ban Mae Sai (Chiang Rai—Kengtung border), January 20, 1937. It will quite possibly prove to be a fairly common winter visitor, at least to Chiang Rai Province.

The adult male of *ethologus* cannot be distinguished from that of *cryptus*, even in the hand. The adult female differs from that of *cryptus* in having the yellow frontal band broader and less clearly defined; the entire upper back dull olive-green, rather than gray; the lower back, rump, and upper tail coverts bright olive-yellow, not golden-orange; the underparts canary yellow, not orange-golden.

PERICROCOTUS SOLARIS SOLARIS Blyth

INDIAN GRAY-THROATED MINIVET

P[ericrocotus] solaris BLYTH, Journ. Asiat. Soc. Bengal, vol. 15, 1846, p. 310 (Darjiling).

Pericrocotus solaris griseigularis, GYLDENSTOLPE, Kungl. Svenska Vet.-Akad. Handl., 1916, p. 73 (Khun Tan); Ibis, 1920, p. 570 (Khun Tan).—DE SCHAUENSEE, Proc. Acad. Nat. Sci. Philadelphia, 1928, p. 569 (Doi Suthep).

Pericrocotus solaris solaris, DEIGNAN, Journ. Siam Soc. Nat. Hist. Suppl., 1931, p. 146 (Doi Suthep).—CHASEN and BODEN KLOSS, Journ. Siam Soc. Nat. Hist. Suppl., 1932, p. 241 (Doi Suthep).—DEIGNAN, Journ. Siam Soc. Nat. Hist. Suppl., 1936, p. 100 (Doi Suthep).—DE SCHAUENSEE, Proc. Acad. Nat. Sci. Philadelphia, 1934, p. 224 (Doi Suthep, Doi Chiang Dao).

Pericrocotus solaris solaris [*partim*], RILEY, U. S. Nat. Mus. Bull. 172, 1938, p. 270, (Doi Langka [*partim*], Khun Tan, Doi Hua Mot).

With the addition of Doi Ang Ka, the localities listed above give the complete range of this minivet in Thailand so far as it is now known. It is fairly common at the edge of the evergreen, in the open hill-forest, and among the pines, chiefly from 4,500 to 5,500 feet but occurring on Doi Khun Tan as low as 4,000 feet and on Doi Ang Ka up to 7,000 feet.

Two females in postjuvenal molt were taken on July 14 and August 23; two males assuming the plumage of the old adult, July 14 and September 4. A long series collected between July 10 and November 20 are in postnuptial molt. An apparently adult female of April 25 is molting the feathers of the throat.

My specimens had the irides brown; the bill, feet, toes, and claws black.

The adult male resembles the adult males of the preceding species but differs from them in having the crown, upper back, scapulars, and upper wing coverts slaty black with little gloss, not glossy blue-black; the red portions of the plumage bright red-orange (the lower back, rump, and upper tail coverts orange-red), not scarlet or scarlet-crimson; the throat and sides of the head and neck gray (the throat strongly suffused with orange). The adult female is scarcely distinguishable from that of *P. e. ethologus* but differs, *inter alia*, in wholly lacking yellow on the forehead and in having the second innermost pair of rectrices tipped yellow, not black.

PERICROCOTUS ROSEUS ROSEUS (Vieillot)

INDIAN ROSEATE MINIVET

Muscicapa rosea VIEILLOT, Nouveau dictionnaire d'histoire naturelle, nouv. éd., vol. 21, 1818, pp. 486–487 (Bengal).

Pericrocotus brevirostris affinis [*partim*], DE SCHAUENSEE, Proc. Acad. Nat. Sci. Philadelphia, 1929, p. 551 (Chiang Saen).

Pericrocotus roseus roseus, DE SCHAUENSEE, Proc. Acad. Nat. Sci. Philadelphia, 1929, p. 551 (Doi Suthep, Chiang Rai).—DEIGNAN, Journ. Siam Soc. Nat. Hist. Suppl., 1931, p. 146 (Doi Suthep) ; 1936, p. 100 (Doi Suthep).—RILEY, U. S. Nat. Mus. Bull. 172, 1938, p. 272 (Khun Tan, Doi Ang Ka, Doi Suthep).

This lovely bird is an uncommon winter visitor, recorded so far only from Chiang Mai and Chiang Rai Provinces but probably occurring throughout our area. It has been found from the level of the plains (numerous localities) to 4,000 feet (Doi Khun Tan), between November 21 (Doi Suthep) and March 4 (Doi Langka).

All my specimens taken between January 11 and March 4 are molting the feathers of head and throat.

A male had the irides dark brown; the bill, feet, toes, and claws black; the soles yellow.

The adult male has the general plumage pattern of the preceding forms but has the crown, upper back, and scapulars ashy (all but the crown faintly suffused with pink) ; the red of the lower back, rump, upper tail coverts, wings, and tail scarlet; the throat pale gray, suffused with pink; the remaining underparts scarlet-pink. The adult female resembles others of the group but has the ashy of the back changing imperceptibly to olive-yellow on the rump and upper tail coverts, each feather margined with brighter yellow; the throat gray, faintly suffused with yellow; the remaining underparts a washed-out yellow, much mixed with white. The immature male differs from the adult in having the rump patch ashy gray, the feathers suffused and tipped with scarlet; the immature female in having the underparts a deeper and more uniform yellow.

PERICROCOTUS ROSEUS CANTONENSIS Swinhoe

SOUTHERN GRAY MINIVET

Pericrocotus cantonensis SWINHOE, Ibis, 1861, pp. 42–43 (Canton, China).

Campophaga neglecta, GYLDENSTOLPE, Kungl. Svenska Vet.-Akad. Handl., 1913, p. 33 (Ban Huai Hom).

Pericrocotus cinereus cantonensis, GYLDENSTOLPE, Ibis, 1920, p. 570 (Ban Huai Hom).

This migratory form seems to be a very rare winter visitor to the northern provinces. The only specimens known from the area are Gyldenstolpe's female taken at Ban Huai Hom, February 13, 1912; a pair collected by me on Doi Suthep, 2,500 feet, October 17, 1936; and an unsexed example at the Raffles Museum shot by a Thai collector at Ko Klang (near Chiang Mai), March 26, 1937.

My birds were two of a number of gray minivets accompanying a flock of *Pericrocotus peregrinus vividus* through open mixed-deciduous forest.

The gray minivet differs from the roseate race chiefly in its complete lack of lipochromatic coloration. The adult male has the lores blackish; the anterior half of the crown, the chin, and the throat white, this color extending onto the sides of the neck behind the ear coverts to form an incomplete collar; the posterior crown, upper back, and scapulars ashy gray; the lower back, rump, and upper tail coverts pale ashy brown; the central pair of rectrices deep brown, the remaining pairs with an outwardly increasing amount of brownish white; the wings blackish brown, with the innermost secondaries and a barely indicated wing bar ashy brown; the underparts white, suffused (especially on the breast) with pale ashy brown. The adult female differs from the male in having the entire crown ashy gray, paler anteriorly; in lacking the partial collar on the sides of the neck; in having a whitish wing bar. Immature birds resemble the adult female but have the innermost secondaries narrowly margined with white and the wing bar (at least in the female) suffused with yellow.

PERICROCOTUS PEREGRINUS VIVIDUS Stuart Baker

BURMESE SMALL MINIVET

Perecrocotus [*sic*] *peregrinus vividus* STUART BAKER, Bull. Brit. Orn. Club, vol. 40, 1920, p. 114 (Attaran River, Burma).

Pericrocotus peregrinus, GYLDENSTOLPE, Journ. Nat. Hist. Soc. Siam, 1915, p. 168 (listed) ; Kungl. Svenska Vet.-Akad. Handl., 1916, p. 73 (Khun Tan) ; Ibis, 1920, p. 570 ("Northern Siam").

Pericrocotus peregrinus vividus, DE SCHAUENSEE, Proc. Acad. Nat. Sci. Philadelphia, 1929, p. 551 (Doi Suthep).

Pericrocotus cinnamomeus vividus, DEIGNAN, Journ. Siam Soc. Nat. Hist. Suppl., 1931, p. 147 (Doi Suthep) ; 1936, p. 100 (Doi Suthep).—DE SCHAUENSEE, Proc. Acad. Nat. Sci. Philadelphia, 1934, p. 225 (Doi Suthep).

The status and distribution in our provinces of this small minivet are far from clear. In the neighborhood of Chiang Mai it has been found only in the deciduous and mixed-deciduous forests of Doi Suthep from 1,200 to 2,800 feet, between October 17 (1936) and the end of March (1932). I have collected it in dry, lowland forest at Chom Thong, Sala Mae Tha, and Ban Mae Mo and on a low, waterless hill (Doi Kasu) near Ban Sa-iap. Gyldenstolpe, however, who took a pair on Doi Khun Tan, April 28, 1914, states that "most often it was observed . . . visiting the pine forests on the tops of the higher hills . . ." The species is not known to be migratory, but it should be noted that there is no record for its occurrence anywhere in the North between April 28 and September 1.

The only indication of this bird's breeding in our provinces was given by a male with greatly enlarged gonads, taken by me from a flock on Doi Suthep at 2,400 feet, March 1, 1932. All specimens collected between September 1 and November 9 are in molt.

My examples had the irides dark brown; the bill, feet, toes, and claws black.

The adult male has the entire head and throat, the upper back, scapulars and upper wing coverts ashy gray; the lower back, rump, and upper tail coverts scarlet-orange; the central pair of rectrices black, the remaining pairs with an outwardly increasing amount of creamy orange; the wing quills black, the inner primaries with a creamy-orange patch near the base. the secondaries with a similar patch, which is red-orange; the underparts, below the throat, scarlet-orange, gradually changing to orange-suffused yellow on the vent and under tail coverts; the under wing coverts yellow. The adult female is similar but has the gray of the upperparts much paler; the rump patch more orange less scarlet; the light wing markings yellow (on the secondaries suffused with orange); the underparts yellow, fading to grayish on the breast and almost white on the throat. My material is insufficient to describe the plumages of immature birds.

HEMIPUS PICATUS CAPITALIS (McClelland)

Brown-backed Bar-winged Flycatcher-shrike

Muscicapa? capitalis McClelland, Proc. Zool. Soc. London, pt. 7, 1839 [=1840], p. 157 (Assam).

Hemipus picatus, de Schauensee, Proc. Acad. Nat. Sci. Philadelphia, 1928, p. 571 (Doi Suthep).

Hemipus picatus capitalis, de Schauensee, Proc. Acad. Nat. Sci. Philadelphia, 1929, p. 550 (Chiang Saen, Doi Suthep).—Deignan, Journ. Siam Soc. Nat. Hist. Suppl., 1931, p. 146 (Doi Suthep).—Chasen and Boden Kloss, Journ. Siam Soc. Nat. Hist. Suppl., 1932, p. 246 (Doi Suthep).—Greenway, Bull. Mus. Comp. Zool., 1940, p. 186 ("Mae Wan River near Mt. Saket," Doi Ang Ka, Doi Nang Kaeo).

Hemipus picatus picatus, Deignan, Journ. Siam Soc. Nat. Hist. Suppl., 1931, p. 146 (Doi Suthep).

Hemipus picatus [*partim*], de Schauensee, Proc. Acad. Nat. Sci. Philadelphia, 1934, p. 222 (Doi Suthep, Doi Chiang Dao).—Riley, U. S. Nat. Mus. Bull. 172, 1938, p. 483 (Doi Langka, Doi Hua Mot).

Hemipus picatus subsp., Deignan, Journ. Siam Soc. Nat. Hist. Suppl., 1936, p. 123 (Doi Suthep).

Despite published assertions (based upon sight records) to the contrary, study of long series of adult males from Thailand has shown that there is no geographical overlap in the distributions of *picatus* and *capitalis* and that the two must be considered valid subspecies. Ticehurst has stated (Ibis, 1940, p. 412) that "*capitalis* is found from the Assam Hills, Manipur, Chindwin, Kachin Hills, Shwebo, Maymyo, and Shan States." In Thailand its known range is restricted to a narrow strip along the Chiang Rai–Shan States border from Chiang Saen Kao to Doi Pha Hom Pok and from there south through the hills of Chiang Mai and Mae Hong Son Provinces to the Hua Mot–Langka–Nang Kaeo mountain-complex, Doi Ang Ka, and Doi Mae Kong Ka. It frequents the edge of the evergreen and forest clearings, usually on the mountains from 2,000 to 5,000 feet, but, where vegetation is suitable, also reaching the plains.

This little bird travels slowly in loose bands among the lower branches of trees. In feeding, it combines the habits of flycatchers with those of the American vireos, now craning its neck to examine the under surface of a leaf, then flying out after a passing insect to catch it with a snap of the bill and return to the same perch.

A male, molting directly from the barred juvenal dress to that of the adult, was taken on Doi Hua Mot, August 24. Adults in postnuptial molt were taken between August 24 and November 29.

My specimens had the irides dark brown; the bill, feet, toes, and claws black.

The adult male has the upper half of the head and the nape glossy blue-black; the scapulars, back, and rump dull brown, the feathers of the last broadly tipped with white to make an irregular band; the upper tail coverts glossy greenish black; the central pair of rectrices black, the others black with an outwardly increasingly broadened white tip; the wings black, with a conspicuous longitudinal band formed by white edges to certain coverts and the inner secondaries; the chin, sides of the throat, and sides of the lower neck white; the remaining underparts dull gray-brown, paling to white on the under tail coverts. The adult female differs in having the crown and nape dull, dark brown; the wings and tail as in the male but dark brown instead of black.

HEMIPUS PICATUS PICATUS (Sykes)

BLACK-BACKED BAR-WINGED FLYCATCHER-SHRIKE

Muscicapa picata SYKES, Proc. Comm. Sci. Corr. Zool. Soc. London, pt. 2, 1832, p. 85 ("The Dukhun" [= The Deccan]).

Hemipus picatus, GYLDENSTOLPE, Kungl. Svenska Vet.-Akad. Handl., 1913, p. 32 ("Northern provinces"); 1916, p. 41 (Khun Tan, Pha Hing, Pha Kho); Journ. Nat. Hist. Soc. Siam, 1915, p. 167 (listed); Ibis, 1920, p. 470 ("Northern Siam").

Hemipus picatus picatus, DE SCHAUENSEE, Proc. Acad. Nat. Sci. Philadelphia, 1929, p. 549 (Chiang Rai).

Hemipus picatus [*partim*], RILEY, U. S. Nat. Mus. Bull. 172, 1938, p. 483 (Khun Tan).

The black-backed flycatcher-shrike is common in all parts of our area outside the range of the brown-backed form.

A female in postjuvenal molt was collected at Ban Huai Thae, June 12. Adults in postnuptial molt were taken at Doi San Huai Wai, Ban Mae Mo, and Doi Khun Tan between June 4 and September 2.

The adult male differs from that of *capitalis* only in having the scapulars, back, and rump glossy green-black instead of dull brown. The adult female and the juvenile are indistinguishable from those of *capitalis*.

TEPHRODORNIS PONDICERIANA THAI Boden Kloss and Chasen

INDO-CHINESE WHITE-TAILED WOOD-SHRIKE

Tephrodornis pondicerianus thai BODEN KLOSS and CHASEN, Bull. Brit. Orn. Club, vol. 46, 1925, p. 58 (Tha Chang Tai, near Rahaeng, West Thailand).

Tephrodornis pondicerianus, GYLDENSTOLPE, Kungl. Svenska Vet.-Akad. Handl., 1913, p. 32 (Phrae); 1916, p. 42 (Khun Tan); Journ. Nat Hist. Soc. Siam, 1915, p. 168 (listed); Ibis, 1920, p. 470 (Khun Tan, Phrae).

Tephrodornis pondiceriana thai, RILEY, U. S. Nat. Mus. Bull. 172, 1938, p. 483 (Mae Khan, Mae Sariang, foot of Doi Pata).

The lesser wood-shrike, while rather local, has been collected at numerous localities in Mae Hong Son, Chiang Mai, Lampang, and Phrae Provinces and may confidently be expected to occur also in Nan Province.

The present species is found at feeble elevations in parklike, deciduous forest, just such as is inhabited by *Dryobates h. hyperythrus* (and, in fact, my two specimens of that woodpecker were taken within sight of flocks of the wood-shrike). The small, loose bands move quietly from tree to tree, diligently searching for their insect food in the crevices of bark and beneath the leaves, exactly in the manner of so many vireos.

Birds in postjuvenal molt were collected, June 20, at Nong Phung (about 46 km. north of Chiang Mai); adults in postnuptial molt at various places, between June 20 and September 28.

Gyldenstolpe notes that his examples had the irides brown; the bill black; the feet and toes plumbeous.

Adults have the lores, cheeks, and ear coverts blackish brown; a white supercilium, which broadens posteriorly; the forehead, crown, visible portions of wings, back, and rump ashy gray, the feathers of the last tipped with white to form a band; the upper tail coverts black; the central pair of rectrices gray-brown, the next three pairs almost wholly blackish brown, the two outermost pairs almost wholly white; the entire underparts white, suffused with ashy gray on the breast.

TEPHRODORNIS GULARIS VERNAYI Kinnear

THAI BROWN-TAILED WOOD-SHRIKE

Tephrodornis pelvicus verneyi [*sic*] KINNEAR, Bull. Brit. Orn. Club, vol. 44, 1924, pp. 101–102 (Um Phang, West Thailand).

Tephrodornis pelvicus, GYLDENSTOLPE, Kungl. Svenska Vet.-Akad. Handl., 1913, p. 32 (Den Chai); 1916, p. 42 (Khun Tan, Pha Hing, Doi Pha Sakaeng); Journ. Nat. Hist. Soc. Siam, 1915, p. 168 (listed); Ibis, 1920, p. 470 ("Throughout northern Siam").

Tephrodornis gularis annectens, DE SCHAUENSEE, Proc. Acad. Nat. Sci. Philadelphia, 1928, p. 562 (Doi Suthep); 1929, p. 550 (Doi Suthep); 1934, p. 222 (Mae Taeng, Khun Tan, Doi Suthep).—DEIGNAN, Journ. Siam Soc. Nat. Hist. Suppl., 1931, p. 146 (Doi Suthep).—CHASEN and BODEN KLOSS, Journ. Siam Soc. Nat. Hist. Suppl., 1932, p. 246 (Doi Suthep).

Tephrodornis gularis vernayi, DEIGNAN, Journ. Siam Soc. Nat. Hist. Suppl., 1936, p. 123 (Doi Suthep).

Tephrodornis gularis pelvica, RILEY, U. S. Nat. Mus. Bull. 172, 1938, p. 481 (Doi Suthep, Doi Langka, Doi Hua Mot, Khun Tan, Thattafang, Mae Kong Ka valley).

The larger wood-shrike has not yet been recorded from Chiang Rai Province but is common in all other parts of our area. Its normal range is the more open evergreen from 2,000 to 4,600 feet, but during the cold weather it may be found in the dry, deciduous forest of the plains and foothills, and then it *might* be seen in exactly the same places as its smaller relative.

The habits of this bird do not seem to differ greatly from those of the preceding species, although the flocks are usually larger (up to as many as 50 individuals) and are certainly noisier.

Examples in postjuvenal molt were collected June 3 at Doi San Huai Wai, and numerous older specimens from all parts of the northern range, taken between March 31 and October 17, are in molt. Those shot between May 5 and June 13 are so badly worn and bleached as scarcely to have taxonomic value.

An adult male had the irides red-brown; the bill black; the feet and toes dark plumbeous; the soles yellowish; the claws horny black. An immature male had the irides gray-brown; the bill pinkish brown, darker at the tip; the feet, toes, and claws dark brown. Gyldenstolpe notes that his adults had the irides yellowish brown, while immatures had them grayish yellow.

The adult male has a broad, black line along the side of the head from the base of the bill to behind the ear coverts; the crown and nape ashy gray; the scapulars, back, and rump ashy brown, the feathers of the last tipped white to form, together with the white shorter tail coverts, a white patch or band; the feathers of wings and tail ashy brown, edged with ashy rufous; the underparts white, suffused on the breast with ashy gray or ashy fawn. The adult female resembles the male but has the crown and nape concolorous with the back and the eye stripe blackish brown.

The birds of Thailand (north of Ko Lak) are exactly intermediate between *pelvica* and *annectens* but form so stable a population that Kinnear's name cannot properly be disregarded. From *pelvica* they differ in just the characters pointed out by Kinnear (*loc. cit.*); from *annectens*, in their superior size and ashy-brown (*not* ashy-gray) upperparts. There is, however, a real possibility that *vernayi* may prove to be inseparable from *sylvicola* of South India; at this time I have not enough material of the latter race to form a definite opinion.

CAMPEPHAGA FIMBRIATA POLIOPTERA Bowdler Sharpe

INDO-CHINESE GRAY CATERPILLAR-SHRIKE

Campophaga [*sic*] *polioptera* BOWDLER SHARPE, Catalogue of the birds in the British Museum, vol. 4, 1879, p. 69 (Cochin-China).

Campophaga melanoptera, GYLDENSTOLPE, Journ. Nat. Hist. Soc. Siam, 1915, p. 168 (listed).

Volvocivora melanoptera avensis, GYLDENSTOLPE, Kungl. Svenska Vet.-Akad. Handl., 1916, p. 71 (Khun Tan).

Volvocivora lugubris saturata [*partim*], GYLDENSTOLPE, Ibis, 1920, p. 569 (Khun Tan [*partim*]).

Lalage melaschista avensis [*partim*], DE SCHAUENSEE, Proc. Acad. Nat. Sci. Philadelphia, 1929, p. 551 (Doi Suthep [*partim*]); 1934, p. 225 (Doi Suthep [*partim*], Mae Taeng, Chiang Dao, 55 km. northeast of Lampang).—DEIGNAN, Journ. Siam Soc. Nat. Hist. Suppl., 1931, p. 147 (Doi Suthep [*partim*]).

Lalage melaschista [*partim*], DEIGNAN, Journ. Siam Soc. Nat. Hist. Suppl., 1936, p. 101 (Doi Suthep [*partim*]).

Volvocivora melanoptera [*partim*], RILEY, U. S. Nat. Mus. Bull. 172, 1938, p. 273 (Doi Hua Mot, Doi Langka, Khun Tan [*partim*]).

The present form of the gray caterpillar-shrike is a rather common resident of the more open evergreen, possibly throughout our area. On the hills of the Thanon Thong Chai range it has been found between 2,500 and 4,500 feet, but in districts where the jungle is suitable it occurs also on the plains, at least in winter.

This bird is found singly or in pairs, quietly hunting for caterpillars and other insects along the branches of the lower trees, at the edge of the forest or beside the trails—in fact, inhabiting much the same places as *Hemipus*.

Nothing certain is known of the breeding season, but specimens in postnuptial molt have been taken between August 20 and November 19.

My examples had the irides bright brown (males) or brownish red (females); the bill black (males) or horny brown (females); the feet, toes, and claws slaty black (males) or blackish brown (females).

The adult male has the general coloration, above and below, slate gray, fading gradually to white on the under tail coverts; the remiges black, outwardly margined with slate gray and narrowly tipped with grayish white; the inner primaries often with an indefinite white area near the center of the inner web (invisible in the closed wing); the central pair of tail feathers slate gray with an indefinite blackish area near the tip along the shaft, the remaining pairs black, broadly tipped with white. The adult female differs in having a narrow eye ring of white feathers; the ear coverts and the feathers below the eye with white shaft streaks; the remiges more conspicuously tipped and margined with grayish white; the entire underparts obsolescently barred with slate gray and grayish white (more definitely posteriorly). Immatures of either sex resemble the adult female but have the general coloration rather paler; the remiges still more broadly margined with white; the entire underparts whitish, narrowly barred everywhere with blackish.

This race seems to be resident in suitable territory throughout Thailand proper. I cannot separate my northern material, even on size, from a topotypical series of Kloss's *indochinensis*, which, itself, appears to be identical with *polioptera* of Sharpe.

CAMPEPHAGA FIMBRIATA MELASCHISTA (Hodgson)

NEPALESE GRAY CATERPILLAR-SHRIKE

[*Volvocivora*] *melaschistos* HODGSON, India Rev., vol. 1, 1837 [=1836], p. 328 (Nepal).

Volvocivora lugubris saturata, GYLDENSTOLPE, Kungl. Svenska Vet.-Akad. Handl., 1916, p. 71 (Khun Tan).

Volvocivora lugubris saturata [*partim*], GYLDENSTOLPE, Ibis, 1920, p. 569 (Khun Tan [*partim*]).

Lalage melaschista avensis [*partim*], DE SCHAUENSEE, Proc. Acad. Nat. Sci. Philadelphia, 1929, p. 551 (Doi Suthep [*partim*], Chiang Saen); 1934, p. 225 (Doi Suthep [*partim*]).—DEIGNAN, Journ. Siam Soc. Nat. Hist. Suppl., 1931, p. 147 (Doi Suthep [*partim*]).

Lalage melaschista, CHASEN and BODEN KLOSS, Journ. Siam Soc. Nat. Hist. Suppl., 1932, p. 242 (Doi Suthep).

Lalage melaschista [*partim*], DEIGNAN, Journ. Siam Soc. Nat. Hist. Suppl., 1936, p. 101 (Doi Suthep [*partim*]).

Volvocivora melanoptera [*partim*], RILEY, U. S. Nat. Mus. Bull. 172, 1938, p. 273 (Doi Suthep, Khun Tan [*partim*]).

Volvocivora melaschistos, RILEY, U. S. Nat. Mus. Bull. 172, 1938, p. 275 (Khun Tan).

This large caterpillar-shrike is a rather common winter visitor to the hills of the Thanon Thong Chai and Khun Tan ranges (4,000 to 5,500 feet) and to the lowland evergreen of Chiang Rai (and perhaps of other provinces). A series of 15 specimens before me was collected between October 24 and February 13, and if Gyldenstolpe's *Volvocivora lugubris saturata* (1916) has been correctly placed with the present race the bird arrives in our districts as early as September 5.

The migratory form occurs, in season, in exactly the same places as the preceding, from which it seems not to differ at all in habits.

C. f. melaschista is a larger bird than *polioptera:* The wings of 15 specimens of the former (both sexes) range from 119 to 127 mm.; of 13 northern examples of the latter (both sexes), from 110 to 118 mm. The fully adult male differs from that of *polioptera* in having the general coloration averaging darker; the remiges and central pair of rectrices uniform black with a slightly greenish gloss. The adult female differs from that of *polioptera* in rather darker coloration; in having the central pair of rectrices usually with much more black suffusion on the apical half; in having the barring of the underparts even more obsolescent and not visible at all on the throat and breast. In younger birds, obsolescent bars show on the throat and breast, as well as elsewhere.

I cannot separate my specimens from topotypical *melaschista*, but the wintering bird of eastern and peninsular Thailand seems to be the equally large but somewhat paler *melanoptera* (which may occur also in the northern provinces east of the Khun Tan chain). The individual listed by Riley (1938) as *melaschista* is extraordinarily dark and must be considered a case of melanism.

I have no reason to believe that two or more forms of this group occur together anywhere during the breeding season and am of the opinion that *melaschista*, *melanoptera*, *polioptera*, *neglecta*, and *culminata* are all races of the Javanese *fimbriata*.

CORACINA NOVAEHOLLANDIAE SIAMENSIS (Stuart Baker)

INDO-CHINESE ASHY CUCKOO-SHRIKE

Graucalus macei siamensis STUART BAKER, Bull. Brit. Orn. Club, vol. 38, 1918, p. 69 ("Mi-Nam-Kabren" [=Krabin river], Central Thailand).

Graucalus macei, GYLDENSTOLPE, Kungl. Svenska Vet.-Akad. Handl., 1913, p. 34 ("Vang Nun"); 1916, p. 70 (Pha Hing, Khun Tan, Pha Kho); Journ. Nat. Hist. Soc. Siam, 1915, p. 168 (listed).

Graucalus macei siamensis, GYLDENSTOLPE, Ibis, 1920, p. 569 ("Throughout the whole country").—DE SCHAUENSEE, Proc. Acad. Nat. Sci. Philadelphia, 1928, p. 569 (Doi Suthep); 1929, p. 551 (Doi Suthep).

Coracina javensis siamensis, DEIGNAN, Journ. Siam Soc. Nat. Hist. Suppl., 1931, p. 147 (Doi Suthep, Chiang Mai).—CHASEN and BODEN KLOSS, Journ. Siam Soc. Nat. Hist. Suppl., 1932, p. 242 (Doi Suthep).—DEIGNAN, Journ. Siam Soc. Nat. Hist. Suppl., 1936, p. 101 (Doi Suthep, Chiang Mai).—DE SCHAUENSEE, Proc. Acad. Nat. Sci. Philadelphia, 1934, p. 225 (Doi Suthep, Khun Tan).

Graucalus javensis siamensis, RILEY, U. S. Nat. Mus. Bull. 172, 1938, p. 277 (Doi Hua Mot, "Doi Phra Chao" [=Doi Saket ?], Khun Tan).

The cuckoo-shrike occurs throughout the North wherever the jungle is both tall and open, at whatever altitude it may be; it is necessarily commonest in the deciduous forest of the plains and foothills and again in the open hill-forest of oak and pine on the high ridges of the mountains, at least to 5,500 feet.

This is the large, heavy-set, gray bird that perches at the very top of some tall tree or flies above the forest with a deliberate, crowlike wing beat, frequently uttering, whether in flight or at rest, a series of loud, liquid, whistling calls. It is usually seen alone or in pairs but, where the species is particularly common, may appear to be in small, loose flocks.

A specimen from Khun Tan, August 25, is in postjuvenal molt; seven adults from various localities, taken between August 3 and September 4, are in postnuptial molt.

A male had the irides brown; the eyelids plumbeous; the bill black; the interior of the mouth flesh; the feet, toes, and claws black.

The old male is generally ashy gray but has the lores and eye ring black; the ear coverts slaty; the primaries black, narrowly margined along the outer web with pale gray; the rectrices (except the central pair) black, narrowly margined and broadly tipped with pale gray; the under tail coverts and under wing coverts white. The old female is similar but has the lores and eye ring slaty, like the ear coverts. Younger birds of either sex have the lores as in the old female; the remiges and rectrices more conspicuously edged with pale gray or white; the underparts marked with narrow, wavy bars of gray and white.

Family DICRURIDAE

DICRURUS LEUCOPHAEUS MOUHOTI (Walden)

INDO-CHINESE PALE ASHY DRONGO

Buchanga mouhoti WALDEN, Ann. Mag. Nat. Hist., ser. 4, vol. 5, 1870, p. 220 (Cambodia; type locality restricted to Angkor, by Riley, Proc. Biol. Soc. Washington, vol. 53, 1940, p. 132).

Dicrurus cineraceus, GYLDENSTOLPE, Kungl. Svenska Vet.-Akad. Handl., 1913, p. 27 (Ban Huai Hom, Phrae); Journ. Nat. Hist. Soc. Siam, 1915, p. 167 (listed).

Buchanga cineracea mouhoti, GYLDENSTOLPE, Kungl. Svenska Vet.-Akad. Handl., 1916, p. 21 (Khun Tan, Doi Pha Sakaeng).

Buchanga cineracea nigrescens, GYLDENSTOLPE, Ibis, 1920, p. 451 ("Northern Siam").

Buchanga cineracea cineracea, DE SCHAUENSEE, Proc. Acad. Nat. Sci. Philadelphia, 1928, p. 557 (Doi Suthep).

Dicrurus leucophaeus hopwoodi, DE SCHAUENSEE, Proc. Acad. Nat. Sci. Philadelphia, 1929, p. 552 (Doi Suthep, Chiang Mai, Chiang Saen, Chiang Rai); 1934, p. 226 (Doi Suthep, Doi Chiang Dao).—DEIGNAN, Journ. Siam Soc. Nat. Hist. Suppl., 1931, p. 147 (Doi Suthep, Chiang Mai).

Dicrurus leucophaeus hopwoodi [*partim*], CHASEN and BODEN KLOSS, Journ. Siam Soc. Nat. Hist. Suppl., 1932, p. 247 (Doi Suthep [*partim*]).

Dicrurus leucophaeus mouhoti, DEIGNAN, Journ. Siam Soc. Nat. Hist. Suppl., 1936, p. 101 (Doi Suthep).

Dicrurus leucophaeus mouhoti [*partim*], RILEY, U. S. Nat. Mus. Bull. 172, 1938, p. 281 (Huai Mae Lao, Song Khwae valley, Doi Langka).

The resident form of the pale ashy drongo is common in the more open evergreen, in overgrown clearings, and even in bamboo brakes, throughout the northern provinces, chiefly from 4,500 to 2,000 feet but ranging onto the plains, at least during the cold weather, wherever suitable vegetation can be found.

The habits and notes of this species seem not to differ essentially from those of the common black drongo, which supplants it in lowland cultivated areas.

Nothing is definitely known of the breeding season, which probably falls in spring. All specimens taken between July 25 and November 23 are in molt.

My examples had the irides bright red or brownish red; the bill, feet, toes, and claws black.

This drongo has the lores and frontal area blackish; the rest of the plumage (except for the blackish primaries) blue-gray with a steely sheen (the underparts paler and with much less gloss).

The species is highly migratory and comparative series of measurements have little significance unless based upon resident adults. The breeding bird of South Annam (*rocki*) is smaller (especially in length of tail) than that of our provinces; the latter may be considered an intermediate between *rocki* and *hopwoodi* and is best called *mouhoti*. The measurements given by Walden for the type specimen of *mouhoti* show it to have been just such an intermediate bird, and I am of the opinion that it occurred in Cambodia merely as a winter visitor from some more northern locality.

DICRURUS LEUCOPHAEUS HOPWOODI Stuart Baker

ASSAMESE PALE ASHY DRONGO

Dicrurus leucophaeus hopwoodi STUART BAKER, Nov. Zool., vol. 25, 1918, p. 294 (Dacca, Bengal).

Dicrurus leucophaeus hopwoodi [*partim*], CHASEN and BODEN KLOSS, Journ. Siam Soc. Nat. Hist. Suppl., 1932, p. 247 (Doi Suthep [*partim*]).

Dicrurus leucophaeus hopwoodi, RILEY, U. S. Nat. Mus. Bull. 172, 1938, p. 280 (Doi Suthep).

Dicrurus leucophaeus mouhoti [*partim*], RILEY, U. S. Nat. Mus. Bull. 172, 1938, p. 281 (Khun Tan).

During the cold season a darker race of the pale ashy drongo appears in small numbers on the hills of the western provinces. I have examined specimens of this migratory form, taken between October 9 and March 14, from Doi Khun Tan (3,000–4,400 feet), Doi Suthep (5,400–5,500 feet), and Doi Mae Kong Ka.

The ashy drongo has been observed on Doi Suthep above 4,500 feet only during the winter months, and every specimen from that elevation has proved to be of the darker type. This will doubtless prove to be the case also upon other high mountains.

Full-plumaged adults of the Assamese pale ashy drongo differ from the Indo-Chinese "in being just a shade darker and in having the wings a trifle longer and the tails distinctly longer" (Ticehurst, Ibis, 1936, p. 280).

Thai examples, all of which seem to be immature, cannot be separated on measurements from the resident population of pale ashy drongo but agree in color with a series of *hopwoodi* from Yunnan. Ticehurst has shown (Journ. Bombay Nat. Hist. Soc., vol. 36, 1933, pp. 927–928) that in the genus *Dicrurus* the measurements of first-year birds are without value in subspecific identification.

DICRURUS LEUCOPHAEUS LEUCOGENIS (Walden)

Hupeh White-cheeked Pale Ashy Drongo

Buchanga leucogenis Walden, Ann. Mag. Nat. Hist., ser. 4, vol. 5, 1870, pp. 219–220 (Nagasaki, Japan, error; type locality corrected to China, by Stuart Baker, Journ. Bombay Nat. Hist. Soc., vol. 27, 1921, p. 474; here restricted to Ichang, Hupeh).

Dicrurus leucogenis leucogenis, Riley, U. S. Nat. Mus. Bull. 172, 1938, p. 282 (Ban Nam Khian).

The two examples recorded by Riley, a male and a female taken by Smith, April 18 and 21, 1930, in the vicinity of Nan, are the only ones yet recorded from our provinces. This race may prove to be a rare but regular migrant through the more eastern districts.

From the preceding forms it differs in having the general coloration a soft, pale gray (without sheen); the lores, sides of head, and ear coverts white. The female is slightly darker than the male and has the white on the head less clearly defined from the surrounding gray.

I am wholly in accord with Riley (1938) in believing *Buchanga leucogenis* Walden to be the paler race of the continental white-cheeked drongo. It is said to have the "general colour pale, delicate slate-grey, or French grey"; immediately following this, *Buchanga mouhoti* is described as having the upperparts "ashy grey or plumbeous, rather darker than in *B. leucophaea*, ex Java." The fact is that *mouhoti* and the darker type of white-cheeked drongo have the upperparts much the same color; since not only is this not brought out but the two are described in wholly different terms, one may assume that Walden was indeed naming the lighter type, which has the upperparts markedly different in color from those of *mouhoti*.

If this be the case, *Buchanga leucogenys cerussata* Bangs and Phillips (paratype examined) is an unwarranted renaming of *Buchanga leucogenis* Walden, and the darker form is left without a name unless, as seems probable, *salangensis* of Reichenow be applicable to it.

Walden's type specimen was erroneously stated to have come from Nagasaki, and Stuart Baker has properly altered the type locality to China (*loc. cit.*). Boden Kloss has attempted to restrict it to Yunnan (Treubia, vol. 13, 1931, p. 358), but since *Dicrurus leucophaeus leucogenis* of Kloss (darker form) is not, according to my views, the same as *Buchanga leucogenis* of Walden (paler form), his restriction seems to be without standing. I now restrict the type locality of *Buchanga leucogenis* Walden to Ichang, Hupeh, which is also the type locality of *Buchanga leucogenys cerussata* Bangs and Phillips.

DICRURUS ADSIMILIS CATHOECUS Swinhoe

CHINESE BLACK DRONGO

Dicrurus cathoecus SWINHOE, Proc. Zool. Soc. London, 1871, p. 377 ("China, Hainan, and Formosa"; type locality restricted to South China, by Hartert, Vögel der paläarktischen Fauna, vol. 3, 1921, p. 2017).

Dicrurus ater, GYLDENSTOLPE, Journ. Nat. Hist. Soc. Siam, 1915, p. 167 (listed).

Buchanga atra longus, GYLDENSTOLPE, Ibis, 1920, p. 451 ("Throughout the whole country").

Buchanga atra cathoeca, GYLDENSTOLPE, Ibis, 1920, p. 451 (Pang Hua Phong).

Dicrurus macrocercus thai, DE SCHAUENSEE, Proc. Acad. Nat. Sci. Philadelphia, 1928, p. 556 (Chiang Mai); 1934, p. 226 (Chiang Mai).—DEIGNAN, Journ. Siam Soc. Nat. Hist. Suppl., 1936, p. 101 (Chiang Mai).

Dicrurus macrocercus cathoecus, DE SCHAUENSEE, Proc. Acad. Nat. Sci. Philadelphia, 1929, p. 552 (Chiang Mai).—DEIGNAN, Journ. Siam Soc. Nat. Hist. Suppl., 1931, p. 147 (Chiang Mai); 1936, p. 101 (Chiang Mai).

The *nok saeo hang pla* has been taken once in Lampang Province, once in Mae Hong Son, and frequently in Chiang Mai but has not yet been recorded at all from the remaining portions of our area. It is likely to occur, at least as a migrant or winter visitor, in any deforested lowland district.

On the plain of Chiang Mai this drongo is one of the most conspicuous birds and can be observed anywhere, perching upon fence posts, on the bunds of the open ricefields, and on the backs of grazing cattle, whence it makes flights after passing insects. Like others of the family, it is a noisy bird, combining harsh shrieks and chattering calls with melodious whistles and flutelike notes. The name "king-crow" is derived from its habit of attacking and driving from the neighborhood crows, hawks, dogs, and other potential enemies.

At Chiang Mai, during the months of October and November, great numbers of immature birds arrive, presumably from farther north, and congregate at ponds and marshes, together with the migratory flocks of bee-eaters. These visitors gradually disappear, and no corresponding return-movement has been noted in spring, possibly because of the aridity of the countryside at that season.

An example in postjuvenal molt was taken at Chiang Mai, July 5.

An adult male had the irides red; the bill, feet, toes, and claws black. The postjuvenal male had the irides brown; the bill black; the rictus and interior of the mouth fleshy; the feet, toes, and claws black.

Adults have the entire plumage black, glossed with steel blue. Immatures have the upperparts rather less glossy; the edge of the wing white; the underparts little glossed and the feathers tipped with gray, especially on the abdomen and under tail coverts.

My series of this common species is highly inadequate for taxonomic purposes. With the exception of a few specimens mentioned under the following form, my adult examples are inseparable from Chinese birds in length of wing and tail, but all are winter-taken and *might* be visitors. My summer-taken material, on the other hand, is immature and not certainly identifiable. A series of breeding adults might show that the resident population is not *cathoecus* at all; until specimens be available, however, I must assume that our summer birds are of the Chinese race.

DICRURUS ADSIMILIS ALBIRICTUS (Hodgson)

HIMALAYAN BLACK DRONGO

[*Bhuchanga*] *albirictus* HODGSON, India Rev., vol. 1, 1837 [= 1836], p. 326 (Nepal).

The Himalayan race of the common black drongo occurs regularly, although in small numbers, in the dry, deciduous forest on the lower slopes of Doi Suthep. I took a male and a female at 1,600 feet, December 12, 1931, and a second male at 1,300 feet, February 22, 1936.

These birds had the irides red; the bill, feet, toes, and claws black.

D. a. albirictus is distinguishable from *cathoecus* only by its relatively longer tail. The tail length of the former ranges from 152 to 180 mm.; of the latter, from 137 to 154 mm.

The tails of my specimens, all fully adult, measure 160, 165, and 171 mm. Two of the three show the white rictal spot.

DICRURUS LEUCOPHAEUS LEUCOGENIS (Walden)

CROW-BILLED DRONGO

[*Bhuchanga*] *annectans* [*sic*] HODGSON, India Rev., vol. 1, 1837 [= 1836], p. 326 (Nepal).

Dicrurus annectans, DEIGNAN, Journ. Siam Soc. Nat. Hist. Suppl., 1936, p. 169 (Nan Province).

In the largely uncultivated lowlands of Phrae and Nan Provinces, where I failed to find any form of *Dicrurus adsimilis*, the crow-billed drongo proved to be extremely common in the dry, deciduous forest.

My specimens, taken in March and September, had the gonads inactive, but I have no doubt that the species breeds in those districts.

An adult female had the irides red; the bill, feet, toes, and claws black.

In coloration this drongo resembles *Dicrurus a. cathoecus* of corresponding age, but it is glossed with steel green rather than blue. From *cathoecus* it is best distinguished by its less slender form, its much more robust bill, and its relatively shorter tail, with the outermost pair of rectrices more distinctly curved upward.

DICRURUS HOTTENTOTTUS HOTTENTOTTUS (Linnaeus)

INDIAN HAIR-CRESTED DRONGO

[*Corvus*] *hottentottus* LINNAEUS, Systema naturae, ed. 12, vol. 1, 1766, p. 155 ("Cap. b. spei," error; type locality corrected to Sikkim, by Stuart Baker, Nov. Zool., vol. 26, 1919, p. 44).

Chibia hottentotta, GYLDENSTOLPE, Kungl. Svenska Vet.-Akad. Handl., 1913, p. 28 (Pak Pan); 1916, p. 20 (Doi Pha Sakaeng, Khun Tan, Pang Hua Phong); Journ. Nat. Hist. Soc. Siam, 1915, p. 167 (listed); Ibis, 1920, p. 450 ("Northern Siam").

Chibia hottentotta hottentotta, DE SCHAUENSEE, Proc. Acad. Nat. Sci. Philadelphia, 1928, p. 556 (Doi Suthep); 1929, p. 553 (Chiang Rai, Chiang Saen Kao); 1934, p. 226 (Khun Tan, Chiang Dao, Chiang Saen).—DEIGNAN, Journ. Siam Soc. Nat. Hist. Suppl., 1931, p. 147 (Doi Suthep); 1936, p. 101 (Doi Suthep).—RILEY, U. S. Nat. Mus. Bull. 172, 1938, p. 286 (Ban Nam Khian).

The resident race of the hair-crested drongo is rather common in flocks throughout our area, occurring in the dry, deciduous forest of the plains and foothills and ascending the mountains only to about 2,700 feet, the altitudinal limit of this type of vegetation.

Where such a tree as *Bombax* is in bloom, this drongo tends to collect into noisy flocks, probing the flowers for insects and getting its face well dusted with the yellow pollen. At other times it takes much of its prey on the wing or even from the branches and trunks of trees, momentarily supporting itself with beating pinions like a huge, black butterfly. Stanford has well observed (Ibis, 1938, p. 417) that "in flight the shape of this bird, especially of the upturned tail feathers, is remarkably like that of an aeroplane, and this resemblance is more pronounced by the 'vertical nose-dives,' with which it is constantly displaying."

A male from the foot of Doi Suthep, April 29, had the gonads enlarged, but some individuals must breed much earlier in the year for, while a bird from Ban Huai Thae, June 12, is just beginning the postjuvenal molt, three others from Nan Province, April 18 and 22, have virtually completed the same molt. An adult in postnuptial molt was collected near Wiang Pa Pao, August 1.

My adult specimens had the irides brownish red; the eyelids slaty; the bill, feet, toes, and claws black.

This is a large drongo with a conspicuously long, curved bill; a group of long, hairlike feathers arising from the base of the bill and extending to the upper back (not visible in the field); the outermost pair of rectrices curved upward even more strongly than in the preceding species. It has the entire plumage black, highly glossed on the posterior crown and the hacklelike feathers at the side of the neck with steel blue, on the wings with bronze-green, on the tail with steel green; the feathers of the lower throat and the breast glossed with steel blue at the tips to form spangles. Immatures are duller in color and have the outer tail feathers much less recurved.

Boden Kloss (Journ. Federated Malay States Mus., vol. 10, 1921, pp. 222–223) believes that Thai birds are separable from those of Sikkim by lesser size. If his views be correct, our resident population must probably be known as *D. h. barbatus* (J. E. Gray). In default of suitable comparative material I am unable to form an opinion.

DICRURUS HOTTENTOTTUS BREVIROSTRIS (Cabanis and Heine)

CHINESE HAIR-CRESTED DRONGO

T[richometopus] brevirostris CABANIS and HEINE, Museum Heineanum, pt. 1, 1850 [=1851], p. 112 (China).

Chibia hottentotta brevirostris, DE SCHAUENSEE, Proc. Acad. Nat. Sci. Philadelphia, 1929, p. 553 (Doi Suthep) ; 1934, p. 227 (Doi Chiang Dao).—DEIGNAN, Journ. Siam Soc. Nat. Hist. Suppl., 1931, p. 148 (Doi Suthep) ; 1936, p. 101 (Doi Suthep).—RILEY, U. S. Nat. Mus. Bull. 172, 1938, p. 287 (Doi Langka).

The Chinese hair-crested drongo occurs not uncommonly in winter (October to January or later) on some of the higher hills of the Thanon Thong Chai and Khun Tan ranges. On Doi Chiang Dao it has been taken at 4,600 and 5,000 feet and on Doi Suthep at 5,500 feet, but, on the latter mountain, it may descend as low as 3,500 feet, at which elevation I have frequently observed a form of the species in tall flowering trees during cold weather.

At the summit of Doi Suthep, late in December and early in January, flocks of this bird, together with numerous unrelated species, can always be observed feeding and fluttering about among the blossoms of a beautiful pink-flowered tree (*Cassia* sp.), which grows just below the bungalows, on the eastern slope of the mountain.

My specimens had the irides dark brown; the bill, feet, toes, and claws black.

From the resident subspecies this race is distinguishable only by having the bill shorter and less robust and by having the long frontal hairs finely barbed instead of naked.

CHAPTIA AENEA AENEA (Vieillot)

INDIAN BRONZED DRONGO

Dicrurus aeneus VIEILLOT, Nouveau dictionnaire d'histoire naturelle, nouv. éd., vol. 9, 1817, p. 586 (Bengal; type locality restricted to Dacca, eastern Bengal, by Stuart Baker, Nov. Zool., vol. 25, 1918, p. 304).

Chaptia aenea, GYLDENSTOLPE, Kungl. Svenska Vet.-Akad. Handl., 1913, p. 28 (Ban Huai Hom) ; 1916, p. 19 (Pang Hua Phong, Khun Tan, Doi Pha Sakaeng) ; Journ. Nat. Hist. Soc. Siam, 1915, p. 167 (listed).

Chaptia aenea malayensis, GYLDENSTOLPE, Ibis, 1920, p. 450 ("Northern Siam"). —DEIGNAN, Journ. Siam Soc. Nat. Hist. Suppl., 1936, p. 101 (Doi Suthep).

Chaptia aenea aenea, DE SCHAUENSEE, Proc. Acad. Nat. Sci. Philadelphia, 1929, p. 552 (Doi Suthep, Chiang Saen) ; 1934, p. 226 (Doi Suthep, Doi Chiang Dao).—DEIGNAN, Journ. Siam Soc. Nat. Hist. Suppl., 1931, p. 147 (Doi Suthep).—GREENWAY, Bull. Mus. Comp. Zool., 1940, p. 187 (Doi Ang Ka, Doi Nang Kaeo).

Chaptia aenea>malayensis, CHASEN and BODEN KLOSS, Journ. Siam Soc. Nat. Hist. Suppl., 1932, p. 247 (Doi Suthep).

Chaptia aenea aenea [*partim*], RILEY, U. S. Nat. Mus. Bull. 172, 1938, p. 284 (Doi Langka [*partim*], Khun Tan).

The bronzed drongo is very common in evergreen jungle throughout our area, on the western hills ranging from 3,000 to 5,500 feet but, in the more eastern districts, occurring also in similar forest on the plains.

Our smallest drongo, which is a conspicuous bird along the trails and at clearings and even in upland pine-forest, does not seem to differ in habits from others of its family. It has the usual medley of harsh and melodious notes and, like *Bhringa*, is often heard singing on moonlight nights.

Specimens with the gonads greatly enlarged were taken on April 17 and 18 and examples in postnuptial molt between August 26 and November 21.

A breeding male had the irides brownish red; the bill, feet, toes, and claws black.

This species has the entire plumage black, everywhere (except on the more grayish abdomen and under tail coverts) highly glossed with steel blue, which, in certain lights, shows reflections of green, bronze, and purple. During molt, while the flaring outermost rectrices are only partly grown, the tail loses its normal, forked appearance and takes on a curious shape.

Northern birds, with wing length ranging from 119 to 126 mm., are really intermediate between *aenea* and *malayensis* and might equally well be called by either name.

BHRINGA REMIFER TECTRIOSTRIS Hodgson

INDIAN LESSER RACQUET-TAILED DRONGO

[*Bhringa*] *tectirostris* HODGSON, India Rev., vol. 1, 1837 [=1836], pp. 325–326 (Nepal).

Bhringa remifer, GYLDENSTOLPE, Kungl. Svenska Vet.-Akad. Handl., 1916, p. 22 (Doi Pha Sakaeng, Khun Tan); Ibis, 1920, p. 450 (Doi Pha Sakeng, Khun Tan).

Bhringa remifer latispatula DE SCHAUENSEE, Proc. Acad. Nat. Sci. Philadelphia, vol. 81, 1929, pp. 475–476 (Doi Suthep, North Thailand); p. 553 (Doi Suthep, Chiang Saen); 1934, p. 227 (Doi Suthep, Doi Chiang Dao).—DEIGNAN, Journ. Siam Soc. Nat. Hist. Suppl., 1931, p. 148 (Doi Suthep); 1936, p. 101 (Doi Suthep).—RILEY, U. S. Nat. Mus. Bull. 172, 1938, p. 287 (Khun Tan, Sop Phung, Doi Langka, Doi Hua Mot).

Bhringa remifer tectirostris, CHASEN and BODEN KLOSS, Journ. Siam Soc. Nat. Hist. Suppl., 1932, p. 247 (Doi Suthep).

Chaptia aenea aenea [*partim*], RILEY, U. S. Nat. Mus. Bull. 172, 1938, p. 284 (Doi Langka [*partim*]).

This fine species is very common in the evergreen of the western mountains (east to and including the Khun Tan range) and also on Phu Kha, from 2,700 to 8,000 feet (more numerous above 3,300 feet).

Like other drongos, this form haunts forest clearings and trailsides, where it is easily seen and heard. When it pursues insects on the wing, a most elegant effect is given by the apparently disjoined racquets fluttering far behind the tail.

A bird still in postnatal molt was taken May 3, and others in postjuvenal molt were obtained between August 13 and 24. Adults in postnuptial molt were collected between August 30 and October 20.

Old individuals had the irides crimson; the bill, feet, toes, and claws black. Immatures seem to have the irides brown.

Bhringa remifer is separated from others of its family by having a dense tuft of frontal feathers directed forward to cover the basal half of the bill and by having the outermost pair of rectrices prolonged beyond the others by a wirelike shaft terminated with a long, slender racquet. It has the general coloration black, highly glossed with steel blue (except on the lower flanks, where the feathers are silky and silver-gray).

DISSEMURUS PARADISEUS RANGOONENSIS (Gould)

Burmese Greater Racquet-tailed Drongo

Edolius Rangoonensis Gould, Proc. Zool. Soc. London, 1836, p. 5 (Rangoon, Burma).

Dissemurus paradiseus, Gyldenstolpe, Journ. Nat. Hist. Soc. Siam, 1915, p. 167 (listed).

Dissemurus paradiseus malabaricus, Gyldenstolpe, Kungl. Svenska Vet.-Akad. Handl., 1916, p. 21 (Khun Tan, Pha Kho).

Dissemurus paradiseus rangoonensis, Gyldenstolpe, Ibis, 1920, p. 450 ("Throughout the north of Siam").—de Schauensee, Proc. Acad. Nat. Sci. Philadelphia, 1928, p. 556 (Chiang Mai) ; 1929, p. 554 (Doi Suthep, Chiang Mai, Chiang Saen Kao) ; 1934, p. 228 (Chiang Mai, Chiang Saen).—Deignan, Journ. Siam Soc. Nat. Hist. Suppl., 1931, p. 148 (Chiang Mai, Doi Suthep) ; 1936, p. 101 (Chiang Mai, Doi Suthep).—Riley, U. S. Nat. Mus. Bull. 172, 1938, p. 291 (Khun Tan, Doi Hua Mot, Muang Pai, Sop Phung).

The larger racquet-tailed drongo is very common throughout our provinces in the bamboo and dry, deciduous forest of the plains and the lower mountain slopes to 2,700 feet, rather less so in light evergreen to 3,500 feet.

The mixed aggregations of babblers, woodpeckers, etc., which travel noisily through the *pa daeng*, are almost always accompanied by a pair of the *nok saeo yai hang buang*, which fly from tree to tree in advance of their more terrestrial companions, uttering an endless series of melodious whistles and liquid calls.

A specimen still in postnatal molt was taken June 1 and another in postjuvenal molt, July 25. Adults in postnuptial molt were collected between May 27 and November 8.

My examples had the irides brown or brownish red; the bill, feet, toes, and claws black.

Dissemurus p. rangoonensis has the frontal feathers lengthened, the shorter ones in front directed forward, the longer ones behind arched backward above the crown to make a conspicuous crest; the wirelike shafts of the elongated outermost rectrices gradually spiralled and terminated by a twisted racquet, much broader than that of *Bhringa remifer*. It has the general coloration black, glossed almost everywhere with steel blue.

Family ORIOLIDAE

ORIOLUS CHINENSIS TENUIROSTRIS Blyth

Assamese Black-naped Oriole

O[riolus] tenuirostris Blyth, Journ. Asiat. Soc. Bengal, vol. 15, 1846, pp. 48–49 ("Central India," error; type locality here corrected to Assam).

Oriolus indicus [*partim*], Gyldenstolpe, Journ. Nat. Hist. Soc. Siam, 1915, p. 168 (listed [=Khun Tan (*partim*)]).

Oriolus tenuirostris, Williamson, Journ. Nat. Hist. Soc. Siam, 1918, p. 21 (Doi Nga Chang).

Oriolus indicus indicus [*partim*], Gyldenstolpe, Ibis, 1920, p. 452 ("Throughout the whole country" [=Khun Tan (*partim*)]).

Oriolus indicus tenuirostris, Gyldenstolpe, Ibis, 1920, p. 452 (Doi Nga Chang).

Oriolus chinensis tenuirostris, de Schauensee, Proc. Acad. Nat. Sci. Philadelphia, 1929, p. 556 (Doi Suthep); 1934, p. 232 (Khun Tan, Doi Suthep, Doi Chiang Dao).—Chasen and Boden Kloss, Journ. Siam Soc. Nat. Hist. Suppl., 1932, p. 248 (Doi Suthep).—Riley, U. S. Nat. Mus. Bull. 172, 1938, p. 295 (Khun Tan, Doi Langka).

Oriolus chinensis tenuirostris [*partim*], Deignan, Journ. Siam Soc. Nat. Hist. Suppl., 1931, p. 150 (Doi Suthep [*partim*]); 1936, p. 102 (Doi Suthep [*partim*]).

The present race of the black-naped oriole is a rather common winter visitor to the districts west of (and including) the Khun Tan range, usually found between 3,000 and 5,500 feet but occasionally occurring down to the very bases of the hills. On Doi Suthep the *species* has been recorded from October 3 (1936) to the end of March (1932).

This bird may be seen at the edge of clearings in the evergreen or in the open hill-forest, often high in the trees but attracting attention by its loud, clear whistles and its brilliant coloration. It is almost always to be observed among the various forms drawn to flowering and fruiting trees.

An adult female had the irides crimson; the bill and interior of the mouth dusky pink; the feet and toes slaty; the claws dull black.

The adult male has a black nuchal band continued on each side of the head, through the eye, to the base of the bill; the crown, the uppermost back, and the entire underparts golden-yellow; the secondary coverts, scapulars, back, rump, and upper tail coverts golden-olive; the primary coverts black, tipped with yellow to form a conspicuous spot near the center of the folded wing; the primaries black, narrowly tipped and margined along the outer web with yellowish white; the secondaries black, broadly margined along the outer web with golden-olive and sometimes narrowly tipped with yellow; the rectrices black with an outwardly increasingly broad golden-yellow tip, which, on the outermost pair, covers over half the feather. The adult female is similar but has the yellow parts more strongly suffused with green; the underparts often with more or less obsolescent dark shaft streaks. Immatures are much duller, lack black markings on the head, and have the underparts largely whitish with heavy blackish streaks.

ORIOLUS CHINENSIS DIFFUSUS Bowdler Sharpe

CHINESE BLACK-NAPED ORIOLE

Oriolus diffusus BOWDLER SHARPE, Catalogue of the birds in the British Museum, vol. 3, 1877, p. 197. New name for *Oriolus indicus* Jerdon 1845 (Malabar), which is, in any case, preoccupied by *Oriolus indicus* Daudin, 1802.

Oriolus indicus [*partim*], GYLDENSTOLPE, Journ. Nat. Hist. Soc. Siam, 1915, p. 168 (listed [=Khun Tan (*partim*)]).

Oriolus indicus, GYLDENSTOLPE, Kungl. Svenska Vet.-Akad. Handl., 1916, p. 22 (Khun Tan, Pha Hing).

Oriolus indicus indicus [*partim*], GYLDENSTOLPE, Ibis, 1920, p. 452 ("Throughout the whole country" [*partim*]).

Oriolus chinensis tenuirostris [*partim*], DEIGNAN, Journ Siam Soc. Nat. Hist. Suppl., 1931, p. 150 (Doi Suthep [*partim*]); 1936, p. 102 (Doi Suthep [*partim*]).

Oriolus chinensis diffusus, RILEY, U. S. Nat. Mus. Bull. 172, 1938, p. 294 (Ban Nam Khian).

The Chinese black-naped oriole presumably occurs throughout our provinces but, up to the present time, is known from the territory *west* of the Khun Tan range only by an adult male that I collected on Doi Suthep, 3,300 feet, January 26, 1937. The northern specimens before me (which I cannot separate from Chinese birds) were taken between September 28 and April 18, and the form is probably only a winter visitor, but it must be noted that Gyldenstolpe took an example at Khun Tan as late as May 1 (1914).

Beyond the fact that this bird is more an inhabitant of lowland deciduous forest than of the mountain evergreen, it seems not to differ in habits from the preceding race.

Gyldenstolpe states (1916) that his specimens had the irides brownish red; the bill pink; the feet and toes plumbeous.

O. c. diffusus is most readily distinguished from *tenuirostris* by its having the bill much more robust and the black nuchal band so wide as to cover the occiput as well as the nape. The fully adult male differs in having the entire upperparts golden-yellow, like the underparts. The adult female and the younger male have the upperparts much like those of the adult male of *tenuirostris*, except that the rump and upper tail coverts are golden-yellow.

ORIOLUS XANTHORNUS XANTHORNUS (Linnaeus)

BENGALESE BLACK-HEADED ORIOLE

[*Coracias*] *Xanthornus* LINNAEUS, Systema naturae, ed. 10, vol. 1, 1758, p. 108 ("America," error=Bengal, *ex* Edwards).

Oriolus melanocephalus, GYLDENSTOLPE, Kungl. Svenska Vet.-Akad. Handl., 1913, p. 34 (Pak Pan, Den Chai); 1916, p. 23 (Pha Kho, Pang Hua Phong, Khun Tan, Tha Chomphu); Journ. Nat. Hist. Soc. Siam, 1915, p. 168 (listed).

Oriolus luteolus thaiacous, GYLDENSTOLPE, Ibis, 1920, p. 452 ("Throughout the whole country").

Oriolus xanthornis thaiacous, DE SCHAUENSEE, Proc. Acad. Nat. Sci. Philadelphia, 1928, p. 557 (Chiang Mai).

Oriolus xanthornus xanthornus, DE SCHAUENSEE, Proc. Acad. Nat. Sci. Philadelphia, 1929, p. 557 (Chiang Mai, Chiang Rai, Chiang Saen); 1934, p. 232 (Khun Tan, Doi Suthep, Doi Chiang Dao).—DEIGNAN, Journ. Siam Soc. Nat. Hist. Suppl., 1931, p. 150 (Chiang Mai, Doi Suthep); 1936, p. 102 (Chiang Mai, Doi Suthep).—RILEY, U. S. Nat. Mus. Bull. 172, 1938, p. 295 (Ban Nam Khian, "Doi Phra Chao" [=Doi Saket ?], Mae Khan).

The black-headed oriole is a very common permanent resident throughout the northern provinces, inhabiting the lowland deciduous and mixed-deciduous forests and ascending the hills in this type of vegetation to about 2,850 feet.

This is the most numerous and best known oriole of our area. Its notes and habits are not markedly different from those of the races of *chinensis*.

Breeding probably takes place during the hot weather, at which season the beautiful whistled song may be heard on all sides in the dry forests. Immatures in postjuvenal molt have been taken between July 25 and August 6; adults in postnuptial molt, between August 4 and September 9.

Gyldenstolpe states that his specimens had the irides crimson (adults) or brown (immatures) the bill rosy pink (adults) or black (immatures); the feet and toes plumbeous (adults) or black (immatures).

Adults resemble a smaller *O. c. diffusus* but may always be known by their having the entire head, neck, and center of the upper breast black. Immatures have the top and sides of the head (except for the yellow forehead) black, indistinctly streaked with yellow; the throat white, streaked with black (these streaks continued onto the yellow breast).

ORIOLUS TRAILLII TRAILLII (Vigors)

HIMALAYAN MAROON ORIOLE

Pastor Traillii VIGORS, Proc. Comm. Sci. Corr. Zool. Soc. London, pt. 1, 1830–1831 [= 1832], p. 175 (Himalayas; type locality restricted to Darjiling by Stuart Baker, Journ. Bombay Nat. Hist. Soc., vol. 27, 1921, p. 698).

Oriolus trailli trailli, DE SCHAUENSEE, Proc. Acad. Nat. Sci. Philadelphia, 1928, p. 557 (Doi Suthep); 1929, p. 557 (Doi Suthep, Chiang Saen).—CHASEN and BODEN KLOSS, Journ. Siam Soc. Nat. Hist. Suppl., 1932, p. 248 (Doi Suthep).

Oriolus traillii traillii, DEIGNAN, Journ. Siam Soc. Nat. Hist. Suppl., 1931, p. 151 (Doi Suthep); 1936, p. 102 (Doi Suthep).—DE SCHAUENSEE, Proc. Acad. Nat. Sci. Philadelphia, 1934, p. 232 (Doi Suthep, Doi Chiang Dao).

Oriolus trailii trailii, RILEY, U. S. Nat. Mus. Bull. 172, 1938, p. 297 (Doi Ang Ka, Doi Suthep, Khun Tan, Doi Langka).

The maroon oriole is rather common in heavy evergreen on the mountains west of (and including) the Khun Tan chain and also on Phu Kha, between 3,300 and 7,500 feet. During the cold weather, some individuals occur in the same type of forest at lower levels, on such a hill as Doi Suthep necessarily not descending below 2,000 feet but, in Chiang Rai Province, appearing even on the plains.

This species gathers in numbers at fruiting and flowering trees, and museum specimens often have the face yellowed with pollen. The only note I have heard is a catlike mew, quite unlike any call of the golden orioles.

A bird from Khun Tan, May 12, has almost completed the postnatal molt; another, from Doi Suthep, July 16, is beginning postjuvenal molt. An apparently adult male from Doi Suthep, February 3, is not in molt but wears a nondescript dress which, especially below, combines the characters of male and female plumages in a most extraordinary way.

My examples had the irides creamy yellow or buffy yellow; the edges of the eyelids and the bill plumbeous-blue; the feet and toes plumbeous; the soles yellow; the claws horny plumbeous.

The adult male has the entire head and neck, the wings, and the thighs black (the head, neck, and shoulders glossed with steel blue); the rectrices dull maroon-crimson; the rest of the plumage shining crimson-maroon, with the pure white bases of the feathers showing through in places. The adult female has the upper half of the head and the nape uniform dull black; the wings and back deep brown, changing to maroon-brown on the rump and to dull maroon-crimson on the upper tail coverts; the rectrices brownish maroon and dull maroon-crimson; the underparts (except for the dull maroon-crimson under tail coverts) grayish white, heavily streaked and spotted, on the throat with blackish, elsewhere with deep brown. Birds in first-winter dress resemble the adult female but have the streaks beneath rather narrower and more clearly defined and not darker on the throat than elsewhere. Juveniles have the throat and breast washed with deep buff and deep buff edgings to the wing coverts and the feathers of the mantle.

Family CORVIDAE

CORVUS MACRORHYNCHOS LEVAILLANTII Lesson

BENGALESE JUNGLE CROW

Corvus Levaillantii LESSON, Traité d'ornithologie, livr. 5, 1831 [= 1830 ?], p. 328 (Bengal).

Corvus macrorhynchus, GYLDENSTOLPE, Kungl. Svenska Vet.-Akad. Handl., 1913, p. 18 ([Mae Raem]); Journ. Nat. Hist. Soc. Siam, 1915, p. 164 (listed).

Corvus macrorhynchus [*partim*], GYLDENSTOLPE, Kungl. Svenska Vet.-Akad. Handl., 1916, p. 16 ("The whole of Siam" [*partim*]).

Corvus coronoides hainanus [*partim*], GYLDENSTOLPE, Ibis, 1920, p. 448 ("Throughout the whole country" [*partim*]).

Corvus coronoides macrorhynchus, DE SCHAUENSEE, Proc. Acad. Nat. Sci. Philadelphia, 1928, p. 555 (Chiang Mai).

Corvas levaillanti andamanensis, DEIGNAN, Journ. Siam Soc. Nat. Hist. Suppl., 1931, p. 134 (Chiang Mai, Doi Suthep).

Corvus macrorhynchus macrorhynchus, DEIGNAN, Journ. Siam Soc. Nat. Hist. Suppl., 1936, p. 102 (Chiang Mai, Doi Suthep).—GREENWAY, Bull. Mus. Comp. Zool., 1940, p. 167 (Doi Ang Ka).

The only true crow of our provinces is common wherever man has gone before to clear the forest and cultivate the land. It is, accordingly, most numerous in towns and villages, but ventures also into clearings in the evergreen and ascends the mountains to as high an elevation as there are inhabited *hai*, on Doi Suthep reaching 3,300 feet, on Doi Ang Ka, 4,400 feet.

At Chiang Mai it was quite fearless in the immediate vicinity of monasteries and dwellings but decidedly wild elsewhere, and for this reason I seldom found it expedient to take a specimen. It occurs in much greater numbers in the towns of Phrae and Nan, where it was said to be highly destructive to fruit and young poultry, than at Chiang Mai, where it was looked upon with indifference. Its harsh *kha-a-a* or *khă-ă-ă* is constantly to be heard at roadside markets, where it gathers refuse from the ground, and in fruiting fig trees about the monasteries, but it will also eat carrion or whatever else is available. While somewhat gregarious at any season, it is especially so during the cold weather when all the crows in a given district spend the night at a common roost, which may be many miles from the feeding grounds of the day; I have more than once followed small roost-bound groups from Chiang Mai as far as Mae Rim and at that point was obviously still miles away from the forest area then being used for the purpose.

An adult female had the irides brown; the bill, feet, toes, and claws black.

Our crow has the plumage wholly black, the underparts glossed with steel blue, the upperparts with steel violet.

Northern birds belong to the form, intermediate between *levaillantii* and *macrorhynchos*, which Mayr designates "Subsp. 2" (Ibis, 1940, p. 695).

GARRULUS GLANDARIUS LEUCOTIS Hume

INDO-CHINESE WHITE-EARED JAY

Garrulus leucotis HUME, Proc. Asiat. Soc. Bengal, No. 5, 1874, p. 106 (no locality given).

Garrulus leucotis HUME, Stray Feathers, vol. 2, 1874, pp. 443–444 ("The hills of the Salween district of the Tenasserim province near Kyoukuyat [=Kyouknyat], at an elevation of about 3,000 feet").

Garrulus leucotis, GYLDENSTOLPE, Kungl. Svenska Vet.-Akad. Handl., 1913, p. 20 ([Pak Pan]); 1916, p. 19 (Khun Tan, Pha Kho, Tha Chomphu, Pang Hua Phong, Doi Pha Sakaeng); Journ. Nat. Hist. Soc. Siam, 1915, p. 164 (listed).

Garrulus leucotis leucotis, GYLDENSTOLPE, Ibis, 1920, p. 449 (Khun Tan, Pha Kho, Tha Chomphu, Pang Hua Phong, Pak Pan, Doi Pha Sakaeng).—DEIGNAN, Journ. Siam Soc. Nat. Hist. Suppl., 1931, p. 135 (Doi Suthep).—CHASEN and BODEN KLOSS, Journ. Siam Soc. Nat. Hist. Suppl., 1932, p. 247 (Doi Suthep).—DEIGNAN, Journ. Siam Soc. Nat. Hist. Suppl., 1936, p. 103 (Chiang Mai, Doi Suthep).—DE SCHAUENSEE, Proc. Acad. Nat. Sci. Philadelphia, 1934, p. 179 (ridge south of Doi Chiang Dao, Doi Suthep).—RILEY, U. S. Nat. Mus. Bull. 172, 1938, p. 309 (Khun Tan, Doi Suthep, Doi Hua Mot, Mae Sariang).

Garrulus leucotis leucotis>*oatesi*, DE SCHAUENSEE, Proc. Acad. Nat. Sci. Philadelphia, 1929, p. 528 (Doi Suthep).

The paragraph dealing with the distribution in our provinces of the ashy cuckoo-shrike (*Coracina n. siamensis*) applies equally well to the white-eared jay, and, in fact, wherever one species is seen the other may be expected to occur also.

This bird is usually seen perched alone at the top of some high tree, but where conditions are particularly favorable a number of individuals may be in sight at once. I have more than once seen such an informal gathering at the edge of a jungle grass fire, where the jays were preying on the numerous small creatures driven out by the flames. It is a rather noisy species, whose commonest note is a rasping *jay*.

I collected a male with the gonads enlarged, March 7, and Gyldenstolpe (1916) obtained at the end of May young birds still in company with the parents. Specimens taken between July 10 and October 17 are in postnuptial molt.

Adults have the irides brown; the bill black; the feet and toes pale brownish gray or dusky flesh.

The present species has the forehead white, each feather with a black shaft streak; the crown and rather short, rounded crest black; the scapulars and back vinaceous-brown, paler and more vinaceous on the rump; the upper tail coverts white; the wings black, with the shoulders chestnut, the remaining coverts narrowly barred black and sky blue, the greater part of the outer web of the outer secondaries more broadly barred black, sky blue, and blue-white, the innermost secondaries largely deep chestnut; the tail black; the throat and sides of the head and neck pure white, except for a broad, black mustachial streak; the breast vinaceous-brown, paling on the abdomen and fading to white on the under tail coverts.

KITTA ERYTHRORHYNCHA MAGNIROSTRIS (Blyth)

BURMESE RED-BILLED BLUE PIE

Ps[ilorhinus] magnirostris BLYTH, Journ. Asiat. Soc. Bengal, vol. 15, 1846, pp. 27–28 ("Ya-ma-dong Mountains, separating Arracan from Pegu").

Urocissa occipitalis, GYLDENSTOLPE, Kungl. Svenska Vet.-Akad. Handl., 1913, p. 19 (Ban Huai Hom, Den Chai, Pak Pan); 1916, p. 17 (Khun Tan); Journ. Nat. Hist. Soc. Siam, 1915, p. 164 (listed).

Urocissa occipitalis magnirostris, GYLDENSTOLPE, Ibis, 1920, p. 448 ("Northern Siam").

Urocissa erythrorhyncha magnirostris, DE SCHAUENSEE, Proc. Acad. Nat. Sci. Philadelphia, 1928, p. 555 (Doi Suthep); 1929, p. 527 (Chiang Mai); 1934, p. 178 (Chiang Mai).—DEIGNAN, Journ. Siam Soc. Nat. Hist. Suppl., 1931, p. 134 (Doi Suthep, Chiang Mai); 1936, p. 102 (Doi Suthep, Chiang Mai).—RILEY, U. S. Nat. Mus. Bull. 172, 1938, p. 303 (Doi Ang Ka, Muang Pai, Mae Suya valley, Doi Musoe).

The red-billed pie is not known to occur in Chiang Rai but is rather common in all the other provinces, haunting deciduous forest and scrubby second growth, from the plains to about 2,700 feet.

This fine bird is shy and avoids the vicinity of human habitation but may often be seen in dry jungle and at uncultivated places along the rivers in flocks of five or six individuals, which follow each other from tree to tree uttering harsh, scolding cries. It often descends to the ground to feed and drink and then carries the exaggerated tail somewhat erected to keep the longest feathers, which naturally curve downward near the tip, from becoming soiled.

Specimens that have almost completed postnatal molt were taken in southern Nan Province on May 25 and 30. An adult from Mae Hong Son Province, October 23, is in postnuptial molt.

De Schauensee notes (1929) that a male had the irides brown; the bill bright sealing-wax red; the feet, toes, and claws bright coral red.

The adult has the head, neck, and upper breast black, with a large and conspicuous white patch from the center of the occiput to the center of the uppermost back; the scapulars, back, and rump dull blue-violet; the upper tail coverts blue-violet with broad, black tips; the wings deep violet-blue, both primaries and secondaries more or less broadly tipped with white; the strongly graduated tail deep violet-blue, each feather with a broad, white tip and all except the central pair with a broad, black, subapical bar; the remaining underparts bluish white, bluer on the lower breast, upper abdomen, flanks, and thighs. In freshly molted examples, the central part of the outer web of the primaries, the center of the abdomen, the under tail coverts, and the tips of the rectrices are suffused with a beautiful but evanescent pinkish-buff hue.

The juveniles from Pak Chong, doubtfully recorded by Riley (1938) as *Urocissa flavirostris robini*, are unquestionably of the present species and can be matched in every detail by young birds that I myself shot from flocks of *K. e. magnirostris*.

A form of the common magpie (*Pica pica*) occurs in Kengtung State within a few miles of our northern border and almost certainly will be found, at least during the cold weather, in the Chiang Saen district.

KITTA CHINENSIS CHINENSIS (Boddaert)

THAI GREEN-BREASTED HUNTING-CROW

Coracias chinensis BODDAERT, Table des planches enluminéez d'histoire naturelle, 1783, p. 38 (China, *ex* d'Aubenton, error; type locality corrected to southern Thailand, by Robinson and Boden Kloss, Journ. & Proc. Asiat. Soc. Bengal, new ser., vol. 18, 1922 [=1923], p. 561).

Cissa chinensis, GYLDENSTOLPE, Journ. Nat. Hist. Soc. Siam, 1915, p. 164 (listed); Kungl. Svenska Vet.-Akad. Handl., 1916, p. 18 (Doi Pha Sakaeng, Khun Tan); Ibis, 1920, p. 448 ("Hills of northern Siam").

Cissa chinensis chinensis, DEIGNAN, Journ. Siam Soc. Nat. Hist. Suppl., 1931, p. 134 (Doi Suthep); 1936, p. 102 (Doi Suthep).—DE SCHAUENSEE, Proc. Acad. Nat. Sci. Philadelphia, 1934, p. 178 (Doi Suthep, Chiang Rai).—RILEY, U. S. Nat. Mus. Bull. 172, 1938, p. 304 (Doi Langka, Doi Hua Mot, Khun Tan, Thattafang, Ban San Pa Yang).

The hunting-crow is fairly common in all our provinces but is restricted in range to districts of dense jungle, whether bamboo or evergreen, in which it occurs both on the plains and on the hills to about 5,000 feet.

This species travels in small bands (accompanied on the plains by *Garrulax l. diardi*, at higher elevations by *Garrulax p. meridionalis* and *Garrulax s. strepitans*), which meticulously quarter the ground, the thickets, vines, and trees. So heavy is the vegetation in which it ordinarily dwells and so retiring the bird that it would seldom be observed at all if it were not for its loud, harsh calls. On Doi Suthep, where it was certainly present at all seasons, it appeared always to be much commoner in the rains and very rare during the autumn months.

An example with the gonads enlarged was taken on Phu Kha, April 7, and another in postnatal molt on Khun Tan, May 16. Specimens collected between August 29 and November 28 are in postnuptial molt.

Adults had the irides dark crimson; the eyelids yellowish brown, edged with deep coral red; the bill, interior of the mouth, feet, and toes deep coral red; the claws horny orange.

Old birds in perfect color have the forehead bright greenish yellow, changing to bright yellow-green on the crown and crest; a broad, black band across the nape and continued on either side of the head, through the eye, to the base of the bill; the scapulars, back, rump, and upper tail coverts glaucous-green; the wings bright chestnut-red, the inner secondaries with a broad, white tip and a broad, black, subterminal bar; the rectrices glaucous-green, all with a broad, whitish tip and all but the central pair also with a broad, black, subterminal bar; the entire underparts light glaucous-green.

Apparently as a result of exposure to sunlight, yellow disappears from the plumage, the green portions change to light blue, and the chestnut-red of the wings becomes gray-brown or even olivaceous-gray. Most specimens, while still alive, show such alteration, and the change is more pronounced in birds taken just before the molt and in those few collected in hot, dry forest with little shade.

CRYPSIRINA VAGABUNDA KINNEARI (Stuart Baker)

Peguan Rufous Tree Pie

Dendrocitta rufa kinneari Stuart Baker, Fauna of British India, Birds, ed. 2, vol. 1, 1922, p. 51 (Toungoo, Burma).

Dendrocitta rufa [*partim*], Gyldenstolpe, Kungl. Svenska Vet.-Akad. Handl., 1916, p. 17 (Khun Tan); Ibis, 1920, p. 449 ("Northern Siam" [*partim*]).

Dendrocitta rufa sakaratensis, de Schauensee, Proc. Acad. Nat. Sci. Philadelphia, 1929, p. 527 (Chiang Mai, Mae Rim).

Dendrocitta rufa sakeratensis, Deignan, Journ. Siam Soc. Nat. Hist. Suppl., 1931, p. 134 (Chiang Mai, Doi Suthep); 1936, p. 103 (Chiang Mai, Doi Suthep).

Dendrocitta rufa sakeratensis [*partim*], de Schauensee, Proc. Acad. Nat. Sci. Philadelphia, 1934, p. 179 (Chiang Mai, Mae Taeng, "Tung Sio").

Dendrocitta vagabunda kinneari [*partim*], Riley, U. S. Nat. Mus. Bull. 172, 1938, p. 306 (Mae Khan).

The Peguan rufous tree pie dwells in exactly the same types of jungle as *Kitta e. magnirostris* but has a much more restricted range: within our provinces it seems to be confined to the lowlands of the Mae Ping basin and, in addition to the localities listed above, has been taken only at Ban Mae Dok Daeng, Chom Thong, Ban Sop Mae Chaem, and Ban Pa Pua. On Doi Suthep I once saw a solitary straggler at 3,000 feet (August 23, 1930), but otherwise it has never been found above 1,500 feet.

This pie lives in the dry forest in small bands, the members of which follow one another from tree to tree with alternate sailing and beating of wings, constantly uttering a rather musical trisyllabic call as well as many harsher notes. It is one of the forms that make up the mixed bands of *Kitta*, *Garrulax*, *Dissemurus*, etc. One of my specimens had the stomach filled with large berries.

Examples taken between July 20 and November 9 are in postnuptial molt.

Two adult females had the irides bright brown; the eyelids slaty gray; the bill dark slate, paler at the rictus; the interior of the mouth black; the feet and toes brownish black; the claws horny black.

The adult of either sex has the head, neck, breast, and upper back sooty gray; the scapulars, back, and upper tail coverts dull rufous-brown; the rump rufous-buff; all the wing coverts and the outer webs of the inner secondaries silvery gray, the rest of the wing black; the long, graduated tail silvery gray, each feather with a broad, black tip; the remaining underparts rufous-buff. Immature birds have the head, neck, breast, and upper back more brownish and not clearly defined from the adjacent color areas; the secondaries narrowly, the rectrices much more broadly, tipped with buff.

As in all species inhabiting the deciduous forests, the plumage of this bird rapidly becomes worn and discolored and properly to understand the geographic variation requires series of freshly molted adults. Too many races have been described from our subregion on unsuitable material and without reference to previously named forms of nearby areas. While single specimens from Thailand can scarcely be differentiated, with series I find it just possible to recognize three subspecies: (1) *saturatior* of southwestern Thailand (Kanchanaburi north to Rahaeng), in which the gray hood is poorly defined from the dull rufous-brown back and the buff underparts are palest; (2) *kinneari* of northwestern Thailand (north of Rahaeng and west of the Khun Tan range), which differs from *saturatior* in having the gray hood more clearly defined from the rather brighter rufous-brown back and the buff underparts deeper in tone; (3) *sakeratensis* of the remaining portions of the country, which differs from *kinneari* in having the hood rather darker (almost slaty), the rufous-brown of the back and the buff of the underparts slightly deeper.

It may be necessary eventually to merge certain of our forms with races described from South India, but I lack the material essential for an investigation of this problem.

CRYPSIRINA VAGABUNDA SAKERATENSIS (Gyldenstolpe)

INDO-CHINESE RUFOUS TREE PIE

Dendrocitta rufa sakeratensis GYLDENSTOLPE, Bull. Brit. Orn. Club, vol. 41, 1920, pp. 32–33 (Ban Chakkarat, East Thailand).

Dendrocitta rufa, GYLDENSTOLPE, Kungl. Svenska Vet.-Akad. Handl., 1913, p. 19 ([Pak Pan, Den Chai]); Journ. Nat. Hist. Soc. Siam, 1915, p. 164 (listed).

Dendrocitta rufa [*partim*], GYLDENSTOLPE, Kungl. Svenska Vet.-Akad. Handl., 1916, p. 17 (Den Chai, Pak Pan, Pha Hing); Ibis, 1920, p. 449 ("Northern Siam" [*partim*]).

The range of the present subspecies seems to coincide closely with that of *Kitta e. magnirostris* in the districts east of the Khun Tan chain. It is noteworthy that neither has yet been found in Chiang Rai and that both have been recorded only from the more southern portions of Lampang, Phrae, and Nan Provinces.

This form differs not at all in habits and habitat from the more western birds.

Two examples taken on August 18 at Ban Mae Mo are in postjuvenal molt.

In series, fresh-plumaged adults of *sakeratensis* are separable from those of *kinneari* in having the head, neck, breast, and upper back rather more slaty; the mantle and underparts slightly deeper in color.

CRYPSIRINA FORMOSAE ASSIMILIS (Hume)

TENASSERIMESE GRAY TREE PIE

Dendrocitta assimilis HUME, Stray Feathers, vol. 5, 1877, p. 117 ("Hill Tenasserim"; specimens recorded from "Kollidoo" and Muleyit, by Hume, *ibid.*, vol. 6, 1878, p. 386).

Dendrocitta himalayensis, GYLDENSTOLPE, Journ. Nat. Hist. Soc. Siam, 1915, p. 164 (Khun Tan).

Dendrocitta sinensis assimilis, GYLDENSTOLPE, Ibis, 1920, p. 449 (Khun Tan).

Dendrocitta formosae assimilis, DE SCHAUENSEE, Proc. Acad. Nat. Sci. Philadelphia, 1929, p. 528 (Doi Suthep); 1934, p. 179 (Doi Suthep, Doi Chiang Dao).—DEIGNAN, Journ. Siam Soc. Nat. Hist. Suppl., 1931, p. 134 (Doi Suthep).—CHASEN and BODEN KLOSS, Journ. Siam. Soc. Nat. Hist. Suppl., 1932, p. 247 (Doi Suthep).—DEIGNAN, Journ. Siam Soc. Nat. Hist. Suppl., 1936, p. 103 (Doi Suthep).

Dendrocitta himalayensis assimilis, RILEY, U. S. Nat. Mus. Bull. 172, 1938, p. 307 (Doi Ang Ka, Doi Langka, Khun Tan).

The southern race of the gray tree pie is known in our provinces only from the higher peaks of the Thanon Thong Chai and Khun Tan ranges, where it inhabits the evergreen from 3,200 feet (Doi Suthep) to 8,000 feet (Doi Ang Ka).

I found this bird common in flocks, usually, but not always, in the tops of tall trees, attracting attention to itself by its noisy calls, some of which have been compared by de Schauensee (1929) to the quack of a mallard, the cheep of a chick, and the "rusty hinge" of an American grackle. One of my specimens had the stomach filled with insects, but I have watched others feeding upon berries.

An example from Doi Ang Ka, April 10, had the gonads enlarged. A bird of August 28 is in postjuvenal molt and another, of November 18, has almost finished the postnuptial molt.

The breeding male mentioned above had the irides red-brown; the bill black; the feet, toes, and claws blackish brown.

Adults have the forehead and a narrow line above the eye black; the crown and nape ashy gray; the scapulars and back light buffy brown; the rump and upper tail coverts pale gray; the wings black, with a small but conspicuous white patch at the center of the primaries; the central pair of rectrices ashy gray with a broad black tip, the next outer pair with only the basal half ashy gray, the remaining pairs usually wholly black; the sides of the head and the throat deep brownish, gradually changing to brownish ashy on the breast and to pale gray on the abdomen; the under tail coverts rufous.

I have been unable to examine topotypes of this form and our birds are possibly intermediate between *assimilis* and *himalayensis*.

CRYPSIRINA FORMOSAE HIMALAYENSIS (Blyth)

East Himalayan Gray Tree Pie

Dendrocitta himalayensis Blyth, Ibis, 1865, p. 45 (Himalayas; type locality restricted to Sikkim, by Ticehurst, Bull. Brit. Orn. Club, vol. 46, 1925, p. 22).

A solitary individual of the gray tree pie, found perched upon a low branch above a trail and giving every indication of being lost, was taken on Doi Suthep at 3,300 feet, March 23, 1937, and was later identified by me at the British Museum as an example of the present race. Although the bird had the testes enlarged, it must nevertheless be considered merely a straggler, perhaps from no great distance, since it is probable that the population of Doi Pha Hom Pok are also of the more northern form, although specimens do not exist to prove this.

It had the irides garnet; the bill black; the feet and toes brownish black; the claws black.

From other Thai specimens, this skin differs in its generally greater proportions; the greater extent of black on the head (covering the forecrown as far as the posterior corner of the eye); its larger white wing patch; the blackish color of the throat; the less sullied, more uniform, gray of the underparts.

CRYPSIRINA TEMIA (Daudin)

Bronzed Spatulate-tailed Tree Pie

Corvus temia Daudin, Traité d'ornithologie, vol. 2, 1800, p. 244 (Java).

Crypsirhina varians, Gyldenstolpe, Kungl. Svenska Vet.-Akad. Handl., 1913, p. 19 (Ban Huai Hom, Phrae); 1916, p. 18 (Khun Tan, Tha Chomphu); Journ. Nat. Hist. Soc. Siam, 1915, p. 164 (listed); Ibis, 1920, p. 449 ("Throughout the whole country").—de Schauensee, Proc. Acad. Nat. Sci. Philadelphia, 1928, p. 556 (Chiang Mai).

Crypsirhina temia, de Schauensee, Proc. Acad. Nat. Sci. Philadelphia, 1929, p. 528 (Chiang Mai, Chiang Saen).

Crypsirina temia, Deignan, Journ. Siam Soc. Nat. Hist. Suppl., 1931, p. 134 (Chiang Mai); 1936, p. 103 (Chiang Mai).—de Schauensee, Proc. Acad. Nat. Sci. Philadelphia, 1934, p. 179 (Chiang Mai, Chiang Rai).—Riley, U. S. Nat. Mus. Bull. 172, 1938, p. 307 (Phrae, Ban Nam Khian).—Greenway, Bull. Mus. Comp. Zool., 1940, p. 168 (Chiang Mai).

While very common throughout our provinces, the spatulate-tailed pie is strictly confined to the plains, where it inhabits brushy waste-lands and the groves of giant bamboo along the streams and in the neighborhood of villages.

This bird travels in small, loose bands among the bamboos, constantly uttering a characteristic whining call. Perhaps the most extraordinary thing in connection with the species is the extreme mobility of the long tail, which is employed as a balancing device while its owner clambers about the branches. The only individual I ever saw on the ground was bathing at a small rain pool and carried the tail directed forward at an angle of 45° to the line of the back.

Gyldenstolpe mentions (1913) taking a male with greatly enlarged gonads; the specimen could not be found in the collection at Stockholm but was probably the mate of a female shot at Phrae, March 1, 1912. I took two examples in postnatal molt at Chiang Mai, July 9, 1935.

Adults have the irides light blue; the bill, feet, toes, and claws black. Immatures differ in having the irides brown.

The adult of either sex has the area immediately around the eye and a frontal band of dense, short, plushy feathers black; the rest of the plumage black, everywhere glossed with deep bronze-green. With wear, the gloss on head and mantle becomes more or less steel blue. Immature birds have the gloss restricted to the remiges and rectrices.

Family PARADOXORNITHIDAE

PARADOXORNIS FLAVIROSTRIS GUTTATICOLLIS David

EASTERN YELLOW-BILLED CROW-TIT

Paradoxornis guttaticollis DAVID, Nouv. Arch. Mus. [Paris], vol. 7, 1871, Bull., pp. 8, 14 (Szechwan; type specimen from "le Setchuan occidentale," *fide* David, Les oiseaux de la Chine, 1877, p. 204).

Paradoxornis guttaticollis, DE SCHAUENSEE, Proc. Acad. Nat. Sci. Philadelphia, 1938, p. 30 (Doi Pha Hom Pok).

This large parrotbill has been found in Thailand only by de Schauensee's collectors, who took three males and two females on Doi Pha Hom Pok, between 6,000 and 6,400 feet, in February, 1938. It is not at all likely to occur at any other locality within our provinces.

The adult has the crown and nape light chestnut-rufous; the remaining upperparts fulvous-brown, with the remiges and rectrices edged rufescent; the ear coverts and the area immediately below them black, forming a large and conspicuous patch; the chin blackish; the remaining underparts fulvous-white, more or less heavily marked on the cheeks, throat, and upper breast with small, anteriorly directed, sagittate, black spots.

PARADOXORNIS GULARIS TRANSFLUVIALIS (Hartert)

BURMESE GRAY-HEADED CROW-TIT

Scaeorhynchus gularis transfluvialis HARTERT, Nov. Zool., vol. 7, 1900, p. 548 (Guilang, North Cachar).

Psittiparus gularis transfluvialis, DE SCHAUENSEE, Proc. Acad. Nat. Sci. Philadelphia, 1929, p. 529 (Doi Suthep); 1934, p. 181 (Doi Suthep).—DEIGNAN, Journ. Siam Soc. Nat. Hist. Suppl., 1931, p. 135 (Doi Suthep).—CHASEN and BODEN KLOSS, Journ. Siam Soc. Nat. Hist. Suppl., 1932, p. 246 (Doi Suthep).—GREENWAY, Bull. Mus. Comp. Zool., 1940, p. 168 (Doi Ang Ka).

Psittiparus gularis gularis, DEIGNAN, Journ. Siam Soc. Nat. Hist. Suppl., 1936, p. 103 (Doi Suthep).

On Doi Ang Ka and Doi Suthep the present form is a common resident of the evergreen from 4,500 to 5,500 feet, occasional as low as 3,500 feet. It has not yet been recorded from the other high mountains of the western provinces.

This parrotbill travels in loose flocks through the forest, at clearings descending into the bushes but in denser places keeping to the tops of the trees. It is a rather silent bird that explores the leaves and hangs head downward from the ends of branchlets in the manner of a titmouse.

I took a very young juvenile on Doi Ang Ka, April 10, and at the same locality an adult in postnuptial molt, September 5.

De Schauensee notes that old birds had the irides dark brown; the bill dull, dark yellow; the feet and toes slaty blue; the claws whitish. My juvenile had the irides brownish gray; the bill orange-yellow; the feet and toes plumbeous-blue; the soles yellow; the claws fleshy.

This species has a frontal patch and a line along each side of the crown to the nape black; the crown, nape, ear coverts, and sides of the neck ashy gray; the remaining upperparts fulvous-brown, suffused with olive; the chin gray; the lores, eye ring, and sides of the throat white; the center of the throat black; the remaining underparts white, more or less suffused (especially on the breast and flanks) with buff.

PARADOXORNIS GULARIS LAOTIANA (Delacour)

LAO GRAY-HEADED CROW-TIT

Psittiparus gularis laotianus DELACOUR, Bull. Brit. Orn. Club, vol. 47, 1926, pp. 19–20 (Chiang Khwang, Laos).

Psittiparus gularis transfluvialis, RILEY, U. S. Nat. Mus. Bull. 172, 1938, p. 310 (Khun Tan, Doi Langka).

The Lao gray-headed parrotbill was found by Smith on Doi Khun Tan and Doi Langka, at the former locality between 3,000 and 4,000 feet. It should be looked for on other high hills of the Khun Tan range and also on Phu Kha.

From the preceding race it differs only in having the bill distinctly longer and higher and in the complete or virtual absence of buffy suffusion from the underparts.

The population of the Khun Tan chain and districts eastward are neither *transfluvialis* nor *fokiensis.* With the former they agree in the gray chin and narrow frontal band; with the latter, in the heavy bill and white underparts (here at the western limit of range occasionally tinged with buff on the breast). For this intermediate form I revive the name *laotiana*, which the describer himself has recently sunk into the synonymy of *fokiensis.*

PARADOXORNIS POLIOTIS FEAE (Salvadori)

Karen Gray-eared Crow-tit

Suthora Feae Salvadori, Ann. Mus. Civ. Stor. Nat. Genova, ser. 2, vol. 7, 1889, p. 363 [in reprint, p. 1] (Taho, in the mountains of Karen-ni).

Suthora poliotis feae, de Schauensee, Proc. Acad. Nat. Sci. Philadelphia, 1934, pp. 3, 181 (Doi Suthep).—Deignan, Journ. Siam Soc. Nat. Hist. Suppl., 1935, p. 64 (Doi Ang Ka); 1936, p. 103 (Doi Suthep).

This diminutive bird, of which few specimens exist in the museums of the world, has been taken on Doi Suthep at 5,500 feet by de Schauensee, February 6 and July 8, 1933 (three males, one female), and on Doi Ang Ka at about 5,000 feet by my collector, September 9, 1935 (one male, two females).

De Schauensee states that his examples were shot from small flocks that occurred in open forest composed of small, gnarled trees; mine were taken from a flock of four in tall lalang grass.

The birds of September 9 are in molt.

De Schauensee notes that a male of February 6 had the maxilla horny black; the mandible yellow; the feet and toes yellow. My specimens of either sex had the irides brown; the eyelids slaty; the maxilla horny black; the mandible flesh, with the apical half plumbeous; the feet and toes horny violet; the claws horn.

The present form has the lores ashy gray; the eye ring and entire upperparts orange-rufous, paler and suffused with olive on the back; an ill-defined black streak at either side of the crown behind the eye; the primary coverts black, the other upper wing coverts olivaceous-brown; the wing quills blackish, the outer ones narrowly margined with white along the outer web, the remainder narrowly margined with orange-rufous along the outer web and with white at the tip and along the inner web; the ear coverts and sides of the neck deep gray; the chin and center of the throat black, bordered at either side by a white mustachial streak of erectile feathers; the breast ashy gray, changing to light orange-rufous on the remaining underparts (albescent on the center of the abdomen); the under wing coverts white.

Family PARIDAE

PARUS MAJOR ALTARUM La Touche

LAO GREEN-BACKED GREAT TIT

Parus major altarum LA TOUCHE, Bull. Brit. Orn. Club, vol. 43, 1922, p. 43 (Mengtze, southeastern Yunnan).

Parus major commixtus, DE SCHAUENSEE, Proc. Acad. Nat. Sci. Philadelphia, 1934, pp. 3, 180 (Doi Chiang Dao).—DEIGNAN, Journ. Siam Soc. Nat. Hist. Suppl., 1935, p. 65 (Doi Ang Ka); 1936, p. 103 (Doi Suthep).

Parus major altarum, RILEY, U. S. Nat. Mus. Bull. 172, 1938, p. 311 (Doi Langka, Doi Hua Mot).

The range of the great tit in our provinces is strictly limited to those districts in which grow fairly extensive pine-forests, with the result that it is a very local form and nowhere really common. I have taken it on the Bo Luang plateau at 3,500 feet and observed it on Doi Ang Ka between 3,500 and 4,500 feet; on Doi Suthep it is known only from a solitary bird at 5,200 feet, January 25, 1936, and a party of four at 3,800 feet, August 8, 1936; on Doi Chiang Dao de Schauensee collected it between 4,500 and 5,500 feet; at the foot of Doi Pha Hom Pok, where the pine descends to the plains, I found it more numerous than at any other locality.

Only rarely is this species seen in some isolated deciduous tree or in open oak-forest and then always in the immediate vicinity of pine. Its acrobatic feeding postures and its cheery notes are quite like those of its congeners throughout the world.

The gonads were enlarged in a specimen from Ban Muang Sum, December 26, and greatly enlarged in one from Doi Suthep, January 25. An example from Doi Suthep, August 8, and another from Doi Hua Mot, August 12, are in postnuptial molt.

Adults have the irides dark brown; the bill black; the feet and toes plumbeous; the claws dark horn.

This titmouse has the crown and nape blue-black; the center of the uppermost back, adjacent to the nape, white; the scapulars and upper back dull olive-green (more yellow anteriorly), changing on the rump and upper tail coverts to blue-gray; the rectrices blackish, with a blue-gray margin along the outer web and a white tip which increases in extent outwardly until the outermost pair are almost wholly white; the folded wing blue-gray with a conspicuous white cross bar and bold white edgings along the outer web of the inner secondaries; the cheeks and ear coverts white, enclosed behind by a narrow blue-black line which connects the black of the nape with that of the breast; the chin, throat, and entire breast blue-black; the remaining underparts vinaceous-white, with a broad black, mesial line extending from the lower breast to the central under tail coverts.

The wing lengths of seven Thai specimens range from 64.5 to 68.8 mm.

PARUS XANTHOGENYS SUBVIRIDIS Blyth

TENASSERIMESE YELLOW-CHEEKED TIT

Parus subviridis "Tickell" BLYTH, Journ. Asiat. Soc. Bengal, vol. 24, 1855, p. 267 ("Mountainous interior of Tenasserim," where it seems to occur only on Muleyit).

Machlolophus spilonotus, WILLIAMSON, Journ. Nat. Hist. Soc. Siam, 1918, p. 15 (Doi Nga Chang).

Parus spilonotus, GYLDENSTOLPE, Ibis, 1920, p. 468 (Doi Nga Chang).

Machlolophus spilonotus subviridis, DE SCHAUENSEE, Proc. Acad. Nat. Sci. Philadelphia, 1929, p. 528 (Doi Suthep).—DEIGNAN, Journ. Siam Soc. Nat. Hist. Suppl., 1931, p. 135 (Doi Suthep).

Parus spilonotus subviridis, CHASEN and BODEN KLOSS, Journ. Siam Soc. Nat. Hist. Suppl., 1932, p. 246 (Doi Suthep).—DE SCHAUENSEE, Proc. Acad. Nat. Sci. Philadelphia, 1934, p. 180 (Doi Suthep).

Machlolophus xanthogenys subviridis, DEIGNAN, Journ. Siam Soc. Nat. Hist. Suppl., 1936, p. 104 (Doi Suthep).

Machlolophus spilonotus subviridis, RILEY, U. S. Nat. Mus. Bull. 172, 1938, p. 312 (Doi Langka, Doi Hua Mot).

With the addition of Doi Ang Ka and Doi Nang Kaeo, the localities listed above give the entire Thai range of this form of the yellow-cheeked tit, so far as it is now known; on these mountains it is common at the edge of the evergreen and in the open hill-forest from 3,300 to 5,500 feet.

It is a social bird that travels in small parties through the bushes and lower trees in company with nuthatches, tree creepers, and such arboreal babblers as *Mesia*, *Stachyris*, and *Alcippe*. De Schauensee observes (1929) that it makes the chattering sounds of other titmice but, in addition, has a loud and cheerful song of three notes, resembling the syllables *chee-chee-pui*, the first two of which are pitched the same, while the third is accented and about two tones lower.

A specimen from Doi Suthep, February 24, had the gonads greatly enlarged. Numerous examples taken between August 26 and November 19 are in postnuptial molt.

Adults have the irides brown; the bill black; the feet, toes, and claws plumbeous-blue or slaty blue.

This species is so typical a titmouse that a detailed description is scarcely necessary. The adult male somewhat resembles the same sex of the great tit but has a conspicuous black crest; the forehead, nape, and sides of the head and body bright yellow; the back heavily streaked with olive-green and black; the upper wing coverts black with bold, white, apical spots. The adult female differs from the male in her generally duller coloration and in the complete absence of black from the underparts.

I have seen, but not collected, some race of the yellow-cheeked tit on Phu Kha; it will perhaps prove to be *Parus x. basileus.*

MELANOCHLORA SULTANEA SULTANEA (Hodgson)

INDIAN SULTAN TIT

[*Parus*] *Sultaneus* HODGSON, India Rev., vol. 2, 1838 [= 1837], pp. 31–32 (no locality given = Nepal).

Melanchlora sultana flavocristata, GYLDENSTOLPE, Journ. Nat. Hist. Soc. Siam, 1915, p. 166 (listed).

Melanochlora sultanea ⪌ *flavocristata*, GYLDENSTOLPE, Kungl. Svenska Vet.-Akad. Handl., 1916, p. 39 (Pha Kho, Khun Tan, Doi Pha Sakaeng).

Melanochlora sultanea sultanea, GYLDENSTOLPE, Ibis, 1920, p. 468 ("Northern Siam).—DE SCHAUENSEE, Proc. Acad. Nat. Sci. Philadelphia, 1929, p. 529 (20 km. south of Muang Phayao, Chiang Saen); 1934, p. 181 (ridge south of Doi Chiang Dao).—DEIGNAN, Journ. Siam Soc. Nat. Hist. Suppl., 1936, p. 104 (Doi Suthep).—RILEY, U. S. Nat. Mus. Bull. 172, 1938, p. 312 (Khun Tan, Doi Pata, Mae Lang valley, "Doi Phra Chao" [= Doi Saket ?]).

The sultan tit is a rather common permanent resident of the lowland evergreen throughout the provinces east of (and including) the Khun Tan range; west of the Khun Tan hills the species is rare, and it is perhaps no coincidence that in these districts all records have been made between October 17 and February 6. To Doi Suthep it is apparently a mere straggler, known only by a solitary bird at 2,850 feet, December 30, 1931, and a second at 2,800 feet, February 6, 1932.

Both Gyldenstolpe and de Schauensee have observed that this species flocks with bulbuls, and I have myself seen it many times with such forms as *Chloropsis* and *Pycnonotus* but am inclined to believe that this is the fortuitous result of a common liking for fruits. On other occasions I have watched it searching the leaves, branches, and trunks of trees, acting much as do the small tits of the genus *Parus*, but whether *Melanochlora* is properly placed with the Paridae is a moot question.

An example from Muang Ngop, April 23, had the gonads enlarged. Specimens in postjuvenal molt were taken between August 6 and October 18; others in postnuptial molt, between August 6 and December 31.

Adults had the irides brown; the bill black, with the maxilla tipped horny; the feet and toes slaty blue; the claws brownish slate.

The old male has the forehead, crown, and lanceolate crest feathers bright yellow; the remaining upperparts, the rest of the head, and the breast black, glossed with steel blue; the remaining underparts bright yellow. The adult female is similar but has the black of the male replaced by deep oily olive, this color suffused on the throat and breast with yellow. Immatures resemble the adults but have the feathers of the crest short and rounded; the primary coverts and secondary coverts narrowly tipped with yellowish white; the yellow parts of the plumage slightly paler; the black portions (of the male) almost without gloss.

The wing lengths of nine adult males from the North range from 107 to 114.5 mm.

Family SITTIDAE

SITTA MAGNA MAGNA Wardlaw Ramsay

SOUTHERN GIANT NUTHATCH

Sitta magna WARDLAW RAMSAY, Proc. Zool. Soc. London, 1876, p. 677, col. pl. 63 (Karen-ni).

Sitta magna, DE SCHAUENSEE, Proc. Acad. Nat. Sci. Philadelphia, 1929, p. 530 (Doi Suthep); 1934, p. 182 (Doi Suthep, Doi Chiang Dao).—DEIGNAN, Journ. Siam Soc. Nat. Hist. Suppl., 1931, p. 135 (Doi Suthep).—CHASEN and BODEN KLOSS, Journ. Siam Soc. Nat Hist. Suppl., 1932, p. 246 (Doi Suthep).—DEIGNAN, Journ. Siam Soc. Nat. Hist. Suppl., 1936, p. 104 (Doi Suthep).—RILEY, U. S. Nat. Mus. Bull. 172, 1938, p. 316 (Doi Ang Ka, Doi Langka).

The giant nuthatch has been found in Thailand only on the high mountains listed above, ranging from 4,000 feet (Doi Ang Ka) to 5,500 feet (Doi Suthep).

I saw this fine species only in or at the edge of dense evergreen forest, where, singly or in pairs, it kept to the tops of huge trees, living or dead. It is apparently not uncommon but, in my experience, is silent and difficult to observe. Smith, Garthwaite, and Smythies state (Journ. Bombay Nat. Hist. Soc., 1940, p. 580) that, in Karen-ni, it occurs in pine and "has a distinctive tri-syllabic call, like the cough of an angry gibbon."

A bird from Doi Ang Ka had the irides brown; the bill black, with the basal half of the mandible plumbeous; the feet and toes light brown; the claws dark brown.

The adult male has a broad, blue-black band on each side of the head from the base of the bill, through the eye, to the upper back; the portions of the forehead and crown between these bands soft blue-gray (more or less streaked with black), changing to a paler gray on the nape and uppermost back; the remaining upperparts slaty blue; the central pair of rectrices slaty blue, the others largely black with white subapical patches; the chin and throat white, changing to soft blue-gray on the breast, abdomen, and flanks (washed with buff at the region of the vent); the thighs chestnut-rufous; the under tail coverts chestnut-rufous with broad, white tips. The adult female resembles the male but has the dark markings of the head dull black, with a tendency to gloss only posteriorly; the pale nuchal area faintly suffused with buff; the mantle paler and less suffused with blue; the underparts pale gray, everywhere more or less suffused with buff.

SITTA EUROPAEA MONTIUM La Touche

La Touche's Eurasian Nuthatch

S[itta] montium La Touche, Ibis, 1899, p. 404 (Kuatun, northwestern Fuhkien).

Sitta europea nagaensis, de Schauensee, Proc. Acad. Nat. Sci. Philadelphia, 1929, p. 530 (Doi Suthep); 1934, p. 182 (Doi Suthep, Doi Chiang Dao).

Sitta europaea nagaensis, Deignan, Journ. Siam Soc. Nat. Hist. Suppl., 1931, p. 135 (Doi Suthep); 1936, p. 104 (Doi Suthep).—Riley, U. S. Nat. Mus. Bull. 172, 1938, p. 315 (Doi Langka).

Sitta castanea neglecta, Chasen and Boden Kloss, Journ. Siam Soc. Nat. Hist. Suppl., 1932, p. 247 (Doi Suthep).

Sitta castanea neglecta [partim], Deignan, Journ. Siam Soc. Nat. Hist. Suppl., 1936, p. 104 (Doi Suthep *[partim]*.

Sitta europaea delacouri Deignan, Journ. Washington Acad. Sci., vol. 28, No. 8, 1938, pp. 371–372 (Doi Suthep, northwestern Thailand).

The present race of this widespread species is strictly confined in Thailand to certain peaks of the Thanon Thong Chai and Khun Tan chains whose elevations exceed 4,500 feet. On Doi Ang Ka, Doi Suthep, Doi Chiang Dao, and Doi Langka it is common from 5,000 to 5,500 feet (occasional as low as 4,500 feet).

I found this little nuthatch in small, loose bands, often accompanied by unrelated forms, both in the evergreen and in tall pine-forest. In addition to a constant, conversational chattering, it frequently utters a note that de Schauensee (1929) compares with the nasal *yank-yank* of the American *S. carolinensis.*

A pair were observed carrying food into a nest hole on Doi Suthep, 5,500 feet, May 10, 1931. Examples in postjuvenal molt were taken on the same mountain, July 13, 14, and 15, 1935.

An adult female had the irides dark brown; the maxilla slaty black, plumbeous-blue at the rictus; the mandible plumbeous-blue, tipped slaty black; the feet and toes slaty gray, tinged olive; the claws horny black.

Adults have a black band along each side of the head from the base of the bill, through the eye, to the upper back; the entire upperparts uniform blue-gray; the rectrices as in the preceding species; the underparts gray, more or less strongly suffused with buff; the lower flanks chestnut; the under tail coverts white, narrowly tipped and edged with chestnut. Immatures differ in having the underparts with more buffy suffusion and in having the lower flanks and margins of the under tail coverts more chestnut-rufous.

Personal examination of the type series of *montium* has shown that my *delacouri* is probably inseparable from La Touche's race.

SITTA EUROPAEA NEGLECTA Walden

Walden's Eurasian Nuthatch

Sitta neglecta Walden, Ann. Mag. Nat. Hist., ser. 4, vol. 5, 1870, p. 218 ("Karen Hills of the Tonghoo district, Burma").

Sitta cinnamoventris, Gyldenstolpe, Kungl. Svenska Vet.-Akad. Handl., 1913, p. 27 (Den Chai, Pak Pan); 1916, p. 37 (Pha Kho); Journ. Nat. Hist. Soc. Siam, 1915, p. 166 (listed); Ibis, 1920, p. 467 ("Northern Siam").

Sitta neglecta, Gyldenstolpe, Journ. Nat. Hist. Soc. Siam, 1915, p. 166 (listed); Kungl. Svenska Vet.-Akad. Handl., 1916, p. 38 (Khun Tan); Ibis, 1920, p. 467 ("Northern and north-western Siam").

Sitta Auto-Sitta siamensis Kleinschmidt, Berajah, Zoographia Infinita, 1928, p. 14 (Khun Tan, North Thailand).

Sitta castanea neglecta, Deignan, Journ. Siam Soc. Nat. Hist. Suppl., 1931, p. 174 (Doi Suthep).—de Schauensee, Proc. Acad. Nat. Sci. Philadelphia, 1934, p. 182 (Mae Taeng).

Sitta castanea neglecta [*partim*], Deignan, Journ. Siam Soc. Nat. Hist. Suppl., 1936, p. 104 (Doi Suthep [*partim*]).—Riley, U. S. Nat. Mus. Bull. 172, 1938, p. 315 (Doi Ang Ka, Mae Khan, Mae Kong Ka valley).

This nuthatch is generally distributed, although only locally common, in the lowland deciduous forest of all our provinces, ranging from the plains to about 2,000 feet (once a solitary bird on Doi Suthep at 2,800 feet). In the neighborhood of Chiang Mai it is confined to the lower slopes of Doi Suthep, where lone individuals have been observed only three times; Chasen and Boden Kloss's record (1932) of a specimen taken by Aagaard at 5,500 feet is here considered referable to *S. e. montium*. My own long series of *neglecta* has been collected from the plains and lower hills of every portion of our area.

It is usually found in small parties in parklike forest, where the trees are tall and well spaced; this preference is doubtless responsible for its absence from certain localities which seem to be otherwise quite suitable. Its habits do not differ in any important way from those of *montium* and the members of the flock converse with the same chattering and twittering.

The breeding season seems to fall early in the year: a male of May 5 is in full juvenal plumage and others, taken between July 10 and 21, are in postjuvenal molt. A female of August 30 has completed the molt and is in fine, unworn feather.

This last specimen had the irides brown; the maxilla black, plumbeous-blue at the base of the culmen; the mandible plumbeous-blue; the feet, toes, and claws slaty. Gyldenstolpe states (1916) that his examples had the irides brown or grayish brown; the bill black or blackish brown; the feet and toes plumbeous.

The adult male *neglecta* has the upperparts like those of *montium;* the underparts rich chestnut-rufous, becoming albescent on the throat and cheeks; the under tail coverts white, narrowly tipped and edged with chestnut-rufous, the longer ones basally slaty. The adult female differs from the adult male in having the entire underparts and the edging of the under tail coverts vinaceous-buff. Juveniles of either sex resemble the adult female.

My adult and subadult males show considerable variation in the depth and extent of the chestnut-rufous below, but such variation seems to bear no relationship to geographical areas and the darkest birds are connected by intermediates with the palest. It seems certain that Kleinschmidt's *siamensis* cannot stand as a valid form.

I do not see how the chestnut-bellied nuthatches can be viewed otherwise than as extremely saturate tropical representatives of *Sitta europaea*. Although, in certain mountainous areas of the Indo-Chinese Subregion, a form of the *europaena*-group may seem to occur together with a form of the *castanea*-group, the fact is that, at such places, the two occupy quite distinct ecological niches, the former holding the high summits, the latter the low elevations.

The mountains of Indo-China are of insufficient altitude to have produced any known example of that type of subspecific variation in which, on a single peak, a lowland form has developed directly from a highland form, or vice versa. Thus, in northern Thailand, we find that *montium* and *neglecta* are so distinct as to indicate a cognate, rather than a direct, relationship: in short, the two are far more distantly separated in time than in space. It may be supposed that, in the isolated southern races of *europaea*-type, we have relict populations whose ranges, for whatever reasons, have been reduced to those few peaks upon which a suitable combination of favorable circumstances still obtains. In the *castanea*-group we have birds that, developed under tropical conditions, have populated the lowlands, wholly surrounding the islandlike areas still held by their distant relatives, and that, wherever the hills proved to be unoccupied by some form of *europaea*-type, have penetrated to higher elevations, to give rise to montane races of their own type.

SITTA EUROPAEA TONKINENSIS Kinnear

KINNEAR'S EURASIAN NUTHATCH

Sitta castanea tonkinensis KINNEAR, Bull. Brit. Orn. Club, vol. 56, 1936, p. 71 (Napé, Laos).

Sitta castanea neglecta [*partim*], RILEY, U. S. Nat. Mus. Bull. 172, 1938, p. 315 (Doi Hua Mot).

A specimen (labeled "female" but almost certainly a male) taken by H. M. Smith on Doi Hua Mot, August 30, 1934, is unquestionably of this form, which has not previously been recorded from Thailand.

S. e. tonkinensis resembles *neglecta* but is somewhat larger and has the coloration, both above and below, decidedly deeper in tone. The male may at once be distinguished from that of any other race by its having the basal portion of the under tail coverts conspicuously *black*, not gray or slaty.

The discovery that *tonkinensis*, a monticolous member of the *castanea*-group, is apparently resident on Doi Hua Mot is of peculiar interest, inasmuch as *montium* (not found on Hua Mot) is the race of the neighboring Doi Langka and *neglecta* is generally distributed over the wide expanse of lowlands which lie between Doi Hua Mot and the mountains of Laos, whence Kinnear's form was described.

SITTA FRONTALIS CORALLINA Hodgson

NEPALESE VELVET-FRONTED NUTHATCH

[*Sitta*] *Corallina* HODGSON, Journ. Asiat. Soc. Bengal, vol. 5, 1836, p. 779 (Nepal).

Sitta frontalis, GYLDENSTOLPE, Journ. Nat. Hist. Soc. Siam, 1915, p. 167 (listed).

Dendrophila frontalis, GYLDENSTOLPE, Kungl. Svenska Vet.-Akad. Handl., 1916, p. 38 (Khun Tan, Doi Pha Sakaeng, Pha Ko, Pang Hua Phong).

Dendrophila frontalis frontalis, GYLDENSTOLPE, Ibis, 1920, p. 467 (Khun Tan, Pang Hua Phong, Pha Kho, Doi Pha Sakaeng).—DE SCHAUENSEE, Proc. Acad. Nat. Sci. Philadelphia, 1929, p. 530 (Doi Suthep, Chiang Saen).

Sitta frontalis frontalis, DEIGNAN, Journ. Siam Soc. Nat. Hist. Suppl., 1931, p. 135 (Doi Suthep).—CHASEN and BODEN KLOSS, Journ. Siam Soc. Nat. Hist. Suppl., 1932, p. 247 (Doi Suthep).—DEIGNAN, Journ. Siam Soc. Nat. Hist. Suppl., 1936, p. 104 (Doi Suthep).—DE SCHAUENSEE, Proc. Acad. Nat. Sci. Philadelphia, 1934, p. 182 (Doi Suthep, Khun Tan, ridge south of Doi Chiang Dao).

Callisitta frontalis frontalis, RILEY, U. S. Nat. Mus. Bull. 172, 1938, p. 313 (Doi Ang Ka, Khun Tan, Doi Langka, Doi Hua Mot, Chiang Dao, Huai Mae Sae).

This pretty species is the common nuthatch of all parts of the northern provinces, occurring from the plains to 5,500 feet, whether in the more open evergreen, in pine-forest, or in parklike deciduous jungle. On Doi Suthep it is very numerous between 3,500 and 4,600 feet, somewhat less so up to 5,500 and down to 2,700 feet; on Doi Ang Ka, it is common from 3,000 to 5,500 feet; in the more eastern districts, however, it regularly occurs at lower elevations.

I found it in loose bands of from 6 to 20 individuals (often accompanied by such small arboreal babblers as *Erpornis*), which, never still, swept from tree to tree uttering a continual *chip-chip-chip*.

Examples in full juvenal plumage were taken between May 1 and 9, but another specimen of May 9 has not quite completed the postnatal molt. Birds in postjuvenal molt were collected between June 1 and September 4 and adults in postnuptial molt between July 31 and December 3.

An adult male had the irides bright yellow; the eyelids plumbeous, tinged yellow; the bill coral red, blackish at the extreme tip of the maxilla; the interior of the mouth coral red; the feet and toes dark brown; the claws dark horny brown. Gyldenstolpe notes (1916) that juveniles had the irides vinaceous-gray and the bill black.

The adult male has the forehead and a narrow line along each side of the crown black; the remaining upperparts violet-blue; the concealed portions of the remiges black, the outer webs of most of the primaries narrowly edged along part of their length with sky blue; the ear coverts pale violet; the throat white, changing to pale violet-vinaceous on the breast and abdomen and to violet-gray on the under tail coverts. The adult female differs in having no black supercilium. Juveniles have the black frontal patch less distinct; the breast and abdomen suffused with buff; the under tail coverts indefinitely barred with gray or white and pale buff.

The wing lengths of 16 northern males range from 74 to 78 mm. and in only four cases does this measurement exceed 76 mm.

Family CERTHIIDAE

CERTHIA DISCOLOR SHANENSIS Stuart Baker

SHAN BROWN-THROATED TREE CREEPER

Certhia discolor shanensis STUART BAKER, Fauna of British India, Birds, ed. 2, vol. 8, 1930, p. 617. New name for *Certhia discolor fuliginosa* Stuart Baker 1922 (Loi Pang Nan [Southern Shan States]), not *C[erthia] fuliginosa* Bechstein, 1811.

Certhia discolor manipurensis, DE SCHAUENSEE, Proc. Acad. Nat. Sci. Philadelphia, 1929, p. 541 (Doi Suthep).—DEIGNAN, Journ. Siam Soc. Nat. Hist. Suppl., 1931, p. 141 (Doi Suthep).

Certhia discolor shanensis, CHASEN and BODEN KLOSS, Journ. Siam Soc. Nat. Hist. Suppl., 1932, p. 247 (Doi Suthep).—DEIGNAN, Journ. Siam Soc. Nat. Hist. Suppl., 1936, p. 104 (Doi Suthep).—DE SCHAUENSEE, Proc. Acad. Nat. Sci. Philadelphia, 1934, p. 207 (Doi Suthep).—RILEY, U. S. Nat. Mus. Bull. 172, 1938, p. 316 (Doi Ang Ka, Doi Langka).

The brown-throated tree creeper, restricted in Thailand to deep evergreen forest at elevations above 4,500 feet, has been found with us only on the three peaks listed above. On Doi Suthep it is not uncommon from 4,500 to 5,000 feet; on Doi Ang Ka it is common from 4,900 to 6,000 feet, somewhat less so up to 8,000 feet.

In the greenish half-light of moss-draped cloud-forest, the soft *seep* of the tree creeper is one of the few sounds to break the silence at the foot of the trees. When hanging motionless against a tree the little bird is scarcely distinguishable from an excrescence of bark; recovered from its alarm, however, it ascends the trunk with quick, jerky movements, describing a wide spiral until the branches are reached, from which point it drops rapidly to the base of another tree and begins again its upward spiral. From March to June may be heard the ringing song: a rather loud *chee-weet, chee-weet, chee-weet, chee-weet*, with the *weet* accented.

A male from Doi Suthep, 5,100 feet, March 12, had the gonads greatly enlarged. An example from Doi Ang Ka, May 4, has almost completed the postnatal molt and two adults from the same mountain, September 3, are in postnuptial molt.

The breeding male had the irides brown; the maxilla black; the mandible flesh; the feet and toes light fleshy brown; the claws pale horny brown.

The adult has the upperparts brown, heavily streaked with black and fulvous, changing on the rump and upper tail coverts to ferruginous and on the tail to a duller red-brown; the remiges with conspicuous black and fulvous markings; the underparts gray-brown, grayer on the abdomen; the under tail coverts rufous-buff. The juvenile is similar but has the feathers of the underparts (except those of the center of the lower abdomen) narrowly tipped with blackish to give an indistinctly scaled appearance.

Family PYCNONOTIDAE

IRENA PUELLA SIKKIMENSIS Whistler and Kinnear

HIMALAYAN FAIRY-BLUEBIRD

Irena puella sikkimensis WHISTLER and KINNEAR, Journ. Bombay Nat. Hist. Soc., vol. 36, No. 3, 1933, p. 582 (Sukna, Darjiling, India).

Irena puella, GYLDENSTOLPE, Kungl. Svenska Vet.-Akad. Handl., 1913, p. 23 (Ban Huai Hom); 1916, p. 65 (Doi Pha Sakaeng, Khun Tan, Pha Kho); Journ. Nat. Hist. Soc. Siam, 1915, p. 166 (listed).

Irena puella puella [*partim*], GYLDENSTOLPE, Ibis, 1920, p. 496 ("Throughout the whole country" [*partim*]).—DE SCHAUENSEE, Proc. Acad. Nat. Sci. Philadelphia, 1934, p. 232 (Khun Tan, Doi Suthep, Doi Chiang Dao).—RILEY, U. S. Nat. Mus. Bull. 172, 1938, p. 300 (Doi Langka, Khun Tan).

Irena puella puella, DE SCHAUENSEE, Proc. Acad. Nat. Sci. Philadelphia, 1928, p. 569 (Doi Suthep); 1929, p. 556 (Doi Suthep, Chiang Saen).—DEIGNAN, Journ. Siam Soc. Nat. Hist. Suppl., 1931, p. 150 (Doi Suthep).—CHASEN and BODEN KLOSS, Journ. Siam Soc. Nat. Hist. Suppl., 1932, p. 242 (Doi Suthep).—DEIGNAN, Journ. Siam Soc. Nat. Hist. Suppl., 1936, p. 102 (Doi Suthep).

This lovely bird is found in the evergreen of all our provinces at comparatively low elevations: it occurs only rarely about 3,500 feet and has not yet been recorded anywhere above 4,600 feet.

The fairy-bluebird ordinarily travels quietly about the forest in pairs but, where some tree, high or low, is laden with ripe fruit, scores may be found together with the hornbills, orioles, smaller bulbuls, and other frugivores that congregate at the place, taking a leading part in the clamor and beating of wings inseparable from such a gathering. While not a migratory species in the strict sense, it almost certainly performs local wanderings in search of fruits, and its numbers at a given locality and elevation seem to be closely correlated with the seasonal abundance of this type of food.

It is said to breed in Burma during the spring months, and this is probably the case also in Thailand, since a long series of adults (all from the Khun Tan range and Nan Province), taken between May 12 and September 3, are in complete molt; it is worthy of record, however, that my only example with the gonads known to have been active was collected on August 3 on Doi Suthep at 3,500 feet. I have no juveniles and my specimens throw no light on the sequence of molts and plumages.

Adults of either sex have the irides bright red; the bill, feet, toes, and claws black.

The adult male has the feathers of the crown, nape, shoulders, scapulars, back, rump, upper and under tail coverts bright violet-blue with an enamellike sheen; the rest of the plumage black. The adult female is quite different: it has the remiges and outer rectrices blackish and the rest of the plumage dull verditer blue.

Thirteen fully adult northern males (of which one is molting the primaries) have the wing length ranging from 127.3 to 140.3 mm., but only two have it under 130 mm. and only two have it over 134 mm. They are thus intermediate between *puella* and *sikkimensis* but rather nearer the latter.

AETHORHYNCHUS LAFRESNAYEI INNOTATUS (Blyth)

BURMESE GREAT IORA

I[ora] innotata, BLYTH, Journ. Asiat. Soc. Bengal, vol. 16, 1847, p. 472 (Arakan).

Aethorhynchus xanthotis, GYLDENSTOLPE, Journ. Nat. Hist. Soc. Siam, 1915, p. 166 (listed).

AEthorhynchus lafresnayei lafresnayei, GYLDENSTOLPE, Ibis, 1920, p. 489 ("Throughout . . . northern Siam").

Aethorhynchus lafresnayi lafresnayi, DE SCHAUENSEE, Proc. Acad. Nat. Sci. Philadelphia, 1929, p. 536 (Chiang Saen).

Aethorhynchus lafresnayanus innotatus, GREENWAY, Bull. Mus. Comp. Zool., 1940, p. 174 (Doi Nang Kaeo).

The great iora is an apparently rare resident of the districts east of (and including) the Khun Tan chain, occurring from the plains to a maximum elevation of 2,800 feet (Doi Nang Kaeo). Eisenhofer took a female at Ban Huai Hom, February 7, 1912 (Hannover), and another at Khun Tan (Stockholm); I have a male from Ban Tong Yang and a female from Ban Huai Som. A single specimen collected by de Schauensee and two recorded by Greenway bring to only seven the total number of examples yet known from our area.

The two birds taken by me were found in fairly open lowland evergreen and, in actions, resembled the following species. The one from Ban Tong Yang, May 4, had the gonads enlarged.

De Schauensee's specimen had the bill slate blue, with the culmen black; the feet and toes slate blue.

The male has the upperparts dull green, washed with yellow on the forehead, forecrown, and tail; the remiges edged along the outer web with yellow-green, along the inner web with white; the outer rectrices narrowly tipped and edged along the inner web with pale greenish yellow; the lores, eye ring, ear coverts, and the entire underparts bright yellow; the under wing coverts and the elongated, silky feathers of the lower flanks white. The female differs in having the yellow underparts duller and suffused with green, especially along the sides of the body.

AEGITHINA TIPHIA TIPHIA (Linnaeus)

BENGALESE SMALL IORA

[*Motacilla*] *Tiphia* LINNAEUS, Systema naturae, ed. 10, vol. 1, 1758, p. 186 (Bengal, *ex* Edwards; type locality restricted to "the neighbourhood of Calcutta," *ex* Latham, by Hume, Stray Feathers, vol. 5, 1877, p. 431).

Aegithina tiphia, GYLDENSTOLPE, Kungl. Svenska Vet.-Akad. Handl., 1913, p. 23 (Phrae); 1916, p. 63 (Khun Tan, Pang Hua Phong).

AEegithina tiphia, GYLDENSTOLPE, Journ. Nat. Hist. Soc. Siam, 1915, p. 166 (listed).

AEgithina tiphia tiphia [*partim*], GYLDENSTOLPE, Ibis, 1920, p. 489 ("Throughout Siam" [*partim*]).

Aegithina tiphia tiphia, DE SCHAUENSEE, Proc. Acad. Nat. Sci. Philadelphia, 1928, p. 567 (Chiang Mai).—DEIGNAN, Journ. Siam Soc. Nat. Hist. Suppl., 1931, p. 139 (Chiang Mai); 1936, p. 108 (Chiang Mai, Doi Suthep).

Aegithina tiphia tiphia [*partim*], DE SCHAUENSEE, Proc. Acad. Nat. Sci. Philadelphia, 1934, p. 199 (Chiang Dao, Chiang Mai).—RILEY, U. S. Nat. Mus. Bull. 172, 1938, p. 366 (Doi Ang Ka, Chiang Mai, Phrae, Nan, Ban Nam Khian).

This race of the common iora is abundant in the lowlands of all our provinces (except Chiang Rai, where it is replaced by the following form) and may also be seen on the mountains in small numbers in the second growth that follows hill-cultivation (on Doi Suthep ascending to 3,800 feet, on Doi Chiang Dao, to about 4,500).

The *nok khamin* is one of the most familiar birds of the northern towns and villages, occurring, in pairs or small parties, in every garden and in the shade trees bordering the streets. It attracts attention both by its bright colors and by its sweet, whistled *whee-e-e-e-ter'* (with the last note an octave lower), one of the characteristic sounds of the rainy season.

The breeding period seems to cover a number of months, for I have taken examples with greatly enlarged gonads as early as May 28 and as late as July 13. A series of males in prenuptial molt were collected between March 20 and April 18; another series, in postnuptial molt, between July 6 and November 3; odd specimens of the same dates, however, were not molting at all.

An adult male had the irides pale gray; the bill plumbeous, with the culmen black; the feet and toes plumbeous.

The male, in nuptial dress, has the upperparts dull green (very rarely, in our provinces, with some feathers of the mantle tipped blackish); the wings black, with two white or yellowish-white bars and the remiges conspicuously edged white or yellowish white; the tail black; the lores, eye ring, ear coverts, and entire underparts bright yellow, more olivaceous along the sides of the body; the under wing coverts and the elongated, silky feathers of the lower flanks white. In nonbreeding plumage, the old male resembles the immature male and the adult female in having the black of the wings very dull; the tail colored like the back; the underparts greenish yellow.

Under *tiphia* I place all Thai populations that are too small for *styani* and never acquire black on the crown in breeding plumage; such birds seem to occur only in the provinces of Mae Hong Son, Chiang Mai, Lampang, Phrae, and Nan. The whole of Thailand, south and east of these districts, is inhabited by a form that is black-capped in nuptial dress and not clearly separable from Oberholser's *micromelaena* of Bangka (1923), which, in turn, is possibly identical with Stuart Baker's *humei* of central India (1922).

AEGITHINA TIPHIA STYANI La Touche

YUNNANESE SMALL IORA

Aegithina tiphia styani LA TOUCHE, Bull. Brit. Orn. Club, vol. 43, 1923, p. 174 ("South Yunnan [Szemao ?], not labelled").

Aeginthina tiphia tiphia [*partim*], DE SCHAUENSEE, Proc. Acad. Nat. Sci. Philadelphia, 1929, p. 536 (Chiang Rai, Chiang Saen).

Aegithina tiphia tiphia [*partim*], DE SCHAUENSEE, Proc. Acad. Nat. Sci. Philadelphia, 1934, p. 199 (Chiang Saen).

The Yunnanese race of the small iora is restricted, in Thailand, to the plains of Chiang Rai Province, where it is quite as common as *tiphia* is in the other portions of our area.

A series taken in the vicinity of Wiang Pa Pao between July 23 and August 3 are in postnuptial molt.

From *tiphia*, *styani* is separable only by its rather greater dimensions, adult males of the latter having the bill noticeably longer and heavier and, in unworn plumage, the wing length normally in excess of 66 mm.

In Chiang Rai, where it reaches the southwestern periphery of its range, *styani* is certainly smaller than at the type locality but nevertheless, in adult males, exceeds the minimum measurements of the race. Most of my adult males, collected in July and August, have the remiges badly worn but are yet separable from *tiphia* by their more robust bills.

CHLOROPSIS AURIFRONS AURIFRONS (Temminck)

BURMESE ORANGE-FRONTED LEAFBIRD

Phyllornis aurifrons TEMMINCK, Nouveau recueil de planches coloriées d'oiseaux, livr. 81, 1829, pl. 484, fig. 1 (Sumatra, error; type locality corrected to "India," *fide* Bowdler Sharpe, Catalogue of the birds in the British Museum, vol. 6, 1881, p. 21; restricted to Cachar, by Stuart Baker, Bull. Brit. Orn. Club, vol. 41, 1920, p. 8).

Chloropsis aurifrons [*partim*], GYLDENSTOLPE, Kungl. Svenska Vet.-Akad. Handl., 1913, p. 23 ("Northern . . . Siam"); 1916, p. 64 (Pha Kho, Khun Tan, Tha Chomphu, Pang Hua Phong, Doi Pha Sakaeng).

Chloropsis aurifrons, GYLDENSTOLPE, Journ. Nat. Hist. Soc. Siam, 1915, p. 166 (listed).

Chloropsis aurifrons aurifrons [*partim*], GYLDENSTOLPE, Ibis, 1920, p. 489 ("Northern Siam").

Chloropsis aurifrons subsp., DE SCHAUENSEE, Proc. Acad. Nat. Sci. Philadelphia, 1928, p. 567 (Doi Suthep).

Chloropsis aurifrons aurifrons, DE SCHAUENSEE, Proc. Acad. Nat. Sci. Philadelphia, 1929, p. 537 ("Chieng Mai" [=Doi Suthep], Doi Suthep, Chiang Rai, Mae Chai); 1934, p. 200 (Doi Suthep).—DEIGNAN, Journ. Siam Soc. Nat. Hist. Suppl., 1931, p. 139 (Doi Suthep); 1936, p. 108 (Doi Suthep).—RILEY, U. S. Nat. Mus. Bull. 172, 1938, p. 368 (Doi Langka, Ban Nam Khian, Mae Suya valley, Mae Hong Son).

This leafbird is very common in all of our provinces, occurring in the deciduous forest of the lowlands and ascending the hills in the same type of vegetation to about 2,500 feet. De Schauensee's immature example from the evergreen of Doi Suthep at 4,600 feet and another collected by me in a Chiang Mai garden must be considered merely stragglers from the normal range.

On the lower slopes of Doi Suthep, the orange-fronted chloropsis is one of the commonest birds, traveling in noisy flocks of as many as 20 individuals and gathering in even greater numbers at the tops of fruiting or flowering trees. Its brilliant colors and sweet voice make it a favorite cage bird at Chiang Mai.

Specimens with the gonads enlarged were taken on Doi Suthep on March 5 and July 12. There is probably an incomplete prenuptial molt, but the protracted breeding season obscures the picture and I can say only that every example in a series of ten, taken at various localities between February 28 and September 29, is undergoing one molt or another.

Breeding males had the irides brown; the bill black; the feet and toes dark plumbeous; the claws slate.

The adult has a conspicuous patch of plushlike, shining golden-orange feathers on the forehead; the chin and upper throat shining ultramarine; the lores, ocular region, anterior ear coverts, and the remainder of the throat black, bordered by an indistinct golden-yellow band (broader and more distinct across the breast); a shining turquoise-blue shoulder patch; the rest of the plumage bright green, slightly more yellow-green on the underparts.

No northern specimen shows any approach to *inornata*.

Since *aurifrons* is common at Chiang Saen Kao and also in Nan Province, it is almost certain to occur in Laos, whence it is still unknown.

CHLOROPSIS COCHINCHINENSIS COCHINCHINENSIS (Gmelin)

INDO-CHINESE GOLDEN-HOODED LEAFBIRD

[*Turdus*] *cochinchinensis* GMELIN, Systema naturae, vol. 1, pt. 2, 1789, p. 825 (Cochin-China).

Chloropsis chlorocephala, GYLDENSTOLPE, Journ. Nat. Hist. Soc. Siam, 1915, p. 166 (listed); Kungl. Svenska Vet.-Akad. Handl., 1916, p. 65 (Pha Kho, Tha Chomphu, Khun Tan).

Chloropsis chlorocephala chlorocephala [*partim*], GYLDENSTOLPE, Ibis, 1920, p. 490 ("Throughout the whole country" [*partim*]).

Chloropsis icterocephala chlorocephala, DE SCHAUENSEE, Proc. Acad. Nat. Sci. Philadelphia, 1928, p. 567 (Doi Suthep); 1929, p. 537 (Doi Suthep, Chiang Saen).

Chloropsis cochinchinensis cochinchinensis, DEIGNAN, Journ. Siam Soc. Nat. Hist. Suppl., 1931, p. 139 (Doi Suthep).—CHASEN and BODEN KLOSS, Journ. Siam Soc. Nat. Hist. Suppl., 1932, p. 242 (Doi Suthep).—DEIGNAN, Journ. Siam Soc. Nat. Hist. Suppl., 1936, p. 108 (Doi Suthep).

Chloropsis cochinchinensis cochinchinensis [*partim*], DE SCHAUENSEE, Proc. Acad. Nat. Sci. Philadelphia, 1934, p. 200 (Doi Suthep, Khun Tan, Doi Chiang Dao, "Foot of Chieng Dao").—RILEY, U. S. Nat. Mus. Bull. 172, 1938, p. 370 (Khuṅ Tan, Mae Hong Son, Mae Sariang).

The golden-hooded chloropsis is restricted to evergreen forest at low elevations, occurring in this type of growth from the plains to 3,500 feet, throughout the northern provinces. In such a neighborhood as that of Chiang Mai it is necessarily found only on Doi Suthep between 2,500 and 3,500 feet (casually as high as 4,600 feet).

The ranges of our species of *Chloropsis* illustrate in a beautiful way the division of territory between closely related forms of precisely similar habits. The two species that dwell at low altitudes keep to wholly independent plant associations; *aurifrons* is restrained, in its ascent of the hills, by the upper limit of the deciduous forest; *cochinchinensis*, which theoretically could thrive at elevations in excess of 3,500 feet, by competition with the montane *hardwickii*. The relative abundance of the three, from one locality to the next, varies directly with the extents of the essential types of forest within given altitudinal limits.

An example of January 3 is in prenuptial molt; others taken between August 25 and September 7 are in postnuptial molt.

Gyldenstolpe's specimens had the irides dark brown; the bill black; the feet and toes plumbeous.

The old male has the forehead and a short supercilium clear yellow, changing gradually to the bright green (suffused with golden on the nape) of the remaining upperparts; the wings deep green, with the shoulder patch shining turquoise blue and the outer webs of the primaries verditer blue; the central pair of rectrices deep green, the others largely verditer blue; a short mustachial streak ultramarine; the lores, the area between the eye and the mustache and the entire throat black, broadly edged with clear yellow, which is followed by a broad, but indistinct, golden gorget; the remaining underparts yellow-green. The adult female and the young male in first-winter dress have no clear yellow on the head and little golden suffusion on the nape and breast; the mustachial streaks verditer blue; the throat bluish green, instead of black.

CHLOROPSIS HARDWICKII HARDWICKII Jardine and Selby

INDIAN ORANGE-BELLIED LEAFBIRD

[*Chloropsis*] *Hardwickii* JARDINE and SELBY, Illustrations of ornithology, sign. C 3, no date [= 1830] (Nepal). (In U. S. Nat. Mus. copy, ser. 1, vol. 2, pt. 7, "Addenda, etc." [p. 131], footnote).

Chloropsis hardwickei, GYLDENSTOLPE, Kungl. Svenska Vet.-Akad. Handl., 1916, p. 64 (Khun Tan).

Chloropsis hardwickii hardwickii, GYLDENSTOLPE, Ibis, 1920, p. 490 (Khun Tan).—DEIGNAN, Journ. Siam Soc. Nat. Hist. Suppl., 1936, p. 108 (Doi Suthep).—RILEY, U. S. Nat. Mus. Bull. 172, 1938, p. 369 (Khun Tan, Doi Langka, Doi Hua Mot, "Doi Kiew Koh Ma").—GREENWAY, Bull. Mus. Comp. Zool., 1940, p. 174 (Doi Nang Kaeo, Doi Ang Ka).

Chloropsis harwicki [*sic*] *malayana*, DE SCHAUENSEE, Proc. Acad. Nat. Sci. Philadelphia, 1929, p. 537 (Doi Suthep).

Chloropsis hardwickii malayana, DEIGNAN, Journ. Siam Soc. Nat. Hist. Suppl., 1931, p. 139 (Doi Suthep).—DE SCHAUENSEE, Proc. Acad. Nat. Sci. Philadelphia, 1934, p. 200 (Khun Tan, Doi Suthep, Doi Chiang Dao).

Chloropsis hardwickii harwickii [*sic*], CHASEN and BODEN KLOSS, Journ. Siam Soc. Nat. Hist. Suppl., 1932, p. 242 (Doi Suthep).

The orange-bellied leafbird is common on all the higher peaks of the North (including Phu Kha), ranging through the evergreen from 4,500 to 5,500 feet and occasionally seen as low as 3,000 feet. On Doi Suthep, where it may be observed in large and noisy flocks at flowering trees, it is one of the most conspicuous birds of the higher ridges.

The relationships between our three species of *Chloropsis* and certain showily flowering trees are noteworthy, and it seems certain that, although attracted to the blossoms solely for the purpose of feeding upon nectarivorous insects, these birds inadvertently play an important part in cross pollination.

A specimen from Doi Ang Ka, April 12, had the gonads enlarged. Examples in postjuvenal molt were taken at various localities between August 12 and November 17; in postnuptial molt, between August 13 and November 23.

Adults have the irides brown; the bill black; the feet and toes plumbeous-blue or dark plumbeous; the soles yellowish gray; the claws horny black or blackish brown.

The old male has the forehead and sides of the crown greenish yellow, the remaining upperparts deep green, more or less suffused with yellow on the crown and nape; the shoulder patch shining turquoise, the primary coverts and the exposed portions of the primaries dark blue, the secondary coverts and the exposed portions of the secondaries deep green; the tail dark blue; a conspicuous mustachial streak ultramarine; the lores, sides of the head and neck, the chin, throat, and breast black (the last suffused with dark blue); the remaining underparts (except for the green flanks) orange. The adult female and the immature male (for at least a year) have the entire upperparts (except for the turquoise shoulder patch) deep green; the mustachial streak paler ultramarine; a broad, central abdominal streak and the under tail coverts orange; the remaining underparts yellow-green. The juvenile of either sex has the upperparts, wings, and tail deep green; the entire underparts yellow-green.

Examination of a long series of this species from every part of its range has shown no trenchant differences in size or color between *hardwickii* and *malayana*, and I do not believe that the latter can be maintained as a valid form. The wings of 17 adult males from our area measure from 85.7 to 96 mm., and similarly wide variation seems to obtain in any other population.

SPIZIXOS CANIFRONS Blyth

CRESTED FINCH-BILLED BULBUL

Sp[izixos] canifrons BLYTH, Journ. Asiat. Soc. Bengal, vol. 14, 1845, pp. 571–572 ("Cherra Poonjee, or the hill ranges bordering on Sylhet to the northward" [=Khasya Hills]).

Spizixos canifrons, ROGERS and DEIGNAN, Proc. Biol. Soc. Washington, 1934, p. 91 (Doi Chiang Dao).

Spizixos canifrons canifrons, DEIGNAN, Journ. Siam Soc. Nat. Hist. Suppl., 1936, p. 170 (Phu Kha).

The finch-billed bulbul is recorded in Thailand only from Doi Chiang Dao, 5,000 feet, and Phu Kha, 4,500 to 5,000 feet; on both of these mountains it is common in the limited areas that afford a suitable environment: the abandoned *hai* of the hillmen, where scattered low trees arise from a heavy growth of lalang and brambles. It is one of the very few truly montane birds that may be deemed to profit by the wasteful agricultural methods of the seminomadic tribes.

This beautiful top-knotted species travels in small flocks through the trees and undergrowth, all the whole uttering soft, musical notes, which are quite different from those of the related forms.

Examples from Phu Kha, April 4, 9, and 11, are undergoing body molt, and the bird of April 4 is also molting the central rectrices.

My specimens had the irides brown; the bill pale fleshy; the feet and toes horny flesh.

This bulbul has the forehead and center of the forecrown ashy gray; the ocular region, sides of the forecrown, and the pointed crest black;

the remaining upperparts bright olive-green, overlaid with gray on the nape and suffused with golden on the outer webs of the remiges and on the rump and upper tail coverts; the rectrices golden-olive, broadly tipped, above and below, with black; the ear coverts ashy gray, sometimes tinged with vinaceous; the chin and throat dark brownish gray; the remaining underparts golden-olive, brighter on the abdomen and under tail coverts.

PYCNONOTUS ATRICEPS CINEREOVENTRIS (Blyth)

BURMESE BLUE-EYED BULBUL

Brachypodius cinereoventris BLYTH, Journ. Asiat. Soc. Bengal, vol. 14, 1845, p. 576 (Tipperah).

Micropus melanocephalus, GYLDENSTOLPE, Kungl. Svenska Vet.-Akad. Handl., 1913, p. 27 (Phrae).

Microtarsus melanocephalus, GYLDENSTOLPE, Kungl. Svenska Vet.-Akad. Handl., 1916, p. 66 (Phrae) ; Ibis, 1920, p. 496 ("Throughout the whole country").

Brachypodius atriceps major, DE SCHAUENSEE, Proc. Acad. Nat. Sci. Philadelphia, 1928, p. 569 (Doi Suthep) ; 1929, p. 541 ("Chieng Mai" [=Doi Suthep], Chiang Saen Kao).—DEIGNAN, Journ. Siam Soc. Nat. Hist. Suppl., 1931, p. 141 (Doi Suthep).

Microtarsus atriceps major, DEIGNAN, Journ. Siam Soc. Nat. Hist. Suppl., 1936, p. 110 (Doi Suthep).

Microtarsus atriceps cinereoventris, GREENWAY, Bull. Mus. Comp. Zool., 1940, p 177 (Chiang Dao).

The blue-eyed bulbul is locally common in our provinces, occurring in districts of mixed-deciduous and second-growth evergreen forest, from the level of the plains to a maximum elevation of 3,000 feet. In addition to the localities named above, it is known from Ban Ton Phung and Ban Hai Huai Som. In the Chiang Mai region it is necessarily rare and restricted in range to a narrow belt of suitable vegetation on Doi Suthep between 2,700 and 3,000 feet.

This is a very sociable species, usually seen (and especially at flowering trees) in large flocks, the members of which keep up a constant conversation of chirps and other musical calls.

De Schauensee has recorded (1929) that the irides are clear, light blue (brown in an immature specimen) ; the bill, feet, and toes black.

In normal plumage, the present form has the uncrested head and the entire neck glossy blue-black; the mantle golden-olive (with black bases to the feathers showing through on the rump), changing to greenish gold on the long upper tail coverts; the primaries wholly black, the secondaries with the inner web black and the outer web greenish gold; the graduated rectrices olive-green, with a very broad, black subapical band and a broad, bright golden-yellow tip; the breast, upper abdomen, and flanks golden-olive, changing gradually to bright golden-yellow on the lower abdomen and long under tail coverts; the under wing coverts golden-yellow.

In the mutant from which the misleading subspecific name is derived, the breast, upper abdomen, and uppermost back are slaty gray instead of golden-olive. This phase is known from Thailand by two females taken in the neighborhood of Muang Chiang Dao, March 21, 1937 (Deignan), and April 26, 1937 (Greenway).

In eastern Thailand certain individuals have been taken in which the bright yellows are replaced by dull orange or yellowish green, and such aberrant examples may also eventually be found in the North.

Northern birds have the wing length varying in males from 82 to 82.8 mm., in females, from 79 to 81 mm., and thus just manage to exceed the lower limit of wing length given by Robinson and Boden Kloss for their race *major* (Journ. Federated Malay States Mus., vol. 11, 1923, p. 55), here considered to be merely the normal yellow phase of *cinereoventris*.

PYCNONOTUS DISPAR MINOR (Boden Kloss)

THAI BLACK-THROATED YELLOW BULBUL

Otocompsa flaviventris minor BODEN KLOSS, Ibis, 1918, p. 200 (Ko Lak [= Prachuap Khirikhan], southwestern Thailand).

Otocompsa flaviventris, GYLDENSTOLPE, Kungl. Svenska Vet.-Akad. Handl., 1913, p. 25 (Den Chai) ; 1916, p. 69 (Pha Kho, Khun Tan, Pang Hua Phong, Tha Chomphu) ; Journ. Nat. Hist. Soc. Siam, 1915, p. 166 (listed).

Otocompsa flaviventris flaviventris, GYLDENSTOLPE, Ibis, 1920, p. 492 ("Northern, north-western . . . Siam").—DE SCHAUENSEE, Proc. Acad. Nat. Sci. Philadelphia, 1928, p. 568 (Doi Suthep) ; 1929, p. 540 (Doi Suthep, Chiang Mai, Chiang Rai, Chiang Saen).—DEIGNAN, Journ. Siam Soc. Nat. Hist. Suppl., 1936, p. 110 (Chiang Mai, Doi Suthep).—RILEY, U. S. Nat. Mus. Bull. 172, 1938, p. 386 (Khun Tan, Mae Khan, Muang Pai).

Elathea flaviventris flaviventris, DEIGNAN, Journ. Siam Soc. Nat. Hist. Suppl., 1931, p. 140 (Chiang Mai, Doi Suthep).—DE SCHAUENSEE, Proc. Acad. Nat. Sci. Philadelphia, 1934, p. 203 (Doi Suthep, Doi Chiang Dao).

The yellow bulbul is very common or even abundant in suitable territory throughout the northern provinces, from the level of the plains to about 3,800 feet. It is most numerous in the mixed-deciduous jungle, somewhat less so in the *pa daeng* of the foothills and plains. At new settlements, where cultivated ground is of small extent and surrounded by only partially cleared forest, it is likely to be as familiar and fearless a dooryard bird as is *Pycnonotus j. erythrotis* in districts that have endured human habitation over a longer period.

Along streams and trails in the submontane regions it will be seen in small, chattering flocks in the bamboos and lower trees. The crested black head and yellow eye make it an unmistakable form.

No definite information on the breeding season is yet available for our provinces, but all adult specimens taken between July 22 and October 28 are in postnuptial molt.

Old birds have the irides yellow; the bill, feet, toes, and claws black. The adult has the entire head and neck black, glossed with steel blue; the remaining upperparts yellowish olive; the rectrices dull dark brown, narrowly edged with yellowish olive; the entire underparts (below the neck) bright yellow, usually suffused with olive on the breast and flanks. The juvenile, *fide* Gyldenstolpe (1916), has the head and crest brownish olive with a faint purplish gloss on the longest feathers of the latter; the chin black, but the throat olive and of the same color as the upperparts; the irides pale gray; the bill horn color.

With a wing length of 87 mm. in the male used as a convenient division between the northern *flaviventris* and the southern *minor*, the population of our provinces just barely fall in with the latter race.

PYCNONOTUS JOCOSUS ERYTHROTIS (Bonaparte)

TENASSERIMESE RED-WHISKERED BULBUL

I[xos] erythrotis BONAPARTE, Conspectus generum avium, vol. 1, 1850, p. 265 (Java, error; type locality corrected to Tavoy, by Chasen, Handlist of Malaysian birds, 1935, p. 204).

Otocompsa emeria, GYLDENSTOLPE, Kungl. Svenska Vet.-Akad. Handl., 1913, p. 25 (Phrae); 1916, p. 70 (Tha Chomphu); Journ. Nat. Hist. Soc. Siam, 1915, p. 166 (listed).

Otocompsa emeria emeria, GYLDENSTOLPE, Ibis, 1920, p. 493 ("Throughout the whole country").

Otocompsa jocosa emeria, DE SCHAUENSEE, Proc. Acad. Nat. Sci. Philadelphia, 1928, p. 568 (Chiang Mai).

Otocompsa jocosa erythrotis, DE SCHAUENSEE, Proc. Acad. Nat. Sci. Philadelphia, 1929, p. 540 (Chiang Mai, Chiang Saen, Chiang Saen Kao).—DEIGNAN, Journ. Siam Soc. Nat. Hist. Suppl., 1936, p. 110 (Chiang Mai, Doi Suthep).—RILEY, U. S. Nat. Mus. Bull. 172, 1938, p. 385 (Ban Nam Khian, Phrae, Lampang, Doi Langka, Doi Hua Mot, Chiang Mai, Muang Pai).—GREENWAY, Bull. Mus. Comp. Zool., 1940, p. 176 (Doi Nang Kaeo, Doi Ang Ka, Chiang Mai, Chiang Dao).

Elathea jocosa erythrotis, DEIGNAN, Journ. Siam Soc. Nat. Hist. Suppl., 1931, p. 140 (Chiang Mai, Doi Suthep).—DE SCHAUENSEE, Proc. Acad. Nat. Sci. Philadelphia, 1934, p. 203 (Chiang Mai, Doi Suthep).

The red-whiskered bulbul is, in our provinces, as truly a symbiont of man as the starling, *Acridotheres t. tristis*, or the sparrow, *Passer m. malaccensis*, and its numbers in a given locality accurately reflect both density of human population and the degree to which human occupation has altered natural environment. In the orchards and gardens of lowland towns and villages (with the curious exception of Chiang Rai, where it is supplanted by the following species) the bird is abundant; on the hills it appears only where some band of hillmen have inhabited the same ground over a long period, as at Ban Nong Lom (4,400 feet) on Doi Ang Ka. About my camp on Phu Kha (4,500 feet), at a site abandoned a few years earlier by the Yao in consequence of pestilence, only two pairs of this bulbul remained within a limited area whose suitability was fast disappearing (1936) before the encroaching lalang. It is not apparently a migratory form, but it should be noted that de Schauensee reported (1934) seeing "loose flocks composed of hundreds" on the lower slopes of Doi Suthep (1,500 feet) in December; such local wanderings may well explain the advent of the species at isolated settlements in the hills.

At Chiang Mai this sprightly bird was always in evidence, its cheerful notes sounding from the trees at the first light of dawn and continuing throughout the day, whether their author was engaged in examining the ripening fruit, hopping about on walks and lawns with tail raised above the line of back in pursuit of beetles and grasshoppers, bathing in some shallow puddle, or hawking at evening for winged termites from the ridgepole of a roof. Owing to its numbers, it must do a certain amount of damage to fruits and vegetables and, since it seems to be the only bird that shows real interest in the fruit of the lantana, it is probably largely responsible for the rapid spread of that beautiful but noxious weed.

I took a male with the gonads greatly enlarged, April 16, and others with them merely enlarged, May 16 and 18. A round, cupshaped nest, made of twigs, pieces of cloth and paper, dry leaves of bamboo, and lined with thin, wiry grass, was found May 13 in the crotch of an *Ixora*, about 3 feet above the ground; it contained two unfledged young, both of which were drowned the same day by a heavy rain. Another nest, discovered July 1, was in a hedge of *Inga dulcis*, about 7 feet from the ground, and held two newly hatched young. Smith took a juvenile at Doi Hua Mot, August 29, and an adult in postnuptial molt at Lampang, November 17.

It has the irides brown; the bill, feet, toes, and claws black.

The adult has the forehead and crested crown black; the upperparts brown, the remiges and the graduated rectrices darker, all except the two central pairs of the latter with an outwardly increasingly broad white tip; a small patch of shining, deep crimson feathers below and behind the eye; the ear coverts pure white, bordered below by a narrow black line; the chin, throat, and center of the upper breast pure white; a broad blackish-brown breast band from the sides of the neck, broken at the center of the breast; the remaining underparts white, more or less sullied with sooty brown, especially along the flanks and on the thighs; the under tail coverts crimson. The juvenile differs in having the forehead and crest blackish brown; the red postocular patch replaced by white; the upper tail coverts suffused with pink; the under tail coverts pale buffy pink.

583136—45——22

The whole of Thailand is occupied by *erythrotis:* 19 adult males from the six northernmost provinces have the wing length 76.5 to 87 mm.; 15 from the Peninsula (south of the Isthmus of Kra), 75.9 to 84.5 mm.

PYCNONOTUS CAFER KLOSSI (Gyldenstolpe)

THAI RED-VENTED BULBUL

Molpastes atricapillus klossi ROBINSON, error=GYLDENSTOLPE, Bull. Brit. Orn. Club, vol. 41, 1920, p. 12 (Khun Tan, North Thailand); vol. 42, 1921, p. 32.

Pycnonotus atricapillus, GYLDENSTOLPE, Kungl. Svenska Vet.-Akad. Handl., 1913, p. 26 (Pak Pan); Journ. Nat. Hist. Soc. Siam, 1915, p. 166 (listed).

Molpastes atricapillus, GYLDENSTOLPE, Kungl. Svenska Vet.-Akad. Handl., 1916, p. 68 (Khun Tan, Tha Chomphu); Ibis, 1920, p. 492 ("Throughout northern Siam").

Molpastes haemorrhous chrysorrhoides, DE SCHAUENSEE, Proc. Acad. Nat. Sci. Philadelphia, 1929, p. 540 (Chiang Mai, Doi Suthep, Chiang Rai, Chiang Saen).

Molpastes cafer chrysorrhoides, DEIGNAN, Journ. Siam Soc. Nat. Hist. Suppl., 1931, p. 140 (Doi Suthep, Chiang Mai, Chiang Rai).

Pycnonotus cafer klossi, DE SCHAUENSEE, Proc. Acad. Nat. Sci. Philadelphia, 1934, p. 205 (Mae Taeng, Khun Tan, Chiang Dao, Chiang Mai).—GREENWAY, Bull. Mus. Comp. Zool., 1940, p. 176 (Doi Nang Kaeo).

Pycnonotus cafer chrysorrhoides, DEIGNAN, Journ. Siam Soc. Nat. Hist. Suppl., 1936, p. 110 (Doi Suthep, Chiang Mai).

Molpastes cafer klossi, RILEY, U. S. Nat. Mus. Bull. 172, 1938, p. 384 (Doi Ang Ka, Chiang Mai, Khun Tan, Mae Hong Son).

Throughout the northern provinces, the red-vented bulbul is locally common, occurring on the plains in *pa daeng* and areas of abandoned cultivation, on the hills to 5,500 feet in open forest of oak and pine.

At Chiang Rai this bulbul proved to be as familiar a garden bird as *Pycnonotus j. erythrotis* is elsewhere; otherwise I have found it to be a rather retiring species, keeping to dry but more or less wooded country and avoiding the neighborhood of human habitation. Its notes and habits are much like those of the red-whiskered bulbul.

A specimen with the gonads slightly enlarged was taken on April 4, another with them greatly enlarged, July 13. Examples in post-juvenal molt were collected between July 6 and October 20; adults in postnuptial molt, between September 28 and November 2.

A breeding male had the irides hazel; the bill black; the feet and toes black; the soles gray; some claws black, the others fleshy white.

The adult has the forehead and slightly crested crown glossy black; the upper parts ashy brown, the feathers of the mantle with somewhat darker centers; the rump and shorter upper tail coverts white or ashy; the rectrices blackish brown, broadly tipped with white; the lores, a narrow subocular line, the chin, and upper throat blackish brown; the ear coverts ashy; the underparts ashy, more or less suffused everywhere with brownish; the under tail coverts crimson. The juvenile is similar but has the feathers of the mantle and the remiges edged with light brown; the rectrices tipped dull brownish; the under tail coverts pale pink or buff; the bill (in the dried skin) yellowish horn.

Some northern specimens have the short supraloral feathers between nostril and eye tipped ashy, to form a narrow, indistinct line.

PYCNONOTUS STRIATUS PAULUS (Bangs and Phillips)

INDO-CHINESE STRIATED BULBUL

Alcurus striatus paulus BANGS and PHILLIPS, Bull. Mus. Comp. Zool., vol. 58, No. 6, 1914, p. 284 (Loukouchai, southeastern Yunnan).

Alcurus striatus, DEIGNAN, Journ. Siam Soc. Nat. Hist. Suppl., 1931, p. 140 (Doi Suthep); 1936, p. 109 (Doi Suthep).—DE SCHAUENSEE, Proc. Acad. Nat. Sci. Philadelphia, 1934, p. 202 (Doi Suthep.)—RILEY, U. S. Nat. Mus. Bull. 172, 1938, p. 383 (Doi Ang Ka, Doi Langka, Doi Hua Mot).

Alcurus leucogarmmicus [*sic*] *striatus*, CHASEN and BODEN KLOSS, Journ. Siam Soc. Nat. Hist. Suppl., 1932, p. 243 (Doi Suthep).

The striated bulbul is uncommon or rare on our loftiest mountains, unknown at elevations below 5,000 feet and, on Doi Ang Ka, ranging as high as 8,000 feet. In addition to the localities named above, it is recorded in Thailand only from Phu Kha.

Along the topmost ridges of Doi Suthep, this species, sometimes accompanied by *Microscelis v. tickelli*, occurred in small parties at the edge of the evergreen or among the pines. Stomachs examined by me contained only insects.

Examples in postnuptial molt have been taken between September 1 and November 10.

An adult female had the irides deep brown; the bill plumbeous-slate; the feet, toes, and claws dark brown.

The present form has the feathers behind the nostrils bright yellow; the crown and ample crest dark olive-green, each feather with a white shaft streak; the remaining upperparts bright olive-green, the feathers of the mantle with white shaft streaks, which become narrower posteriorly and almost disappear on the rump; the remiges narrowly margined yellow along the basal half of the blackish-brown inner web; the outer rectrices narrowly tipped and margined along the inner web with yellow; a narrow eye ring of yellow feathers; the feathers at the base of the mandible, the chin, and the throat bright yellow, the feathers of the last part with small blackish tips; the ear coverts and the feathers of the breast dark olive-gray, with broad yellowish-white central streaks; those of the flanks dark grayish olive with pale yellow central streaks; the center of the abdomen almost immaculate yellow; the under tail coverts bright yellow; the under surface of the tail yellowish olive.

Specimens from southeastern Yunnan and the Indo-Chinese countries are indeed smaller than those of the Himalayas (*striatus*), and Bangs and Phillips's name may properly be used for them.

PYCNONOTUS FINLAYSONI FINLAYSONI Strickland

INDO-CHINESE STREAKED-THROATED BULBUL

Pycnonotus Finlaysoni STRICKLAND, Ann. Mag. Nat. Hist., vol. 13, 1844, pp. 411–412 ("Probably from some of the Malasian islands"; type locality corrected to Malacca, by Hartert, Nov. Zool., vol. 9, 1902, p. 560).

Pycnonotus finlaysoni, GYLDENSTOLPE, Kungl. Svenska Vet.-Akad. Handl., 1913, p. 26 (Ban Huai Hom); 1916, p. 69 (Pha Kho); Journ. Nat. Hist. Soc. Siam, 1915, p. 166 (listed).

Pycnonotus finlaysoni finlaysoni, GYLDENSTOLPE, Ibis, 1920, p. 494 ("Throughout the whole country").—DEIGNAN, Journ. Siam Soc. Nat. Hist. Suppl., 1936, p. 170 ("Districts watered by streams which flow into the Me Khong").

The streaked-throated bulbul is uncommon and perhaps only locally distributed in the lowlands of Chiang Rai and the provinces east of the Khun Tan chain. An example in Hannover was taken by Eisenhofer at Pak Pan, February 16, 1912; I took specimens at Ban Kiu Nak (Nan Province), at Rong Chiang Laeng (Chiang Rai Province), and at Ban Sathan, in the northern part of the French Enclave.

I believed at one time that this species replaced *Pycnonotus b. conradi* in the more eastern provinces but have since learned that the two forms occur in more or less the same areas. Strictly speaking, they do not appear together, for, while *conradi* inhabits the neighborhood of villages and cultivation, *finlaysoni* keeps to almost uninhabited country. It is not really a bird of the evergreen forest, as was implied by Gyldenstolpe (1913, 1916), but prefers such places as roadsides and clearings, where evergreen jungle has been cut back and succeeded by dense thickets of *Eupatorium* and other second growth; on the other hand, it probably never enters the deciduous forest, as *conradi* may sometimes do.

Examples from Ban Kiu Nak, April 1, and Ban Sathan, April 28, had the gonads enlarged; the one from Rong Chiang Laeng, May 1, had them greatly enlarged.

Gyldenstolpe's specimens had the irides brown; the bill black; the feet and toes plumbeous.

The adult has the feathers of the front and forecrown bright yellow (those immediately bordering the lores orange), narrowly edged with olivaceous-brown to give a streaked appearance; the remaining upperparts dull olive-green (brighter on the remiges and rectrices), overlaid with ashy on the posterior crown, nape, and upper part of the mantle; the lores mixed black and bright yellow; the ear coverts, chin, and throat streaked with bright yellow and olivaceous-brown, exactly like the front and forecrown; the breast and upper abdomen ashy, the feathers with narrow whitish shaft streaks and more or less olivaceous suffusion; the flanks ashy, suffused with olivaceous-brown; the bend of the wing, the under tail coverts, and the region of the vent bright yellow, this color sometimes faintly invading the albescent lower abdomen.

Riley's recently taken series of *eous* (Annam) were compared with aged and discolored specimens of *finlaysoni*, and I believe that the supposed differences would not have appeared had he seen truly comparable material. There is some chance, however, that the population of *northern* Thailand and Indochine will prove separable from *finlaysoni* by their rather longer wing; I have unfortunately not examined enough skins to settle this point.

PYCNONOTUS FLAVESCENS VIVIDUS (Stuart Baker)

TENASSERIMESE FLAVESCENT BULBUL

Xanthiscus [*sic*] *flavescens vivida* [*sic*] STUART BAKER, Bull. Brit. Orn. Club, vol. 38, 1917, p. 16 (Salwin; Mount Muleyit).

Xanthixus flavescens vivida [*sic*], WILLIAMSON, Journ. Nat. Hist. Soc. Siam, 1918, p. 19 (Doi Nga Chang).

Xanthiscus [*sic*] *flavescens vivida* [*sic*], GYLDENSTOLPE, Ibis, 1920, p. 492 (Doi Nga Chang).

Xanthixus flavescens vividus, DE SCHAUENSEE, Proc. Acad. Nat. Sci. Philadelphia, 1929, p. 539 (Doi Suthep); 1934, p. 202 (Doi Suthep, Doi Chiang Dao).—RILEY, U. S. Nat. Mus. Bull. 172, 1938, p. 384 (Doi Ang Ka, "Ban Ta Pai," Khun Tan, Doi Langka, Doi Hua Mot).

Xanthixus flavescens flavescens, CHASEN and BODEN KLOSS, Journ. Siam Soc. Nat. Hist. Suppl., 1932, p. 242 (Doi Suthep).

Pycnonotus flavescens vividus, DEIGNAN, Journ. Siam. Soc. Nat. Hist. Suppl., 1936, p. 110 (Doi Suthep).

Xanthixus flavescens berliozi, GREENWAY, Bull. Mus. Comp. Zool., 1940, p. 175 (Doi Ang Ka).

The flavescent bulbul is a bird of the brush and grasslands at elevations in excess of 3,500 feet; it is common, or even abundant, at suitable places on all the higher peaks of the North (including Phu Kha). On Doi Suthep it abounds along the highest ridges in the lalang and stunted trees, is common among the pines on the northern face of the mountain, and occurs in small numbers at an ancient *hai* in the evergreen near H. B. M. Consul's bungalow.

As it travels in loose bands through the thickets, tall grass, and lowest branches of the smaller trees, this species attracts attention to itself by its own curiosity; while at the first alarm the members of the flock seek shelter in the densest undergrowth, whence only soft, cheeping notes give evidence of their presence, first one, then another, comes up to investigate the disturbance—ruffling the crown feathers and nervously twitching the tail for a moment, before diving again into the concealing vegetation.

A male shot on Doi Ang Ka, April 17, had the gonads greatly enlarged. A specimen in late postnatal molt was taken April 7 on

Phu Kha and others in postjuvenal molt at various localities between July 14 and August 29. Birds in postnuptial molt were collected December 3 and 23 and January 30.

A breeding male had the irides brown; the bill black; the feet, toes, and claws blackish brown.

The adult has a short, yellowish-white streak at the sides of the forehead (from nostril to eye); the feathers of the center of the forehead and the crown dark brown, fringed with olive-green and ashy gray to give a scaled appearance; the remaining upperparts dull olive-green, the remiges and rectrices edged with golden-olive along the outer web; the lores blackish; a narrow, interrupted eye ring of white feathers; the chin and throat sullied ashy gray and not clearly defined from the breast; the breast and upper abdomen olivaceous-yellow, sullied by the indistinct, brownish-ashy central portions of the feathers, which give a faintly streaked appearance; the flanks and thighs olivaceous-brown, more or less strongly suffused with yellow; the center of the lower abdomen clear, pale yellow; the bend of the wing and the under tail coverts bright yellow. The juvenile differs from the adult chiefly in having the *entire* forehead and crown uniform olivaceous-brown.

The yellow of the underparts loses much of its brightness with wear and *P. f. berliozi* (Laos) is probably nothing but *vividus* in fine, fresh feather. *P. f. sordidus* of South Annam is likewise doubtfully distinct from *flavescens*, and good topotypes should be critically compared.

PYCNONOTUS BLANFORDI CONRADI (Finsch)

INDO-CHINESE STREAKED-EARED BULBUL

Criniger Conradi FINSCH, Verh. zool.-bot. Ges. Wien, vol. 23, 1873, pp. 349–350 (Bangkok, Thailand).

Pycnonotus blanfordi, GYLDENSTOLPE, Kungl. Svenska Vet.-Akad. Handl., 1913, p. 26 (Den Chai, Phrae); 1916, p. 69 (Khun Tan); Journ. Nat. Hist. Soc. Siam, 1915, p. 166 (listed).

Pycnonotus blanfordi blanfordi, GYLDENSTOLPE, Ibis, 1920, p. 493 ("Throughout Siam proper").—DEIGNAN, Journ. Siam Soc. Nat. Hist. Suppl., 1931, p. 141 (Chiang Mai); 1936, p. 110 (Chiang Mai).—DE SCHAUENSEE, Proc. Acad. Nat. Sci. Philadelphia, 1934, p. 206 (Chiang Mai, "Tung Sio").

Pycnonotus blanfordi robinsoni, RILEY, U. S. Nat. Mus. Bull. 172, 1938, p. 393 (Nan, Ban Nam Khian).

This species is common or abundant at suitable places throughout the northern provinces, with the exceptions of Chiang Rai and Mae Hong Son, from neither of which it has yet been recorded, and from the former of which it is not to be expected. It is a characteristic inhabitant of lowland areas overgrown with brush and bamboo, especially where such country is found in the neighborhood of human habitation. At Chiang Mai it was common in town and village gardens and abounded in the wastelands used for cremations, in the thickets edging irrigation ditches and other watercourses, and in thin deciduous forest.

The streaked-eared bulbul travels in small bands, uttering a harsh, and, in the hot weather, somewhat irritating, conversational *chŭ-chŭ-chŭ;* in flight, the same sound is delivered at rather longer intervals. Stomachs examined by me contained both fruit and insects.

A specimen with the gonads slightly enlarged was taken on June 11, another with them enlarged, June 23; the breeding season, however, begins much earlier than these dates would indicate, for a bird in full juvenal dress was shot April 25. Two in postjuvenal molt were collected July 6 and August 19, while *all* of eight adults taken between April 2 and September 15 are in postnuptial molt.

An adult female had the irides gray; the eyelids plumbeous; the bill dark brown, horny brown at the base of the mandible; the feet and toes slaty brown; the claws blackish. An unsexed adult had the irides brownish gray; the bill purplish flesh; the feet and toes grayish horn. A juvenile male had the irides light grayish brown; the bill horny brown; the rictus and interior of the mouth flesh; the feet and toes plumbeous; the claws fleshy horn.

The present form has the upperparts dull olivaceous-brown, the feathers of the uncrested crown with darker centers, the rump and upper tail coverts suffused with ochraceous, the remiges and rectrices narrowly edged with ochraceous-olive along the outer web; the ear coverts dull olivaceous-brown, with narrow silvery-white shaft streaks; the underparts sullied white, the upper breast and flanks suffused with olivaceous, the lower breast and abdomen indistinctly streaked and suffused with cream color; the bend of the wing and the under tail coverts buffy cream; the undersurface of the tail creamy olivaceous.

The birds of northern Thailand are quite inseparable from those of Bangkok and must be called *conradi*, since this name antedates *robinsoni* by 33 years (*cf.* Deignan, Ibis, 1940, pp. 528–529).

CRINIGER TEPHROGENYS HENRICI Oustalet

YUNNANESE WHITE-THROATED BULBUL

Criniger Henrici OUSTALET, Bull. Mus. Hist. Nat. [Paris], 1896, pp. 185–186 ("entre Manhao et Se-mao [Yunnan], sur les bords de la Rivière-Noire . . . à Nam-Xong, Ban-Moi et Hat-Hoa [Tonkin]").

Criniger gutturalis, GYLDENSTOLPE, Journ. Nat. Hist. Soc. Siam, 1915, p. 166 (listed).

Criniger gutturalis sordidus, GYLDENSTOLPE, Kungl. Svenska Vet.-Akad. Handl., 1916, p. 67 (Pha Kho, Doi Pha Sakaeng, Khun Tan).

Criniger gutturalis henrici, GYLDENSTOLPE, Kungl. Svenska Vet.-Akad. Handl., 1916, p. 67 (Pang Hua Phong, Khun Tan, Doi Pha Sakaeng).—DEIGNAN, Journ. Siam Soc. Nat. Hist. Suppl., 1936, p. 108 (Doi Suthep).

Criniger gutturalis ochraceus, GYLDENSTOLPE, Ibis, 1920, p. 494 ("Throughout Siam proper").—DE SCHAUENSEE, Proc. Acad. Nat. Sci. Philadelphia, 1928.

p. 568 (Doi Suthep).—DEIGNAN, Journ. Siam Soc. Nat. Hist. Suppl., 1931, p. 139 (Doi Suthep).

Criniger tephrogenis henrici, DE SCHAUENSEE, Proc. Acad. Nat. Sci. Philadelphia, 1929, p. 538 (Chiang Saen).

Criniger gularis henrici, DE SCHAUENSEE, Proc. Acad. Nat. Sci. Philadelphia, 1934, p. 201 (Doi Suthep, Khun Tan, "Foot of Chieng Dao," ridge just south of Doi Chiang Dao).

Criniger tephrogenys henrici, RILEY, U. S. Nat. Mus. Bull. 172, 1938, p. 374 (Khun Tan, Huai Mae Sae, Doi Hua Mot).—GREENWAY, Bull. Mus. Comp. Zool., 1940, p. 175 (Doi Ang Ka, Doi Nang Kaeo, "Mae Wan River near Doi Saket," Doi Suthep).

The criniger of the northern provinces is very common throughout the area in districts with light evergreen or mixed-deciduous forest, from the level of the plains to 3,800 (rarely to 4,600) feet.

On Doi Suthep, between 2,400 and 3,800 feet, the loose bands of this bulbul are conspicuous along the jungle tracks and attract attention by their loud notes, which combine melodious whistles with scolding calls. The species may readily be recognized by its somewhat ragged crest and its white throat, the feathers of which stand out as if brushed the wrong way. It is frugivorous and, wherever there is an abundance of food, may be seen in great numbers.

A specimen from Doi Ang Ka, May 4, had the gonads greatly enlarged. An example from Phrae Province, September 9, is in postjuvenal molt and birds collected at various localities between August 29 and October 22 are in postnuptial molt.

A breeding male had the irides dull brown; the maxilla dark horny plumbeous; the mandible plumbeous; the feet and toes horny pink; the claws horny flesh.

This large species has the crown and crest olivaceous-brown; the upperparts brownish olive; the remiges and rectrices brown; the sides of the head brownish gray; the chin and throat white; the remaining underparts pale yellow, washed on the breast and sides of the body with olivaceous and changing to buff on the under tail coverts.

For those who are unwilling to accept the concept of the superspecies, it might be feasible to group the definitely crested, white-throated forms of *Criniger* in the Indo-Chinese countries and Malaysia in four species, as follows:

I. Both crest and tail relatively short.
- *A.* Abdomen bright yellow___1. Criniger xanthizurus balicus+xanthizurus
- *B.* Abdomen buffy or yellowish.
  2. Criniger tephrogenys frater+gutturalis+tephrogenys+robinsoni

II. Both crest and tail relatively long.
- *A.* Abdomen bright yellow_____3. Criniger flaveolus burmanicus+flaveolus
- *B.* Abdomen buffy (southern group) or yellowish (northern group).
  4. Cringer ochraceus ruficrissus+sumatranus+sacculatus +ochraceus+cambodianus (southern group)+griseiceps + annamensis + henrici + pallidus (northern group)

As Ticehurst has correctly observed (Journ. Bombay Nat. Hist. Soc., vol. 36, 1933, p. 924): "On comparing *burmanicus* and *flaveolus* with the Javanese bird (*gularis* of Horsfield) one would hardly hesitate to say that here we have geographical representatives of one species." In the arrangement above, *C. ochraceus* differs from *tephrogenys* precisely as *C. flaveolus* from *xanthizurus* and if the latter pair be united under the name *flaveolus*, consistency demands a similar combination of *ochraceus* and *tephrogenys* to form a second species or superspecies *tephrogenys*.

The alleged overlaps in the ranges of *C. ochraceus* and *C. tephrogenys* seem to be merely superficial—the races of *tephrogenys* keeping to lower elevations everywhere, those of *ochraceus* to higher elevations in the general areas inhabited by *tephrogenys* and appearing in the lowlands only where *tephrogenys* is absent. We have then a problem not unlike that set in the Indo-Chinese countries by the juxtaposition of boreal and tropical representatives of *Sitta europaea* (which see) but more complicated by the fact that within the assemblage of *ochraceus* forms a second trenchant differentiation has taken place, to form what for convenience I have called the northern and southern groups.

A distributional study restricted to these two groups will reveal on a smaller scale the same puzzles that appear in a similar study of the two main branches of the superspecies: thus, in South Annam, a bird near to *C. o. ochraceus* occurs but a few miles from localities at which *C. o. annamensis* is found, without the least sign of intergradation between the two. This may be explained by the assumption that *annamensis* (the extreme representative of the northern group) pressing southward has here met the northward-pressing *ochraceus* (of the southern group), with the result that, in the same general area, we have conspecific forms so remotely related in time as to act like distinct species.

MICROSCELIS CHARLOTTAE PROPINQUUS (Oustalet)

TONGKINESE VIRIDESCENT BULBUL

Criniger propinquus OUSTALET, Nouv. Arch. Mus. [Paris], ser. 4, vol. 5, 1903, pp. 76–77 (Pa-mou, Tongking).

Criniger lönnbergi GYLDENSTOLPE, Kungl. Svenska Vet.-Akad. Handl., vol. 50, No. 8, 1913, p. 24 ("Northern Siam . . . at Bang Hue Hom [= Ban Huai Hom] and Kao Plyng [= Khao Phlung]"; type specimen from Ban Huai Hom, *fide* Gyldenstolpe, Ark. för Zool., vol. 19A, No. 1, 1926, p. 57).

Iole olivacea, GYLDENSTOLPE, Journ. Nat. Hist. Soc. Siam, 1915, p. 166 (listed).

Criniger lönnbergi, GYLDENSTOLPE, Kungl. Svenska Vet.-Akad. Handl., 1916, p. 68 (Khun Tan, Pha Hing, Doi Pha Sakaeng, Pang Hua Phong, Pha Kho).

Iole olivacea lönnbergi, GYLDENSTOLPE, Ibis, 1920, p. 491 ("Northern and northwestern Siam"). — DE SCHAUENSEE, Proc. Acad. Nat. Sci. Philadelphia, 1929, p. 538 (Doi Suthep, Chiang Saen).—CHASEN and BODEN KLOSS, Journ. Siam Soc. Nat. Hist. Suppl., 1932, p. 242 (Doi Suthep).

Iole virescens lönnbergi, DEIGNAN, Journ. Siam Soc. Nat Hist, Suppl., 1931, p. 140 (Doi Suthep) ; 1936, p. 110 (Doi Suthep).

Iole virescens lönnbergi [*partim*], DE SCHAUENSEE, Proc. Acad. Nat. Sci. Philadelphia, 1934, p. 204 (Doi Suthep, Khun Tan, ridge just south of Doi Chiang Dao.)

Iole olivacea cinnamomeoventris [*partim*], RILEY, U. S. Nat. Mus. Bull. 172, 1938, p. 376 (Khun Tan).

Iole olivacea propinqua [*partim*], RILEY, U. S. Nat. Mus. Bull. 172, 1938, p. 377 (Doi Ang Ka, Khun Tan, Huai Mae Sae).

Iole olivacea propinqua, GREENWAY, Bull. Mus. Comp. Zool., 1940, p. 177 (Doi Nang Kaeo, Chiang Dao).

The present race of the viridescent bulbul is fairly common throughout the northern provinces in districts with light evergreen or mixed-deciduous forest, from the level of the plains to 3,500 (rarely to 4,600) feet.

The habits of this species are much like those of *Criniger t. henrici*, with which it sometimes associates, but it is a shier and less noisy form, uttering from time to time merely a soft, whistled note. It is usually seen singly or in pairs but may gather in numbers at fruit-bearing trees.

Gyldenstolpe (1916) took a nestling at Pha Hing, April 11, and a juvenile at Pha Kho, April 7. Specimens collected by Smith at Khun Tan, August 29 and September 7, are in postnuptial molt.

Adults have the irides clear gray; the maxilla blackish brown; the mandible horny gray; the feet and toes fleshy brown.

The viridescent bulbul resembles a smaller, scarcely crested *Criniger*. It has the upperparts dull olivaceous (the tail browner); the underparts olivaceous-gray, albescent on the throat and everywhere washed with light greenish yellow (clearer yellow on the abdomen); the under tail coverts cinnamon-buff.

The race of North Thailand may be separated from that of the more southern districts (north of the Isthmus of Kra) by its greater size (wing length: 85-90 mm., against 80–85 mm.) and slightly darker upperparts. The southern form must probably be known as *cinnamomeoventris* (Tenasserim Town), which, *fide* Ticehurst (Journ. Bombay Nat. Hist. Soc., vol. 36, 1933, p. 925), differs from *propinquus* in exactly these characters.

The numerous specimens from Peninsular Thailand (between the Isthmus of Kra and the Malayan border), which have been recorded by Robinson and Boden Kloss, Chasen, and Riley as *cinnamomeoventris* are, in my opinion, merely slightly aberrant examples of *cryptus*, which bear not the least resemblance to true *cinnamomeoventris*, as here understood.

The unique specimen of "*cinnamomeoventris*" recorded from Khun Tan by Riley (1938) differs, to my eyes, in no particular from *propinquus* of the same locality except insofar as it is the most worn of the series, as might be expected from the date of collection (May 12).

C. lönnbergi seems to be inseparable from *M. c. propinquus*, as has already been pointed out by others. The type specimen of Gyldenstolpe's race was a female from Ban Huai Hom, February 12, 1912; the sole paratype, an unsexed bird from Khao Phlung, January 28, 1912.

MICROSCELIS VIRESCENS TICKELLI (Blyth)

TENASSERIMESE RUFOUS-BREASTED BULBUL

Hypsipetes Tickelli BLYTH, Journ. Asiat. Soc. Bengal, vol. 24, 1855, p. 275 (mountainous interior of Tenasserim).

Ixos macclellandi tickelli, DE SCHAUENSEE, Proc. Acad. Nat. Sci. Philadelphia, 1929, p. 539 (Doi Suthep); 1934, p. 202 (Doi Suthep, Doi Chiang Dao).—RILEY, U. S. Nat. Mus. Bull. 172, 1938, p. 381 (Doi Ang Ka, Doi Khun Tan, Doi Hua Mot).

Ixos mcclellandi tickelli, DEIGNAN, Journ. Siam Soc. Nat. Hist. Suppl., 1931, p. 140 (Doi Suthep).—CHASEN and BODEN KLOSS, Journ. Siam Soc. Nat. Hist. Suppl., 1932, p. 242 (Doi Suthep).—DEIGNAN, Journ. Siam Soc. Nat. Hist. Suppl., 1936, p. 109 (Doi Suthep).

The present race is very common on the higher mountains of the districts west and south of (and including) the Khun Tan chain, ranging through the evergreen from 2,700 feet (Doi Suthep) to 7,000 feet (Doi Ang Ka). In addition to the localities named above, it is known from Doi Pha Hom Pok by a single specimen, which, in my opinion, should be considered merely an aberrant example of *M. v. binghami*.

The rufous-breasted bulbul may be seen in the lower trees along the trails or at the edge of the forest, usually in pairs but, where fruit is plentiful, in small flocks together with others of the family.

As in the case of certain related species, the breeding season of this bulbul seems to cover many months: specimens with the gonads greatly enlarged were taken on February 21, May 31, August 24, and September 3. Birds undergoing body molt have been collected on August 23, September 1, and December 6.

A breeding male from Doi Suthep had the irides crimson; the eyelids edged red; the bill brown; the feet, toes, and claws horny pink; the soles yellowish. Another had the irides dull red; the maxilla horny black; the mandible horn, darker at the tip and lighter at the base; the feet and toes pinkish brown; the soles chrome yellow. De Schauensee notes (1929) that his examples had the irides chestnut; the bill brownish flesh; the feet and toes fleshy brown.

M. v. tickelli has the lanceolate feathers of the crown and crest dull, dark brown, with conspicuous pale shaft streaks; the remaining upperparts bright olive-green; the feathers of the chin and throat ashy gray, with conspicuous white central streaks; the sides of the neck dull rufous; the feathers of the breast pale rufous, with indistinct pale shaft streaks; the remaining underparts whitish, sometimes faintly sullied with pale rufous; the under wing coverts and under tail coverts dull yellow; the under surface of the rectrices bright olive-green, like the upper surface.

MICROSCELIS VIRESCENS BINGHAMI (Hartert)

SOUTHERN SHAN RUFOUS-BREASTED BULBUL

Iole holti binghami HARTERT, Nov. Zool., vol. 9, 1902, p. 558 (Loi San Pa, Möng Köng State, Southern Shan States).

This form of the rufous-breasted bulbul occurs within our limits only on Doi Pha Hom Pok, where de Schauensee's collectors, early in 1938, took three quite typical examples, in addition to a bird that is externally inseparable from *tickelli* but probably represents an aberration of *binghami*.

M. v. binghami differs from *tickelli* only in having the mantle dull gray-brown instead of bright olive-green.

MICROSCELIS VIRESCENS LOQUAX (Deignan)

PHU KHA RUFOUS-BREASTED BULBUL

Ixos mcclellandii loquax DEIGNAN, Smithsonian Misc. Coll., vol. 99, No. 18, 1940, pp. 2–3 (Phu Kha, Nan Province, North Thailand).

The Phu Kha rufous-breasted bulbul is known only from the evergreen of Phu Kha above 4,000 feet but will probably be found to occur also on other high mountains of northern Nan Province.

This race, like *binghami*, differs strikingly from *tickelli* in having the mantle dull gray-brown instead of bright olive-green. "From *binghami* it is separable by the slightly deeper buffy color of the underparts, by having the entire underparts (including the center of the abdomen) suffused with this color, and by having the bend of the wing and the under tail-coverts buffy yellow, not pale yellow" (Deignan, *loc. cit.*).

MICROSCELIS FLAVALA HILDEBRANDTI (Hume)

KAREN BROWN-EARED BULBUL

Hemixus Hildebrandi [*sic*] HUME, Stray Feathers, vol. 2, 1874, p. 508 ("On the banks of the Younzaleen, in the Salween District of the Tenasserim Provinces, on the outskirts of the Pine Forest, at an elevation of about 3,000 feet").

Hemixus hildebrandi, WILLIAMSON, Journ. Nat. Hist. Soc. Siam, 1918, p. 19 (Muang Wang).—GYLDENSTOLPE, Ibis, 1920, p. 492 (Muang Wang).

Pycnonotus hainanus, DEIGNAN, Journ. Siam Soc. Nat. Hist. Suppl., 1931, p. 141 (Doi Suthep).

Ixos flavala hildebrandi, DE SCHAUENSEE, Proc. Acad. Nat. Sci. Philadelphia, 1934, p. 202 (Doi Chiang Dao, Doi Suthep).—DEIGNAN, Journ. Siam Soc. Nat. Hist. Suppl., 1936, p. 109 (Doi Suthep).

Ixos hildebrandi, RILEY, U. S. Nat. Mus. Bull. 172, 1938, p. 381 (Doi Langka, Doi Hua Mot, Khun Tan).

Ixos flavula hildebrandi, GREENWAY, Bull. Mus. Comp. Zool., 1940, p. 176 (Doi Ang Ka, Doi Nang Kaeo).

In the provinces west of, and including, the Khun Tan range, the brown-eared bulbul is a rather common species of the evergreen forest, occurring chiefly on the hills between 2,700 and 4,000 feet, rarely at lower elevations where the jungle is suitable.

This bulbul is one more of those that collect in scolding, chattering flocks at flowering trees on the mountain slopes. Freshly taken examples usually have the face and forecrown well dusted with pollen.

No information on the breeding season is available for our area, but adults undergoing body molt have been collected on February 15 and August 13, which implies that the nuptial period embraces a number of months.

My specimens had the irides red-brown; the bill black; the feet and toes dark brown; the soles yellowish white; the claws blackish brown.

Our race has the short crest blackish brown (appearing black in the field); the ear coverts shining pale brown; the mantle sullied gray; the remiges blackish brown, most of them conspicuously edged along the outer web with greenish yellow; the rectrices similar, edged with olive-green along the outer web near the base; a black mustachial streak; the underparts white, strongly washed with gray across the breast and along the flanks.

M. f. hildebrandti seems to have been named from a specimen which showed approach to *davisoni*, coming as it did from near the periphery of its range, but it is very misleading on this account to discard the later name *davisoni* and use *hildebrandti* for the brown-headed, brown-backed populations of Tenasserim and South Annam, as has been done by Delacour. It seems to me preferable to recognize *davisoni* and *bourdellei*, together with *hildebrandti* as an intermediate race.

M. f. hildebrandti, in North Thailand, is very near *bourdellei* but differs in having the crown blackish brown instead of black. Only newly molted specimens may fairly be compared since, with wear, the crown becomes browner—two *bourdellei* from Tongking, badly worn, are inseparable in color from fresh-plumaged birds of western Thailand.

The specimen from Khao Raem, recorded by Riley (1938) as *hildebrandti*, is, according to my view, true *bourdellei;* this race will probably be found also on the higher peaks of Nan Province.

MICROSCELIS MADAGASCARIENSIS CONCOLOR (Blyth)

TENASSERIMESE BLACK BULBUL

Hypsipetes concolor BLYTH, Journ. Asiat. Soc. Bengal, vol. 18, 1849, p. 816 ("Tenasserim provinces"; type specimen from Moulmein, *fide* Sclater, Ibis, 1892, p. 77, and Finn, List of the birds in the Indian Museum, pt. 1, 1901, p. 94).

Hypsipetes concolor, GYLDENSTOLPE, Journ. Nat. Hist. Soc. Siam, 1915, p. 166 (listed).

Hypsipetes concolor yunnanensis, GYLDENSTOLPE, Kungl. Svenska Vet.-Akad. Handl., 1916, p. 66 (Khun Tan); Ibis, 1920, p. 491 (Khan Tan).

Microscelis psaroides concolor, DE SCHAUENSEE, Proc. Acad. Nat. Sci. Philadelphia, 1929, p. 538 (Doi Suthep); 1934, p. 201 (Doi Suthep, Doi Chiang Dao, Doi Khun Tan).—DEIGNAN, Journ. Siam Soc. Nat. Hist. Suppl., 1931, p. 139 (Doi Suthep); 1936, p. 109 (Doi Suthep).—RILEY, U. S. Nat. Mus. Bull. 172, 1938, p. 379 (Doi Ang Ka, Doi Suthep, Doi Khun Tan, Doi Langka, Doi Hua Mot).

Microscelis leucocephalus concolor, CHASEN and BODEN KLOSS, Journ. Siam Soc. Nat. Hist. Suppl., 1932, p. 243 (Doi Suthep).

The Tenasserimese black bulbul is a common species of the evergreen on the Thanon Thong Chai and Khun Tan chains, at elevations between 2,900 (Doi Suthep) and 8,000 feet (Doi Ang Ka).

The movements of this bird are largely governed by the antheses of such nectariferous trees as *Cassia* and *Bombax*, so that, while it is a permanent resident of the two ranges named above, it is at the same time highly erratic in its appearances and numbers at a given locality. Occurring in flocks, great or small in proportion to the abundance of desirable food, it usually keeps to the tops of quite high trees, in clearings or at the edge of the forest. Whether flying or at rest, it is one of the most clamorous of its family and is almost impossible to overlook.

A female from Doi Suthep, February 13, had the gonads enlarged. Smith took a specimen in advanced postnatal molt on Doi Langka, May 2; de Schauensee reports (1934) a juvenile from Doi Suthep, July 22. Postnuptial molt appears in examples collected between May 12 and August 29.

Adults have the irides brown; the bill, interior of the mouth, tongue, feet, and toes bright coral red; the claws horny brown.

Old birds have the lanceolate feathers of the front and crown black, glossed with steel blue; the remaining upperparts bluish slate (the mantle more or less strongly suffused with blue-black); the feathers of the wings and tail black, their exposed portions narrowly edged with bluish slate; a spot below the anterior ear coverts glossy black (this color sometimes continued as a narrow line beneath and behind the ear coverts); the remaining underparts slaty gray, paler posteriorly (the feathers of the center of the abdomen sometimes edged with white); the under tail coverts slaty gray, always narrowly fringed with white.

MICROSCELIS MADAGASCARIENSIS LEUCOTHORAX Mayr

SZECHWANESE WHITE-HEADED BLACK BULBUL

Microscelis leucocephalus leucothorax MAYR, Journ. für Orn., vol. 89, 1941, p. — ("Chung Chiang Miao, [W ?] Szetschwan").

Microscelis leucocephalus leucocephalus, DE SCHAUENSEE, Proc. Acad. Nat. Sci. Philadelphia, 1929, p. 539 (Doi Suthep).—DEIGNAN, Journ. Siam Soc. Nat. Hist. Suppl., 1931, p. 140 (Doi Suthep).

Microscelis leucocephalus, DEIGNAN, Journ. Siam Soc. Nat. Hist. Suppl., 1936, p. 109 (Doi Suthep).

White-headed black bulbuls of whatever race are known in our area only from Doi Suthep, where they have been noted but three times: A flock of ten at 5,500 feet, December 30, 1928 (de Schauensee); a flock of six at 5,400 feet, May 10, 1930 (Deignan); many, between 2,700 and 3,000 feet, February 22, 1936 (Deignan). A single male taken by de Schauensee has been identified by Mayr as an example of the present form; *M. m. stresemanni* of northwestern Yunnan may, however, be expected to occur in the same flocks as *leucothorax*.

To northern Thailand, these birds are merely rare winter visitors which, like the resident black bulbul, appear erratically at a given locality. In habits they differ not at all from *concolor*, with which they are often associated while feeding; it is interesting then to find *leucothorax* and *stresemanni* much more timid than their black-headed relative and apparently not mingling with it in flight.

De Schauensee's specimen had the irides brown; the eyelids edged orange; the bill deep orange, tinged reddish at the base; the interior of the mouth orange; the feet and toes orange; the claws horn.

This race is polymorphic and not every specimen can be certainly identified to subspecies. The adult male, in its typical form, has the entire head, neck, and breast pure white; the rest of the plumage, above and below, black, glossed (especially on the mantle) with steel blue. The adult female differs in having the upperparts slaty gray, more or less strongly suffused with black, and the underparts (below the breast) deep ashy gray.

M. m. stresemanni, another polymorphic race, is not separable from *leucothorax* in life. The male in typical plumage closely resembles the female *leucothorax* as described above; the female is distinguishable from that of *leucothorax* only by its greater size.

MICROSCELIS THOMPSONI (Bingham)

WHITE-HEADED ASHY BULBUL

FRONTISPIECE: PLATE 1

Cerasophila Thompsoni BINGHAM, Ann. Mag. Nat. Hist., ser. 7, vol. 5, 1900, pp. 358–359 (Loi San Pa, Möng Köng State, Southern Shan States).

Cerasophila thompsoni, DE SCHAUENSEE, Proc. Acad. Nat. Sci. Philadelphia, 1929, p. 539 (Doi Suthep); 1934, p. 202 (Doi Chiang Dao).—DEIGNAN, Journ. Siam Soc. Nat. Hist. Suppl., 1931, p. 140 (Doi Suthep).—RILEY, Journ. Siam Soc. Nat. Hist. Suppl., 1933, p. 156 (Doi Langka).—DEIGNAN, Journ. Siam Soc. Nat. Hist. Suppl., 1935, p. 65 (Doi Ang Ka); 1936, p. 109 (Doi Suthep, Doi Chiang Dao).—RILEY, U. S. Nat. Mus. Bull. 172, 1938, p. 380 (Doi Langka, Doi Hua Mot).

The rare white-headed ashy bulbul has been found in Thailand on the five peaks named above, at elevations between 3,800 and 5,500 feet.

This is a bird of lightly wooded country at high altitudes: On Doi Ang Ka, I noted it in the semicleared valley below Pha Mon; on Doi Chiang Dao, at the poppy gardens of the Musoe and in the thin trees growing from the great precipices of the southern wall (above abysses so deep that specimens could not be taken); on Doi Suthep, in the park-like areas of widely spaced pines. Only on Doi Chiang Dao, where there is plenty of open forest at suitable elevations, it is comparatively common.

On Doi Chiang Dao, in March, 1937, I observed it in loose flocks of a score or more, but on Doi Suthep it was always seen singly or in pairs at any season, possibly because of the small number inhabiting the latter mountain. In flocks it is a clamorous species, in pairs silent and inconspicuous. Stomachs examined by me contained only insects.

On Doi Suthep, 5,500 feet, I took a female with enlarged gonads, April 2, 1931, and, on the same hill, watched a pair at 3,800 feet, May 13 and 14, 1935, which almost certainly had nestling young in the vicinity. Smith took a juvenile on Doi Langka, April 26, 1931, and another in postjuvenal molt on Doi Hua Mot, August 22, 1934. A bird from Doi Ang Ka, 4,500 feet, September 8, 1935, is in postnuptial molt.

Adult females had the irides light yellow or brownish yellow; the eyelids edged bright vermilion-red or coral red; the naked orbital skin gray-brown or slaty brown; the bill coral red, yellowish or horny at the extreme tip; the interior of the mouth coral red; the feet and toes coral red; the claws horny brown or brown with an orange tinge.

The adult of either sex has the entire head and neck pure white; the rest of the plumage ashy gray (the remiges and rectrices darker, almost slaty), except for the dull chestnut-rufous under tail coverts. The immaculate white of the head is a character of maturity; see Riley (*loc. cit.*) for descriptions of the juvenile specimens collected by Smith.

Family TIMALIIDAE

CUTIA NIPALENSIS NIPALENSIS Hodgson

NEPALESE KHATYA

Cutia Nipalensis HODGSON, Journ. Asiat. Soc. Bengal, vol. 5, 1836, pp. 773–775 (Nepal).

Cutia nipalensis nipalensis, DEIGNAN, Journ. Siam Soc. Nat. Hist. Suppl., 1931, p. 138 (Doi Suthep).—CHASEN and BODEN KLOSS, Journ. Siam Soc. Nat. Hist. Suppl., 1932, p. 245 (Doi Suthep.)—DEIGNAN, Journ. Siam Soc. Nat. Hist. Suppl., 1936, p. 107 (Doi Suthep).—DE SCHAUENSEE, Proc. Acad. Nat. Sci. Philadelphia, 1934, p. 196 (Doi Suthep).—RILEY, U. S. Nat. Mus. Bull. 172, 1938, p. 361 (Doi Langka).—GREENWAY, Bull. Mus. Comp. Zool., 1940, p. 174 (Doi Ang Ka).

The khatya is restricted to the evergreen on our highest peaks and seems to be a bird of considerable rarity in Thailand: it has been collected only three times on Doi Suthep, 5,500 feet (five specimens); once on Doi Ang Ka, 7,400 feet (two specimens); twice on Doi Langka (five specimens, four of them taken on the same day).

At the summit of Suthep, all examples have been found eating berries on low trees at the edge of the bungalow clearing, accompanied by bulbuls and other frugivores.

Four adults from Doi Langka, November 6, are in postnuptial molt.

An adult male had the irides red-brown; the bill black, plumbeous-blue at the base of the mandible; the feet and toes intense yellow; the claws yellowish horn.

The male has the forehead and crown slaty blue; the lores and the sides of the head and neck glossy black, this color crossing the nape to form a narrow collar; the scapulars, back, rump, and very long upper tail coverts rufous-chestnut (the scapulars often fading to a dull rufous); the wing coverts glossy black; the remiges largely black but with slaty blue along the outer web, white near the base of the inner web, and minutely tipped white; the rectrices with the apical half black, the basal half slaty blue suffused with rufous-chestnut; a minute tuft of black feathers on the extreme base of the mandible; the remaining underparts white, boldly barred with black on the sides of the breast and along the flanks, and everywhere suffused with buff (this color soon disappearing from the throat and breast after death). The female differs in having the black on the sides of the head replaced by brown; the scapulars and back rufous with conspicuous, elongated black spots, instead of uniform rufous-chestnut.

PTERUTHIUS AENOBARBUS INTERMEDIUS (Hume)

TENASSERIMESE CHESTNUT-FRONTED SHRIKE BABBLER

Allotrius intermedius HUME, Stray Feathers, vol. 5, 1877, p. 112 ("Central Tenasserim Hills"; type specimen from Mount Muleyit, *fide* Hume, *ibid.*, vol. 6, 1878, p. 370).

Pteruthius aenobarbus intermedius, DEIGNAN, Journ. Siam Soc. Nat. Hist. Suppl., 1931, p. 175 (Doi Suthep); 1936, p. 108 (Doi Suthep).—DE SCHAUENSEE, Proc. Acad. Nat. Sci. Philadelphia, 1934, p. 197 (Doi Suthep).—RILEY, U. S. Nat. Mus. Bull. 172, 1938, p. 363 (Doi Khun Tan, Doi Langka, Doi Hua Mot).

With the addition of Doi Nang Kaeo, this pretty bird is recorded only from the mountains named above, on all of which it seems to be rare or uncommon and restricted to a zone between 4,400 and 5,500 feet.

On Doi Suthep I saw it occasionally, singly or in pairs (often in the same flock with *Siva* spp.), in the lower branches of the trees at the edge of the evergreen or in the open hill-forest, acting much like a white-browed shrike babbler.

Examples taken on Doi Hua Mot between August 19 and 26 are in postnuptial molt.

Adults have the irides dark red-brown; the maxilla plumbeous, with the culmen and tip black; the mandible plumbeous; the feet and toes flesh; the claws horn.

The old male has the forehead chestnut, followed by a band of bright yellow across the forecrown; the remaining upperparts bright olive-green; the shoulders black, with two broad white bars; the rest of the folded wing bright olive-green, except that the outer primaries are edged with white along the outer web and the secondaries are narrowly tipped with the same color; the central pair of rectrices bright olive-green, the others black with an outwardly increasingly broad white tip, the outermost pair almost wholly white; a broken eye ring of pure white feathers; the lores and a narrow line edging the lower half of the eye ring black; a streak from above the eye to the sides of the nape ashy, darkening posteriorly; the chin and throat chestnut; the under wing coverts pure white; the flanks and thighs grayish white; the remaining underparts bright yellow. The adult female differs chiefly in having the forehead chestnut-rufous, immediately followed by the olive-green of the remaining upperparts; the shoulders olive-green, with two salmon-buff bars; the black line below the eye merely indicated; the chin suffused with rufous; the remaining underparts grayish white, washed with pale yellowish olive on the breast, flanks, and abdomen; the under tail coverts light yellow.

PTERUTHIUS MELANOTIS MELANOTIS Hodgson

INDIAN YELLOW-FRONTED SHRIKE BABBLER

Pt[eruthius] melanotis HODGSON, *in* Blyth, Journ. Asiat. Soc. Bengal, vol. 16, 1847, p. 448 ("The Terai, at the base of the S. E. Himalaya"; type specimen from Nepal, *fide* Gadow, Catalogue of the birds in the British Museum, vol. 8, 1883, p. 118).

Pteruthius melanotis, DEIGNAN, Journ. Siam Soc. Nat. Hist. Suppl., 1936, p. 169 (Phu Kha).

The only example yet known from Thailand is an adult female, collected by me on Phu Kha, 4,500 feet, April 5, 1936.

This bird, although accompanied by a male, had the ovaries still quite inactive.

The adult male differs from that of the preceding species most conspicuously in having the forehead bright yellow; the ashy streaks from above the eyes joined in a broad band across the nape; the bright yellow ear coverts bordered posteriorly by a black vertical band. The adult female differs from that of *P. a. intermedius* in having the entire upperparts (including the forehead) olive-green, except for a gray nuchal band; a black band indicated behind the ear coverts; the sides of the throat washed with rufous; the flanks grayish white, strongly washed with yellow; the remaining underparts light yellow.

PTERUTHIUS ERYTHROPTERUS AERALATUS Blyth

TENASSERIMESE WHITE-BROWED SHRIKE BABBLER

Pteruthius aeralatus "Tickell" BLYTH, Journ. Asiat. Soc. Bengal, vol. 24, 1855, p. 267 ("Mountainous interior of Tenasserim"; type specimen from Mount Muleyit, *fide* Hume, Stray Feathers, vol. 6, 1878, p. 368).

Pterythias aeralatus, GYLDENSTOLPE, Kungl. Svenska Vet.-Akad. Handl., 1916, p. 63 (Khun Tan).

Pteruthius aeralatus aeralatus, WILLIAMSON, Journ. Nat. Hist. Soc. Siam, 1918, p. 18 (Muang Wang, Doi Nga Chang).—GYLDENSTOLPE, Ibis, 1920, p. 479 (Muang Wang, Doi Nga Chang).—RILEY, U. S. Nat. Mus. Bull. 172, 1938, p. 362 (Doi Ang Ka, Khun Tan, Doi Langka, Doi Hua Mot, Doi Mana, "Doi Kiew Koh Ma").

Pterythius flaviscapis aeralatus, DE SCHAUENSEE, Proc. Acad. Nat. Sci. Philadelphia, 1928, p. 565 (Doi Suthep).

Pteruthius flaviscapis aeralatus, DE SCHAUENSEE, Proc. Acad. Nat. Sci. Philadelphia, 1929, p. 535 (Doi Suthep); 1934, p. 197 (Doi Suthep, Doi Chiang Dao, Ridge just south of Doi Chiang Dao).—DEIGNAN, Journ. Siam Soc. Nat. Hist. Suppl., 1931, p. 138 (Doi Suthep).—CHASEN and BODEN KLOSS, Journ. Siam Soc. Nat. Hist. Suppl., 1932, p. 245 (Doi Suthep).—DEIGNAN, Journ. Siam Soc. Nat. Hist. Suppl., 1936, p. 108 (Doi Suthep).

This form is common on all the mountains of sufficient altitude in the provinces west of (and including) the Khun Tan chain, occurring from 3,300 to 5,500 feet, both at the edge of the evergreen and in the open hill-forest.

It is seen singly or in pairs, silently creeping along a horizontal branch and exploring the underside of the leaves in the deliberate fashion of an American *Vireo*, or perched upon some exposed twig, turning its head from one side to the other, much like a *Tephrodornis*. It utters a churring note when alarmed and the pair, when separated, communicate by a sweet double call; de Schauensee states (1929) that it has also "a very pretty warbling song, generally delivered from an exposed and leafless branch at the top of a tall tree."

An example from Doi Suthep, February 21, had the gonads greatly enlarged. Specimens in postjuvenal molt have been taken between April 24 and July 15 and others in postnuptial molt between May 15 and November 4.

Adults had the irides glaucous-blue, blue-green, olive-green, or brown; the maxilla black, with the commissure edged plumbeous-blue along the basal half; the entire mandible and the interior of the mouth plumbeous-blue; the feet and toes yellowish fleshy or fleshy-pink; the soles yellow; the claws dark horny.

The old male has the forehead, crown, nape, lores, subocular region, and ear coverts black; a broad white band from above the eye to the nape; the mantle gray, the upper tail coverts tipped black; the wings black, the primaries conspicuously tipped and edged along the inner web with white, the inner secondaries with the outer web deep golden, the inner web chestnut, and a narrow black tip; the tail black; the underparts white, more or less strongly washed with gray on the throat, breast, and upper flanks, with vinaceous-pink on the lower flanks. The adult female has the upper half of the head gray (the supercilium merely indicated), this color changing on the nape to the grayish olive of the mantle; the primaries black with white tips and the outer web edged bright olive-green; the inner secondaries bright olive-green, strongly suffused with chestnut-rufous; the inner pairs of rectrices bright olive-green, tipped with black, the outer pairs similar but tipped apically with yellow and subterminally with black; the underparts white, more or less strongly suffused everywhere with pale buff. Juveniles of either sex resemble the old female but have the under tail coverts pale yellow.

PTERUTHIUS ERYTHROPTERUS YUNNANENSIS Ticehurst

YUNNANESE WHITE-BROWED SHRIKE BABBLER

Pteruthius erythropterus yunnanensis TICEHURST, Bull. Brit. Orn. Club, vol. 57, 1937, p. 147 (Shweli-Salwin Divide, northwestern Yunnan).

A race, which may conveniently be placed under this name, is common on Phu Kha between 3,500 and 5,500 feet and will doubtless be found on other suitably high mountains in Nan Province.

From *aeralatus*, it may be known by having (in the male) the throat, breast, and upper flanks washed with a much deeper gray and by having the white mustachial line below the black ear coverts distinctly set off, instead of scarcely demarcated from the color of the throat.

The female differs from that of *aeralatus* in having the throat gray, with little or no buffy suffusion.

The population of Phu Kha is, in fact, intermediate between *yunnanensis* and *aeralatus*, having the coloration of the former and the measurements of the latter.

MESIA ARGENTAURIS GALBANA Mayr and Greenway

THAI SILVER-EARED MESIA

Mesia argentauris galbana MAYR and GREENWAY, Proc. New England Zool. Club, vol. 17, 1938, pp. 3–4 (Doi Ang Ka, North Thailand).

Mesia argentauris argentauris, DE SCHAUENSEE, Proc. Acad. Nat. Sci. Philadelphia, 1929, p. 536 (Doi Suthep); 1934, p. 197 (Doi Suthep).—CHASEN and BODEN KLOSS, Journ. Siam Soc. Nat. Hist. Suppl., 1932, p. 245 (Doi Suthep).—DEIGNAN, Journ. Siam Soc. Nat. Hist. Suppl., 1936, p. 108 (Doi Suthep).

Mesia argentauris, DEIGNAN, Journ. Siam Soc. Nat. Hist. Suppl., 1931, p. 139 (Doi Suthep).

Mesia argentauris galbana, RILEY, U. S. Nat. Mus. Bull. 172, 1938, p. 363 (Doi Ang Ka, Doi Langka).—GREENWAY, Bull. Mus. Comp. Zool., 1940, p. 174 (Doi Ang Ka).

The mesia has until now been recorded in the northern provinces only from Doi Ang Ka, Doi Suthep, Doi Langka, and Phu Kha; on all these mountains it is common within its altitudinal range. On Doi Ang Ka it has been found between 4,000 and 5,700 feet, but on Doi Suthep it is strictly confined to the topmost ridge from 5,000 to 5,500 feet.

This bird requires lalang-covered areas at high elevations, dotted with low trees and brushy thickets, and enters the evergreen only in the immediate proximity of such places. It travels in large bands, usually accompanied by other species of small babblers. A stomach examined by me contained ants and beetles.

The breeding season is very protracted: on Doi Ang Ka I have taken a specimen with gonads enlarged, April 27, and another with them greatly enlarged, September 3. Full-plumaged juveniles have been collected May 1 (Doi Langka), July (Doi Suthep), and September 7 (Doi Ang Ka). The only bird seen in postnuptial molt is from Doi Ang Ka, December 4.

Adults had the irides brownish red; the bill ochreous-yellow (the mandible brighter), tinged greenish at the corners of the mouth; the tarsi horny yellow; the toes horny brown; the claws fleshy yellow or light horny brown.

The adult male in fresh plumage (December–March) has the forehead deep yellow; the ear coverts shining silvery gray; the crown, lores, and mustachial streak below the ear coverts black; the nape and uppermost back deep olivaceous-golden; the mantle gray, strongly suffused with olive-green; the upper tail coverts red; the outermost primaries edged yellow along the outer web, the other remiges (except the innermost secondaries) similarly edged shining red near the base, yellow elsewhere; the rectrices blackish, the outer pairs edged yellowish along the outer web; the chin and throat bright orange-yellow, changing on the breast to the olivaceous-yellow of the remaining underparts; the under tail coverts red. The adult female differs in having the upper and under tail coverts orange-buff. The juvenile resembles the old female but has the top of the head duller black and the nuchal collar pale and indistinct. As the plumage becomes worn during spring and summer, the green suffusion is lost from the mantle and the yellows become much duller, possibly as a result of exposure to sunlight.

Mayr and Greenway (*loc. cit.*) have described *M. a. vernayi* (Hai Bum, Upper Burma) and *galbana* (Doi Ang Ka, North Thailand) as distinct from *argentauris* (Nepal) on characters of size and tone of mantle, nape, and throat.

The alleged size differences are slight or nonexistent in the authors' own tables, while color characters in this species are so much subject to change, both seasonal and *post mortem*, that, unless really striking, it seems unwise to use them as racial criteria at all.

Thanks to Dr. Mayr's courtesy, I have before me the original series (3) of *vernayi*, as well as 20 specimens of *galbana* from every known locality in its Thai range. So far as color is concerned, all examples taken in Thailand between December 4 and January 30 are *galbana*, while those collected between April 6 and July 14 could be *vernayi*, and a breeding topotypical bird of September 3 is so gray that it might belong to an undescribed form. Using the material at hand,

All nonmolting adult males from Thailan agree with *argentauris galbana* is separable from *vernayi* only by its slightly longer wing. in having the wing length 75 mm. or longer but differ from it in their more golden, less orange, nuchal collar, and, on the assumption that this distinction has nothing to do with age of skins, I accept *galbana*, at least for the present. It seems to me highly probable, however, that future workers will find it necessary to combine *galbana* with either *vernayi* or *argentauris*, or even to place both of the more recent names on the synonymy of the Nepalese race.

LIOCICHLA RIPPONI (Oates)

INDO-CHINESE LIOCICHLA

Trochalopterum ripponi OATES, Bull. Brit. Orn. Club, vol. 11, 1900, pp 10–11 ("Shan States").

Trochalopteron phoeniceum ripponi, RILEY, Journ. Siam Soc. Nat. Hist. Suppl., 1933, p. 155 (Doi Langka).

Liocichla ripponi ripponi, RILEY, U. S. Nat. Mus. Bull. 172, 1938, p. 322 (Doi Langka).

This extraordinary species has been found in Thailand only by Smith, who collected, on Doi Langka, a male, November 12, 1930, and a male and a female, April 26, 1931.

Nothing has been recorded of its habits nor have I been able even to learn whether it is a terrestrial or an arboreal form. The example of November 12 is in postnuptial molt.

It has the crown and nape gray (more or less suffused with olivaceous); the remaining upperparts olivaceous-brown; the primaries with the outer web edged crimson basally, yellow apically, the crimson inwardly increasing in extent; the outer secondaries similarly edged olivaceous-brown basally, then gray, crimson apically, the innermost almost wholly olivaceous-brown, all narrowly tipped with buffy white; the *truncate* rectrices olivaceous-brown on the basal half, indistinctly barred with blackish near the center, blackish on the apical half, the outer ones suffused with dull red-orange beneath, all narrowly tipped with buff; the lores, supercilium, and sides of the head and neck crimson, this color tending to invade the chin, upper throat, and sides of the lower throat; the remaining underparts grayish olive, more or less suffused with golden; the under tail coverts black, broadly tipped with dull orange.

GARRULAX MILNEI SHARPEI (Rippon)

BURMESE RED-TAILED LAUGHING-THRUSH

Trochalopterum sharpei RIPPON, Bull. Brit. Orn. Club, vol. 12, 1901, p. 13 ("The Kauri-Kachin tract, to the east of Bhamo, and bordering on the south of the Tapeng River").

Trochalopterum milnei sharpei, RILEY, Journ. Siam Soc. Nat. Hist. Suppl., 1933, p. 155 (Doi Langka).

Trochalopteron milnei sharpei, RILEY, U. S. Nat. Mus. Bull. 172, 1938, p. 322 (Doi Langka).

The beautiful red-tailed garrulax has been found only on Doi Langka and Doi Pho Hom Pok, but, on these two mountains at least, it is a common bird at the higher elevations. At the former locality Smith saw it in large flocks and collected no less than 15 specimens between April 22 and 27, 1931; at the latter, de Schauensee's men took a fine series during an equally short period.

Nothing has been recorded of its habits in Thailand, and I myself never had the good fortune to see this species in life. One of Smith's examples from Doi Langka, November 9, is undergoing postnuptial molt.

The adult has the forehead, crown, and nape orange-rufous; the mantle ashy olive, becoming olivaceous-brown on the rump and upper tail coverts, the feathers of the back narrowly edged with dull blackish brown to give a scaled appearance; the remiges with the outer web largely bright, shining red, the inner web black (except the innermost secondaries, which have the inner web largely white); the rectrices red above, blackish beneath; the lores and a narrow supercilium black, the latter becoming white near the posterior end; the ear coverts silvery gray; the chin and throat blackish, changing on the remaining underparts to dark ashy gray, posteriorly more or less suffused with olivaceous-brown.

GARRULAX ERYTHROCEPHALUS MELANOSTIGMA Blyth

TENASSERIMESE CHESTNUT-CAPPED LAUGHING-THRUSH

G[arrulax] melanostigma BLYTH, Journ. Asiat. Soc. Bengal, vol. 24, 1855, p. 268 (Mount Muleyit).

Trochalopteron erythrocephalum melanostigma, DEIGNAN, Journ. Siam Soc. Nat. Hist. Suppl., 1931, p. 174 (Doi Suthep).

Garrulax erythrocephalus melanostigma, DEIGNAN, Journ. Siam Soc. Nat. Hist. Suppl., 1936, p. 105 (Doi Suthep).—GREENWAY, Bull. Mus. Comp. Zool., 1940, p. 169 (Doi Ang Ka).

Trochalopteron melanostigma melanostigma, Riley, U. S. Nat. Mus. Bull. 172, 1938, p. 322 (Doi Ang Ka, Doi Suthep).

Birds that, though atypical, may conveniently be known by this name, are numerous on Doi Ang Ka between 4,300 feet and the summit (8,400 feet), and rather less common on Doi Suthep between 4,600 and 5,500 feet.

I found them always in the densest undergrowth, whether evergreen or bamboo, traveling in small parties and carrying on an endless conversation of melodious notes in which one would whistle and another immediately reply with a similar but different song.

A male had the irides with a violet-brown outer ring and a chestnut inner ring; the eyelids plumbeous; the bill blackish brown; the feet, toes, and claws wood brown.

In the forest shadows it appears to be a black bird with a gray head. In the hand, it proves to have the crown and center of the nape chestnut; the remaining upperparts grayish olive; the wings golden-olive, with an orange-rufous patch near the shoulder, followed by a black patch on the primary coverts; the sides of the head and nape deep silvery gray, finely streaked with blackish; the chin and sides of the upper throat black, changing to maroon-chestnut on the rest of the throat, which color, in turn, changes on the remaining underparts to grayish olive, suffused with tawny.

I have already shown (Proc. Biol. Soc. Washington, vol. 51, 1938, p. 90) that Doi Ang Ka and Doi Suthep are inhabited by distinct populations, neither of which, strictly speaking, is *melanostigma*, but I still feel that no useful purpose would be served by the erection of new names for them.

Greenway's discovery (*loc. cit.*) that, on Doi Ang Ka, "specimens taken above 6,000 ft. have rather longer and stouter bills, (26–28 mm. as against 24–25 mm.) and as a rule, have less brown on the throat and upper breast than those from lower altitudes" is of especial interest, inasmuch as it indicates that birds at the summit of this more southern mountain are acquiring two characters regularly found in the race (*schistaceus*) inhabiting peaks farther north.

GARRULAX ERYTHROCEPHALUS SCHISTACEUS Deignan

Southern Shan Chestnut-capped Laughing-thrush

Garrulax erythrocephalus schistaceus Deignan, Proc. Biol. Soc. Washington, vol. 51, 1938, pp. 89–90 (Doi Chiang Dao, Chiang Mai Province, North Thailand).

The present race, in its typical form known only from Doi Chiang Dao and Doi Pha Hom Pok, between 5,000 and 7,000 feet, will probably not be found elsewhere in Thailand.

At the type locality I collected it in the dense evergreen of the crater-like valley at the western base of the southwestern pinnacle and again in the thickets of gnarled shrubs growing among huge, broken rocks at the summit of the same pinnacle.

Prenuptial molt of the feathers of head and neck is shown in examples taken on March 19 and 20.

G. e. schistaceus differs from *melanostigma* in having the general coloration, above and below, deep mouse gray, instead of grayish olive; the under parts almost without tawny suffusion; the maroon-chestnut of the throat more restricted in extent; the bill slightly longer.

GARRULAX ERYTHROCEPHALUS SUBCONNECTENS Deignan

PHU KHA CHESTNUT-CAPPED LAUGHING-THRUSH

Garrulax erythrocephalus subconnectens DEIGNAN, Proc. Biol. Soc. Washington, vol. 51, 1938, pp. 90–91 (Phu Kha, Nan Province, North Thailand).

The subspecies *subconnectens* is known, within our limits, only from Phu Kha, where it is common in the heavy evergreen between 4,500 feet and the summit (5,500 feet).

Specimens of April 6, 7, and 9 are undergoing prenuptial molt of the feathers of head and neck.

This form resembles *melanostigma* in having the general coloration grayish olive but differs widely from both *melanostigma* and *schistaceus* in having the feathers of the breast broadly edged with brownish gray to give a distinctly scaled appearance. From *connectens* of Laos, which has the breast similarly marked, it is separable by having the primary coverts black, instead of dark golden-green.

GARRULAX MERULINUS LAOËNSIS de Schauensee

SHAN SPOTTED-BREASTED LAUGHING-THRUSH

Garrulax (Stactocichla) merulinus laoënsis DE SCHAUENSEE, Proc. Acad. Nat. Sci. Philadelphia, vol. 90, 1938, p. 27 (Doi Pha Hom Pok, North Thailand).

This form, described from a series of three (one male, two females) taken by de Schauensee's collectors on Doi Pha Hom Pok, 6,000 feet, January 21 and 31, 1938, is not at all likely to occur at any other Thai locality.

It has the entire upperparts olivaceous-brown, except for a narrow, white postocular streak; the underparts, except for the olivaceous-brown flanks, buffy white, boldly marked on the throat and breast with guttate black spots; the under tail coverts rufous-buff.

The validity of *laoënsis*, named after comparison of fresh material with "foxed" *obscurus* and *merulinus*, is by no means established, and the name is here adopted only with reservations.

GARRULAX CHINENSIS LOCHMIUS Deignan

LAO BLACK-THROATED LAUGHING-THRUSH

Garrulax chinensis lochmius DEIGNAN, Zoologica, vol. 26, pt. 3, 1941, p. 241 (Chiang Saen Kao, North Thailand).

Dryonastes chinensis, GYLDENSTOLPE, Journ. Nat. Hist. Soc. Siam, 1915, p. 164 (listed); Kungl. Svenska Vet.-Akad. Handl., 1916, p. 55 (Khun Tan, Chiang Rai).

Dryonastes chinensis [*partim*], GYLDENSTOLPE, Ibis, 1920, p. 486 (Khun Tan, Chiang Rai).

Dryonastes chinensis propinquus, DEIGNAN, Journ. Siam Soc. Nat. Hist. Suppl., 1931, p. 136 (Chiang Mai).

Garrulax chinensis propinquus, DE SCHAUENSEE, Proc. Acad. Nat. Sci. Philadelphia, 1934, p. 183 (Chiang Rai).—DEIGNAN, Journ. Siam Soc. Nat. Hist. Suppl., 1936, p. 104 (Chiang Mai).

Garrulax chinensis propinquus [*partim*], RILEY, U. S. Nat. Mus. Bull. 172, 1938, p. 317 (Khun Tan, Doi Hua Mot, Muang Pai).

This laughing-thrush is locally common throughout our provinces, chiefly on the plains but, on Doi Ang Ka and Phu Kha, occurring as high as 4,000 and 4,500 feet in areas of abandoned cultivation grown up to *Rubus* and *Eupatorium*.

Except during the breeding season, the bird is found in small flocks in the densest cover and especially in thick hedgerows bordering cart tracks, whence it may sometimes come out to feed in the open road. Its habits are quite like those of *G. l. diardi*, but it is a rather more retiring species and its calls are very different: melodious, conversational whistles, interspersed with harsher notes.

A pair from Ban Wang Mo, March 31, had the gonads enlarged. A specimen from Muang Fang, July 20, is in full juvenal dress; examples from Doi Hua Mot and Doi Ang Ka, September 4 and 8, are in postnuptial molt.

An adult female had the irides deep red; the orbital skin slaty; the bill black; the feet and toes brown; the claws horny brown.

The adult has the bushy feathers of the forehead, the lores, orbital region, postocular streak, chin, and central portion of the throat to the upper breast black; the crown and nape slaty gray, a narrow area immediately behind the forehead streaked with white; the remaining upperparts olivaceous-brown, except for the blackish apical quarter of the tail; the ear coverts and the sides of the upper throat white; the ring of feathers around the vent rufous; the remaining underparts gray, changing to olivaceous-brown on the flanks and under tail coverts. The juvenile differs from the adult in having the gray of the crown paler and less clearly defined from the mantle; the upperparts more rufescent, less olivaceous; the underparts washed with dull rufous and the under tail coverts wholly of this color.

GARRULAX LEUCOLOPHUS DIARDI (Lesson)

INDO-CHINESE WHITE-CRESTED LAUGHING-THRUSH

Turdus Diardi LESSON, Traité d'ornithologie, 1831, p. 408 (Cochin-China).
Garrulax diardi, GYLDENSTOLPE, Journ. Nat. Hist. Soc. Siam, 1915, p. 164 (listed).
Garrulax leucolophus diardi, GYLDENSTOLPE, Kungl. Svenska Vet.-Akad. Handl., 1916, p. 53 (Pha Kho, Khun Tan, Pang Hua Phong, Tha Chomphu); Ibis, 1920, p. 486 ("The whole of Siam").—DE SCHAUENSEE, Proc. Acad. Nat. Sci. Philadelphia, 1928, p. 567 (Doi Suthep); 1929, p. 530 (Chiang Mai, Chiang Saen, Chiang Saen Kao); 1934, p. 183 (Chiang Mai, "Tung Sio," Chiang Saen).—DEIGNAN, Journ. Siam Soc. Nat. Hist. Suppl., 1931, p. 136 (Doi Suthep, Chiang Mai); 1936, p. 105 (Doi Suthep, Chiang Mai).—CHASEN and BODEN KLOSS, Journ. Siam Soc. Nat. Hist. Suppl., 1932, p. 243 (Doi Suthep).—RILEY, U. S. Nat. Mus. Bull. 172, 1938, p. 317 (Doi Ang Ka, Mae Khan, Chiang Dao, Khun Tan, Muang Pai, Phrae, Ban Nam Khian).

This large babbler occurs abundantly in the dry deciduous forest of all our provinces from the plains to about 2,700 feet, rarely in mixed-deciduous jungle as high as 3,200 feet, and has once been seen in open pinewoods on Doi Ang Ka at 3,500 feet.

Travel through the hot *pa daeng* is enlivened by the large flocks of these birds, which, at the approach of the wayfarer, scuttle like rats across the trail or skim the ground on stiffly set wings, one after the other, then move along through the bushes before him to the accompaniment of hysterical "laughter." Far from showing timidity, they often first intimate their presence by raising a general babble and approaching for a nearer view. Their excitement is shown by beating the wings and jumping off the ground, while others ascend into the undergrowth and lower branches of the trees, constantly cackling and laughing; as the uproar begins to die down in one quarter, it arises again from another, as in a musical round. If one waits quietly, the party soon loses interest in the stranger and, with conversational notes, begins hunting for food, peering under the vegetation or rising into the air and kicking backward with both feet at once, causing loud cracklings and rustlings of the dry leaves.

The only actual breeding record for our area is that of Gyldenstolpe (1916), who discovered at Tha Chomphu, May 2, 1914, "a nest containing 4 pure white eggs. The nest was placed in a low tree and rather difficult to detect among the leaves though it was fairly large. The whole structure of the nest somewhat resembled that of our common Song Thrush." Since I took a male with the gonads enlarged, July 16, and another with the organs greatly enlarged, July 29, it is evident that the breeding season covers a number of months, and, in fact, Riley (1938) has shown that, in the more southern districts of Thailand, it runs from March to August.

There is a prenuptial molt of the feathers of the head and neck, and birds in this condition have been taken between April 10 and 19, while examples in postnuptial molt have been collected between August 18 and December 2. The plumage becomes badly worn from the coarse vegetation, and the white portions are usually somewhat soiled by mud and dust.

An adult male had the irides dark brown; the orbital skin slate; the bill black; the feet and toes slaty blue; the claws slaty horn. An adult female differed in having the feet, toes, and claws brownish slate.

This species has the crested crown white; a broad black band from the base of the bill, through the eye, to the posterior ear coverts, where it joins a broad gray nuchal collar; the mantle deep ferruginous, becoming rufous-brown on the rump and upper tail coverts; the remiges brown, edged with rufous; the rectrices dark olivaceous-brown; the underparts white, more or less suffused with gray at the sides of the breast and more or less strongly washed with rufous on the flanks; the thighs olivaceous-brown.

I have seen no specimen from our area that shows approach to *G. l. belangeri.*

GARRULAX PECTORALIS MERIDIONALIS Robinson and Boden Kloss

TENASSERIMESE BLACK-GORGETED LAUGHING-THRUSH

Garrulax pectoralis meridionalis ROBINSON and BODEN KLOSS, Bull. Brit. Orn. Club, vol. 40, 1919, pp. 11–12 (Hat Sanuk, near Ko Lak [Prachuap Khirikhan], southwestern Thailand).

Garrulax pectoralis, GYLDENSTOLPE, Journ. Nat. Hist. Soc. Siam, 1915, p. 164 (listed); Kungl. Svenska Vet.-Akad. Handl., 1916, p. 54 (Khun Tan, Doi Pha Sakaeng); Ibis, 1920, p. 487 ("Throughout northern Siam").

Garrulax pectoralis meridionalis, DE SCHAUENSEE, Proc. Acad. Nat. Sci. Philadelphia, 1929, p. 531 (Doi Suthep); 1934, p. 183 (Doi Suthep, Khun Tan, Doi Chiang Dao).—CHASEN and BODEN KLOSS, Journ. Siam Soc. Nat. Hist. Suppl. 1932, p. 243 (Doi Suthep).—RILEY, U. S. Nat. Mus. Bull. 172, 1938, p. 319 (San Pa Yang, Mae Suya valley, Thattafang, Mae Hong Son).

Garrulax pectoralis meridionalis [*partim*], DEIGNAN, Journ. Siam Soc. Nat. Hist. Suppl., 1931, p. 136 (Doi Suthep); 1936, p. 105 (Doi Suthep).

Although stated by Gyldenstolpe (1920) to be "commonly distributed throughout northern Siam," the black-gorgeted laughing-thrush is, in fact, restricted to the districts west of, and including, the Khun Tan chain. Owing to the risk of confusion with the following species, sight records are almost without value, but, to judge by specimens at hand, it is almost confined to evergreen forest, at whatever altitude. On Doi Suthep it has been taken between 2,700 and 5,000 feet and reaches its greatest abundance at about 3,500 feet, but where there is suitable vegetation it occurs also at much lower elevations.

Outside of the difference in habitat, there is nothing in the account of the habits of the white-crested laughing-thrush that will not apply well enough to the present form, even to the description of its notes.

Nothing certain is known of the breeding season in our area but two specimens of September 30 are in postnuptial molt.

Examples collected by me had the irides maroon or dark red (males) or orange-brown (a female); the eyelids edged bright yellow; the orbital skin plumbeous-blue; the maxilla dark slate with the extreme tip horn; the mandible with the basal half horny white, bluish horn, or pale bluish, the apical half slaty horn or bluish horn, the tip sometimes horny white; the rictus and interior of the mouth yellow; the feet and toes gray-blue or greenish plumbeous; the claws fleshy white.

This bird has the upperparts olivaceous-brown with an ill-defined rufous nuchal collar; the primary coverts usually more or less blackish brown; the rectrices olivaceous-brown, all except the central pair with a broad buff or buffy-white tip and a broad black subapical bar; a narrow postocular streak with the upper half buffy white, the lower half black; the ear coverts silvery gray, usually streaked with black, and bordered below by a narrow black mustachial streak; a conspicuous black gorget, connected on the sides of the neck with both the mustachial streak and the black portion of the postocular streak; the remaining underparts rufous-buff, more or less albescent on the center of the abdomen.

So extraordinary is the resemblance of this species to the following that the points of difference will be dealt with in detail in the description of the black-necklaced laughing-thrush.

I believe that Williamson's collectors took specimens of a black-gorgeted laughing-thrush in the lowlands of Chiang Rai Province; they should be compared with *G. p. robini* Delacour.

GARRULAX MONILEGER FUSCATUS Stuart Baker

Tenasserimese Black-necklaced Laughing-thrush

Garrulax moniliger [*sic*] *fuscata* [*sic*] Stuart Baker, Bull. Brit. Orn. Club, vol. 38, 1918, p. 64 (Tavoy).

Garrulax moniliger [*partim*], Gyldenstolpe, Kungl. Svenska Vet.-Akad. Handl., 1916, p. 54 (Khun Tan).

Garrulax moniliger fuscata [*partim*], Gyldenstolpe, Ibis, 1920, p. 487 ("Throughout the northern parts of Siam" [*partim*]).

Garrulax pectoralis meridionalis [*partim*], Deignan, Journ. Siam Soc. Nat. Hist. Suppl., 1931, p. 136 (Chiang Mai); 1936, p. 105 (Chiang Mai).

Garrulax moniliger fuscata, de Schauensee, Proc. Acad. Nat. Sci. Philadelphia, 1934, p. 184 (Chiang Mai).

Garrulax moniliger bakeri, de Schauensee, Proc. Acad. Nat. Sci. Philadelphia, vol. 87, 1935, pp. 409–410 (Chiang Mai, Northern Thailand).

Garrulax moniliger bakeri, Deignan, Journ. Siam Soc. Nat. Hist. Suppl., 1936, p. 105 (Doi Suthep, error! Chiang Mai).—Riley, U. S. Nat. Mus. Bull. 172, 1938, p. 320 ("Doi Phra Chao" [=Doi Saket?], Huai Mae Sae).

The present race inhabits, in our area, the deciduous forest of the provinces west of, and including, the Khun Tan chain, not ascending the mountains beyond the altitudinal limit of the *pa daeng*. Its range scarcely impinges upon that of *meridionalis*, and the specimen recorded by me (1936) as having been taken on Doi Suthep at 2,700 feet was, in fact, collected on the Chiang Mai plain, where it was almost certainly with a flock of its own kind. I took other examples at Ban Samoeng, Doi Chiang Dao, and Muang Fang.

The flocks of *G. m. fuscatus* sometimes accompany those of *G. l. diardi* through the dry forest; the two species seem to have identical notes and habits.

Specimens in postjuvenal molt have been taken on July 14, 22, and 23; others in postnuptial molt between August 4 and December 24. The plumage becomes astonishingly worn and bleached from contact with the rough leaves among which the bird dwells.

An adult female had the irides creamy yellow; the orbital skin slaty; the bill blackish brown, with the edges of the commissure horny brown and the tip horny white; the interior of the mouth plumbeous; the feet, toes, and claws fleshy white.

This species is smaller in all its parts than *G. p. meridionalis*, but the size difference is not apparent in the field. *G. p. meridionalis* has the ear coverts usually streaked with black and bordered below by a distinct black mustachial streak, while *fuscatus* has them plain silvery gray, with no black line to separate them from the buffy-white throat; *meridionalis* has the primary coverts more or less blackish brown, while *fuscatus* has them olivaceous-brown like all the other coverts; *meridionalis* has the irides red and the eyelids edged with bright yellow, while *fuscatus* has the irides yellow and the eyelids without conspicuous color.

De Schauensee seems to have named *bakeri* as a result of comparing fresh Thai material with "foxed" Burmese and Indian skins. I find much individual variation in my series but no constant character by which they can be separated from *fuscatus*.

GARRULAX MONILEGER SCHAUENSEEI Delacour and Greenway

LAO BLACK-NECKLACED LAUGHING-THRUSH

Garrulax moniliger [*sic*] *schauenseei*, DELACOUR and GREENWAY, Bull. Brit. Orn. Club, vol. 59, 1939, pp. 132–133 (Chiang Khwang, Laos).

Garrulax moniliger, GYLDENSTOLPE, Kungl. Svenska Vet.-Akad. Handl., 1913, p. 20 (Den Chai); Journ. Nat. Hist. Soc. Siam, 1915, p. 164 (listed).

Garrulax moniliger [*partim*], GYLDENSTOLPE, Kungl. Svenska Vet.-Akad. Handl., 1916, p. 54 (Pha Kho).

Garrulax moniliger fuscata [*partim*], GYLDENSTOLPE, Ibis, 1920, p. 487 ("Throughout the northern parts of Siam" [*partim*]).

The Lao black-necklaced garrulax is widely distributed over the lowlands of the provinces east of the Khun Tan range. Eisenhofer sent to Hannover a male from Pha Hing, May 5, 1912, and to Stockholm an unsexed skin from Huai Pu, May 24, 1912; Gyldenstolpe took it at Den Chai and Pha Kho and I found it at Chiang Saen Kao.

Gyldenstolpe records that, near Pha Kho, "a nest containing 3 pale blue eggs was found . . . on the 16th of April 1914 . . . The nest was placed in a low tree within a bamboo-jungle and could easily be reached from the ground."

Gyldenstolpe's birds had the irides yellow or yellowish red; the bill horn color; the feet and toes plumbeous-gray.

G. m. schauenseei differs from *fuscatus* in having the upperparts generally, but especially the nuchal collar, deeper in color; the rectrices tipped with dark buff, not buffy white.

GARRULAX STREPITANS STREPITANS Blyth

TENASSERIMESE BROWN-BREASTED LAUGHING-THRUSH

Garrulax strepitans "Tickell" BLYTH, Journ. Asiat. Soc. Bengal, vol. 24, 1855, p. 268 (mountainous interior of Tenasserim).

Garrulax strepitans, GYLDENSTOLPE, Journ. Nat. Hist. Soc. Siam, 1915, p. 164 (Khun Tan); Ibis, 1920, p. 487 (Khun Tan).—DE SCHAUENSEE, Proc. Acad. Nat. Sci. Philadelphia, 1929, p. 531 (Doi Suthep).—DEIGNAN, Journ. Siam Soc. Nat. Hist. Suppl., 1931, p. 136 (Doi Suthep).—RILEY, U. S. Nat. Mus. Bull. 172, 1938, p. 321 (Khun Tan, Doi Langka, Doi Hua Mot).

Dryonastes strepitans, GYLDENSTOLPE, Kungl. Svenska Vet.-Akad. Handl., 1916, p. 55 (Khun Tan).

Garrulax strepitans strepitans, CHASEN and BODEN KLOSS, Journ. Siam Soc. Nat. Hist. Suppl., 1932, p. 244 (Doi Suthep).—DEIGNAN, Journ. Siam Soc. Nat. Hist. Suppl., 1936, p. 105 (Doi Suthep).—DE SCHAUENSEE, Proc. Acad. Nat. Sci. Philadelphia, 1934, p. 184 (Doi Suthep, Doi Chiang Dao).

This laughing-thrush is rather common in heavy evergreen from 3,300 to 5,500 feet but has until now been found in our provinces only on those few peaks of the Khun Tan and Thanon Thong Chai ranges that are listed above.

If it did not possess in full measure the curiosity characteristic of its genus, the present species would be known only by scratching sounds and conversational calls proceeding from ravines and thickets. Intrusion on its haunts, however, at once produces a clamor like that of species already dealt with, and individual birds climb up the vines for a nearer view before ducking again into the foliage. De Schauensee (1929) records that it has a loud, clear, whistled song of three short notes on the same pitch, followed by a longer note three tones lower.

A male from Doi Suthep, March 23, had the gonads enlarged; another from Doi Ang Ka, April 27, had them greatly enlarged. Specimens in postjuvenal molt have been taken between September 3 and

November 11; adults in postnuptial molt, between August 28 and December 11. Examples collected between February 14 and March 4 are undergoing prenuptial molt of the feathers of head and neck. Spring birds with the rufous-edged remiges of immaturity indicate that postjuvenal molt is incomplete.

A breeding male had the irides crimson-lake; the orbital region dull black; the bill black, with the commissure edged gray at the tip; the feet and toes blackish brown; the claws horny gray.

In the deep shade of the forest, this appears to be a black bird with a conspicuous white patch at each side of the neck. In fact, it has the top of the head and the nape rich brown, suffused with blackish on the front and forecrown; the remaining upperparts dull olivaceous-brown, strongly suffused with ashy on the upper portion of the back; the cheeks and anterior ear coverts black, this color changing to rich chestnut on the remaining ear coverts; on either side of the neck, adjacent to the ear coverts, an indefinite area of pure white that becomes ashy posteriorly; the throat and upper breast wholly covered by a deep chocolate-brown area, which is posteriorly edged with rufous; the remaining underparts dull olivaceous-brown, irregularly and variably suffused with ashy and rufous, especially on the lower breast and the abdomen.

GAMPSORHYNCHUS RUFULUS TORQUATUS Hume

INDO-CHINESE WHITE-HEADED BABBLER

Gampsorhynchus torquatus HUME, Proc. Asiat. Soc. Bengal, No. 5, 1874, p. 107 (no locality given; type specimen collected "on the banks of the Younzaleen below the Pine forests in the Salween district," *fide* Hume, Stray Feathers, vol. 2, 1874, p. 446).

Gampsorhynchus torquatus, GYLDENSTOLPE, Journ. Nat. Hist. Soc. Siam, 1915, p. 165 (Khun Tan); Kungl. Svenska Vet.-Akad. Handl., 1916, p. 56 (Khun Tan).

Gampsorhynchus rufulus torquatus, GYLDENSTOLPE, Ibis, 1920, p. 480 (Khun Tan).—DEIGNAN, Journ. Siam Soc. Nat. Hist. Suppl., 1931, p. 174 (Doi Suthep); 1936, p. 105 (Doi Suthep).—DE SCHAUENSEE, Proc. Acad. Nat. Sci. Philadelphia, 1934, p. 188 (Doi Suthep).—RILEY, U. S. Nat. Mus. Bull. 172, 1938, p. 328 (Khun Tan, Doi Langka).

The white-headed babbler has been found in all our provinces but is common only in districts that have extensive bamboo-brakes in the vicinity of water. In many parts of the lowlands of Nan and on such a hill as Doi Khun Tan it is numerous; on Doi Suthep, on the other hand, where its preferred habitat is almost wholly lacking, it is decidedly rare and local—occurring only between 3,000 and 4,500 feet and compelled to haunt the edges of evergreen clearings and the thickets and low trees along small streams. One may almost say that its occurrence at a given locality is contingent upon the presence of suitable bamboo jungle and that its numbers, in a given area, vary directly with the extent of this type of growth.

The habits of this bird are so much like those of the more arboreal scimitar babblers that it is of considerable interest to find it, on the mountains, constantly associating with *P. o. ochraceiceps* and, in the lowlands of Nan Province, with *P. s. humilis.*

A specimen of March 24 is undergoing prenuptial molt of the feathers of head and neck. Immatures collected by me, May 4 and June 13, are both in the final stages of the postnatal molt, but de Schauensee has taken an example, July 15, in which this molt is much less advanced. All of a series of seven adults shot between May 13 and October 19 are in postnuptial molt.

An adult male had the irides dull yellow; the eyelids white, edged slate; the maxilla horny brown, pale fleshy in the narial region, the culmen dark brown, the extreme tip white; the mandible and interior of the mouth pale fleshy; the tarsi brown; the toes plumbeous-blue; the soles yellow; the claws pale fleshy.

The old adult of either sex has the entire head and neck, the edge of the wing, and some of the upper wing coverts pure white; the remaining upperparts rufescent olivaceous-brown; the long and strongly graduated tail olivaceous-brown, each rectrix tipped with white; at each side of the upper breast a black spot or bar, often produced to form a more or less complete gorget; the remaining underparts rufous-buff, deepest next to the spots or gorget, albescent on the center of the abdomen and the under tail coverts. The juvenile differs from the adult chiefly in having the upperparts, including most of the crown, rufous-brown; the rectrices tipped with grayish rufous instead of white.

The description given above will apply, in general, to any northern specimen, but it is noteworthy that, though the birds of each locality agree well with each other and even, in some cases, with the members of one or more geographically distant populations, they tend, nevertheless, to differ in important degree from their nearest neighbors. It is probable that three or four names will eventually be required to reflect these distinctions; for the present, I leave all Thai aggregates under the oldest available designation.

ACTINODURA EGERTONI RAMSAYI (Walden)

KAREN SPECTACLED BARWING

Actinura Ramsayi WALDEN, Ann. Mag. Nat. Hist., ser. 4, vol. 15, 1875, pp. 402–403 (Karen-ni; type specimen from Kyai-pho-gyi, *fide* Wardlaw Ramsay, *in* The Ornithological Works of Arthur, Ninth Marquis of Tweeddale, 1881, p. 415, footnote).

Actinodura ramsayi ramsayi, ROGERS and DEIGNAN, Proc. Biol. Soc. Washington, 1934, p. 91 (Doi Ang Ka).

This evidently rare form is known as a Thai bird by only two examples from Doi Ang Ka: an adult female collected by me at about 6,000 feet, April 24, 1931, and an adult male taken by Griswold (Asiatic Primate Expedition) at the summit of the mountain, April 1, 1937.

My specimen was one of a pair feeding quietly in a dense thicket of grass, briers, and low shrubs at an old clearing. The bill, feet, and some of the feathers were stained with the purple juice of a berry.

The female had the irides light brown; the bill slaty gray; the feet, toes, and claws horny plumbeous. Griswold has noted that his male had the irides chestnut; the bill, feet, and toes gray.

The adult of either sex has the upperparts dull olivaceous-brown, the feathers of the crown (and especially of the forehead) suffused with rufous, those of the mantle faintly and narrowly barred darker; the primary coverts black; the primaries and outer secondaries with the outer web basally rufous, apically ashy, and barred with black throughout, the inner web black, broadly margined with rufous-buff along the basal half; the inner secondaries regularly barred with ashy olivaceous-brown and black and narrowly tipped with white; the strongly graduated rectrices olivaceous-brown, suffused with rufous toward the base, all narrowly but distinctly barred throughout with blackish and tipped with white; a conspicuous eye ring of white feathers; the sides of the head and neck brownish ashy; the underparts ochraceous-buff, cinerescent on the center of the abdomen.

Specimens from Laos, listed (L'Oiseau et la Revue Française d'Ornithologie, 1940, p. 185) by Delacour and Jabouille as of this race, are really almost exactly intermediate between *ramsayi* and *yunnanensis;* they should perhaps be called *radcliffei.*

HETEROPHASIA PICAOIDES CANA (Riley)

INDO-CHINESE LONG-TAILED SIBIA

Sibia picaoides cana, RILEY, Proc. Biol. Soc. Washington, vol. 42, 1929, p. 166 (Doi Ang Ka, North Thailand).

Sibia picaoides cana, DE SCHAUENSEE, Proc. Acad. Nat. Sci. Philadelphia, 1929, p. 533 (Doi Suthep).

Heterophasia picaoides cana, DEIGNAN, Journ. Siam Soc. Nat. Hist. Suppl., 1931, p. 138 (Doi Suthep).—CHASEN and BODEN KLOSS, Journ. Siam Soc. Nat. Hist. Suppl., 1932, p. 244 (Doi Suthep).—DEIGNAN, Journ. Siam Soc. Nat. Hist. Suppl., 1936, p. 107 (Doi Suthep).—RILEY, U. S. Nat. Mus. Bull. 172, 1938, p. 356 (Doi Ang Ka, Doi Suthep, Doi Langka, Doi Hua Mot).

Heterophasa picaoides cana, DE SCHAUENSEE, Proc. Acad. Nat. Sci. Philadelphia, 1934, p. 194 (Doi Suthep).

The range of the long-tailed sibia in northern Thailand is restricted to those peaks that have evergreen forest at altitudes in excess of 4,500 feet; the species occurs from that elevation to about 7,500 feet (Doi Ang Ka). It is common on Phu Kha but is unknown from Doi

Khun Tan (whose summit is too low) and from Doi Chiang Dao (which lacks suitable forest on the higher slopes).

This bird travels in flocks of as many as 20 individuals, which keep to the tops of the highest trees but attract attention by their constant outcry and incessant flirting of the tail as they run along the branches. De Schauensee observes (1929) that "their notes consist of a series of jumbled whistles and squeaks and a rolling sound like *krrr* reminiscent of the winding of a large clock." Like other sibias, this species congregates at flowering trees but may sometimes also be seen feeding on berries.

A specimen from Doi Ang Ka, April 15, had the testes greatly enlarged. Examples in postnuptial molt have been taken at various localities between November 12 and December 15.

A breeding male had the irides brown-orange; the bill black; the feet and toes dark plumbeous; the claws blackish brown.

The long-tailed sibia has the entire upperparts deep slaty gray (the wings and tail blackish); the outer secondaries with a large white spot at the center of the outer web, forming a conspicuous speculum; the graduated rectrices broadly tipped ashy gray, above and below; the underparts ashy gray, somewhat albescent on the center of the abdomen.

LEIOPTILA CAPISTRATA MELANOLEUCA (Blyth)

TENASSERIMESE BLACK-CAPPED SIBIA

Sibia melanoleuca "Tickell" BLYTH, Journ. Asiat. Soc. Bengal, vol. 28, 1859, p. 413 ("Mountainous interior of the Tenasserim provinces"; type specimen from Mount Muleyit, *fide* Tickell, Journ. Asiat. Soc. Bengal, vol. 28, 1859, p. 451).

Leioptila melanoleuca laeta DE SCHAUENSEE, Proc. Acad. Nat. Sci. Philadelphia, 1929, p. 470 (Doi Suthep, North Thailand).

Leioptila melanoleuca laeta, DE SCHAUENSEE, Proc. Acad. Nat. Philadelphia, 1929, p. 534 (Doi Suthep); 1934, p. 194 (Doi Suthep, Doi Chiang Dao).—DEIGNAN, Journ. Siam Soc. Nat. Hist. Suppl., 1931, p. 138 (Doi Suthep); 1936, p. 107 (Doi Suthep).—RILEY, U. S. Nat. Mus. Bull. 172, 1938, p. 357 (Doi Ang Ka, Doi Suthep, Doi Langka).

Leioptila melanoleuca melanoleuca, CHASEN and BODEN KLOSS, Journ. Siam Soc. Nat. Hist. Suppl., 1932, p. 244 (Doi Suthep).

The present form is very common or even abundant in evergreen forest at elevations in excess of 4,400 feet, on Doi Ang Ka occurring from that altitude up to about 7,500 feet; it reaches its eastern periphery of range on the highest peaks of the Khun Tan chain.

At the summit of Doi Suthep, this delightful bird is rivaled in numbers only by the bulbul, *Pycnonotus f. vividus*, and, thanks to its complete lack of timidity, no species is more easily observed. In small, loose bands (often accompanied by the other sibias) it explores the epiphyte-laden trees, now ascending an upright trunk like a *Yuhina*, again swinging head-downward from the extremity of a branch like a titmouse, in between running lengthwise along a bough, investigating every leaf and blossom and getting its head well dusted with pollen at the same time, all the while opening and closing the flabelliform tail and uttering an endless variety of notes, both sweet and discordant, one of the commonest of which is a curious, shrill *k-r-r-r-r-r-r*. De Schauensee (1929) has perfectly described its "pretty and eerie song" as "six notes, the first four on the same tone, the first about twice as long as the succeeding three, the fifth note one tone lower and the sixth, which is a long note, one tone lower than the fifth"; heard on all sides from the mists that enshroud the peaks after the beginning of the rains, this is one of the most melancholy sounds imaginable.

No specimens in breeding condition were taken, but I collected examples in postjuvenal molt between July 11 and 14 and have seen birds, shot between November 2 and December 6, in postnuptial molt.

The adult has the irides red-brown; the bill, feet, and toes black; the claws dark horny brown.

In life it has the upper half of the head and the entire upperparts glossy black, suffused with ashy on the rump and upper tail coverts; the primaries with a white or whitish area on the inner web at the base (invisible in the closed wing); the central rectrices with narrow pale gray tips, the others with outwardly increasingly broad grayish-white tips (conspicuous from beneath); the point of the chin black; the remaining underparts pure white. After death the mantle soon becomes deep brown.

Ticehurst has discussed (Journ. Bombay Nat. Hist. Soc., 1940, pp. 582–583) the post-mortem color change in this race and the relationship of *laeta* to *melanoleuca*.

I find no reason why *capistrata*, *gracilis*, *melanoleuca*, and *desgodinsi* should be considered otherwise than as conspecific forms.

LEIOPTILA ANNECTENS SATURATA Walden

KAREN CHESTNUT-BACKED SIBIA

L[eioptila] saturata WALDEN, *in* Wardlaw Ramsay, Ibis, 1875, p. 352, footnote (Karen-ni).

Leioptila annectens saturata, DE SCHAUENSEE, Proc. Acad. Nat. Sci. Philadelphia, 1929, p. 535 (Doi Suthep); 1934, p. 195 (Doi Suthep).—DEIGNAN, Journ. Siam Soc. Nat. Hist. Suppl., 1931, p. 138 (Doi Suthep).—CHASEN and BODEN KLOSS, Journ. Siam Soc. Nat. Hist. Suppl., 1932, p. 244 (Doi Suthep).—RILEY, U. S. Nat. Mus. Bull. 172, 1938, p. 357 (Doi Suthep, Doi Langka, Doi Hua Mot).

Leioptila annectans saturata, DEIGNAN, Journ. Siam Soc. Nat. Hist. Suppl., 1936, p. 107 (Doi Suthep).

This sibia is restricted to those high peaks that are clothed with extensive evergreen forest at elevations in excess of 4,600 feet, on

Doi Suthep occurring commonly from that altitude to the summit and on Doi Ang Ka uncommonly from 5,500 to 6,500 feet.

It is a less numerous and rather more silent bird than the black-capped sibia, and it is accordingly less often observed. The habits of the two seem to differ in no important particulars.

All of a series of seven adults collected between July 13 and November 12 are in postnuptial molt.

An adult male had the irides brown; the eyelids plumbeous; the bill black, with the basal half of the mandible yellow; the feet and toes bright yellow; the claws brownish horn.

The adult has the upper half of the head and the anterior half of the back black, the feathers of the center of the nape and upper back with broad ashy-white edges to give a streaked appearance; the scapulars and the lower back, rump, and upper tail coverts chestnut, sometimes more or less maculated with black on the scapulars and the center of the back; the wings black, the greater coverts tipped with chestnut, the remiges narrowly edged along the outer web with ashy-white, the inner secondaries with narrow white tips as well; the rectrices black, with outwardly increasingly broad white tips (conspicuous from beneath); the underparts white, changing to rich buff on the flanks, lower abdomen, and under tail coverts.

This is a poorly defined race, variably intermediate between *davisoni* (of which *eximia* is doubtless a synonym) and *annectens* and recognizable only in series. De Schauensee has a unique example from Doi Suthep (Acad. Nat. Sci. Philadelphia No. 112261) which might well be called true *davisoni*, and it is quite possible that *davisoni* will prove to be the form of Doi Ang Ka, whence no skins are yet known; on the other hand, a *worn* specimen from Doi Hua Mot could easily be considered *annectens*. A series of six from Doi Pha Hom Pok, in good plumage, are consistently paler than *saturata* and they alone may perhaps properly be placed with the following race.

LEIOPTILA ANNECTENS ANNECTENS Blyth

INDIAN CHESTNUT-BACKED SIBIA

L[eioptila] annectans [*sic*] BLYTH, Journ. Asiat. Soc. Bengal, vol. 16, 1847, p. 450 (Darjiling).

De Schauensee's collectors, between January 22 and February 18, 1938, took five males and one female on Doi Pha Hom Pok, 6,000 to 6,400 feet. This subspecies is not likely to occur at any other Thai locality.

In series, *annectens* differs from *saturata* in having the chestnut of the scapulars, lower back, rump, and upper tail coverts somewhat paler.

SIVA STRIGULA CASTANICAUDA Hume

TENASSERIMESE CHESTNUT-TAILED SIVA

Siva castanicauda HUME, Stray Feathers, vol. 5, 1877, p. 100 (Mount Muleyit, Tenasserim).

Siva strigula castanicauda, ROGERS and DEIGNAN, Proc. Biol. Soc. Washington, 1934, p. 91 (Doi Ang Ka).—RILEY, U. S. Nat. Mus. Bull. 172, 1938, p. 358 (Doi Ang Ka).

Siva strigula castaneicauda, GREENWAY, Bull. Mus. Comp. Zool., 1940, p. 173 (Doi Ang Ka).

This siva is rather common in the low trees which surround the sphagnum bog at the summit of Doi Ang Ka (8,400 feet, once at 8,000 feet), but it has not yet been recorded from any other locality in our provinces.

I found it in small flocks in the almost impenetrable thickets of arboreous rhododendrons, quietly feeding and acting much like the blue-winged siva.

Greenway (*loc. cit.*) lists a juvenile taken sometime between March 22 and 31. An example of December 5 has not quite completed postnuptial molt.

An adult male had the irides brown; the maxilla blackish brown; the mandible dark brown, with the basal half fleshy; the tarsi horny plumbeous; the toes slaty; the claws brown.

It has the crown dull rufous-orange, suffused with olivaceous, gradually changing at the nape to the grayish olive of the mantle; the primary coverts black; the remiges black, the outer primaries with the outer web narrowly edged bright yellow, the inner ones similarly edged but bright orange toward the base, the outer secondaries edged bright orange and tipped with white, the inner ones similarly tipped but without orange and with the basal half of the outer web ashy gray; the two central pairs of rectrices largely chestnut, otherwise black, and tipped with yellowish white, the others black with an outwardly increasingly broad yellow tip (the outermost pairs with the outer web also largely bright yellow); the chin bright yellow; the throat white, with crescent-shaped cross bars formed by the narrow black tips and exposed dark bases of the feathers; an indistinct black mustachial streak separating the grayish-olive ear coverts from the chin and throat; the remaining underparts yellow, suffused with olivaceous on the breast and flanks.

SIVA CYANOUROPTERA SORDIDA Hume

TENASSERIMESE BLUE-WINGED SIVA

Siva sordida HUME, Stray Feathers, vol. 5, 1877, pp. 104–105 (Mount Muleyit, Tenasserim).

Siva cyanuroptera oatesi, DE SCHAUENSEE, Proc. Acad. Nat. Sci. Philadelphia, 1929, p. 535 (Doi Suthep); 1934, p. 196 (Doi Suthep, Doi Chiang Dao).

Siva cyanouroptera oatesi, DEIGNAN, Journ. Siam Soc. Nat. Hist. Suppl., 1931, p. 138 (Doi Suthep); 1936, p. 107 (Doi Suthep).—CHASEN and BODEN KLOSS, Journ. Siam Soc. Nat. Hist. Suppl., 1932, p. 245 (Doi Suthep).

Examples which are best placed under this name have been collected on Doi Ang Ka (4,900 feet), Doi Suthep (4,600 to 5,500 feet), and Doi Chiang Dao (4,500 to 6,900 feet).

It is an apparently rare bird in Thailand, haunting the more open evergreen and the hill-forest of oak and chestnut, singly or in pairs, but often in company with other small arboreal babblers. It is a very silent form and probably frequently escapes notice through its quiet ways.

A specimen just beginning postjuvenal molt was taken on Doi Suthep, July 13, 1935.

A male from Doi Ang Ka had the irides creamy white; the maxilla horny black, with the narial region horny brown and the edges of the commissure horny gray; the mandible with the apical half horny gray, the rest horny white; the feet, toes, and claws horny gray-brown.

The adult (in our provinces) has the forehead, crown, and nape dull brown, more or less strongly washed with violet-blue (especially at the sides), the front sometimes with faint indications of dark shaft streaks; the mantle dull olivaceous-brown, suffused with fulvous on the rump and upper tail coverts (this color sometimes invading the back); the primaries black, with the outer web deep blue; the secondaries black, the outermost with the outer web narrowly edged violet-ashy, the following with the outer web narrowly edged violet-blue, the innermost with the entire outer web brownish ashy; the central pair of the graduated, truncated rectrices wholly deep blue, the following pairs with the inner web blackish and the outer web deep blue, the three outermost pairs with an increasing amount of white on the inner web until the shortest has the inner web wholly white (and the outer web black); a narrow violet-white supercilium; the ear coverts and sides of the neck violet-ashy; the entire underparts white (in the spring months, often sullied from contact with burned trees). The juvenile differs from the adult chiefly in having the forehead, crown, and nape uniform dull brown.

SIVA CYANOUROPTERA OATESI Harington

SHAN BLUE-WINGED SIVA

Siva cyanuroptera oatesi HARINGTON, Bull. Brit. Orn. Club, vol. 33, 1913, p. 62 (Mount Byingyi, Loilong State, Southern Shan States).

Siva cyanouroptera oatesi, RILEY, U. S. Nat. Mus. Bull. 172, 1938, p. 358 (Doi Hua Mot, Doi Langka).

A form of the blue-winged siva, which may most conveniently be called *oatesi*, has been taken on Doi Hua Mot, Doi Langka, and Doi Pha Hom Pok (6,400 feet). It seems to be rather common on these more northern peaks, for Smith collected six examples on Langka between November 10 and 17, 1930, while de Schauensee's men shot ten on Pha Hom Pok between February 6 and 24, 1938.

Smith took a specimen in postjuvenal molt on Doi Hua Mot, August 30, 1931; his November birds from Langka are all adults in postnuptial molt.

From the preceding race this one differs (in our provinces) in having the front, crown, and nape more strongly suffused with violet-blue (this color so deep immediately above the supercilium as to form a definite stripe), the forehead and forecrown with ill-defined blackish shaft streaks; the whole mantle strongly suffused with fulvous; the white underparts more or less suffused everywhere (except on the lower belly and the under coverts of wings and tail) with violet-ashy.

SIVA CYANOUROPTERA WINGATEI Ogilvie Grant

YUNNANESE BLUE-WINGED SIVA

Siva wingatei OGILVIE GRANT, Bull. Brit. Orn. Club, vol. 10, 1900, p. 38 (Yunnan-fu, Yunnan).

Three specimens taken by me at high elevations on Phu Kha, April 9 and 10, 1936, are in badly worn and somewhat discolored plumage but seem to be inseparable from *S. c. wingatei*.

A bird of April 9 had the ovaries greatly enlarged.

From the examples that I have called *oatesi* these differ in having the supercilium edged above by a blue-washed black stripe and the feathers of front and forecrown with clearly defined black shaft streaks; the mantle olivaceous-brown, with rather less fulvous suffusion; the suffusion over the underparts somewhat stronger and more vinaceous-ashy.

For a discussion of the difficulties attendant upon subspecific determination of northern Thai populations of the blue-winged siva, *cf.* Deignan, Notulae Naturae Acad. Nat. Sci. Philadelphia, No. 100, May 1942.

SIVA CASTANICEPS STRIATA (Blyth)

TENASSERIMESE STRIATED SIVA

Ixulus striatus BLYTH, Journ. Asiat. Soc. Bengal, vol. 28, 1859, pp. 413–414 ("Mountainous interior of the Tenasserim provinces"; type specimen "obtained . . . near Tretoungplee, a place at an elevation of about 3,000 feet, about 10 miles W. N. W. from the Peak of Mooleyit," *fide* Hume, Stray Feathers, vol. 6, 1878, p. 374).

Staphidia striata striata, DE SCHAUENSEE, Proc. Acad. Nat. Sci. Philadelphia, 1929, p. 535 (Doi Suthep); 1934, p. 195 (Doi Suthep).—CHASEN and BODEN KLOSS, Journ. Siam Soc. Nat. Hist. Suppl., 1932, p. 245 (Doi Suthep).—RILEY, U. S. Nat. Mus. Bull. 172, 1938, p. 357 (Khun Tan, Doi Langka).

Staphida striata striata, DEIGNAN, Journ. Siam Soc. Nat. Hist. Suppl., 1931, p. 138 (Doi Suthep) ; 1936, p. 107 (Doi Suthep).

The present race of the striated siva is restricted, within our area, to the mountains west of (and including) the Khun Tan chain, occurring rather commonly from 4,500 to 5,500 feet, and rarely down to 3,300 feet. In addition to the localities listed above, it is known from Doi Ang Ka and Doi Chiang Dao.

This little bird is seen in flocks, often accompanied by other small arboreal babblers, which, constantly chattering, sweep rapidly through the tops of the bushes and the lower branches of the trees, whether at the edge of the evergreen or in the open hill-forest. De Schauensee (1929) records having seen a band of at least 50 feeding among the flowers of a tree of the genus *Cassia* at the summit of Doi Suthep.

De Schauensee took two juveniles on Doi Suthep, July 12. I have examples in postnuptial molt, collected between June 15 and November 19.

My specimens had the irides brown; the bill horny brown; the feet and toes dark fleshy or orange-flesh; the claws orange-horn.

The adult has the forehead and crest dark grayish brown, each feather with a grayish-white shaft streak; the mantle olivaceous-brown, with each feather (except on the rump and upper tail coverts) similarly streaked; the remiges and graduated rectrices deep brown, the latter(except the central pair) with outwardly increasingly broad white tips; an indistinct superciliary area ashy-gray, this color suffusing the occiput beneath the crest; the ear coverts dull chestnut (with white shaft streaks), this color often invading the nape to form an indistinct collar; the entire underparts grayish white, somewhat sullied with gray on the breast and flanks.

SIVA CASTANICEPS TORQUEOLA Swinhoe

CHINESE STRIATED SIVA

Siva torqueola SWINHOE, Ann. Mag. Nat. Hist., ser. 4, vol. 5, 1870, pp. 174–175 (Tingchow mountains, about 100 miles from Amoy, Fuhkien).

The Chinese form of the striated siva is known, in Thailand, only from Phu Kha, where, in April 1936, I found it common between 4,000 and 5,000 feet and collected four specimens.

Examples with the gonads enlarged were taken April 4 and a juvenile, which has all but finished postnatal molt, April 11.

From *striata* this race differs in having the crest a purer gray; the mantle darker and suffused with rufous; the ear coverts and well-marked nuchal collar rich chestnut.

The population of Phu Kha tends to be rather smaller than *torqueola* of Fuhkien but not sufficiently so to justify subspecific separation.

YUHINA FLAVICOLLIS ROGERSI Deignan

PHU KHA FERRUGINOUS-COLLARED YUHINA

Yuhina flavicollis rogersi DEIGNAN, Proc. Biol. Soc. Washington, vol. 50, 1937, pp. 217–218 (Phu Kha, Nan Province, North Thailand).

This bird is rather common in the humid evergreen between 5,000 and 5,500 feet (the summit) on Phu Kha, but it is not yet known from any other locality.

In forest so dark that only scattered ferns grew beneath the trees, I found the yuhina usually perched quietly upon some high branch but occasionally fluttering up a mossy trunk in the manner of *Alcippe castaneceps exul*. In that remote upland jungle, where probably the report of a gun had never yet been heard and where the smaller creatures had no knowledge of man, it proved to be a bird almost without fear.

Specimens taken on April 10 and 11 had the gonads highly active.

It has the forehead and crest dark brown; the ear coverts and the occiput, beneath the crest, gray-brown; a distinct nuchal collar, beginning at the sides of the neck behind the ear coverts, ferruginous; the remaining upperparts olivaceous-brown; an incomplete eye ring of pure white feathers; the lores and a narrow mustachial streak, extending to the ferruginous collar, black; the chin, throat, and center of the breast and abdomen, white; the sides of the breast olivaceous-brown with white streaks; the flanks similar but gradually changing to pale grayish fulvous on the under tail coverts.

ERPORNIS ZANTHOLEUCA ZANTHOLEUCA Hodgson

INDIAN HERPORNIS

Erp[*ornis*] *zantholeuca* HODGSON, *in* Blyth, Journ. Asiat. Soc. Bengal, vol. 13, 1844, p. 380 (Nepal).

Herpornis xantholeuca, GYLDENSTOLPE, Kungl. Svenska Vet.-Akad. Handl., 1916, p. 62 (Khun Tan).

Herpornis xantholeuca tyrannulus, GYLDENSTOLPE, Ibis, 1920, p. 479 ("Northern Siam").

Erpornis zantholeuca tyrannula, DEIGNAN, Journ. Siam Soc. Nat. Hist. Suppl., 1931, p. 138 (Doi Suthep).

Erpornis xantholeuca xantholeuca, DE SCHAUENSEE, Proc. Acad. Nat. Sci. Philadelphia, 1934, p. 196 (Khun Tan).

Erpornis zantholeuca zantholeuca, DEIGNAN, Journ. Siam. Soc. Nat. Hist. Suppl., 1936, p. 107 (Doi Suthep).—RILEY, U. S. Nat. Mus. Bull. 172, 1938, p. 359 (Doi Langka, Doi Hua Mot, Khun Tan).

The herpornis is common in the more open evergreen and the mixed-deciduous forest throughout our provinces. On Doi Ang Ka and Doi Khun Tan it has been recorded at 3,500 feet and on Doi Suthep, from 2,700 to 4,000 feet (rarely as low as 2,100 feet); in Phrae and Nan

Provinces, where suitable jungle grows at feeble elevations, it occurs at the very bases of the hills.

This is a wholly arboreal form that, in flocks, large or small, and often accompanied by tits and nuthatches, travels rapidly along the edges of clearings and forest tracks, busily investigating the leaves and cracks in the bark or even hanging head-downward from the ends of twigs, all the while uttering notes not unlike those of a titmouse.

A specimen with the gonads enlarged was taken on April 18, but another with them greatly enlarged was collected as early as March 23. Birds in full juvenal plumage were found on April 25 and May 10. Postnuptial molt is shown in examples of August 27 and 29 and postjuvenal molt in one of September 9.

An adult female had the irides brown; the maxilla horn, with the edges of the commissure fleshy; the mandible fleshy; the interior of the mouth bright yellow; the feet, toes, and claws fleshy.

The adult of either sex has the entire upperparts, including the crest, golden-olive, the remiges and rectrices narrowly margined with yellow along the inner web; the lores, narrow eye ring, ear coverts, and underparts white, more or less strongly suffused with ashy; the under coverts of wings and tail yellow. The juvenile is similar but has the nape and mantle strongly suffused with tawny.

I can distinguish only four continental races of this species: *tyrannula*, *zantholeuca*, *interposita*, and *canescens*, of which only the last may be known definitely by color characters. Among the other three we find, from north to south, a gradual increase in length of wing and heaviness of bill, with *tyrannula* and *interposita* representing the extreme forms and *zantholeuca* the intermediate. *E. z. sordida* (paratypes examined), described from worn specimens (March, May), seems to be quite inseparable from *zantholeuca*.

ALCIPPE CASTANECEPS EXUL Delacour

INDO-CHINESE CHESTNUT-CAPPED BABBLER

Alcippe castaneiceps exul DELACOUR, L'Oiseau et la Revue Française d'Ornithologie, new ser., vol. 2, No. 3, 1932, pp. 427–428 (Phu Kong Ntoul, Bolovens plateau, Bas-Laos).

Pseudominla castaneiceps castaneiceps, DE SCHAUENSEE, Proc. Acad. Nat. Sci. Philadelphia, 1934, p. 194 (Doi Suthep).—DEIGNAN, Journ. Siam Soc. Nat. Hist. Suppl., 1936, p. 107 (Doi Suthep).

Pseudominla castaneceps castaneceps, RILEY, U. S. Nat. Mus. Bull. 172, 1938, p. 356 (Doi Ang Ka, Doi Langka, Doi Hua Mot).

Pseudominla castaneiceps exsul, GREENWAY, Bull. Mus. Comp. Zool., 1940, p. 173 (Doi Ang Ka).

This diminutive babbler probably occurs on all the northern peaks whose slopes are heavily forested above an elevation of 5,000 feet.

On Doi Ang Ka it is very common from about 5,000 to 6,800 feet, somewhat less so thence to the summit; on Doi Suthep it has been recorded but twice (at 5,500 feet): February 6, 1933, and February 6, 1936; east of the Khun Tan range it is known only from Phu Kha, where it is rather rare.

On Ang Ka Luang it is one of the most conspicuous forms of the dense evergreen and may be seen in large flocks (usually accompanied by other small timaliine species). It has the titlike habit of fluttering jerkily up the trunks of the larger trees, uttering a ceaseless conversational chippering.

An example with the gonads enlarged was taken on Doi Ang Ka, April 29; another, which has virtually completed the postnatal molt, on Doi Langka, April 24. The only specimen seen in postnuptial molt was collected on Doi Hua Mot, August 17.

A breeding male had the irides brown; the maxilla black; the mandible with the apical half plumbeous, otherwise pale yellowish; the rictus and interior of the mouth bright yellow; the feet and toes horny yellow; the claws yellowish horn. An adult female had the irides maroon; the maxilla dark brown; the mandible with the apical half brown, then fleshy white, and yellow at the base; the rictus and interior of the mouth bright yellow; the feet, toes, and soles dull yellow; the claws horny.

This species has the forehead, crown, and nape chestnut, the feathers of the forehead with broad white centers, those of the crown and nape with rufous-white shaft streaks; the mantle olive, more or less suffused with rufous; the primary coverts black; the outermost primaries with the outer web grayish white, the others with the outer web largely orange-rufous; the exposed portions of the wing otherwise olive; the tail dark gray, washed with olive; a white supercilium; the ear coverts silvery white, bordered above by a broad, black postocular streak, below by a narrow, black mustachial streak; the underparts white, heavily washed on the sides of the neck and breast and along the flanks with olivaceous-buff.

Without recently collected material of *castaneceps*, it is really impossible to decide whether *exul* is a valid form. Old skins of the former differ from fresh skins of the latter in having the underparts washed with ochraceous-buff, not olivaceous-buff, so, at least for the present, I accept Delacour's race. Since birds taken east and west of the Khun Tan chain are inseparable, one may assume that *exul*, if distinct, ranges from Laos to Tenasserim.

ALCIPPE RUFOGULARIS MAJOR (Stuart Baker)

MOYEN-LAOS RUFOUS-THROATED BABBLER

Schoeniparus rufigularis major STUART BAKER, Bull. Brit. Orn. Club, vol. 41, 1920, p. 11 (Pak Mat, "Siam" [=Pak Mat, Moyen-Laos]).

S[choeniparus] r[ufogularis] major [partim], DE SCHAUENSEE, Proc. Acad. Nat. Sci. Philadelphia, 1938, p. 28 (Ban Huai Som).

In the moist evergreen of the little Huai Som valley, at the eastern base of the Nan-Phrae border-range, this bird is apparently not uncommon, and I collected three males there, March 28 and 29, 1937.

It is a terrestrial feeder, which usually stays beneath the densest thickets but, occasionally, may come out onto some narrow trail whence, at the first alarm, it takes refuge again in the undergrowth. At least when disturbed, it utters a continual *chur-r-r*, *chur-r-r*, *chur-r-r*.

All my specimens had the gonads greatly enlarged.

It has the crown, nape, and uppermost back dull chestnut-rufous, this area completely bordered by a narrow black band (which tends to be disconnected on the upper back); the remaining upperparts rufous-brown, washed with olivaceous on the mantle; a narrow white supercilium below the black coronal border; the ear coverts olivaceous-brown; the sides of the neck ferruginous, this area joined with a deep chestnut-rufous gorget across the lower threat (often broken at the center); the chin and the rest of the throat pure white; the breast olivaceous-gray; the flanks olivaceous-brown; the abdomen white; the under tail coverts pale ferruginous.

The birds of Ban Huai Som, taken about 56 miles west of Pak Mat, are undoubtedly *major*. On the other hand, a pair from Ban Nam Puat, in the French Enclave, about 90 miles northwest of Pak Mat, erroneously identified by me, and also by de Schauensee (*loc. cit.*), as *major*, are probably of the race *blanchardi*. The latter is described (Bull. Brit. Orn. Club, vol. 48, 1928, p. 132) as differing from *major* "in its smaller size, more olivaceous, less yellowish underparts, browner breast, dull brown under tail-coverts." The Nam Puat specimens have, in fact, the underparts less olivaceous, more rufous, than *major* and I strongly suspect that a *lapsus calami* has caused the characters to be reversed in the original description. *A. r. blanchardi*, as here understood, may be known from *major* by its smaller size; deeper color of the upperparts, gorget, and under tail coverts; paler brown ear coverts; and more rufous flanks.

ALCIPPE POIOICEPHALA HARINGTONIAE Hartert

SHAN GRAY-EYED QUAKER BABBLER

Alcippe haringtoniae HARTERT, Bull. Brit. Orn. Club. vol. 25, 1909, p. 10 (Bhamo. Upper Burma).

Alcippe phayrei, GYLDENSTOLPE, Kungl. Svenska Vet.-Akad. Handl., 1913, p. 21 (Khao Phlung).

Alcippe phaeocephala magnirostris, GYLDENSTOLPE, Kungl. Svenska Vet.-Akad. Handl., 1936, p. 58 (Doi Pha Sakaeng); Ibis, 1920, p. 482 (Doi Pha Sakaeng, Khao Phlung).

Alcippe sp., GYLDENSTOLPE, Kungl. Svenska Vet.-Akad. Handl., 1916, p. 59 (Doi Pha Sakaeng).

Alcippe poioicephala harringtoniae, DE SCHAUENSEE, Proc. Acad. Nat. Sci. Philadelphia, 1929, p. 533 (Chiang Saen).

Alcippe poioicephala magnirostris, DE SCHAUENSEE, Proc. Acad. Nat. Sci. Philadelphia, 1934, p. 193 (Chiang Dao, Khun Tan).

Alcippe poioicephala karenni, DEIGNAN, Journ. Siam Soc. Nat. Hist. Suppl., 1936, p. 107 (Doi Suthep).

Alcippe poioicephala haringtoniae, RILEY, U. S. Nat. Mus. Bull. 172, 1938, p. 352 (Khun Tan).

Alcippe poiocephala haringtoniae, GREENWAY, Bull. Mus. Comp. Zool., 1940, p. 172 (Chiang Dao, Doi Nang Kaeo).

This quaker babbler is found only at those localities where evergreen forest grows below 3,500 feet. It is very common on the plains and lower hills of the districts north and east of the Khun Tan chain and at such places as Samoeng and Chiang Dao; on Doi Suthep, whose lower slopes are covered with deciduous jungle, it is necessarily very rare (three records) and restricted to the lowest fringe of the evergreen (3,300 to 3,500 feet).

The habits of the present species differ in no important way from those of the following one, and just where their altitudinal limits of range come together the two forms may sometimes be seen in the same flock.

An example with the gonads greatly enlarged was taken on Doi Suthep, 3,500 feet, March 12, 1932. At other localities have been collected a bird completing postnatal molt, April 24; one in full juvenal plumage, May 10; and a long series of adults in postnuptial molt, between June 17 and December 5. Gyldenstolpe's "*Alcippe* sp." from Doi Pha Sakaeng, July 17, 1914, has been examined and found to be a specimen of this form in postjuvenal molt.

A breeding male had the irides gray; the maxilla horny brown; the mandible horny yellow; the feet and toes fleshy yellow; the claws horn.

Our two species of quaker babbler are extraordinarily similar but *A. p. haringtoniae* may readily be known by its not having a white eye ring. It differs also in somewhat greater size and in having the crown and nape brownish gray, the sides of the head and neck brownish buff.

ALCIPPE MORRISONIA LAOTIANA Delacour

LAO RED-EYED QUAKER BABBLER

Alcippe nipalensis laotianus DELACOUR, Bull. Brit. Orn. Club, vol. 47, 1926, p. 19 (Chiang Khwang, Laos).

Alcippe nepalensis fratercula, DE SCHAUENSEE, Proc. Acad. Nat. Sci. Philadelphia, 1929, p. 533 (Doi Suthep); 1934, p. 193 (Doi Suthep, Doi Chiang Dao).

Alcippe nipalensis fratercula, DEIGNAN, Journ. Siam Soc. Nat. Hist. Suppl., 1931, p. 138 (Doi Suthep).—CHASEN and BODEN KLOSS, Journ. Siam Soc. Nat. Hist. Suppl., 1932, p. 244 (Doi Suthep).—DEIGNAN, Journ. Siam Soc. Nat. Hist.

Suppl., 1936, p. 107 (Doi Suthep).—RILEY, U. S. Nat. Mus. Bull. 172, 1938, p. 351 (Doi Ang Ka, Doi Khun Tan, Doi Langka, Doi Hua Mot).

Alcippe fratercula fratercula, GREENWAY, Bull. Mus. Comp. Zool., 1940, p. 172 (Doi Ang Ka, Doi Nang Kaeo).

The red-eyed quaker babbler is very common or even abundant on all the higher peaks, including Phu Kha, ranging through the evergreen from 3,500 to 8,000 feet.

The large flocks of this fearless bird, usually accompanied by other small babblers and, sometimes, by bulbuls, nuthatches, and tits as well, swarm through the undergrowth and lower trees with a continual conversational chatter. It frequently follows the forest tracks and, thanks to its consuming curiosity, is one of the most easily observed members of the family.

A specimen with the gonads enlarged was taken on Phu Kha, April 13. I collected juveniles, April 16 and May 2, and adults in postnuptial molt between July 14 and November 28.

An adult male had the irides red-brown; the bill horny brown; the feet, toes, and claws horny brown. De Schauensee's birds had the irides red; the bill gray, tinged pink at the base of the mandible; the feet, toes, and claws fleshy brown or fleshy yellow.

This form, in fresh plumage, has the crown, nape, uppermost back, and sides of the head and neck sooty gray, with a more or less distinct dull black streak from above each eye to the upper back; the remaining upperparts olivaceous-brown; a ring of grayish-white feathers around the eye (obvious in life); the entire underparts buff.

I follow Mayr (Ibis, 1941, p. 73) in the assumption that Rippon's *fratercula* is the rather larger, more northern race, in which case the name *laotiana* becomes available for the birds of our area.

CHRYSOMMA SINENSE SINENSE (Gmelin)

CHINESE YELLOW-EYED BABBLER

[*Parus*] *sinensis* GMELIN, Systema naturae, vol. 1, pt. 2, 1789, p. 1012 (China; type locality restricted to Kwangtung, by Stresemann and Heinrich, Mitt. Zool. Mus. Berlin, vol. 24, 1940, p. 205).

Pyctoris sinensis major, DE SCHAUENSEE, Proc. Acad. Nat. Sci. Philadelphia, 1928, p. 566 (Chiang Mai).

Chrysomma sinensis sinensis, DEIGNAN, Journ. Siam. Soc. Nat. Hist. Suppl., 1931, p. 136 (Chiang Mai); 1936, p. 106 (Chiang Mai).

Chrysomma sinensis major, DE SCHAUENSEE, Proc. Acad. Nat. Sci. Philadelphia, 1934, p. 188 (Chiang Mai).

This babbler has been found only at Muang Fang and Chiang Mai and on Doi Ang Ka at about 4,300 feet (in the brush of the cleared valley below Pha Mon).

At Chiang Mai and Muang Fang I met with it in parties of as many as a dozen individuals, in exactly the same places as, and almost always in company with, the commoner *Timalia p. intermedia*.

Specimens with the gonads enlarged were taken at Chiang Mai, May 3, and on Doi Ang Ka, September 8. An example from Muang Fang, July 15, is in juvenal dress.

An adult female of July 6 had the irides golden-orange; the eye ring red-orange; the orbital region bright yellow; the bill black, with the narial region yellow; the rictus and skin of the chin yellow; the interior of the mouth black; the feet and toes bright yellow; the claws horny flesh. The interior of the mouth is said to be yellow in winter.

The yellow-eyed babbler has the entire upperparts rufous-brown; the exposed portions of the remiges cinnamon; the lores and a short, indistinct supercilium white; the underparts white, suffused with buffy on the lower breast, abdomen, flanks, and under tail coverts and with cinnamon-buff on the thighs.

PELLORNEUM RUFICEPS VIVIDUM La Touche

INDO-CHINESE STREAKED-BREASTED BABBLER

Pellorneum nipalense vividum LA TOUCHE, Bull. Brit. Orn. Club, vol. 42, 1921, p. 17 (Hokow, southeastern Yunnan).

Pellorneum subochraceum, GYLDENSTOLPE, Kungl. Svenska Vet.-Akad. Handl., 1913, p. 20 (["Vang Nun," Den Chai]); 1916, p. 56 (Pha Kho, Khun Tan, Pang Hua Phong); Journ. Nat. Hist. Soc. Siam, 1915, p. 165 (listed).

Pellorneum ruficeps subochraceum [*partim*], GYLDENSTOLPE, Ibis, 1920, p. 481 ("Throughout the whole country" [*partim*]).—DE SCHAUENSEE, Proc. Acad. Nat. Sci. Philadelphia, 1934, p. 189 (Chiang Mai, Doi Suthep).

Pellorneum ruficeps subochraceum, DE SCHAUENSEE, Proc. Acad. Nat. Sci. Philadelphia, 1929, p. 532 (Chiang Saen).—DEIGNAN, Journ. Siam Soc. Nat. Hist. Suppl., 1931, p. 137 (Chiang Mai, Doi Suthep); 1936, p. 106 (Chiang Mai, Doi Suthep).

Pellorneum ruficeps vividum, RILEY, U. S. Nat. Mus. Bull. 172, 1938, p. 330 (Khun Tan, Ban Nam Khian).

The spotted babbler is fairly common in every part of our area, chiefly at low elevations but, where the vegetation is suitable, occurring also on the mountains to about 5,000 feet. On the plains, it is a characteristic inhabitant of the bamboo, whether in pure stands or mixed with deciduous trees; on the hills, it dwells both in bamboo and in the high grass of the open forest of oak and pine. I have never found it in true evergreen jungle at any locality.

This bird, singly or in pairs, keeps to the dense lower portions of the bamboo clumps or to the deep shade of the ground beneath them, only rarely venturing onto an open trail and thence, at the first alarm, scuttling again into the nearest cover. During the hot months of spring its sweet song, delivered from some concealed perch in the heart of the canes, is repeated again and again, asking: *Where have' you'' been?* In life, the pure white feathers of the throat are always partially erected, much like those of *Criniger*.

An example with the gonads greatly enlarged was taken by Gyldenstolpe at an unspecified locality, March 5, 1912. I collected specimens in postjuvenal molt between July 3 and August 27 and others in postnuptial molt between July 3 and December 2.

An adult male had the irides red; the maxilla horny brown, horn at the tip; the mandible horn, with the basal half yellow; the feet and toes light brownish yellow; the claws horny yellow. An adult female from Doi Suthep, 2,400 feet, had the irides crimson-lake; the maxilla horny brown; the mandible with the basal half yellowish fleshy, the apical half plumbeous-blue; the feet, toes, and claws fleshy.

The adult has the crown and nape dull chestnut-rufous; the remaining upperparts olivaceous-brown; a conspicuous supercilium pale buffy, posteriorly mixed with olivaceous-brown; the ear coverts light brown, indistinctly edged above and below by blackish streaks; the throat immaculate white; the remaining underparts pale buffy (albescent on the center of the abdomen), on the breast and sides of the body more or less heavily streaked with blackish brown or dark olivaceous-brown; the under tail coverts with dark or light olivaceous-brown centers. The juvenile, which is unstreaked below, is colored much like the adult of *P. t. ochraceum;* within a short time, however, it can be distinguished from older birds only by the unmarked under tail coverts.

PELLORNEUM ALBIVENTRE CINNAMOMEUM (Rippon)

INDO-CHINESE SPOTTED-THROATED BABBLER

Drymocataphus cinnamomeus RIPPON, Bull. Brit. Orn. Club, vol. 11, 1900, p. 12 (Loi Mai, Southern Shan States).

Pellorneum ignotum cinnamomeum, DE SCHAUENSEE, Proc. Acad. Nat. Sci. Philadelphia, 1934, pp. 3, 189 (Doi Chiang Dao).—DEIGNAN, Journ. Siam Soc. Nat. Hist. Suppl., 1936, p. 106 (Doi Suthep).

This babbler, which is evidently one of our rarest forms, is known from Thailand by only two specimens: A female taken by me on Doi Suthep, 5,500 feet, September 10, 1931 (now in the Princeton Museum of Zoology), and a female collected by de Schauensee on Doi Chiang Dao, 5,000 feet, January 18, 1933. Another was shot by me on Doi Suthep, 5,300 feet, sometime prior to September 10, 1931, but was too nearly destroyed for preservation; despite constant search for the species during subsequent years, it was never met with again.

It seems to occur only in extensive stands of lalang, keeping to the ground and not likely to be noted unless it darts across a path, looking exactly like a mouse.

My specimen had the irides brownish red; the maxilla dark horny brown; the mandible white; the tarsi dusky flesh; the toes fleshy; the claws horny flesh.

583136—45——25

The adult has the entire upperparts dark olivaceous-brown (slightly more rufous on the wings and tail), the feathers of the forehead and crown narrowly edged darker to give a scaly appearance; the lores and superciliary region ashy; the ear coverts ashy brown; the chin and throat grayish white, the feathers tipped with small sagittate marks; the remaining underparts rufous-buff, albescent on the center of the abdomen.

PELLORNEUM TICKELLI OCHRACEUM (Kinnear)

LAO BUFF-BREASTED BABBLER

Drymocataphus tickelli ochraceus KINNEAR, Bull. Brit. Orn. Club, vol. 55, 1934, p. 53. New name for *Drymocataphus tickelli olivaceus* Kinnear, 1924 (Bao Ha, Tongking), not *P[ellorneum] olivaceum* Jerdon, 1839, nor *Mixornis olivaceus* Tickell, 1859 [=*Pellorneum tickelli* Blyth 1859].

Drymocataphus tickelli, GYLDENSTOLPE, Kungl. Svenska Vet.-Akad. Handl., 1916, p. 58 (Pha Kho).

Drymocataphus tickelli tickelli [*partim*], GYLDENSTOLPE, Ibis, 1920, p. 481 (Pha Kho).

Pellorneum tickelli (apparently *P. t. olivaceum*), ROGERS and DEIGNAN, Proc. Biol. Soc. Washington, 1934, p. 92 (Doi Ang Ka).

Pellorneum tickelli olivaceum, DE SCHAUENSEE, Proc. Acad. Nat. Sci. Philadelphia, 1934, p. 190 (Doi Chiang Dao).

Drymocataphus tickelli olivaceus, RILEY, U. S. Nat. Mus. Bull. 172, 1938, p. 332 (Khun Tan).

The buff-breasted babbler is generally distributed across the northern provinces in districts of dense evergreen or even mixed-deciduous forest but is everywhere apparently rare and especially so in the country west of the Khun Tan range. Specimens have been taken at Doi Mae Kong Ka, Ban Samoeng, Doi Ang Ka at 4,400 feet, Doi Suthep at 3,800 feet (sole record), Doi Chiang Dao at 4,000 feet, Doi Nang Kaeo, Doi Khun Tan at 3,000 feet, Pha Kho, Huai Oi, Ban Hai Huai Som, Phu Kha, and Kiu Chang Kong.

This retiring species feeds silently on or near the ground in the most tangled thickets and is, accordingly, seldom seen. De Schauensee states (1934) that he captured one example in a trap set for pittas.

I collected specimens with the gonads enlarged at Ban Hai Huai Som, March 28, and at Huai Oi, April 5, and others in postnuptial molt between October 22 and November 7.

An adult female had the irides bright brown; the eyelids edged pale orange; the maxilla dark horny brown, with the edges of the commissure fleshy white; the mandible with the apical half fleshy, the basal half fleshy white; the interior of the mouth light yellow; the feet, toes, and claws fleshy.

It has the entire upperparts olivaceous-brown (slightly more rufous on the wings and tail), the feathers of the forehead and crown with buffy shaft streaks; the sides of the head brownish buff, the ear coverts with buffy shaft streaks; the underparts buff, albescent on the throat and the center of the abdomen.

STACHYRIS STRIOLATA HELENAE Delacour and Greenway

LAO SPOTTED-NECKED BABBLER

Stachyris striolata helenae DELACOUR and GREENWAY, Bull. Brit. Orn. Club, vol. 59, 1939, pp. 130–131 (Ban Nam Khuang, 20 km. west of Ban Huai Sai, on the left bank of the Mae Khong, Haut-Laos).

The Lao spotted-necked babbler is known from Thailand only by a pair I collected on Phu Kha, about 4,500 feet, April 9, 1936.

They were taken at the edge of a trail in the narrow belt between an overgrown *hai* and a stand of undisturbed evergreen—where scrubby bamboo and tangled vines concealed scattered rocks and long-felled trees. I found them not at all shy but almost impossible to see in the heavy cover.

Although the birds were obviously paired, I found their gonads to be quite inactive.

My specimens had the irides red-brown; the maxilla black, with the edges of the commissure plumbeous; the mandible plumbeous; the tarsi horn; the toes horny yellow; the claws horn.

This species has the crown and nape dull chestnut-brown (streaked with black on the forehead); the remaining upperparts dark olivaceous-brown, more rufous on the wings and tail; the supercilium black, the feathers with broad white centers, joining, on the sides of the neck, a postauricular patch, which anteriorly has the feathers black with broad white centers, and posteriorly has them dull chestnut-brown but with similar centers; a white area below the eye, bordered behind by the slaty ear coverts, below, by a black mustachial streak; the throat pure white; the remaining underparts orange-rufous, brightest on the breast and washed with brown along the flanks.

STACHYRIS NIGRICEPS YUNNANENSIS La Touche

YUNNANESE GRAY-THROATED BABBLER

Stachyris nigriceps yunnanensis LA TOUCHE, Bull. Brit. Orn. Club, vol. 42, 1921, p. 18 (Hokow, southeastern Yunnan).

Stachyris nigriceps, GYLDENSTOLPE, Kungl. Svenska Vet.-Akad. Handl., 1913, p. 21 (Ban Huai Hom).

Stachyris nigriceps davisoni, GYLDENSTOLPE, Ibis, 1920, p. 484 ("Northern Siam").—DE SCHAUENSEE, Proc. Acad. Nat. Sci. Philadelphia, 1934, p. 191 (Doi Suthep).—DEIGNAN, Journ. Siam Soc. Nat. Hist. Suppl., 1936, p. 106 (Doi Suthep).

Stachyris nigriceps coltarti, DE SCHAUENSEE, Proc. Acad. Nat. Sci. Philadelphia, 1929, p. 532 (Doi Suthep).—DEIGNAN, Journ. Siam Soc. Nat. Hist. Suppl., 1931, p. 137 (Doi Suthep).—CHASEN and BODEN KLOSS, Journ. Siam Soc. Nat. Hist. Suppl., 1932, p. 244 (Doi Suthep).—RILEY, U. S. Nat. Mus. Bull. 172, 1938, p. 344 (Doi Langka).

Stachyris nigriceps yunnanensis, GREENWAY, Bull. Mus. Comp. Zool., 1940, p. 170 (Doi Ang Ka, Doi Nang Kaeo).

The gray-throated babbler is found chiefly in the mountain evergreen between 3,500 and 5,500 feet (usually above 4,500 feet) but, in districts of lowland evergreen, occurs also at feeble elevations. It seems to be generally, although locally, distributed throughout our provinces.

It is seen in flocks, often with *Alcippe* spp. and other small babblers, in the densest undergrowth, moving with such rapidity through the tangled vegetation that it can rarely be observed satisfactorily.

Examples with the gonads greatly enlarged were taken in Nan Province, March 29 and April 5. A specimen in full juvenal dress was collected June 22 and others, in postjuvenal molt, between August 17 and September 2.

My birds had the irides tan; the maxilla black; the mandible plumbeous, with the extreme tip blackish horn; the feet and toes light greenish brown; the claws light horny brown.

This species has the crown black, each feather fringed with ashy white to give a streaked appearance; the center of the nape and the remaining upperparts olivaceous-brown, more rufous on the wings and tail; a supercilium, white immediately above the eye, ashy white posteriorly, separated from the crown by a conspicuous black line, which begins above the eye and reaches the side of the nape, where it is divided from the olive-brown portion of the nape by an edging of ashy white; the ear coverts light brown; the throat gray, bordered at each side by a short grayish-white mustachial streak; the remaining underparts rich buff, brightest on the breast and washed with olivaceous-brown along the flanks.

S. n. yunnanensis is distinguishable from *coltarti* in having the underparts paler and the throat patch uniformly gray, not blackish posteriorly; from *davisoni*, in having the dark markings of the head black, not blackish brown, thus contrasting more with the pale edgings of the feathers.

STACHYRIS CHRYSAEA ASSIMILIS Walden

KAREN GOLDEN-HEADED BABBLER

S[trachyrhis] assmilis [*sic*] WALDEN, *in* Blyth, Catalogue of the mammals and birds of Burma, Journ. Asiat. Soc. Bengal, vol. 43, pt. 2, extra no., 1875, p. 116 (Karen-ni).

Stachyris chrysaea assimilis, DEIGNAN, Journ. Siam Soc. Nat. Hist. Suppl., 1931, p. 137 (Doi Suthep); 1936, p. 106 (Doi Suthep).—DE SCHAUENSEE, Proc. Acad. Nat. Sci. Philadelphia, 1934, p. 191 (Doi Suthep, Doi Chiang Dao).—RILEY, U. S. Nat. Mus. Bull. 172, 1938, p. 347 (Doi Langka, Doi Hua Mot).

The Karen golden-headed babbler has been found, in addition to the localities named above, only on Doi Ang Ka and Phu Kha. On all these mountains it is uncommon and restricted to the heavy evergreen between 4,600 and 5,500 feet.

Its habits are quite like those of *Stachyris n. yunnanensis* and *Alcippe m. laotiana*, two species with which it is usually associated.

An example from Phu Kha, April 8, had the gonads greatly enlarged; two from Doi Hua Mot, August 30, are in postnuptial molt.

De Schauensee records (1934) that his specimens had the irides red-brown; the bill black, fleshy at the base of the mandible; the feet, toes, and claws yellow.

In fresh plumage, the adult has the forehead and crown dull golden, the feathers with ill-defined blackish central streaks; the remaining upperparts olive; the lores and, sometimes, a more or less distinct short mustachial streak slaty gray; the entire underparts bright yellow. In worn plumage and after death, the yellow becomes much less bright.

STACHYRIS CHRYSAEA AURATA de Schauensee

Southern Shan Golden-headed Babbler

Stachyris chrysaea aurata de Schauensee, Proc. Acad. Nat. Sci. Philadelphia, vol. 90, 1938, p. 29 (Doi Pha Hom Pok, North Thailand).

This race is still known only from the original series of three adults (two males, one female), taken by de Schauensee's collectors on Doi Pha Hom Pok, 6,400 feet, in February, 1938.

From *assimilis*, *aurata* differs in having the pileum bright golden and the mantle golden-olive.

S. c. aurata seems to be a valid form, intermediate between *assimilis* and *chrysaea*. *S. c. assimilis* has the lores and mustachial streak slaty gray, the pileum dull golden with ill-defined blackish streaks, the mantle olive; *aurata* has the lores and mustachial streak slaty gray, the pileum bright golden with ill-defined blackish streaks, the mantle golden-olive; *chrysaea* has the lores and mustachial streak black, the pileum blight golden with well-defined black streaks, and the mantle olive-golden. It is, of course, essential that specimens of approximately the same date of collection be used for comparison.

STACHYRIS RUFIFRONS RUFIFRONS Hume

Peguan Rufous-fronted Babbler

Stachyris rufifrons Hume, Stray Feathers, vol. 1, 1873, pp. 479–480 ("On the dry western slopes of the Pegu Hills").

A single mummified specimen (Princeton), collected by me on Doi Ang Ka, 4,400 feet, in April 1931, agrees best with the present race, which is not otherwise known from Thailand.

The species, always at that season in pairs, was observed several times in a dense stand of lalang.

The adult of either sex has the forehead and forecrown rufous, the feathers with obsolescent black shaft streaks; the remaining upperparts light olivaceous-brown; the lores whitish; the ear coverts pale buff; the chin and upper throat white (this color contrasting with the rest of the lower plumage), the feathers with conspicuous black shaft streaks; the remaining underparts warm buff; the edge of the wing, the under wing coverts, and the axillaries pure white.

STACHYRIS RUFIFRONS RODOLPHEI Deignan

Doi Chiang Dao Rufous-fronted Babbler

Stachyris rodolphei Deignan, Publ. Field Mus. Nat. Hist., zool. ser., vol. 24, 1939, p. 110 (Doi Chiang Dao, Chiang Mai Province, northwestern Thailand).

Stachyris rufifrons rufifrons, de Schauensee, Proc. Acad. Nat. Sci. Philadelphia, 1934, p. 192 (Doi Chiang Dao).

This bird is known by only three specimens, all from Doi Chiang Dao: A female collected by de Schauensee at 5,500 feet, January 14, 1933, and two males taken by me at 3,825 and 3,525 feet, March 21, 1937. Though it may prove to be restricted in range to the type locality, I suspect that it will be found to occur also on Doi Pha Hom Pok and perhaps on other northwestern peaks.

My examples, each of which had the gonads greatly enlarged, were obtained in tall bamboo forest; they conducted themselves quite like *Mixornis g. sulphurea.*

De Schauensee has noted that his specimen had the irides red; the bill dark gray; the feet, toes, and claws olive.

Following my original description, this form has the "front and crown dull, dark rufous, with inconspicuous dark shaft-streaks; upperparts, including wings and tail, dark olivaceous-brown; lores and feathers above eye pure gray; ear coverts olive-brown; edge of wing, under wing coverts, and axillaries pale gray; chin and upper throat pale gray with conspicuous black shaft-streaks and sharply defined from the remaining under parts; lower throat and upper breast olivaceous-buff, changing to a dull, light olivaceous-brown on rest of breast, abdomen, flanks, and under tail coverts—the whole bird below darker and duller than any [other] race of *rufifrons.*"

I am now of the opinion that *Stachyris rodolphei* may properly be considered a mere subspecies of the *rufifrons* group. Such treatment, however, for reasons stated under the following form, requires that *Stachyris "rufifrons" insuspecta* be attached to the species *ruficeps* (*cf.* Deignan, *loc. cit.*, p. 112).

STACHYRIS RUFICEPS INSUSPECTA Deignan

Thai Rufous-crowned Babbler

Stachyris rufifrons insuspecta Deignan, Publ. Field Mus. Nat. Hist., zool. ser., vol. 24, 1939, p. 111 (Thateng, Bolovens plateau, Bas-Laos).

Stachyridopsis rufifrons, GYLDENSTOLPE, Kungl. Svenska Vet.-Akad. Handl., 1916, p. 59 (Pha Kho, Doi Pha Sakaeng).
Stachyridopsis rufifrons rufifrons, GYLDENSTOLPE, Ibis, 1920, p. 482 ("Northern and northwestern Siam").

I place with this rare and little-known form of the rufous-crowned babbler three specimens from northern Thailand: A male taken by de Schauensee's men on Doi Pha Hom Pok, 6,400 feet, February 18, 1938 (a paratype) and two males collected by Gyldenstolpe at Pha Kho and Doi Pha Sakaeng, respectively, April 13 and July (*not* April) 23, 1914.

Gyldenstolpe has stated (1916) that "these birds kept to the undergrowth among the valleys which were mostly clothed with dense evergreen forests. I never saw them skulking about among the lower trees or bushes as *Mixornis gularis minor*" [=*M. g. sulphurea*].

The example from Doi Pha Hom Pok had the irides chestnut; the bill gray; the feet and toes yellowish gray. That from Pha Kho had the irides reddish brown; the bill plumbeous; the feet and toes light brown. The one from Doi Pha Sakaeng had the irides brown; the bill horn color; the feet and toes dirty yellow.

I originally described this race as having the "front and crown orange-rufous with conspicuous black shaft-streaks; upper plumage medium olivaceous-brown; lores yellowish-gray; ear-coverts olivaceous-fulvous; edge of wing, wing-coverts, and axillaries white washed with buffy; chin and upper throat buffy-white (or buff) with conspicuous black shaft-streaks and merging into remainder of lower plumage, which is nearest antimony yellow (Ridgway) and slightly more olivaceous on the flanks."

In December 1931, on the steep, grass-covered slopes of Doi Chiang Dao at some 6,000 feet, I met with a small party of a strange *Stachyris*, of which I succeeded in collecting one mutilated specimen; it was identified in the flesh as a form of *Stachyris ruficeps*, as understood by Stuart Baker (Fauna of British India, Birds, ed. 2, vol. 1, 1922, p. 268), and my identification of the fragments was subsequently confirmed by Chasen at the Raffles Museum. I now have no doubt that this example belonged to the race later named *insuspecta*, and since de Schauensee took *S. rufifrons rodolphei* in the grasslands at 5,500 feet, I find it impossible to agree with Mayr in his view that the forms of *rufifrons* and those of *ruficeps* are conspecific. Inasmuch as *insuspecta* seems to have an extensive range in our provinces, it is highly likely to occur with *rufifrons* or with *rodolphei* also at other localities.

It was suggested by Gyldenstolpe (1916, but not 1920) that the two specimens in Stockholm might represent distinct races, but my examination of them in 1939 revealed to me no important differences. In the absence of comparative material and pertinent literature, I made the following notes on them: "Whole crown (not nape) rufous, but merging on hinder part with olive-brown of back. Throat patch small, not well defined, buffy white; lores buffy gray. All below tawny-buff, more intense on breast. Coronal shafts black, conspicuous only at forehead." These remarks seem to place them with *S. r. insuspecta* in the table of characters prepared by me at the original description (pp. 113–114).

Since the type series of *insuspecta* came from only two localities so remote from each other as Doi Pha Hom Pok and the Bolovens plateau, it was made imperative by the facts of Indo-Chinese zoogeography that the race be found also at intermediate stations. Its presumable occurrence at Pha Kho (east of the Khun Tan chain) now goes far to rationalize the extensive and anomalous range indicated for the bird by my original material.

MIXORNIS GULARIS SULPHUREA (Rippon)

SHAN YELLOW-BREASTED BABBLER

Stachyridopsis sulphurea RIPPON, Bull. Brit. Orn. Club, vol. 11, 1900, p. 11 ("Namehet" [=Nam Chet], Southern Shan States).

Mixornis rubricapillus, GYLDENSTOLPE, Kungl. Svenska Vet-Akad. Handl., 1913, p. 21 (Den Chai, Ban Huai Hom); Journ. Nat. Hist. Soc. Siam, 1915, p. 165 (listed).

Mixornis gularis minor GYLDENSTOLPE, Kungl. Svenska Vet.-Akad. Handl., vol. 56, No. 2, 1916, pp. 60–61 (Pha Kho, North Thailand, Khun Tan, Doi Pha Sakaeng).

Mixornis gularis minor, DEIGNAN, Journ. Siam Soc. Nat. Hist. Suppl., 1931, p. 137 (Doi Suthep, Chiang Mai); 1936, p. 106 (Doi Suthep, Chiang Mai).

Mixornis sumatrana minor, GYLDENSTOLPE, Ibis, 1920, p. 484 ("Throughout northern Siam").

Mixornis gularis sulphurea, DE SCHAUENSEE, Proc. Acad. Nat. Sci. Philadelphia, 1928, p. 566 (Chiang Mai); 1934, p. 192 (Chiang Mai).—RILEY, U. S. Nat. Mus. Bull. 172, 1938, p. 350 (Doi Ang Ka, Khun Tan, Ban Nam Khian).—GREENWAY, Bull. Mus. Comp. Zool., 1940, p. 171 (Doi Nang Kaeo).

Mixornis rubricapilla minor [*partim*], DE SCHAUENSEE, Proc. Acad. Nat. Sci. Philadelphia, 1929, p. 533 (Chiang Mai).

This race of the yellow-breasted babbler is very common throughout all the northern provinces except Chiang Rai in lowland areas overgrown with bushy scrub, coarse grass, and especially bamboo; it is somewhat less common at similar territory in the hills, reaching 3,500 feet on Doi Suthep, 4,000 feet on Doi Ang Ka, 4,500 feet on Phu Kha, and 5,000 feet on Doi Chiang Dao.

This species is by far the most numerous of its family in submontane districts and can almost always be found in the great clumps of bamboo that line stream courses and irrigation canals and in the tangled brush that follows the abandonment of cultivation. It occurs in flocks of a dozen or more individuals and is rather parine in actions, as it flits rapidly from twig to twig (usually not far above the ground), all the while spreading and twitching the tail. The common call note is a buzzing *shĭ-shĭ-shĭ-shĭ* in descending scale; the song, a whistled *sweet'-chŭ-chŭ-chŭ-chŭ-chŭ* or *chĭ'-choo͝-choo͝-choo͝*, with the opening note higher, the others uttered rapidly in a monotone.

An example of March 6 had the gonads greatly enlarged. Juveniles that had not yet completed the postnatal molt were taken April 4 and June 4. Postnuptial molt is shown by specimens collected between October 18 and 27.

An adult female from Doi Suthep had the irides pale creamy; the bill slate, with the extreme tip and the edges of the commissure horn; the feet and toes light horny brown; the claws light horny yellow.

The adult in fresh plumage has the center of the forehead and the crown orange-rufous, this color intergrading on the nape with the brownish olive of the remaining upperparts (the wings and tail more olivaceous-brown); the lores blackish; the sides of the forehead, the supercilium, and the entire underparts sulphur yellow, the feathers of the throat and upper breast with fine black shaft streaks, the sides of the head, neck, and body and the under tail coverts washed with olivaceous.

MIXORNIS GULARIS LUTESCENS Delacour

LAO YELLOW-BREASTED BABBLER

Mixornis rubricapilla lutescens DELACOUR, Bull. Brit. Orn. Club, vol. 47, 1926, p. 18 (Bao Ha, Tongking).

Mixornis rubricapilla minor [*partim*], DE SCHAUENSEE, Proc. Acad. Nat. Sci. Philadelphia, 1929, p. 533 (Chiang Rai, Chiang Saen).

A form best known by this name replaces *M. g. sulphurea* in the lowlands of Chiang Rai Province, where, although definitely known only from Chiang Saen, Chiang Rai, and Wiang Pa Pao, it is probably common and generally distributed.

Two specimens in postnuptial molt were taken at Wiang Pa Pao, August 1, 1935.

M. g. lutescens, in Chiang Rai and the adjacent parts of Kengtung State, shows approach to *sulphurea*, and some birds can be identified only by locality. Typical examples differ from *sulphurea* in having the crown chestnut-rufous instead of orange-rufous and the mantle rather darker, with a somewhat oily tinge.

The continental races of *Mixornis gularis* are a most difficult group, in which one form intergrades insensibly with the next, considerable individual variation appears within any given population, and specimens are subject to great alteration in color (in life resulting from wear and sunlight, in death from "foxing" and fading). In studying such birds, it is wholly impossible to arrive at satisfactory conclusions without examination of long series from critical areas and I am fortunate in having before me, in addition to the skins deposited in

Washington, valuable material from the museums of Philadelphia, New York, and Cambridge.

It is evident that, in Thailand (except in those regions occupied by the well-marked race *connectens*), we are concerned with two only slightly differentiated forms with finely streaked throat and breast, one of which has the crown and mantle darker than the other and cannot be distinguished from topotypes of *lutescens* (which, incidentally, do not agree at all with the original diagnosis of the subspecies!). I have seen specimens of this darker bird from Khemmarat, Channuman, Hin Lap, Khorat, Pak Chong, Kaeng Khor, and Lat Bua Khao, in eastern Thailand, from Chiang Saen, Chiang Rai, and Wiang Pa Pao in northern Thailand, and from Muang Len, Sop Lao, and Kengtung Town in the State of Kengtung; those from the last two areas are atypical, yet, in my opinion, nearer *lutescens* than *sulphurea*. All these localities have in common the fact that they lie in territory drained by the Mae Khong and its tributaries and show that the range of *lutescens* is bounded, not by the river itself, as suggested by Delacour (L'Oiseau et la Revue Française d'Ornithologie, 1936, p. 11), but by the limits of its watershed.

The paler bird, which I call *sulphurea*, occurs in Thailand across the North from the basin of the Mae Nan to that of the Salwin, in the more western districts south as far as the Gorges of the Mae Ping. In the West, below the Gorges, we find another population, distinguished from *sulphurea* by their more chestnut-rufous crown and from both *sulphurea* and *lutescens* by their rather heavier streaking of throat and breast; they are intermediate between *sulphurea* and *connectens* and, in default of sufficient material, I hesitate to use a definite name for them.

Judging from analogies, we should expect, in northern Thailand, so plastic a species to be represented by distinct forms to east and west of the Khun Tan chain, but I have been unable to find any important difference between "*minor*" and *sulphurea* and am forced to believe that racial distribution, in this case, is governed wholly by drainage systems. Such correlation is supported by the fact that this babbler finds its most congenial habitat along streams, large or small—to such an extent that, in the most constricted river-gorges, where dry-land vegetation is reduced to a narrow fringe of bamboo between water's edge and lofty precipice and few birds can exist at all, it is usually the most abundant nonaquatic species.

TIMALIA PILEATA INTERMEDIA Kinnear

BURMESE RED-CAPPED BABBLER

Timalia pileata intermedia KINNEAR, Bull. Brit. Orn. Club, vol. 45, 1924, p. 9 (Toungoo, Pegu).

Timelia pileata jerdoni, WILLIAMSON, Journ. Nat. Hist. Soc. Siam, 1918, p. 17 (Chiang Mai).—GYLDENSTOLPE, Ibis, 1920, p. 480 (Chiang Rai, error = Chiang Mai).

Timalia pileata bengalensis, DEIGNAN, Journ. Siam Soc. Nat. Hist. Suppl., 1931, p. 136 (Chiang Mai).

Timalia pileata intermedia, DEIGNAN, Journ. Siam Soc. Nat. Hist. Suppl., 1936, p. 105 (Chiang Mai).

Within our area, the red-capped babbler is known only from the basins of the Mae Ping (Chiang Mai, Ban Mae Klang) and the Mae Khong (Muang Fang, Wiang Pa Pao, Ban Hong Khaeo). At Chiang Mai it is locally common and, at Muang Fang, almost abundant.

This species is strictly confined to the plains, where it occurs in small flocks at places overgrown with bamboo, clumps of bushes, and tall grass. The song, heard from the depths of the thickets, is a squealing *eek'-eek-eek-eek-eek* or *wră-ă-reek*, *eek'-eek-eek-eek-eek*, the notes descending the scale; the alarm note is a sharp *chink;* one hears also a sharp *peek*, by which the members of the group keep in touch with one another as they work their way through the dense vegetation.

Young, just learning to fly, were observed at Chiang Mai, May 28, but an example in postnatal molt was collected at Muang Fang as late as July 16. Birds in postjuvenal molt have been taken between July 15 and August 2; others, in postnuptial molt, between July 16 and 20.

An adult male had the irides bright red; the eyelids blue-gray; the bill black; the feet and toes horn brown; the soles yellowish; the claws dark horn. A juvenile had the irides light grayish brown; the maxilla dull black; the mandible fleshy yellow, blackish horn at the tip; the interior of the mouth bright yellow; the feet, toes, and claws light horn brown; the soles more yellowish.

The adult has a narrow frontal band and a short supercilium white; the crown chestnut-rufous; the remaining upperparts olivaceous-brown, the rectrices indistinctly rayed; the lores conspicuously black; the ear coverts, sides of the neck, and the sides of the upper breast ashy gray; the chin and upper throat white; the lower throat and the breast grayish white with black shaft streaks; the abdomen rufous-buff; the lower flanks and under tail coverts olivaceous-brown, sometimes suffused with rufous-buff. The juvenile differs in having the forehead, superciliary region, and crown olivaceous-brown like the remaining upperparts.

POMATORHINUS HYPOLEUCOS TICKELLI Hume

TENASSERIMESE LONG-BILLED SCIMITAR BABBLER

Pomatorhinus (. . . *Orthorhinus*) *Tickelli* HUME, Stray Feathers, vol. 5, 1877, pp. 32–33 (Mount Muleyit, Tenasserim).

Pomatorhinus tickelli, GYLDENSTOLPE, Journ. Nat. Hist. Soc. Siam, 1915, p. 165 (Khun Tan, Huai Pu).

Pomatorhinus hypoleucus tickelli, GYLDENSTOLPE, Kungl. Svenska Vet.-Akad. Handl., 1916, p. 52 (Khun Tan) ; Ibis, 1920, p. 488 (Khun Tan).

Pomatorhinus hypoleucos tickelli, DE SCHAUENSEE, Proc. Acad. Nat. Sci. Philadelphia, 1934, p. 188 (Doi Chiang Dao).

Pomatorhinus hypoleucos laotianus, RILEY, U. S. Nat. Mus. Bull. 172, 1938, p. 326 (Khun Tan).

The long-billed scimitar babbler is apparently uncommon and very locally distributed in our provinces. Eisenhofer sent to Stockholm a female from Huai Pu, May 27, 1912, and two unsexed examples collected in 1914 at Khun Tan; Gyldenstolpe, at the last-named locality, got two males and two females between September 7 and 23, 1914, and Smith two males at 3,000 feet, February 22, 1932, and May 11, 1933; de Schauensee took a female on Doi Chiang Dao, 4,000 feet, January 17, 1933; I myself shot an adult female in the low hills at Ban Huai Som, March 28, 1937.

The species seems to be restricted to extensive areas of bamboo, where it occurs singly or in pairs (sometimes in company with *Garrulax* spp.), feeding on the ground and flying up into the thorny clumps when alarmed. Gyldenstolpe observes (1916) that it has "a very nice and peculiar and flute-like note which it utters now and then."

Smith's specimen of May 11 is in postjuvenal molt.

De Schauensee's female had the irides reddish brown; the bill horny gray; the feet and toes gray; the claws flesh.

Adults have the upperparts olivaceous-brown, the mantle suffused with rufous (the feathers of the nape sometimes with white central streaks) ; the wings and tail rufous-brown; the feathers at the sides of the crown and nape with white central streaks and tips (more or less strongly tinged with chestnut-rufous, especially anteriorly), to form a narrow supercilium from above the eye; the ear coverts rufous-brown or grayish brown; the sides of the neck anteriorly chestnut-rufous, posteriorly olivaceous-brown streaked with white; the chin, throat, center of breast and the belly white; the feathers at the sides of the breast first white with blackish margins, then deep ashy gray, with broad, black-bordered white central streaks; the lower flanks olivaceous-brown; the under tail coverts rufous or rufous-brown.

This is a variable form, and individuals agreeing with the description of *laotianus* occur in every part of Thailand side by side with *tickelli*; it seems certain that Delacour's race cannot be maintained.

POMATORHINUS ERYTHROGENYS CELATUS Deignan

THAI FERRUGINOUS-CHEEKED SCIMITAR BABBLER

Pomatorhinus erythrogenys celatus DEIGNAN, Zoologica, vol. 26, pt. 3, 1941, p. 241 (Doi Chiang Dao, Chiang Mai Province, northwestern Thailand).

Pomatorhinus erythrogenys imberbis, ROGERS and DEIGNAN, Proc. Biol. Soc. Washington, 1934, p. 91 (Doi Chiang Dao).—DE SCHAUENSEE, Proc. Acad. Nat. Sci. Philadelphia, 1934, pp. 3, 187 (Doi Chiang Dao).

This species has been found in Thailand only on Doi Chiang Dao, where it is rather common between 4,500 and 6,800 feet.

It is chiefly a bird of the heavy lalang growth beneath the somewhat stunted oaks that dot the highest slopes of the mountain but occurs also in the impenetrable *Eupatorium*, which has covered abandoned *hai* of the Musoe people.

A specimen taken March 21 at 4,500 feet has not yet completed postnatal molt.

An adult male had the irides red; the orbital skin plumbeous; the bill gray, with the basal half dark slate; the feet, toes, and claws horny brown. An adult female had the irides pinkish brown; the orbital skin plumbeous; the maxilla slaty, with the apical half of the culmen and the edges of the commissure horn; the mandible plumbeous-white; the tarsi dusky flesh, yellowish white behind; the toes dusky flesh; the soles light yellow; the claws dusky flesh.

This form has the entire upperparts dark olivaceous-brown, suffused with ferruginous on the forehead, superciliary region, and ear coverts; the lores dark gray; the sides of the throat, neck, breast and belly, the flanks, thighs, and under tail coverts bright ferruginous; the remaining underparts white, sometimes with a faint, narrow mustachial line at either side of the throat; the feathers of the lower throat and upper breast occasionally with blackish shafts.

POMATORHINUS OCHRACEICEPS OCHRACEICEPS Walden

KAREN OCHRACEOUS-HEADED SCIMITAR BABBLER

Pomatorhinus ochraceiceps WALDEN, Ann. Mag. Nat. Hist., ser. 4, vol. 12, 1873, p. 487 (Karen Hills).

Pomatorhinus ochraceiceps, GYLDENSTOLPE, Journ. Nat. Hist. Soc. Siam, 1915, p. 165 (Khun Tan).—WILLIAMSON, Journ. Nat. Hist. Soc. Siam, 1918, p. 16 (Muang Wang).

Pomatorhinus ochraceiceps ochraceiceps, GYLDENSTOLPE, Ibis, 1920, p. 488 (Khun Tan, Muang Wang).—DE SCHAUENSEE, Proc. Acad. Nat. Sci. Philadelphia, 1929, p. 532 (Doi Suthep); 1934, p. 187 (Doi Suthep).—DEIGNAN, Journ. Siam Soc. Nat. Hist. Suppl., 1931, p. 136 (Doi Suthep); 1936, p. 105 (Doi Suthep).—CHASEN and BODEN KLOSS, Journ. Siam Soc. Nat. Hist. Suppl., 1932, p. 244 (Doi Suthep).—RILEY, U. S. Nat. Mus. Bull. 172, 1938, p. 326 (Khun Tan).

The ochraceous-headed scimitar babbler is a rather rare inhabitant of evergreen forest between 3,000 and 4,500 feet but is likely to occur in any part of our area in which suitable conditions are found. In addition to localities listed above, I have it from Huai Mae Chan and Phu Kha.

On Doi Suthep I observed it in small bands, almost always accompanied by *Gampsorhynchus*, in dense thickets and low trees along small streams or at the edge of overgrown clearings. While the members of the flock explore the vines and branches they constantly utter a low double whistle but, when frightened, give vent also to a harsh *chur-chur* and other discordant notes.

On Phu Kha at about 4,000 feet, April 7, 1936, I discovered a nest containing three immaculate white eggs. This nest was a domed structure with a large opening on the only exposed side, made externally of coarse grass but lined with much finer grass, sunk into a hollow of the ground on a steep, stony slope overgrown with thin bamboo. The eggs, which were heavy-set, were taken after dark, together with the incubating female.

Adults in postnuptial molt have been collected on Doi Suthep between August 24 and October 27.

A male had the irides yellowish pink; the eyelids slaty; the bill vermilion, with the narial membranes blackish; the feet and toes brownish olive; the claws light horny brown.

This species has the entire upperparts ochraceous-brown, brighter on the head and nape; a white supercilium; the lores and feathers immediately below the eye black; the ear coverts deep brown; the underparts white, washed on the flanks with ochraceous; the under tail coverts olivaceous-brown.

POMATORHINUS FERRUGINOSUS ALBOGULARIS Blyth

TENASSERIMESE CORAL-BILLED SCIMITAR BABBLER

P[*omatorhinus*] *albogularis* BLYTH, Journ. Asiat. Soc. Bengal, vol. 24, 1855, p. 274 (Mount Muleyit).

Pomatorhinus ferruginosus mariae, RILEY, Journ. Siam Soc. Nat. Hist. Suppl., 1933, p. 156 (Doi Langka); U. S. Nat. Mus. Bull. 172, 1938, p. 325 (Doi Langka).

The only record for this bird in Thailand is based upon two specimens taken by Smith on Doi Langka, April 23 and 25, 1931.

The example of April 25 has not yet completed the postnatal molt.

The adult has the entire upperparts olivaceous-brown, the crown and nape somewhat deeper in color; the lores and a supercilium extending to the nape white, narrowly edged above with black; the ear coverts and sides of the neck black; the throat white, changing to pale rufous-buff on the remaining underparts, this color suffused with blackish at the extreme sides of the breast and with olivaceous-brown on the flanks and under tail coverts. The juvenile differs only in its generally more rufous coloration.

P. f. mariae, apparently described without knowledge of Blyth's name, is almost certainly a synonym.

POMATORHINUS SCHISTICEPS RIPPONI Harington

SHAN YELLOW-BILLED SCIMITAR BABBLER

Pomatorhinus ripponi HARINGTON, Bull. Brit. Orn. Club, vol. 27, 1910, pp. 9–10 (Shan States; type specimens, in British Museum, from Pyaunggaung, Northern Shan States).

Pomatorhinus olivaceus ripponi, WILLIAMSON, Journ. Nat. Hist. Soc. Siam, 1918, p. 16 (Doi Nga Chang, Muang Wang).—GYLDENSTOLPE, Ibis, 1920, p. 488 (Doi Nga Chang, Muang Wang).—DE SCHAUENSEE, Proc. Acad. Nat. Sci. Philadelphia, 1929, p. 532 (Doi Suthep).—DEIGNAN, Journ. Siam Soc. Nat. Hist. Suppl., 1931, p. 136 (Doi Suthep).

Pomatorhinus olivaceus olivaceus, DE SCHAUENSEE, Proc. Acad. Nat. Sci. Philadelphia, 1928, p. 567 (Doi Suthep).—CHASEN and BODEN KLOSS, Journ. Siam Soc. Nat. Hist. Suppl., 1932, p. 244 (Doi Suthep).

Pomatorhinus schisticeps nuchalis, DE SCHAUENSEE, Proc. Acad. Nat. Sci. Philadelphia, 1934, p. 185 (Doi Suthep, Doi Chiang Dao).—RILEY, U. S. Nat. Mus. Bull. 172, 1938, p. 323 (Khun Tan, Doi Langka).—GREENWAY, Bull. Mus. Comp. Zool., 1940, p. 169 (Doi Ang Ka, Doi Nang Kaeo).

Pomatorhinus nuchalis, DEIGNAN, Journ. Siam Soc. Nat. Hist. Suppl., 1936, p. 105 (Doi Suthep).

The present form is rather common, wherever it finds a satisfactory environment, throughout the districts west of, and including, the Khun Tan range, occurring chiefly on the mountains between 3,300 and 5,500 feet but, in the neighborhood of Muang Fang, descending into the lowland evergreen.

Outside of the breeding season, the yellow-billed scimitar babbler is found in noisy flocks of as many as a dozen individuals, which keep to such cover as patches of lalang grass and fallen trees overgrown with vines. The ordinary call is the soft double whistle of the genus but it has also many harsh, chattering notes and I once took a solitary bird from the top of a high tree, where it was uttering loud, melodious whistles. Stomachs examined by me contained only insects.

An example from Ban Muang Sum, December 24, and another from Doi Suthep, January 23, had the gonads slightly enlarged, but still others taken at that season had them inactive. Juveniles have been collected on Doi Ang Ka, April 10 and 27, and on Doi Khun Tan, October 20; the Khun Tan specimen is just beginning postjuvenal molt. A long series of adults, taken at various localities between July 11 and December 17, are in postnuptial molt. It appears that, although the majority of birds breed during the spring months, odd pairs do so in the cold weather and yet others in the rainy season.

Adults had the irides pinkish yellow; the bill bright wax yellow, with the narial membranes and the base of the culmen blackish; the feet and toes plumbeous, tinged violet or greenish; the soles yellow; the claws horny white or yellowish horn. Juveniles differed in having the irides creamy gray or tan and the claws horny brown.

This species has the upperparts olivaceous-brown, with an indistinct chestnut-rufous nuchal collar; a white supercilium, extending to the nape; the lores, feathers immediately below the eye, and ear coverts black; at either side of the neck, following the ear coverts, a conspicuous patch of bright chestnut-rufous, connected with the nuchal collar; the underparts white, changing to olivaceous-brown on the lower flanks and the under tail coverts; the sides of the breast and the upper flanks frequently (in our provinces) more or less streaked, or at least suffused, with chestnut-rufous.

I have elsewhere discussed the geographical variation of this scimitar babbler in Thailand (Auk, 1942, p. 117).

POMATORHINUS SCHISTICEPS HUMILIS Delacour

BAS-LAOS YELLOW-BILLED SCIMITAR BABBLER

Pomatorhinus schisticeps humilis DELACOUR, L'Oiseau et la Revue Française d'Ornithologie, new ser., vol. 2, No. 3, 1932, pp. 424–425 (Thateng, Bas-Laos).

I collected specimens, inseparable from topotypes of *humilis*, at Ban San Pa Haeng and Ban Wang Mo, localities on the Mae Nan, and also on Phu Kha at 4,500 feet. It seems to be really a lowland bird, and its presence on Phu Kha (together with a number of other species characteristic of feeble elevations), at an old *hai* overgrown with *Rubus*, may well have been a result of the clearing of forest by the Yao.

In the river valley I found this form in small flocks in extensive jungles of bamboo and always in company with *Gampsorhynchus*. In the absence of undergrowth beneath the clumps, it was possible to observe the bird as it fed upon the ground, something unusual in the genus, but it made up for it by greater wariness.

A juvenile was taken on Phu Kha, April 4, 1936.

An adult male had the irides gray; the bill yellow, with the narial membranes blackish brown; the feet and toes plumbeous; the claws horn.

From *ripponi*, the present race is distinguished by its generally lesser size and smaller bill and by having the sides of the body dull olivaceous-brown without any rufous suffusion.

NAPOTHERA CRISPIFRONS CRISPIFRONS (Blyth)

TENASSERIMESE LIMESTONE BABBLER

Turdinus crispifrons BLYTH, Journ. Asiat. Soc. Bengal, vol. 24, 1855, pp. 269–272 (mountainous interior of Tenasserim; type specimen from Muleyit, *fide* Sclater, Ibis, 1892, p. 76).

Gypsophila crispifrons, WILLIAMSON, Journ. Nat. Hist. Soc. Siam, 1916, p. 59 (Muang Song).—GYLDENSTOLPE, Ibis, 1920, p. 481 (Muang Song).

A male and two females were taken by Williamson's collector, during April 1916, "in the Muang Song forest"; the bird has not since that time been found in Thailand.

These specimens were presumably collected in the neighborhood of limestone crags, which are numerous in that portion of Phrae Province. They are, however, likewise numerous at many other northern localities, and it is noteworthy that the bird has never been rediscovered, although I looked for it constantly over a period of years.

Williamson believed that his examples represented "young birds of the year," but all are, in my opinion, normally colored adults of a population in which partial albinism is exceptional—rather than the rule, as in Tenasserim.

In default of specimens at hand, I quote here the description of "birds of the first year," as given by Stuart Baker (Fauna of British India, Birds, ed. 2, vol. 1, 1922, p. 249): "The forehead to back olive-brown, each feather margined with black; the rump, upper tail-coverts, tail and exposed portions of wing olive-brown; the sides of the forehead and a short supercilium . . . greyish white with black specks; chin, throat and upper breast white, streaked with dark brown, especially on the breast; remainder of lower plumage ochraceous olive-brown."

I have examined Sir Walter's skins in London and agree with him that they show no approach to *annamensis* and must be placed with the nominate form.

NAPOTHERA BREVICAUDATA BREVICAUDATA (Blyth)

TENASSERIMESE STREAKED-THROATED WREN BABBLER

T[urdinus] brevicaudatus BLYTH, Journ. Asiat. Soc. Bengal, vol. 24, 1855, p. 272 (mountainous interior of Tenasserim; type from Muleyit, *fide* Sclater, Ibis, 1892, p. 76).

Corythocichla brevicaudata, GYLDENSTOLPE, Kungl. Svenska Vet.-Akad. Handl., 1916, p. 58 (Doi Pha Sakaeng).

Corythocichla brevicaudata brevicaudata, GYLDENSTOLPE, Ibis, 1920, p. 485 (Doi Pha Sakaeng).

Napothera brevicaudata (probably *N. b. venningi*), ROGERS and DEIGNAN, Proc. Biol. Soc. Washington, 1934, p. 91 (Doi Ang Ka).

Napothera brevicaudata brevicaudata, DEIGNAN, Journ. Siam. Soc. Nat. Hist. Suppl., 1931, p. 137 (Doi Suthep); 1936, p. 106 (Doi Suthep).—DE SCHAUENSEE, Proc. Acad. Nat. Sci. Philadelphia, 1934, p. 190 (Doi Chiang Dao).

Corythocichla brevicaudata venningi, RILEY, U. S. Nat. Mus. Bull. 172, 1938, p. 334 (Doi Langka).

The present form probably occurs wherever, on our mountain slopes, moist evergreen forest arises from a confusion of tumbled boulders and broken rock, whether limestone or granite; owing to its timidity and the nature of its haunts, however, its true status at any given locality is uncertain. On Doi Ang Ka it has been found fairly commonly between 4,600 and 5,500 feet; on Doi Suthep once at 3,800 feet (a pair at the Hermit's Cave, March 7, 1931); on Doi Chiang Dao twice, at 3,000 and 5,000 feet; on Phu Kha once at about 4,500 feet; at Ban Huai Ki once in lowland evergreen.

On Doi Ang Ka I watched it climb silently about fallen trees and investigate crannies and crevices in the rocks, acting quite like other members of the genus. A flock of five or six individuals observed by Gyldenstolpe at Doi Pha Sakaeng communicated with each other by faint whistling notes.

Examples with the gonads enlarged were taken on Phu Kha, April 12, and on Doi Ang Ka, April 22 and 26; at the latter locality, a bird in postnatal molt was collected April 22 and another in postnuptial molt, September 5.

Males in breeding condition had the irides brownish red or red-brown; the maxilla blackish brown, tipped dark gray; the mandible brown, horny at the base, or plumbeous-gray, gray-white at the base; the tarsi fleshy brown or horny brown; the toes brown or horny brown with a fleshy tinge; the claws fleshy horn or horny brown. A juvenile female had the irides dull brown; the maxilla blackish brown with the extreme tip yellow; the mandible with the anterior half dark brown, the rest fleshy; the rictus and interior of the mouth yellow; the tarsi fleshy brown; the toes dark brown; the claws horny brown.

The adult has the upperparts dark olivaceous-brown, changing to dark rufous-brown on the rump, upper tail coverts, and tail, the feathers of the crown and upper half of the back with conspicuous brownish-ashy centers and fairly broad blackish margins; the upper wing coverts and most of the remiges with small, but distinct, white or brownish-white tips; the lores, indistinct supercilium, and sides of the head dark ashy; the feathers of the chin and throat ashy, with dark brown central streaks; the remaining underparts ferruginous, paler on the center of the breast and belly, deeper along the flanks and on the under tail coverts.

I find so much variation in coloration and length of wing among even a small series of Thai birds that it seems to be impossible at present to recognize more than one race from our area. The two specimens from Doi Chiang Dao and one from Doi Langka are more saturate throughout than true *brevicaudata* and thus approach *venningi*, which will probably prove to be the form of Doi Pha Hom Pok; in wing length, on the other hand, they agree well with Tenasserimese birds. The single example from Ban Huai Ki appears to be different from that of Phu Kha and fits the description of *proxima* (Bas-Laos); it is, however, badly worn (June 23) and can be matched perfectly with certain Tenasserimese skins.

NAPOTHERA EPILEPIDOTA BAKERI (Harington)

SHAN STREAKED-BREASTED WREN BABBLER

Turdinulus epilepidotus bakeri HARINGTON, Bull. Brit. Orn. Club, vol. 33, 1913, pp. 44–45 (Na Noi ["near Loimaw," *fide* Ticehurst, Ibis, 1938, p. 207], Southern Shan States).

Turdinulus epilepidotus bakeri, WILLIAMSON, Journ. Nat. Hist. Soc. Siam, 1918, p. 18 (Muang Wang).—GYLDENSTOLPE, Ibis, 1920, p. 485 (Muang Wang).—DE SCHAUENSEE, Proc. Acad. Nat. Sci. Philadelphia, 1929, p. 532 (Doi Suthep).

Napothera epilepidota bakeri, DEIGNAN, Journ. Siam. Soc. Nat. Hist. Suppl., 1931, p. 137 (Doi Suthep); 1936, p. 106 (Doi Suthep).—DE SCHAUENSEE, Proc. Acad. Nat. Sci. Philadelphia, 1934, p. 190 (Doi Suthep, Doi Chiang Dao).—RILEY, U. S. Nat. Mus. Bull. 172, 1938, p. 336 (Doi Langka).

This wren babbler is a not uncommon resident of heavy evergreen jungle (and immediately adjacent areas of open hill-forest) in the districts west of (and including) the Khun Tan chain, at whatever elevations suitable conditions are found; while, on such a hill as Doi Suthep, it occurs only from 4,600 to 5,500 feet, at Ban Pang An and Huai Mae Chan it has been taken in evergreen at the very foot of the mountains.

I found it in pairs or family groups in rather less moist locations than those preferred by *Pnoëpyga*, but showing similarly wrenlike habits—clambering about on fallen trees or turning over dead leaves on the ground, with a constant *chur-r-r*, *chur-r-r*. Although difficult to watch beneath the undergrowth and against the dark background of the forest floor, it is, once discovered, quite tolerant of observation and continues its explorations without the least evidence of shyness.

De Schauensee collected a bird in postjuvenal molt on Doi Suthep, July 16, while I took three examples in the same condition on Doi Ang Ka, between September 2 and 7. A specimen from Doi Suthep, October 26, is in postnuptial molt.

An adult male had the irides hazel; the maxilla with the apical half plumbeous, the basal half slaty; the mandible plumbeous; the feet and toes brownish horn; the claws fleshy horn.

The adult has the upperparts dark olivaceous-brown, changing to dark rufous-brown on the rump and upper tail coverts, the feathers of the crown and mantle with narrow, indistinct blackish margins, those of the mantle also with distinct brownish-white shaft streaks, the coverts and the secondaries with small, but distinct, white or brownish tips; the lores and a long streak behind the eye blackish, bordered above by a rufous-buff suffused white supercilium, which extends to the side of the nape; the throat and sides of the head white, washed (especially on the latter parts) with rufous-buff; the remaining underparts white, the feathers of the breast and sides with broad, dark olivaceous-brown margins (which, on the lower flanks, restrict the white to a mere streak along the shaft), those of the belly narrowly edged with pale rufous-buff; the under tail coverts dull rufous-brown.

My specimens differ from a Tenasserimese skin (*davisoni*) in just the characters attributed by Harington to *bakeri*, so that, although no topotypical material has been examined, I have no hesitation in placing them with the race of the Shan States.

NAPOTHERA EPILEPIDOTA LAOTIANA (Delacour)

LAO STREAKED-BREASTED WREN BABBLER

Turdinulus epilepodotus laotianus DELACOUR, Bull. Brit. Orn. Club, vol. 47, 1926, pp. 17–18 (Chiang Khwang, Laos).

An adult male from Phu Kha, 4,500 feet, April 8, 1936, and another from Kiu Chang Kong, April 29, 1936, are best placed under this name. The race is probably fairly common and well distributed in the evergreen of the more eastern provinces.

From the preceding form it differs in having the supercilium and throat white, the former with a very slight wash of rufous-buff, the latter wholly free of this color; the olivaceous-brown of the lower flanks more or less suffused with rufous; the under tail coverts brighter rufous-brown.

N. e. laotiana has recently been synonymized with *amyae* but is readily separable therefrom by its lesser dimensions and especially by its smaller bill. In coloration it lies, as might be expected, between *amyae* and *clara*, but since it cannot possibly be confused with either one it may properly be restored to valid subspecific rank.

De Schauensee and Ripley have suggested (Proc. Acad. Nat Sci. Philadelphia, 1939, pp. 352–353) that either *exsul* or *roberti* must be employed as the specific name for these birds. I suspect, however, that *diluta* at Blangnanga and *lucilleae* at Meloewak may no more correctly be said to occur "together" in Sumatra than *bakeri* and *laotiana* (and numerous other pairs of races) in northern Thailand.

PNOËPYGA PUSILLA PUSILLA Hodgson

INDIAN LESSER SCALY-BREASTED WREN BABBLER

[*Pnoëpyga*] *pusillus* [*sic*] HODGSON, Proc. Zool. Soc. London, pt. 13, 1845, p. 25 (Nepal).

Pnoëpyga pusilla pusilla, RILEY, U. S. Nat. Mus. Bull. 172, 1938, p. 398 (Doi Langka).

This tiny, apparently tailless bird is rather common in dense evergreen forest, between 4,400 and 5,500 feet, on Doi Ang Ka, Doi Chiang Dao, and Doi Langka; it may confidently be expected to occur upon other northern mountains where suitable conditions obtain.

In deep, humid jungle, watered by small streams, I found the present species, in the fashion of a true wren, creeping about moss-grown rocks beneath arching fern fronds and exploring the tangles of fallen trees, now disappearing completely into a crevice among the boulders, again investigating the epiphytes, which lined some decaying log. On Doi Ang Ka, in April and May, it was quite fearless and constantly attracted attention to itself by a loud, ringing song delivered from the top of a rock or stump.

A male with the gonads greatly enlarged was taken on Doi Ang Ka at 5,000 feet, April 26, 1931.

This specimen had the irides brown; the maxilla black; the mandible with the apical half horny black, the basal half horny gray; the feet and toes horn brown, tinged fleshy; the claws pale horny.

The adult of either sex has the upperparts deep, rich brown, the feathers of the crown and mantle with narrow, indistinct blackish margins, the wing coverts, inner secondaries, and the feathers of the lower back with small, subapical buff tips, which broaden into bars on the rump; the throat, breast, and belly white *or* vivid buff, each feather with a narrow blackish margin, those of the breast and belly also with a more or less concealed blackish central area; the flank feathers deep brown with a buff submarginal band and a narrow blackish margin. Of six Thai males before me, two have the throat, breast, and belly white and four have these parts buff.

Family CINCLIDAE

CINCLUS PALLASII DORJEI Kinnear

Burmese Brown Dipper

Cinclus pallasi dorjei Kinnear, Ibis, 1937, p. 263 (Sakden, East Bhutan).
Cinclus pallasii ?marila, Deignan, Journ. Siam Soc. Nat. Hist. Suppl., 1935, p. 65 (Doi Ang Ka).

The dipper has been recorded in Thailand only from the immediate vicinity of a huge fall of the Mae Klang, at about 3,500 feet on Doi Ang Ka. At this place I found a pair in September 1930, and again in April and May 1931, and saw a single example on August 31, 1935. The sole Thai specimen, taken by Aagaard at the same locality sometime in 1931, is probably now deposited in the collection of Chulalongkon University at Bangkok.

This small colony haunted a wider portion of the stream, where the racing water boiled among great broken rocks and where the swift current made it improbable that any dead bird could be retrieved. The sharp, shrill call, uttered as its author bobbed up and down on some spray-drenched boulder or flew above the torrent, carried easily over the roar of the cataracts.

The dippers are plump, short-tailed, thrush-like species, which, unlike all other land birds, spend much of their time *beneath* the water.

The present form has the plumage wholly dark chocolate-brown, except for a more or less distinct eye ring of small white feathers.

Kinnear (*loc. cit.*) states that "five [specimens] from the Shan States may for the present be considered the same as [those from] Bhutan." In the absence of material, Thai birds are merely provisionally placed under this name.

Family TURDIDAE

ENICURUS LESCHENAULTI INDICUS Hartert

INDIAN WHITE-CROWNED FORKTAIL

Enicurus leschenaulti indicus HARTET, Vögel der paläarktischen Fauna, vol. 1, 1910, p. 760 (Margherita, Upper Assam).

Henicurus leschenaulti, GYLDENSTOLPE, Journ. Nat. Hist. Soc. Siam, 1915, p. 170 (Khun Tan).

Henicurus leschenaulti indicus, GYLDENSTOLPE, Kungl. Svenska Vet.-Akad. Handl., 1916, p. 48 (Khun Tan, Doi Pha Sakaeng).

Enicurus leschenaulti indicus, GYLDENSTOLPE, Ibis, 1920, p. 476 (Khun Tan, Doi Pha Sakaeng).—DE SCHAUENSEE, Proc. Acad. Nat. Sci. Philadelphia, 1929, p. 542 (Chiang Saen); 1934, p. 209 (Doi Suthep, Doi Chiang Dao).—DEIGNAN, Journ. Siam Soc. Nat. Hist. Suppl., 1931, p. 142 (Doi Suthep); 1936, p. 111 (Doi Suthep).—RILEY, U. S. Nat. Mus. Bull. 172, 1938, p. 402 (Doi Langka, Khun Tan).

The status of the beautiful white-crowned forktail, in Thailand recorded only from Chiang Mai and Chiang Rai Provinces, is difficult to define. In the former province, where it is known only from the mountains, I considered it to be rather rare on Doi Ang Ka at 4,900 feet (April) and an uncommon permanent resident on Doi Suthep between 3,500 and 4,600 feet (occasionally as low as 2,500 feet); Smith took one example on Doi Khun Tan at 3,000 feet (February); de Schauensee found it "extraordinarily abundant" on Doi Chiang Dao, 2,000 feet, January 23, 1933, "side by side with *E. schistaceus* but . . . much commoner than the latter." The few specimens known from Chiang Rai, however, have been collected (January) in submontane districts (Chiang Saen, Huai Mae Chan), a fact that may indicate that it is also resident where mountain streams debouch into lowland evergreen or may merely reflect a tendency to descend to lower levels during the cold weather.

On Doi Suthep the normal altitudinal range of this species (3,500 to 4,600 feet) scarcely overlapped with that of its only competitor, *E. schistaceus* (2,000 to 3,600 feet); while *indicus* haunted tiny streams flowing through ravines in dense evergreen jungle, *schistaceus* dwelt along the same brooks where, at lower levels, they broadened and ran through more open evergreen and mixed-deciduous forest; it is possible that only in winter will *indicus* be found in exactly the same environment as *schistaceus*.

Beyond the fact that it is less strictly confined to the immediate vicinity of watercourses than its relatives and may often be seen running nervously along some forest track, especially one that crosses and recrosses a small stream, the habits of this species are much like those of *schistaceus*.

Gyldenstolpe took juveniles at Doi Pha Sakaeng, July 16, and at Khun Tan, September 13, while de Schauensee collected one on Doi Suthep, July 18.

My specimens had the irides dark brown; the bill black; the feet, toes, and claws fleshy white.

The adult has the forehead and semierectile feathers of the forecrown white; the rest of the head (including the throat and neck), the breast, and upper back black; the lower back, rump, and upper tail coverts white; the wings black, the greater coverts broadly tipped with white to form a wing bar (which seems to be connected with the white of the back), the inner secondaries with broad concealed white bases and narrow white tips; the deeply forked tail with the two outermost pairs of feathers white, the others black with conspicuous white tips; the abdomen, flanks, and under tail coverts white. The juvenile differs in having the head, upper back, throat, and breast deep brown, the feathers of the two last parts with fulvous shaft streaks; the white wing band suffused with buff.

ENICURUS SCHISTACEUS (Hodgson)

SLATY-BACKED FORKTAIL

[*Motacilla* (*Enicurus*)] *Schistaceus* HODGSON, Asiatick Researches, vol. 19, 1836, pp. 189–190 (Nepal).

Henicurus schistaceus, GYLDENSTOLPE, Journ. Nat. Hist. Soc. Siam, 1915, p. 170 (listed); Kungl. Svenska Vet.-Akad. Handl., 1916, p. 49 (Khun Tan, Doi Pha Sakaeng).

Enicurus schistaceus, GYLDENSTOLPE, Ibis, 1920, p. 476 (Khun Tan, Doi Pha Sakaeng).—DE SCHAUENSEE, Proc. Acad. Nat. Sci. Philadelphia, 1928, p. 564 Doi Suthep); 1934, p. 209 (Doi Suthep, Doi Chiang Dao).—DEIGNAN, Journ. Siam Soc. Nat. Hist. Suppl., 1931, p. 142 (Doi Suthep).

Enicurus schistaceus schistaceus, DEIGNAN, Journ. Siam Soc. Nat. Hist. Suppl., 1936, p. 111 (Doi Suthep).—RILEY, U. S. Nat. Mus. Bull. 172, 1938, p. 401 (Doi Langka, Doi Hua Mot, "Ban Padieng," Huai Lak, Song Khwae valley).

The slaty-backed forktail, known only from the provinces of Mae Hong Son, Chiang Mai, and Chiang Rai (Kiu Chang Kong, on the border of the French Enclave), is the commonest of its genus in our area. It is numerous on Doi Ang Ka from 3,500 to 5,000 feet and on Doi Suthep between 2,000 and 3,600 feet and, at least in winter, occurs also where brooks debouch from the hills into heavy forest at the level of the plains, just as does the preceding species.

Within its range on Doi Ang Ka and Doi Suthep, pairs of this forktail inhabited every stream, both where it tumbled torrentially down the rock-strewn slopes and where it temporarily followed a more or less level course. The bird flits gracefully from stone to stone, with a sharp, monosyllabic cry, rests for a moment with tail bobbed rapidly up and down, runs this way and that across some wet shelf of rock in pursuit of insect prey, and, finally alarmed, takes off with dipping flight through the low, overhanging branches to vanish around a bend, where the performance is repeated. It is rather less shy than *indicus* and is much more likely to be seen where the brook is comparatively wide and the rocks are unsheltered by the vegetation of the banks.

Gyldenstolpe took juveniles at Khun Tan, May 29, and at Doi Pha Sakaeng, July 16; I have examples in postjuvenal molt from the country between Ban Choeng Doi and Doi Langka, July 21 and August 26. A specimen in postnuptial molt was collected at the base of Doi Mae Kong Ka, October 22.

Gyldenstolpe notes (1916) that his juveniles had the irides blackish brown; the bill black; the feet and toes flesh color.

The adult has the forehead white, this color continued as a supercilium above and down behind the eye; the crown, nape, upper and lower back slaty blue-gray; the rump and upper tail coverts white; the wings much as in the preceding species but with the primaries narrowly tipped white (in unworn plumage) and with broad white bases to form a speculum; the tail as in the preceding species; the lores, chin, upper throat, and sides of the head and neck black; the remaining underparts white, the feathers of the breast often with faint, narrow dark tips. The juvenile lacks the white frontal area and has the upper half of the head, nape, and back uniform dark sooty gray; the chin, throat, and breast buffy, the feathers of the last part narrowly edged darker; the white wing band suffused with buff.

ENICURUS IMMACULATUS (Hodgson)

BLACK-BACKED FORKTAIL

[*Motacilla* (*Enicurus*)] *Immaculatus* HODGSON, Asiatick Researches, vol. 19, 1836, p. 190 (Nepal).

Enicurus immaculatus, RILEY, U. S. Nat. Mus. Bull. 172, 1938, p. 402 (Mae Kong Ka valley).

A female collected by Smith at the base of Doi Mae Kong Ka, January 19, 1933, and two males and one female taken by me at the same locality, October 18 and 19, 1936, are the only specimens of this forktail yet known from Thailand.

It seems to be restricted throughout its range to feeble elevations but, like others of the genus, requires swift-flowing streams and is not likely to be found away from the broken country at the foot of the mountains.

A female of October 18 retains traces of the juvenal dress in having the feathers of the forecrown suffused with deep brown, the center of the lower breast and the wing band suffused with buff. A male of October 19 is in postnuptial molt.

The adult differs from that of *schistaceus* chiefly in having the crown, nape, and back black, instead of slaty blue-gray, and the primaries without a visible speculum.

It is interesting to note that an example of *schistaceus* was collected, October 22, 1936, at the same locality as the series of *immaculatus*.

MYOPHONUS CAERULEUS CAERULEUS (Scopoli)

CHINESE SPANGLED WHISTLING THRUSH

Gracula (*caerulea*) SCOPOLI, Deliciae florae et faunae insubricae, pt. 2, 1786, p. 88, sp. 42 (China, *ex* Sonnerat; type locality restricted to Canton, by Stresemann, Abh. Ber. Mus. Tierk. Völkerk. Dresden, vol. 16, No. 2, 1923–1924 [=1924], p. 28).

Myiophoneus caeruleus, GYLDENSTOLPE, Kungl. Svenska Vet.-Akad. Handl., 1916, p. 61 (Khun Tan); Ibis, 1920, p. 479 (Khun Tan).

Myiophoneus coeruleus coeruleus, CHASEN and BODEN KLOSS, Journ. Siam Soc. Nat. Hist. Suppl., 1932, p. 245 (Doi Suthep).

Myophonus caeruleus caeruleus, DE SCHAUENSEE, Proc. Acad. Nat. Sci. Philadelphia, 1934, p. 212 (Doi Chiang Dao).—RILEY, U. S. Nat. Mus. Bull. 172, 1938, p. 419 (Doi Ang Ka, Doi Langka).

Myophonus coeruleus coeruleus, DEIGNAN, Journ. Siam Soc. Nat. Hist. Suppl., 1936, p. 113 (Doi Suthep).

Myiophoneus caeruleus caeruleus, GREENWAY, Bull. Mus. Comp. Zool., 1940, p. 169 (Doi Ang Ka).

The black-billed whistling thrush seems to be a fairly common winter visitor to the higher mountains of the provinces west of (and including) the Khun Tan chain, occurring from October 17 (Doi Suthep) to March 15 (Doi Ang Ka), at elevations between 4,000 and 7,000 feet. Gyldenstolpe's example, taken at Doi Khun Tan in May 1914, is of such exceptionally late date that it must represent a case of delayed migration.

My specimens of this race were collected, not along the mountain streams where the resident *M. c. eugenei* is dominant, but in deep, moist evergreen forest, where they fed on the ground among mossy rocks and fallen trees and were not observed until, alarmed, they flew up onto some low branch or rotting stump, before vanishing into the fastnesses of the jungle.

A male had the irides dark brown; the bill black; the interior of the mouth bright yellow; the feet and toes black; the claws horny black.

From *M. c. temminckii*, the present form differs only in its shorter and less robust bill, which is wholly black in color.

I cannot distinguish *immansuetus* (Ichang, Hupeh) from topotypical material of *caeruleus*.

MYOPHONUS CAERULEUS TEMMINCKII Vigors

HIMALAYAN SPANGLED WHISTLING THRUSH

Myophonus Temminckii VIGORS, Proc. Comm. Sci. Corr. Zool. Soc. London, pt. 1, 1830–1831 [= 1832], p. 171 (Himalayas; type locality restricted to Simla-Almora district, by Ticehurst and Whistler, Ibis, 1924, p. 471).

Myiophoneus temmincki, GYLDENSTOLPE, Journ. Nat. Hist. Soc. Siam, 1915, p. 165 (listed).

Myiophoneus temminckii, GYLDENSTOLPE, Ibis, 1920, p. 479 (Khun Tan).

Myophonus caeruleus rileyi DEIGNAN, Proc. Biol. Soc. Washington, vol. 51, 1938, pp. 25–26 (Doi Ang Ka, Chiang Mai Province, North Thailand).

Myophonus temminckii rileyi, RILEY, U. S. Nat. Mus. Bull. 172, 1938, p. 417 (Doi Ang Ka).

The specimen recorded (1915, 1920) by Gyldenstolpe is an unsexed, undated bird, collected in "Siam" by Eisenhofer and now deposited in the museum at Hannover. The type of "*rileyi*" was taken by Smith on Doi Ang Ka, 7,000 feet, December 6, 1928, while the sole paratype, from the same mountain, was shot on the same day at 8,400 feet. The only other examples known from Thailand are two gotten by de Schauensee's collectors above 6,000 feet on Doi Pha Hom Pok early in 1938. The status of this form seems to be that of a rare winter visitor.

It has the irides brown; the bill yellow, with the culmen and basal half of the maxilla (except along the edges of the commissure) blackish; the feet, toes, and claws black.

This large thrush appears black in the field, but in reality it has the upper plumage deep purplish blue (the remiges and rectrices brighter), the feathers of the head and mantle with glossy tips of a lighter purplish blue; the front, forecrown, and lesser upper wing coverts (shoulder patch) shining cobalt blue; the median upper wing coverts with white or violet-white tips; the underparts black, washed with deep purplish blue, the feathers of the throat, breast, and upper abdomen spangled like those of the head and mantle; the feathers of the lower back, flanks, and lower abdomen with concealed pure white bases and shafts; the undersurface of the remiges and rectrices black.

MYOPHONUS CAERULEUS EUGENEI (Hume)

BURMESE SPANGLED WHISTLING THRUSH

Myiophoneus Eugenei HUME, Stray Feathers, vol. 1, 1873, pp. 475–476 (Thayetmyo, Pegu, Burma).

Myiophoneus eugenii, GYLDENSTOLPE, Journ. Nat. Hist. Soc. Siam, 1915, p. 165 (listed).

Myiophoneus eugenei, GYLDENSTOLPE, Kungl. Svenska Vet.-Akad. Handl., 1916, p. 62 (Khun Tan).

Myiophoneus eugenei eugenei, GYLDENSTOLPE, Ibis, 1920, p. 479 ("Different localities").—DE SCHAUENSEE, Proc. Acad. Nat. Sci. Philadelphia, 1928, p. 566 (Doi Suthep).

Myiophoneus stonei DE SCHAUENSEE, Proc. Acad. Nat. Sci. Philadelphia, 1929, pp. 469–470 (Chiang Mai [=foot of Doi Suthep], North Thailand).

Myiophoneus eugenii eugenii, DE SCHAUENSEE, Proc. Acad. Nat. Sci. Philadelphia, 1929, p. 544 (Chiang Mai [=foot of Doi Suthep]).

Myiophoneus stonei, DE SCHAUENSEE, Proc. Acad. Nat. Sci. Philadelphia, 1929, p. 544 (Chiang Mai [=foot of Doi Suthep]).

Myophonus coeruleus eugenei, DEIGNAN, Journ. Siam Soc. Nat. Hist. Suppl., 1931, p. 143 (Doi Suthep).

Myophonus stonei, DEIGNAN, Journ. Siam Soc. Nat. Hist. Suppl., 1931, p. 143 (Doi Suthep).

Myophonus temminckii eugenei, DE SCHAUENSEE, Proc. Acad. Nat. Sci. Philadelphia, 1934, p. 212 (Doi Suthep, Doi Chiang Dao). — DEIGNAN, Journ. Siam Soc. Nat. Hist. Suppl., 1936, p. 113 (Doi Suthep).

Myophonus eugenei eugenei, RILEY, U. S. Nat. Mus. Bull. 172, 1938, p. 418 (Doi Langka, Doi Suthep, Mae Khan, Song Khwae valley).

This is the common whistling thrush of our area, occurring at suitable localities throughout the northern provinces, with the curious exception of Chiang Rai, whence it has never been recorded. Eisenhofer sent to Stockholm four unsexed skins, collected at Khun Tan in 1914, and to Hannover, a male from Pha Hing, May 11, 1912; Boden Kloss mentions (Ibis, 1918, p. 208) a bird from Phrae in the Williamson collection; I have specimens from Ban Na Noi (Chiang Mai Province) and Ban Huai Ki.

This species ranges along mountain torrents from the level at which they debouch onto the plains up to their sources, on Doi Chiang Dao reaching 4,500 feet, on Doi Suthep, 5,500 feet, and on Doi Ang Ka, 5,500 feet or higher, but it is found in greater numbers at the lower elevations where the streams are broader and more turbulent. On Doi Suthep it dwells in pairs at every waterfall and along every reach, hopping about on mossy logs and spray-drenched rocks and from time to time uttering loud calls or a wild, whistled song which carries above the roar of rushing water and re-echoes from the walls of the ravines. It is a timid bird, as befits a species whose first intimation of approaching danger must frequently be wholly visual, and, at the least alarm, flies strongly into the forest to circle back to the water's edge beyond the nearest bend.

Adults have the irides brown; the bill deep yellow, with the culmen and basal half of the maxilla dark horny brown or blackish; the feet and toes dark brown or blackish brown; the soles yellow; the claws black or blackish brown.

The present form, which is scarcely distinguishable in life from the much rarer *temminckii*, differs in having the general color of the plumage more blue, less violet or purplish (seen only by direct comparison of specimens); in always lacking the white or violet-white tips to the median upper wing coverts; in having the bases of the feathers of the lower back, flanks, and lower abdomen dark sooty gray, without the least trace of concealed white.

BRACHYPTERYX CRURALIS CRURALIS (Blyth)

INDIAN INDIGO-BLUE SHORTWING

Calliope (? Gould) *cruralis* BLYTH, Journ. Asiat. Soc. Bengal, vol. 12, 1843, pp. 929, 933–934 (Darjiling).

Brachypteryx cruralis, ROGERS and DEIGNAN, Proc. Biol. Soc. Washington, 1934, p. 91 (Doi Ang Ka).

Brachypteryx cruralis cruralis, GREENWAY, Bull. Mus. Comp. Zool., 1940, p. 177 (Doi Ang Ka).

Our larger shortwing is fairly common on Doi Ang Ḳa from 6,000 feet to the summit but is known from no other Thai locality.

I found it only in the dense, moss-bedecked cloud-forest of these high altitudes, feeding on the ground beneath the tall ferns or, at small clearings, in the *Eupatorium* which had somehow found its way thither. In the deep shade it appears to be a black bird with a white crown.

Specimens of either sex had the irides brown; the eyelids plumbeous-blue; the bill black; the feet, toes, and claws wood brown.

The old male has the lores and the feathers immediately about the eye black; a conspicuous, long white supercilium; the rest of the plumage deep indigo-blue, the feathers of the center of the abdomen and the under tail coverts more or less distinctly margined with ashy gray. The adult female has the forehead, lores, and an indistinct superciliary line bright ferruginous, this color changing gradually to the olivaceous-brown of the remaining upperparts; the remiges and rectrices dark rufous; the underparts dull gray-brown, albescent on the abdomen; the under tail coverts ferruginous-buff. Between the juvenal and adult plumages, the male assumes a dress similar to that of the adult female, from which it may be at once distinguished by the white eyebrow.

BRACHYPTERYX LEUCOPHRIS CAROLINAE La Touche

CHINESE SLATE-BLUE SHORTWING

Brachypteryx carolinae LA TOUCHE, Bull. Brit. Orn. Club, vol. 8, 1898, pp. 9–10 (Kuatun, northwestern Fuhkien).

Heteroxenicus nangka RILEY, Proc. Biol. Soc. Washington, vol. 45, 1932, pp. 59–60 (Pang Mae Ton, Doi Langka, North Thailand).

Brachypteryx leucophris nangka, RILEY, U. S. Nat. Mus. Bull. 172, 1938, p. 398 (Doi Langka).—GREENWAY, Bull. Mus. Comp. Zool., 1940, p. 178 (Doi Ang Ka, Chiang Dao).

This little bird probably occurs in suitable territory throughout the provinces west of (and including) the Khun Tan chain. Smith collected four examples on Doi Langka; I found it common on Doi Ang Ka between 4,400 and 4,900 feet and the members of the Asiatic Primate Expedition took one there at an elevation of 6,000 feet. The fact that the last-named group got one also at the very base of Doi Chiang Dao (1,280 feet) and Smith another at the foot of Doi Langka seems to show that its distribution is governed wholly by the presence of dense, evergreen forest, without regard to altitude.

Those observed by me on Doi Ang Ka looked and acted like true wrens, occurring in pairs in the heaviest jungle, where they stayed near the ground, creeping about stumps, roots, and the tangle of fallen trees. The usual call was a soft *seep-seep* but, during April, the males frequently delivered a sweet song, loud out of all proportion to the size of the singer.

A male with the gonads greatly enlarged was taken on Doi Ang Ka, April 28, while a bird in postjuvenal molt was collected there September 3.

The breeding male had the irides dark brown; the maxilla blackish brown; the mandible lighter brown, with the base and the corners of the mouth fleshy white; the feet, toes, and claws fleshy. A male with inactive gonads differed in having the entire bill blackish brown; the tarsi dusky flesh; the toes fleshy plumbeous; the claws light horny brown. A nonbreeding female differed from the last only in having the mandible paler than the maxilla and fleshy at the base.

The adult of *either* sex has a short, ill-defined and partially concealed white supraloral streak, usually ending somewhere above the eye; the entire upperparts ferruginous olive-brown, the wings and abbreviated tail more rufous; the sides of the head and neck fulvous-brown; the underparts white, heavily and irregularly sullied with fulvous-brown on the breast and sides of the body (this color forming a broad but indefinite breast band).

The present form, in my opinion, differs from *nipalensis* only in that the adult male seems never to acquire a slate-blue plumage. Between *carolinae* and *nangka* I can find no difference at all.

PHOENICURUS FULIGINOSUS FULIGINOSUS Vigors

INDIAN SLATY-BLUE WATER REDSTART

Phoenicura fuliginosa VIGORS, Proc. Comm. Sci. Corr. Zool. Soc. London, pt. 1, 1830–1831 [=1831], p. 35 (Himalayas; type locality restricted to Simla-Almora district, by Ticehurst and Whistler, Ibis, 1924, p. 471).

Rhyacornis fuliginosa fuliginosa, ROGERS and DEIGNAN, Proc. Biol. Soc. Washington, 1934, p. 91 (Doi Ang Ka).

This water redstart occurs in small numbers along the Mae Klang (Doi Ang Ka), at least between 2,800 and 3,500 feet, and commonly along the Mae Mao and the Mae Chan, where these streams debouch onto the plains.

On Doi Ang Ka it associated with *Phoenicurus leucocephalus*, *Enicurus schistaceus*, *Myophonus c. eugenei*, and *Cinclus pallasii*, at a place where the current was swift and strong. It is one of the most active birds imaginable, dashing about on the wet rocks in mid-current with constantly flirted tail or making butterflylike flights into the air after some passing insect.

An adult female had the irides dark brown; the bill black; the feet horny brown; the toes darker; the claws dark brown.

The adult male has the wings blackish, the outer webs of the feathers narrowly edged slaty blue and the greater coverts with small white tips; the rectrices and upper and under tail coverts chestnut-rufous; the rest of the plumage slaty blue, somewhat paler on the abdomen. The adult female has the forehead, crown, and mantle bluish ashy, sometimes suffused with brownish; the upper tail coverts white; the wings blackish brown, the feathers edged light brown along the outer web (the inner secondaries sometimes edged ashy white), the coverts and inner secondaries with small white tips; the rectrices blackish brown with broad white bases, the white portion outwardly increasing in extent until the outermost pair are almost wholly of this color; the underparts ashy white, each feather with a bluish-ashy subterminal bar which gives this area its predominant hue (the chin, sides of the upper throat, cheeks, lores, and front often suffused with ferruginous); the under tail coverts white.

PHOENICURUS LEUCOCEPHALUS Vigors

White-capped Water Redstart

Phoenicura leucocephala Vigors, Proc. Comm. Sci. Corr. Zool. Soc. London, pt. 1, 1830–1831 [=1831], p. 35 (Himalayas; type locality restricted to Simla-Almora district, by Ticehurst and Whistler, Ibis, 1924, p. 471).

Chaimarrornis leucocephala, Greenway, Bull. Mus. Comp. Zool., 1940, p. 179 (Doi Ang Ka).

I watched a pair of white-capped redstarts at the top of the great waterfall of the Mae Klang (at the foot of Doi Ang Ka), March 15, 1930, and in April 1931 found the species occurring uncommonly along the same stream from the waterfall up to an elevation of 3,500 feet. The members of the Asiatic Primate Expedition took a female on Doi Ang Ka (probably along the Mae Klang) at 4,300 feet, February 27, 1937. The only other Thai locality from which the bird has been recorded is Doi Suthep, where a male was collected by a Thai skinner at the waterfall of Huai Kaeo (1,100 feet), March 27, 1937; this specimen was deposited in the Raffles Museum at Singapore.

The delayed discovery of so conspicuous a form on Doi Suthep, at the very spot where I had sought it unsuccessfully over a period of years, leads me to believe that it is wholly or partially migratory in Thailand and, in this connection, it is noteworthy that every observation of it on Doi Ang Ka has been made during the cold weather.

This is not quite so active a bird as the preceding species but shares with it the habit of incessant tail movement. Those seen by me fed not only on rocks jutting out of the churning water but waded about in the shallow pools at the margin of the stream. The call note is a sharp *ping*.

The adult of either sex has the crown and nape white; the rest of the head, the neck, breast, back, and wings glossy black; the rump, upper tail coverts, belly, flanks, and under tail coverts rich maroon; the tail rufous-maroon, with the apical third black; the thighs blackish brown.

PHOENICURUS AUROREUS LEUCOPTERUS Blyth

SZECHWANESE SLATY-CROWNED REDSTART

Phoenicura leucoptera BLYTH, Journ. Asiat. Soc. Bengal, vol. 12, 1843, p. 962 ("The Malay Peninsula").

Phoenicurus auroreus, DE SCHAUENSEE, Proc. Acad. Nat. Sci. Philadelphia, 1929, p. 532 (Chiang Saen Kao); 1934, p. 209 (Doi Suthep).—DEIGNAN, Journ. Siam Soc. Nat. Hist. Suppl., 1936, p. 111 (Doi Suthep).

This land redstart seems to be a rather rare winter visitor to our provinces, known by only three specimens: De Schauensee collected a male at Chiang Saen Kao, January 13, 1929, and a female on Doi Suthep, 1,500 feet, February 1, 1933, while I took a male on Doi Suthep, 5,500 feet, November 7, 1936.

My example was found perched at the top of a tangle of shrubs, thorny vines, and tall grass, shivering the tail just as does the common redstart of western Europe.

The adult male has the crown, nape, and upper back slaty gray; the center of the back black (the feathers edged with dull rufous in winter); the rump and upper tail coverts orange-rufous; the wings black, the secondaries with a large white area at the base to form a conspicuous patch; the central pair of tail feathers black, the others orange-rufous; the forehead, lores, ear coverts, sides of the neck, the chin, throat, and upper breast black; the remaining underparts orange-rufous (the feathers of the breast and belly edged with rufous-white in winter). The adult female has the upperparts dull olivaceous-brown, except for the orange-rufous rump and upper tail coverts; the wings and tail as in the adult male but with the black replaced by dark brown; the underparts gray-brown (albescent on the throat and center of the abdomen), washed with buff on the breast and upper flanks and changing to buff on the lower flanks and under tail coverts.

The breeding population of Szechwan and western Yunnan and the wintering birds of northern Thailand agree in every character with Blyth's description of *leucopterus* and are easily separable from *auroreus* of Kansu, Kiangsu, Manchuria, and Japan. The most obvious difference at any season lies in the color of the throat, which is jet black in *leucopterus* and blackish slate in *auroreus*.

RHODOPHILA FERREA (G. R. Gray)

IRON-GRAY BUSHCHAT

Saxicola ferrea G. R. GRAY, Catalogue of . . . Mammalia and birds of Nepal and Thibet . . . British Museum, 1846, pp. 71, 153 (Nepal).

Oreicola ferrea, GYLDENSTOLPE, Journ. Nat. Hist. Soc. Siam, 1915, p. 170 (listed).

Oreicola ferrea haringtoni, GYLDENSTOLPE, Kungl. Svenska Vet.-Akad. Handl., 1916, p. 52 (Khun Tan) ; Ibis, 1920, p. 475 (Khun Tan).

Oreicola ferrea ferrea, DE SCHAUENSEE, Proc. Acad. Nat. Sci. Philadelphia, 1928, p. 564 (Doi Suthep).

Oreicola ferrea harringtoni, DE SCHAUENSEE, Proc. Acad. Nat. Sci. Philadelphia, 1929, p. 542 (Doi Suthep).

Rhodophila ferrea haringtoni, DEIGNAN, Journ. Siam Soc. Nat. Hist. Suppl., 1931, p. 142 (Doi Suthep).—CHASEN and BODEN KLOSS, Journ. Siam Soc. Nat. Hist. Suppl., 1932, p. 245 (Doi Suthep).—DEIGNAN, Journ. Siam Soc. Nat. Hist. Suppl., 1936, p. 111 (Doi Suthep).—DE SCHAUENSEE, Proc. Acad. Nat. Sci. Philadelphia, 1934, p. 208 (Doi Suthep, Khun Tan, Doi Chiang Dao, ridge just south of Doi Chiang Dao).—RILEY, U. S. Nat. Mus. Bull. 172, 1938, p. 400 (Doi Ang Ka, Khum Tan, Doi Suthep, Mae Hong Son, Doi Mana, Umong valley).

The gray bushchat is a very common winter visitor to the provinces of Mae Hong Son, Chiang Mai, and Chiang Rai, occurring in suitable territory from the level of the plains to at least 5,500 feet. On Doi Suthep it has been recorded between October 10 (1936) and March 25 (1931).

This bird avoids cultivated areas—in Chiang Rai keeping to the tall grass of the open plains, in Chiang Mai haunting the deciduous jungle of the lower mountain slopes, the brush and lalang of the open hill-forest, abandoned *hai*, etc. On Doi Suthep it is a most conspicuous form during the cold weather and, while it is not truly gregarious, numbers may be found together at favored places, perched on grass and bushes or feeding on the ground along the trails. Its habits are much like those of the various species of *Saxicola*.

My specimens had the irides dark brown; the bill, feet, toes, and claws black.

The adult male, as seen with us, has the entire upperparts iron gray, the feathers of the crown and mantle more or less conspicuously fringed with dark ferruginous and each one with a sagittate black subterminal band which makes these parts appear streaked; the wings black, most of the feathers narrowly margined along the outer web with dark ashy or grayish white (this color often strongly suffused with rufous on the secondaries), the innermost coverts pure white to form a conspicuous patch; the rectrices black, narrowly margined with dark ashy or grayish white; a conspicuous white supercilium; the lores, sides of head, and ear coverts black; the chin and throat pure white; the remaining underparts ashy, changing to white on the center of the abdomen and the under tail coverts. The female differs in having the upper parts brown, this color changing to deep rufous on the upper tail coverts; the remiges and rectrices edged with rufous; the supercilium poorly defined; the lores, sides of head, and ear coverts deep brown; the underparts, below the white throat, pale brown, tinged with rufous on the lower flanks and under tail coverts.

SAXICOLA CAPRATA BURMANICA Stuart Baker

INDO-CHINESE PIED STONECHAT

Saxicola caprata burmanica STUART BAKER, Bull. Brit. Orn. Club, vol. 43, 1922, p. 19 (Pegu).

Pratincola caprata bicolor, GYLDENSTOLPE, Journ. Nat. Hist. Soc. Siam, 1915, p. 170 (listed); Kungl. Svenska Vet.-Akad. Handl., 1916, p. 51 (Khun Tan, Chiang Rai); Ibis, 1920, p. 475 ("Northern Siam").—DE SCHAUENSEE, Proc. Acad. Nat. Sci. Philadelphia, 1928, p. 563 (Chiang Mai).

Saxicola caprata burmanica, DE SCHAUENSEE, Proc. Acad. Nat. Sci. Philadelphia, 1929, p. 541 (Chiang Mai, Chiang Rai, Chiang Saen); 1934, p. 208 (Chiang Mai, "Tung Sio").—DEIGNAN, Journ. Siam Soc. Nat. Hist. Suppl., 1931, p. 141 (Chiang Mai); 1936, p. 111 (Chiang Mai).—RILEY, U. S. Nat. Mus. Bull. 172, 1938, p. 400 (Chom Thong, Chiang Mai, Chiang Dao, Muang Pai, Mae Hong Son).

On the open plains of Mae Hong Son, Chiang Mai, and Chiang Rai Provinces the pied stonechat is a common or locally abundant permanent resident; I found it numerous in the cleared valley below Pha Mon on Doi Ang Ka, 4,200 to 4,400 feet, but it is otherwise known only from the lowlands. It is extraordinary that no form of the species has been recorded from the districts east of the Khun Tan range, although the present race occurs again in the southern parts of Indochine.

This is a conspicuous bird in the vicinity of Chiang Mai, seen, usually in pairs, perched upon hedges and fences along roadsides, on tall grass and thorny shrubs at areas of abandoned cultivation, and, especially after harvest, on bunds and bushes in the ricefields, from which points of vantage it repeatedly makes short flights after insects, whether these be in the air or on the ground.

I took a bird in full juvenal dress at Chiang Mai, July 1, and Gyldenstolpe has recorded (1916) a similar specimen from Chiang Rai, August 1.

An adult female had the irides brown; the bill, feet, and toes blackish brown; the claws black.

The adult male has the entire plumage black, except for a large patch on the wing coverts and inner secondaries and the upper and under tail coverts, all of which are pure white. The adult female has the crown and mantle dark grayish brown, the feathers with darker centers; the upper tail coverts ferruginous; the remiges and rectrices blackish brown, the former narrowly edged with pale rufous; the underparts grayish brown (the feathers of the throat, breast, upper abdomen, and flanks usually with darker centers), more or less suffused with pale rufous; the under tail coverts and thighs pale rufous. Juveniles of either sex resemble the adult female but the young male may be known by his whitish wing patch.

S. c. burmanica was originally separated from *caprata* on slight size differences alleged to exist between adult males of the two forms; Ticehurst, showing that these distinctions do not hold, has synonymized *burmanica* with *caprata* (Ibis, 1938, pp. 221–222). Comparison of adult females, however, shows that continental birds are easily separable by their darker underparts, this character appearing most markedly on the breast, the feathers of which have broader dark centers, with resultant reduction of the amount of pale rufous.

SAXICOLA TORQUATA STEJNEGERI (Parrot)

Japanese Rufous-breasted Stonechat

Pr[atincola] rubicola stejnegeri Parrot, Verh. Orn. Ges. Bayern, vol. 8, 1908, p. 124 ("Iterup" [Yetorofu] and "Jesso" [Hokkaido], Northern Japan).

Pratincola torquata stejnegeri, Gyldenstolpe, Kungl. Svenska Vet.-Akad. Handl., 1916, p. 51 ("Ban Kia"); Ibis, 1920, p. 475 ("Several parts of Siam").

Saxicola torquata stejnegeri [*partim*], de Schauensee, Proc. Acad. Nat. Sci. Philadelphia, 1929, p. 542 (Chiang Mai, Chiang Rai [*partim*], Chiang Saen); 1934, p. 208 ("Tung Sio").

Saxicola torquata stejnegeri, Deignan, Journ. Siam Soc. Nat. Hist. Suppl., 1931, p. 142 (Chiang Mai); 1936, p. 111 (Doi Suthep, Chiang Mai).—Riley, U. S. Nat. Mus. Bull. 172, 1938, p. 400 (Nan).

The Japanese stonechat is a common winter visitor to the lowlands of all our provinces between September 16 (Chiang Mai) and April 16 (Nan). It has, however, also been found several times on the high mountains of Chiang Mai Province: at "Ban Kia," 4,600 feet, August 24; on Doi Ang Ka, 4,200 feet, *ca.* September 2; on Doi Suthep, 5,500 feet, September 7; on the same hill, 3,300 feet, March 7. I suggest that these montane individuals, which vanish from the area in advance of the first arrival of lowland wintering birds and pass again to the North before the latter's departure, have their origin in some northern territory more or less remote geographically from that of their racial brethren of the plains. Stanford has noted (Ibis, 1938, p. 222) a similar small migration through the hills of the Myitkyina district of northern Burma, between March 15 and April 21.

The account of the habits of the pied stonechat will apply equally well to this species. It may be said here that the English vernacular name of the genus is quite inappropriate to the birds seen in Thailand, inasmuch as rocks are infrequent or wholly lacking in the cultivated lands inhabited by them.

My specimens had the irides dark brown; the bill black; the interior of the mouth whitish; the feet, toes, and claws black; the soles yellow.

The adult male, as seen in our region, has the entire head, the chin and throat, and the upperparts black, the feathers with more or less broad buffy-brown edgings; the inner upper wing coverts and most of the basal half of the innermost secondaries white (more or less suffused with rufous-buff), to form a conspicuous wing patch; the upper tail coverts white, more or less suffused with rufous-buff; the tail black; the sides of the breast and lower throat pure white, this color extending onto the sides of the neck to form a broadly interrupted nuchal collar; the center of the breast buffy rufous or chestnut-rufous, this color more or less strongly suffusing the white of the remaining underparts; the under wing coverts and the axillaries black, narrowly tipped with white. The winter female has the feathers of crown and mantle blackish brown, broadly edged with buffy brown; the wing patch as in the male; the upper tail coverts rufous-buff; the tail blackish brown; an ill-defined buffy-white superciliary line; the chin and throat white, sometimes tinged with buff; the remaining underparts, including the under wing coverts and axillaries, rufous-buff. The young male is at first like the female but, in spring, begins to assume color characters of the adult.

SAXICOLA TORQUATA YUNNANENSIS (La Touche)

YUNNANESE RUFOUS-BREASTED STONECHAT

Pratincola torquata yunnanensis LA TOUCHE, Bull. Brit. Orn. Club, vol. 43, 1923, pp. 134–135 (Shuitang and Mengtz, southeastern Yunnan).

Saxicola torquata stejnegeri [*partim*], DE SCHAUENSEE, Proc. Acad. Nat. Sci. Philadelphia, 1929, p. 542 (Chiang Rai [*partim*]).

An adult female collected by de Schauensee at Chiang Rai, January 5, 1929, and an adult male taken by his men on Doi Pha Hom Pok, 6,400 feet, February 7, 1938, are the only examples of this race yet known from our provinces.

Typical specimens of *yunnanensis* differ from *stejnegeri* in their greater dimensions and in having the chestnut-rufous of the underparts decidedly deeper everywhere.

The male recorded (1934) by de Schauensee from Kiu Loi, 3,500 feet, Kengtung State, is also of the present form.

LUSCINIA CYANE (Pallas)

BLUE GROUNDCHAT

Motacilla Cyane PALLAS, Reise durch verschiedene Provinzen des russischen Reichs, vol. 3, 1776, pp. 220 (footnote), 697 ("In Dauuriæ extremis campis inter Ononem et Argunum").

Larvivora cyanea, GYLDENSTOLPE, Kungl. Svenska Vet.-Akad. Handl., 1916, p. 49 (Khun Tan).—DE SCHAUENSEE, Proc. Acad. Nat. Sci. Philadelphia, 1929, p. 541 (Doi Suthep, Chiang Saen).

Larvivora cyane, DEIGNAN, Journ. Siam Soc. Nat. Hist. Suppl., 1931, p. 141 (Doi Suthep).—DE SCHAUENSEE, Proc. Acad. Nat. Sci. Philadelphia, 1934, p. 208 (Doi Suthep, Foot of Doi Chiang Dao).—RILEY, U. S. Nat. Mus. Bull. 172, 1938, p. 399 (Mae Khan).

Larvivora cyane cyane, DEIGNAN, Journ. Siam Soc. Nat. Hist. Suppl., 1936, p. 111 (Doi Suthep).

This chat is an apparently rare winter visitor, at least to the provinces of Chiang Mai and Chiang Rai, between September 22 (1914) and May 6 (1914), ranging from the level of the plains to 2,800 feet. Specimens taken on the extreme dates at Khun Tan by Gyldenstolpe led him to believe that the species is resident in our area but it seems rather to be one of a small number of Siberian forms which arrive early in autumn and depart late in spring. It has been recorded by other observers only in January and February.

It is a silent and retiring bird, found by Gyldenstolpe in the undergrowth of dense forest and by de Schauensee and myself in extensive brakes of bamboo; the only one collected by me was discovered walking about, with occasional jerks of the tail, in the deep shade of overarching bamboos near the ruins of Wat Umong, at the base of Doi Suthep.

Dried museum skins indicate that there is seasonal change in the colors of the soft parts of this species, which may account for discrepancies in published descriptions. My example, an old male (February 9), had the irides dark brown; the maxilla blackish brown, horny brown toward the tip; the mandible with the apical half pale fleshy, the basal half white; the feet, toes, and claws pale fleshy. One of Gyldenstolpe's specimens (taken in May?) had the irides brown; the bill horny black; the feet and toes pale brown.

The adult male has the entire upperparts and the sides of the head, neck, and breast dark slaty blue; the remiges and rectrices blackish, suffused with slaty blue; the lores and a narrow line edging the ear coverts and the blue of neck and sides of breast black; the sides of the body bluish slate; the remaining underparts pure white. The adult female has the upperparts olivaceous-brown, suffused with rufous on the upper tail coverts; the wing feathers olivaceous-brown, narrowly edged with rufous; the underparts white, the feathers of the throat, breast, and sides of the body more or less strongly suffused with buff, those of the breast with narrow, faintly darker edges to give a squamated appearance. The first-winter male resembles the adult female but often has the upper tail coverts and rectrices suffused with slaty blue.

Shulpin has separated the population of South Ussuri-land, under the name *Larvivora cyane bochaiensis* (Ezhegodnik Zoologicheskogo Muzeia, Akademiia Nauk SSSR, vol. 27, 1927, pp. 404–405), as being darker and less grayish than *cyane*. All specimens seen from Hokkaido answer to this description, in contrast to those from other localities, but I am informed by Delacour and Mayr (*in epist.*) that topotypical material is unstable and that the race cannot be maintained. Since Japanese ornithologists list only the nominate form from their islands, it seems best to assume that the uniformity of coloration shown by my Hokkaido skins is accidental and that the species cannot be divided.

LUSCINIA CALLIOPE CALLIOPE (Pallas)

SIBERIAN RUBYTHROAT

Motacilla Calliope PALLAS, Reise durch verschiedene Provinzen des russischen Reichs, vol. 3, 1776, pp. 261, 325, 697 ("A Ienisea vsque ad Lenam").

Calliope calliope, DEIGNAN, Journ. Siam Soc. Nat. Hist. Suppl., 1931, p. 142 (Chiang Mai); 1936, p. 112 (Chiang Mai, Doi Suthep).—DE SCHAUENSEE, Proc. Acad. Nat. Sci. Philadelphia, 1934, p. 210 (Doi Suthep, Chiang Mai, Doi Chiang Dao).—RILEY, U. S. Nat. Mus. Bull. 172, 1938, p. 404 (Chiang Mai, Doi Langka).

The Siberian rubythroat is common in migration (October, March) and somewhat less so during the intervening months, at least in the provinces of Mae Hong Son and Chiang Mai; it occurs chiefly on the plains but has been taken once on Doi Suthep at 2,500 feet (January) and twice on Doi Chiang Dao at 4,500 feet (November, January). At Chiang Mai the extreme dates are October 7 (1936) and April 3 (1931).

This bird, like the preceding, haunts dense thickets and bamboo brakes, especially such as follow abandonment of cultivation, rarely ascending so high as 2 feet above ground and keeping its back turned to the observer in such a way as to conceal the red throat patch.

My winter-collected specimens had the irides brown; the bill dark brown, light horny brown at the base; the tarsi horny brown or light pinkish brown, whitish behind; the toes and claws light horny brown.

The adult male, as seen in Thailand, has the entire upper plumage olivaceous-brown, the wing feathers narrowly edged with rufous; a narrow supercilium white; the lores and area immediately below the eye black; a conspicuous mustachial line white; the chin and throat shining crimson-scarlet, narrowly edged with black; the upper breast, next to the black, dark gray, changing to buffy brown on the lower breast and upper flanks, the last-named color changing to buff on the lower flanks and to white on the center of the abdomen; the under tail coverts white, more or less strongly washed with buff. The adult female and first-winter male differ in having the supercilium and indistinct mustachial streak buffy white; the lores and area below the eye blackish brown; the chin and throat white, more or less suffused with buffy brown and not clearly defined from the buffy-brown breast and sides of neck.

LUSCINIA SVECICA WEIGOLDI Kleinschmidt

MANCHURIAN BLUETHROAT

Luscinia svecica weigoldi KLEINSCHMIDT, Author's abstract of "Turdinæ, I. Teil," *ex* Abh. Ber. Mus. Tierk. Völkerk. Dresden, vol. 16, No. 2, 1923–1924 [=*ante* October 3, 1924, when a copy was received at Washington from Germany], p. 8 (Bago, 90 km. east of Jehol [Ch'êng-tê-fu]).

Luscinia svecica weigoldi KLEINSCHMIDT, Abh. Ber. Mus. Tierk. Völkerk. Dresden, vol. 16, No. 2, 1923–1924 [=December 1, 1924], p. 43 (Bago, 90 km. east of Jehol [Ch'êng-tê-fu]).

Cyanosylvia suecica robusta, DEIGNAN, Journ. Siam Soc. Nat. Hist. Suppl., 1931, p. 142 (Chiang Mai); 1936, p. 111 (Chiang Mai).

The bluethroat has been taken only at Sala Mae Tha and Chiang Mai; at the latter place it is a regular winter visitor in small numbers at suitable localities and has been recorded between October 24 (1931) and March 28 (1931).

I found this species only at the edges of drying *nong*, feeding on the ground at muddy places in company with stints and wagtails and, at the least alarm, vanishing into the dense cover of rushes and sedges, where it was as well concealed as any small rail. It seems to be a solitary bird, although some numbers may occur in close proximity as favorable areas become reduced by drought and the harvesting of marsh vegetation.

A male had the irides brown; the bill black, yellow at the base; the interior of the mouth yellow; the feet and toes brown; the soles yellowish; the claws black.

The adult male, in full plumage, has the entire upperparts grayish brown, the feathers of the forehead and crown with blackish centers, those of the rump and upper tail coverts sometimes partly rufous; the wings grayish brown, the greater coverts narrowly tipped with pale rufous; the central pair of rectrices wholly blackish brown, the remainder similar but with the basal half rufous (conspicuous in flight); a narrow white supercilium; the chin and upper throat shining bright blue; the center of the lower throat and the upper breast covered by a large patch of rufous, narrowly bordered by shining bright blue; a narrow black breast band succeeding the blue border and this followed by a narrow white band and a broad band of rufous; the remaining underparts white, washed with buff, especially along the flanks and on the under tail coverts. The adult female differs chiefly in having a white mustachial streak; the chin and throat buffy white, more or less washed with rufous below, this area edged at the sides by a narrow black line and below by a band of mixed black and blue, which, in turn, is followed by a narrow and poorly defined rufous band. As seen in Thailand, the adult male has the blue of the chin and upper throat and the rufous of the lower throat and upper breast more or less completely replaced by white. A juvenile female from Chiang Mai (January 30) differs from the adult in the complete absence of blue and rufous below and in having the breast feathers blackish brown with white edgings to form a broad speckled gorget.

Thai males, differing from *robusta* in rather shorter wing length (70 to 75 mm.) and decidedly shorter *wing tip*, agree perfectly with a series of Chihli specimens taken late in May and early in September.

TARSIGER CYANURUS RUFILATUS (Hodgson)

NEPALESE ORANGE-FLANKED BUSHROBIN

N[emura] rufilatus HODGSON, Proc. Zool. Soc. London, 1845, pt. 13, p. 27 (Nepal).
Ianthia rufilata rufilata, DEIGNAN, Journ. Siam Soc. Nat. Hist. Suppl., 1936, p. 112 (Doi Suthep).
Tarsiger cyanurus rufilatus, GREENWAY, Bull. Mus. Comp. Zool., 1940, p. 180 (Doi Ang Ka).

The present race of the orange-flanked bushrobin is known from Thailand by only four specimens: a female taken by me on Doi Suthep, 4,500 feet, February 8, 1936, and a juvenile male and two females collected by the Asiatic Primate Expedition at the summit of Doi Ang Ka, March 23 and 28, 1937.

My example was found alone at a clearing, just where the evergreen gave way to pine, flitting about the vine-tangled branches of a fallen tree.

The full-plumaged male has the forehead, supercilium, shoulder area, rump, and upper tail coverts shining bright blue; the upperparts otherwise deep cobalt blue or ultramarine; the sides of the head, neck, throat, and breast deep cobalt blue (sometimes almost blackish blue at the sides of the breast); the chin and center of the throat pure white; the sides of the body golden-orange; the remaining underparts white, sullied with gray (most strongly on the breast and upper abdomen). The adult female has the crown and mantle olivaceous-brown, changing to olivaceous gray-blue on the rump and upper tail coverts; the tail dull blue; the chin and center of the throat white; the sides of the body golden-orange; the remaining underparts pale olivaceous-brown, changing to sullied white on the center of the lower abdomen and the under tail coverts.

T. c. practicus, described from southeastern Yunnan, apparently ranges as far north as Shensi, but northwestern Yunnan and southern

Szechwan are inhabited by *rufilatus*. *T. c. albocoeruleus*, the white-browed race of Kansu, seems not to occur, even in winter, south of northern Szechwan.

TARSIGER CYANURUS USSURIENSIS Stegmann

JAPANESE ORANGE-FLANKED BUSHROBIN

Tarsiger cyanurus ussuriensis "Sushk. (in litt.)" STEGMANN, Ezhegodnik Zoologicheskogo Muzeia, Akademiia Nauk SSSR [Ann. Musée Zool. Acad. Sci. U. R. S. S.], vol. 29 [for] 1928, 1929, p. 229 (Ussuri-land and Manchuria).

Ianthia cyanura cyanura, DE SCHAUENSEE, Proc. Acad. Nat. Sci. Philadelphia, 1929, p. 543 (Doi Suthep).—DEIGNAN, Journ. Siam Soc. Nat. Hist. Suppl., 1931, p. 142 (Doi Suthep).—RILEY, U. S. Nat. Mus. Bull. 172, 1938, p. 404 (Doi Ang Ka).

Ianthia cyanura, DEIGNAN, Journ. Siam Soc. Nat. Hist. Suppl., 1936, p. 112 (Doi Suthep).

Tarsiger cyanurus cyanurus, GREENWAY, Bull. Mus. Comp. Zool., 1940, p. 179 (Doi Ang Ka).

Like the preceding form, the Japanese orange-flanked bushrobin is known from Thailand by only four examples: De Schauensee took an adult male (observed in company with a female several times between December 7 and 12) on Doi Suthep, 5,500 feet, December 12, 1928; Smith collected an adult female on Doi Ang Ka, 8,000 feet, December 5, 1928, and an adult male the following day at 8,400 feet; the members of the Asiatic Primate Expedition shot a female at the summit of Doi Ang Ka, March 30, 1937.

The old male differs from that of *rufilatus* chiefly in having the upperparts cerulean blue, the feathers of the mantle often narrowly tipped with olivaceous-brown; that portion of the supercilium between the base of the bill and the eye white (sometimes washed with pale blue); the white streak down the center of the throat broader and more flaring on the upper breast; the white portions of the underparts often more or less strongly suffused with buff. The adult female differs from that of *rufilatus* in having the white streak down the center of the throat broader and more flaring on the breast; the olivaceous-brown portions of the underparts usually strongly tinged with buff.

According to Stegmann (*loc. cit.*), the adult male of *cyanurus* is customarily colored like the female—only in rare instances assuming a blue plumage; that of *ussuriensis* is "always" blue. The two males taken in Thailand have both been blue and it may be assumed that of the two only *ussuriensis* occurs with us.

MYIOMELA LEUCURA LEUCURA (Hodgson)

INDIAN WHITE-TAILED GROUNDROBIN

M[uscisylvia] leucura HODGSON, Proc. Zool. Soc. London, pt. 13, 1845, p. 27 (Nepal).

Notodela leucura, DE SCHAUENSEE, Proc. Acad. Nat. Sci. Philadelphia, 1929, p. 543 (Chiang Saen).

Muscisylvia leucura, DEIGNAN, Journ. Siam Soc. Nat. Hist. Suppl., 1931, p. 142 (Doi Suthep); 1935, p. 65 (Doi Ang Ka); 1936, p. 112 (Doi Suthep).—DE SCHAUENSEE, Proc. Acad. Nat. Sci. Philadelphia, 1934, p. 210 (Khun Tan).—RILEY, U. S. Nat. Mus. Bull. 172, 1938, p. 405 (Doi Langka, "Ban Padieng").

The groundrobin occurs in dense, damp evergreen forest (rarely in adjacent areas of thick bamboo), at elevations from the level of the plains (Chiang Saen) to 5,200 feet (Doi Ang Ka). In addition to the localities named above, it has been found at Doi Nang Kaeo, Doi Chiang Dao, and Phu Kha. The sole record for Doi Suthep is a female taken at 3,200 feet, February 24, 1931.

This shy species keeps to the ground in heavy forest along streams or in shady ravines and is not likely to be seen unless it comes out for a moment onto some jungle track. On Doi Ang Ka, between 4,400 and 5,200 feet, in April, I often heard it singing; the song, short but sweet and strong, is reminiscent of the songs of the American thrushes of the genus *Hylocichla*.

A male of November 12 is in postnuptial molt; others of September 2 and December 5 are in postjuvenal molt. Young birds of either sex molt directly from the juvenal dress to that of the adult but the change is not always complete the first year: a male of December 7 (not molting) is in wholly adult plumage except for the retention of the juvenal greater upper wing coverts; another of May 6 (not molting) has not only these juvenal wing coverts but the feathers at the sides of the upper back colored exactly as in the adult female and the feathers of the breast tipped full rufous. An old female of February 28 has some of the scapulars blue, as in the male, and the rectrices suffused with blue.

An adult male had the irides brown; the bill black; the feet, toes, and claws blackish brown. An adult female had the irides dark brown; the bill black, with the base of the mandible fleshy; the rictus and interior of the mouth yellow; the feet and toes horny violet; the soles white; the claws horn.

The adult male has the forehead, forecrown, eyebrow, and point of the shoulder shining blue; the remaining upperparts (including the wings) deep blue; the rectrices black, all except the central and outermost pairs with a patch of pure white at the base of the outer web (outwardly decreasing in extent); some of the feathers at each side of the lower throat with pure white bases, to form two small, concealed patches; the feathers of the lower flanks with at least part of the bases white, to form larger concealed patches; the remaining underparts deep blue (so dark on the breast, throat, and chin as to be almost black). The adult female has the upperparts olivaceous-brown, suffused with rufous on the mantle; the remiges edged with bright rufous; the tail as in the male but with the black replaced by olivaceous-brown; the same concealed white patches at the sides of the lower throat and on the lower flanks as in the male; the throat and breast olivaceous-brown (the throat usually paler), more or less strongly suffused with rufous; the remaining underparts olivaceous-brown, changing to ashy on the center of the abdomen and albescent on the under tail coverts. The juvenile has the feathers of the crown and mantle dark rufous-brown with light rufous shaft streaks; the remiges and rectrices exactly as in the adult of corresponding sex; the underparts light rufous, changing to buff on the center of the abdomen, all the feathers with blackish edgings; the under tail coverts ashy, suffused with buff.

COPSYCHUS SAULARIS ERIMELAS Oberholser

INDO-CHINESE MAGPIE ROBIN

Copsychus saularis erimelas OBERHOLSER, Smithsonian Misc. Coll., vol. 76, No. 6, 1923, pp. 1–2 ("Kankarit, Houndraw Branch, Tenasserim"; type specimen from "Kaukarit, Houndraw R^r^" [=Kaukareyit, Haungdaraw river, Amherst District]).

Copsychus saularis, GYLDENSTOLPE, Kungl. Svenska Vet.-Akad. Handl., 1913, p. 39 (Ban Huai Hom); Journ. Nat. Hist. Soc. Siam, 1915, p. 170 (listed).

Copsychus saularis saularis, GYLDENSTOLPE, Kungl. Svenska Vet-Akad. Handl. 1916, p. 50 (Khun Tan, Ban Mae Na); Ibis, 1920, p. 477 (Northern . . . Siam").—DE SCHAUENSEE, Proc. Acad. Nat. Sci. Philadelphia, 1928, p. 564 (Chiang Mai); 1929, p. 543 (Chiang Mai); 1934, p. 210 (Chiang Mai).—DEIGNAN, Journ. Siam Soc. Nat. Hist. Suppl., 1931, p. 142 (Chiang Mai); 1936, p. 112 (Chiang Mai).—RILEY, U. S. Nat. Mus. Bull. 172, 1938, p. 406 (Ban Nam Khian).

The magpie robin may sometimes be seen along trails in wild bamboo jungle, but its true home is in the immediate vicinity of human dwellings, whether in large towns or diminutive settlements. Throughout our provinces it is really a lowland form, but I found it common also on Doi Ang Ka, between 4,200 and 4,400 feet, near the Karen village of Ban Nong Lom, and a few pairs still dwelt in the abandoned Yao clearing on Phu Kha at 4,500 feet.

This is the charming black and white (or gray and white) bird that hunts for earthworms and insects on lawns and garden plots, constantly elevating the tail perpendicularly to the line of the back or spreading it broadly like a fan. It is an indefatigable singer almost throughout the year but chiefly from January to July, and its sweet strains may be heard in a veritable chorus at dawn and again at dusk from the tops of trees, the ridgepoles of houses, the posts of fences, or wherever else it finds an exposed perch. Its numbers, familiarity with man, and preference for a diet of insects make it, economically, one of our most valuable species.

At Chiang Mai, specimens with the gonads active have been collected between February 25 and May 8, while examples in full juvenal plumage have been taken there July 5.

A juvenile female had the irides dark brown; the bill black; the rictus and interior of the mouth light yellow; the feet and toes slate; the claws horny slate.

The adult male has the entire head and neck, breast, and mantle glossy blue-black; the wings black, with a conspicuous, longitudinal white stripe; the two central pairs of rectrices black, the next pair white with a black margin along the inner web, the remaining pairs pure white; the underparts, below the breast, pure white. The adult female differs only in having the upper half of the head and the mantle blue-gray with a steely sheen; the chin, throat, and breast deep ashy gray. The juvenile differs from the adults in having the upperparts slaty brown; the remiges outwardly edged with pale rufous and the white of the coverts sullied with this color; the third pair of rectrices from the center with a black margin along both inner and outer webs; the chin, throat, and breast rufous-buff, each feather narrowly margined with blackish; the white of the remaining underparts more or less washed with rufous-buff.

Since the birds of nonpeninsular Thailand are intermediate between *musicus* (Sumatra) and *saularis* (Bengal), with just the characters attributed by Oberholser to his *erimelas*, this name may properly be employed for them.

In this species the amount of black on the rectrices gradually decreases from south to north and it is instructive to find that, at any given latitude in Thailand, juveniles tend to have more black on these feathers than their parents, thus seeming to belong with a more southern population.

KITTACINCLA MALABARICA INTERPOSITA Robinson and Boden Kloss

INDO-CHINESE SHAMA

Kittacincla malabarica interposita ROBINSON and BODEN KLOSS, Journ. Federated Malay States Mus., vol. 10, 1922, p. 262 (Daban, South Annam).

Copsychus macrurus, SCHOMBURGK, Ibis, 1864, p. 262 (Chiang Mai).

Cittocincla macrura, GYLDENSTOLPE, Kungl. Svenska Vet.-Akad. Handl., 1913, p. 39 (Den Chai, Ban Huai Hom); Journ. Nat. Hist. Soc. Siam, 1915, p. 170 (listed).

Kittocincla macrurus tricolor, GYLDENSTOLPE, Kungl. Svenska Vet.-Akad. Handl., 1916, p. 50 (Pha Kho, Khun Tan, Doi Pha Sakaeng).

Kittacincla macrura tricolor, GYLDENSTOLPE, Ibis, 1920, p. 477 ("Throughout Siam").

Kittocincla malabarica interposita, DE SCHAUENSEE, Proc. Acad. Nat. Sci. Philadelphia, 1928, p. 564 (Chiang Mai); 1929, p. 543 (Chiang Mai, Doi Suthep).

Kittacincla malabarica interposita, DEIGNAN, Journ. Siam Soc. Nat. Hist. Suppl., 1931, p. 143 (Chiang Mai, Doi Suthep); 1936, p. 112 (Chiang Mai, Doi Suthep).

Kittacincla malabarica malabarica, DE SCHAUENSEE, Proc. Acad. Nat. Sci. Philadelphia, 1934, p. 210 (Chiang Mai).

The shama is a common resident of all the northern provinces from the level of the plains to about 4,600 feet (Doi Suthep), occurring chiefly in bamboo jungle at whatever elevation but frequently seen also in the evergreen, if it be not too dense.

This species is sometimes found in villages, where ancient clumps of giant bamboo overhang the drainage ditches and the gardens are deeply shaded by mango and longan, but it is not really a dooryard form, preferring to dwell rather in wild bamboo brakes at a distance from human habitation. Its singing, often continued without pause for minutes at a time, is, in my opinion, superior in sweetness and variety to that of any other bird of our forests and, heard from some dark thicket at early evening, is one of the loveliest sounds imaginable. In habits, the shama seems to differ in no important way from the magpie robin.

I took a male with the gonads greatly enlarged, May 30, and specimens in full juvenal dress, June 13 and July 21, but Eisenhofer sent to Stockholm juveniles shot as early as May 25. Postjuvenal molt is shown by a bird of July 2, postnuptial molt by examples of July 26 and August 31.

A breeding male had the irides dark brown; the bill black; the feet, toes, and claws fleshy.

The adult male has the entire head and neck, breast, and mantle glossy blue-black; the rump and upper tail coverts pure white; the remiges black; the long, strongly graduated tail with the two central pairs of feathers black, the next two pairs with the basal half black and apical half white, the two remaining pairs pure white; the underparts, below the breast, chestnut-rufous; the thighs white, sometimes more or less suffused with rufous. The adult female differs in having the head and neck, breast, and mantle slaty gray (the crown and mantle sometimes with a steely sheen); the underparts, below the breast, orange-rufous. The juvenile may readily be known by its white rump and long tail, patterned like that of the adult. The changes from the immature plumage to that of the old adult are complicated and should be studied by someone with suitable material at hand.

Gyldenstolpe (1916) and de Schauensee (1934) have each considered northern Thai birds to be distinct from more southern ones (*interposita*), but my own material does not support this view. If they be correct, our shama must, at least in part, be known either as *indica* or *pellogyna*. Whistler and Kinnear (Journ. Bombay Nat. Hist. Soc., vol. 36, 1932, p. 75) have recognized *indica* as separable from *mala-*

barica but have not shown how it may be distinguished from *pellogyna*. I strongly suspect, however, that these putative races will prove to be one and the same thing as *interposita*, which will then have a range exactly coinciding with that of *Copsychus s. erimelas*.

MONTICOLA GULARIS (Swinhoe)

WHITE-THROATED ROCK THRUSH

Oroecetes gularis SWINHOE, Proc. Zool. Soc. London, 1862, p. 318 (Tientsin, China).

Monticola gularis, GYLDENSTOLPE, Kungl. Svenska Vet.-Akad. Handl., 1916, p. 48 (Khun Tan); Ibis, 1920, p. 478 (Khun Tan).

Monticola gularis gularis, DE SCHAUENSEE, Proc. Acad. Nat. Sci. Philadelphia, 1934, p. 212 (Doi Suthep).—DEIGNAN, Journ. Siam. Soc. Nat. Hist. Suppl., 1936, p. 113 (Doi Suthep).

This little rock thrush is hardly more than a straggler to northern Thailand, whence it has been recorded only twice: An undated male shot by Eisenhofer's collector at Khun Tan (specimen in Stockholm); a male taken by de Schauensee on Doi Suthep, 1,500 feet, December 18, 1932.

The male, in winter dress, has the forehead, crown, nape, and center of the upper back violet-blue, each feather with a narrow black subterminal bar and narrow grayish-buff tip; the mantle black, each feather with a conspicuous grayish-buff margin, changing on the rump and upper tail coverts to chestnut-rufous, each feather with a buffy margin; the tail slaty; the wings blackish with a large violet-blue shoulder patch, the outer secondaries with a conspicuous white area near the base of the outer web, the inner secondaries and the greater coverts tipped and margined along the outer web with white or buffy white; the ear coverts black, tipped with grayish buff; the throat with a white central streak which flares broadly on the uppermost part of the breast; the remaining underparts chestnut-rufous, paling on the center of the abdomen and the under tail coverts, the feathers of the sides of the throat, breast, and flanks narrowly margined with grayish buff. The female in winter has the upperparts grayish brown, the feathers of the mantle with crescentic black subterminal bars and grayish-buff tips, the upper tail coverts barred grayish buff and black throughout; the throat patch exactly as in the male; the feathers beneath and behind the ear coverts with broad buffy-white tips and central streaks, to form a light area at either side of the neck; the remaining underparts buffy white, the feathers conspicuously marked with crescentic black bars except on the center of the abdomen, the under tail coverts, the under wing coverts, and the axillaries.

MONTICOLA RUFIVENTRIS (Jardine and Selby)

CHESTNUT-BELLIED ROCK THRUSH

Petrocincla rufiventris JARDINE and SELBY, Illustrations of ornithology, ser. 1, vol. 3, pt. 9, no date [=1833], pl. 129 and text ("The Himmalayan district").

Monticola erythrogastra, DE SCHAUENSEE, Proc. Acad. Nat. Sci. Philadelphia, 1929, p. 543 (Doi Suthep).

Monticola rufiventris, DEIGNAN, Journ. Siam Soc. Nat. Hist. Suppl., 1931, p. 143 (Doi Suthep).—DE SCHAUENSEE, Proc. Acad. Nat. Sci. Philadelphia, 1934, p. 211 (Doi Chiang Dao).—RILEY, U. S. Nat. Mus. Bull. 172, 1938, p. 415 (Khun Tan, Doi Langka).

Monticola rufiventris sinensis, DEIGNAN, Journ. Siam Soc. Nat. Hist. Suppl., 1936, p. 113 (Doi Suthep).

The chestnut-bellied rock thrush is of regular but uncommon occurrence on the higher mountains of the Thanon Thong Chai and Khun Tan ranges, from 4,000 to 5,500 feet; it has been found only between November 4 (Doi Langka) and February 6 (Doi Suthep) but probably arrives earlier and departs later than these dates would imply.

I have observed this bird, not at rocky places, but at clearings in the evergreen and along forest trails.

An apparently adult male of November 23 has the central pair of rectrices only half-grown.

De Schauensee states (1929) that an immature male had the irides brown; the bill horn; the feet and toes brownish black.

The adult male has the entire upperparts rich blue, brighter on the forecrown, shoulder, rump, and upper tail coverts (in winter with narrow ashy tips to the feathers of the mantle and narrow white tips to the remiges and greater coverts); the lores, ocular region, and ear coverts black; the chin and throat dull blue (the feathers with narrow ashy tips in winter); the remaining underparts, including the under wing coverts and axillaries, rich chestnut. The adult female has the entire upperparts plumbeous-gray, the feathers of the mantle with narrow blackish shaft streaks and crescentic subterminal bars, the upper tail coverts barred plumbeous-gray and blackish throughout; the throat with a pale buffy or buffy-white central streak, which flares somewhat on the uppermost part of the breast; the feathers beneath and behind the ear coverts buff, with narrow black tips, forming an indefinite mustachial streak and a conspicuous light patch at each side of the neck; the remaining underparts pale buffy or buffy white, each feather with broad, crescentic blackish bars.

MONTICOLA SOLITARIUS PANDOO (Sykes)

INDIAN BLUE ROCK THRUSH

Petrocincla Pandoo SYKES, Proc. Comm. Sci. Corr. Zool. Soc. London, pt. 2, 1832, p. 87 ("The Dukhun").

Monticola cyanea, GYLDENSTOLPE, Journ. Nat. Hist. Soc. Siam, 1915, p. 170 (listed).
Monticola cyanus solitaria, DE SCHAUENSEE, Proc. Acad. Nat. Sci. Philadelphia, 1928, p. 565 (Chiang Mai).
Monticola solitaria pandoo, GYLDENSTOLPE, Ibis, 1920, p. 478 ("Siam").—DE SCHAUENSEE, Proc. Acad. Nat. Sci. Philadelphia, 1929, p. 544 (Chiang Mai, Doi Suthep, Chiang Saen); 1934, p. 212 (Chiang Mai, Doi Suthep, Khun Tan, Doi Chiang Dao).—DEIGNAN, Journ. Siam Soc. Nat. Hist. Suppl., 1931, p. 143 (Chiang Mai, Doi Suthep); 1936, p. 113 (Chiang Mai, Doi Suthep).—RILEY, U. S. Nat. Mus. Bull. 172, 1938, p. 416 (Khun Tan, Doi Ang Ka, Chiang Mai, Mae Khan, "Ban Padieng").—GREENWAY, Bull. Mus. Comp. Zool., 1940, p. 181 (Chiang Mai, Doi Ang Ka).

The Indian blue rock thrush is a very common winter visitor to the provinces west of (and including) the Khun Tan chain; I place here also certain specimens taken by de Schauensee and myself in Chiang Rai Province, though it should be noted that no adult male has yet been collected in that area and that their subspecific identification is therefore subject to revision. The race occurs from the level of the plains up to at least 5,500 feet (Doi Suthep); the extreme dates of its stay in the Chiang Mai district are September 5 (1931) and April 2 (1931).

This thrush will probably never be found in the evergreen, but it is likely to occur in any other type of forest and also in cultivated areas. Its chief requirement is the presence of rock faces, and man-made masonry forms so satisfactory a substitute for natural walls that it is perhaps even more numerous about the monasteries of towns and villages than at mountain cliffs. At Chiang Mai it was constantly to be seen on the ridgepoles of houses and the tops of garden walls, whence it would dash from time to time in pursuit of some insect on the ground or in the air. The only note heard in the cold season is a low clucking sound, accompanied by an upward flick of the tail.

A male from Doi Suthep, March 23, is undergoing molt of the feathers of throat and upper back; another from the same locality, April 2, had the testes enlarged. There is no good reason to believe, however, that any individuals remain to breed within our provinces.

Adult males had the irides dark brown; the bill black; the interior of the mouth yellow; the feet and toes dark brown or black; the claws black.

The old male has the entire plumage bright deep blue (the remiges and rectrices black, narrowly edged with blue and tipped with white), in winter with most of the body feathers tipped white and then black to give a more or less squamate appearance. Certain individuals from our provinces show approach to *M. s. philippensis* by having the under wing coverts and especially the under tail coverts wholly or partly chestnut-rufous instead of blue. The adult female and the immatures of either sex are similar to the old female of *M. rufiventris* but differ in the lack of striking markings on the center of the throat and the sides of the neck and by having the upperparts (and sometimes the underparts) more or less strongly washed with blue.

MONTICOLA SOLITARIUS PHILIPPENSIS (P. L. S. Müller)

Chinese Blue Rock Thrush

Turdus Philippensis P. L. S. Müller, Natursystems Supplements- und Register-Band, 1776, p. 145 (Philippine Islands, *ex* Buffon).

Monticola solitaria philippensis, Gyldenstolpe, Journ. Nat. Hist. Soc. Siam, 1915, p. 170 (listed); Ibis, 1920, p. 478 ("Siam").

Monticola solitarius philippensis, Gyldenstolpe, Kungl. Svenska Vet.-Akad. Handl., 1916, p. 48 (Pha Kho).

Two male specimens in Stockholm, one taken by Eisenhofer at Khun Tan, the other by Gyldenstolpe at Pha Kho (March 21, 1914), are best placed with this more eastern race of the blue rock thrush, which is probably the form wintering commonly in those provinces east of the Khun Tan chain.

The adult male of *philippensis* differs from that of *pandoo* in its rather brighter shade of blue and by having the under wing coverts, upper flanks, abdomen, and under tail coverts chestnut-rufous instead of blue. Females and immatures seem to be indistinguishable from those of other races.

All degrees of intergradation occur between typical *philippensis* and typical *pandoo* and it is not likely that many specimens from our area will show the extreme plumage phase of the former race.

TURDUS BOULBOUL BOULBOUL (Latham)

Indian Gray-winged Blackbird

[*Lanius*] *Boulboul* Latham, Index ornithologicus, vol. 1, 1790, p. 80 (India; type locality restricted to Darjiling, by Stuart Baker, Fauna Brit. India, Birds, ed. 2, vol. 2, 1924, p. 130).

Turdus boulboul, Deignan, Journ. Siam Soc. Nat. Hist. Suppl., 1936, p. 112 (Doi Suthep).

The gray-winged thrush is known from Thailand only by an adult male that I collected on Doi Suthep, 5,500 feet, January 25, 1936. It is probably a very rare winter visitor.

My specimen was found hopping about on the bare ground of the bungalow colony just at the summit of the mountain, acting much like the blackbirds of more northern countries.

It had the irides brown; the eyelids edged yellow; the bill orange; the tarsi brown in front, yellow behind; the toes brown; the soles yellow; the claws horn.

The adult male has the tips of the median upper wing coverts, the outer webs of the greater coverts and inner secondaries, and the outer edges of the outer secondaries ashy white, to form a broad and conspicuous longitudinal bar in the folded wing; the rest of the upper plumage, including the wings and tail, jet black; the underparts dull black, washed with brown on the breast and belly, the feathers of the abdomen narrowly fringed with ashy, the under tail coverts more broadly margined with ashy white. The adult female differs in having the general coloration olivaceous-brown, with the wing markings dull rufous.

TURDUS OBSCURUS Gmelin

WHITE-BROWED THRUSH

[*Turdus*] *obscurus* GMELIN, Systema naturae, vol. 1, pt. 2, 1789, p. 816 ("in Sibiriae silvis, ultra lacum Baical").

Turdus obscurus obscurus, DEIGNAN, Journ. Siam Soc. Nat. Hist. Suppl., 1931, p. 143 (Doi Suthep).—CHASEN and BODEN KLOSS, Journ. Siam Soc. Nat. Hist. Suppl., 1932, p. 245 (Doi Suthep).—DE SCHAUENSEE, Proc. Acad. Nat. Sci. Philadelphia, 1934, p. 211 (Khun Tan, Doi Suthep, Doi Chiang Dao).—RILEY, U. S. Nat. Mus. Bull. 172, 1938, p. 410 (Doi Ang Ka, Doi Langka).—GREENWAY, Bull. Mus. Comp. Zool., 1940, p. 180 (Doi Ang Ka).

Turdus obscurus, DEIGNAN, Journ. Siam Soc. Nat. Hist. Suppl., 1936, p. 112 (Doi Suthep).

Smith took a specimen of the white-browed thrush on Doi Ang Ka, 8,000 feet, December 5, 1928, but all other northern records have been made betwen January 3 (Khun Tan) and April 18 (Phu Kha). So common a migrant is this bird in March and April (when hundreds may sometimes be seen in a single day) that its rarity or absence during the autumn months can only be explained by assuming that its southbound passage follows some other route. It is a species of the more open evergreen and occurs in suitable territory from the level of the plains (1,214 feet at Chiang Rai) to the summits of the highest hills (8,400 feet on Doi Ang Ka).

I found it usually in large, loose flocks, feeding quietly on the ground beneath the ferns or in low berry-bearing trees. It is excessively shy and, at the slightest alarm, takes refuge in the tops of the highest trees at hand.

Two males had the irides brown; the maxilla blackish brown, with the edges of the commissure yellow on the basal half; the mandible yellow, with the tip blackish brown; the rictus and interior of the mouth yellow; the feet, toes, and soles yellow; the claws pinkish horn or light brown.

The adult male has the entire upperparts, including the wings and tail, olivaceous-brown, the forehead, crown, and nape more or less strongly suffused with ashy; the supercilium white; the lores black; a patch beneath the eye and another below the lores white; the chin white, edged at each side by a short, indistinct black mustachial streak;

the throat dark gray; the upper breast, the sides of the lower breast, and the flanks orange-rufous; the center of the lower breast and the abdomen white; the under tail coverts white, broadly margined with olivaceous-brown toward the base. The adult female differs chiefly in having the forehead, crown, and nape concolorous with the back and in having the chin and throat white, more or less heavily streaked, especially at the sides, with dark gray. Younger birds of either sex resemble the old female but have the greater upper wing coverts and the inner secondaries narrowly tipped with ashy white.

TURDUS DISSIMILIS Blyth

BLACK-BREASTED THRUSH

T[urdus] dissimilis BLYTH, Journ. Asiat. Soc. Bengal, vol. 16, 1847, pp. 144–145 (Lower Bengal; Himalayas).

Turdus dissimilis, DE SCHAUENSEE, Proc. Acad. Nat. Sci. Philadelphia, 1938, p. 30 (Doi Pha Hom Pok).

De Schauensee's collectors took an adult male and an adult female of this thrush on Doi Pha Hom Pok, 6,000 feet, January 23 and 28, 1938.

The specimens are labeled as having the irides light brown; the bill, feet, and toes orange.

The old male has the entire head, neck, and breast black; the remaining upperparts slaty gray; the remaining underparts bright orange-rufous, becoming white on the center of the abdomen; the under tail coverts white, more or less suffused with orange-rufous; the under wing coverts and axillaries orange-rufous. The adult female has the entire upperparts olivaceous-brown; the chin white, changing on the throat and breast to light brown, each feather with a blackish-brown terminal spot; the remaining underparts as in the male.

GEOKICHLA CITRINA INNOTATA Blyth

INDO-CHINESE ORANGE-HEADED GROUND THRUSH

Geocichla innotota [*sic*] BLYTH, Journ. Asiat. Soc. Bengal, vol. 15, 1846, p. 370 (Nicobar Islands and Malaya; type locality restricted to the Malay Peninsula, by Blyth, *ibid.*, vol. 16, 1847, p. 146).

Geocichla innotata, GYLDENSTOLPE, Kungl. Svenska Vet.-Akad. Handl., 1916, p. 46 (Khun Tan).

Geocichla citrina innotata, GYLDENSTOLPE, Ibis, 1920, p. 478 (Khun Tan).

Geokichla citrina innotata, DE SCHAUENSEE, Proc. Acad. Nat. Sci. Philadelphia, 1934, p. 211 (Doi Suthep).—DEIGNAN, Journ. Siam Soc. Nat. Hist. Suppl., 1936, p. 112 (Doi Suthep).—RILEY, U. S. Nat. Mus. Bull. 172, 1938, p. 411 (Khun Tan).

Geokichla citrina citrina, RILEY, U. S. Nat. Mus. Bull. 172, 1938, p. 411 (Khun Tan).

This ground thrush is an apparently rare and local inhabitant of the more western provinces, known only from Doi Khun Tan, 3,000 feet, and Doi Suthep, 4,500 feet. The few dated specimens from the North have been taken between May 9 and July 21 and there is just a possibility that the species is present with us only in summer.

A male collected by de Schauensee on Doi Suthep, 4,500 feet, July 21, is in postjuvenal molt.

The same author states that a male had the irides dark brown; the feet and toes pale yellow.

The adult male has the entire head and neck and the underparts bright orange-rufous, albescent on the throat and center of the abdomen and changing to white on the region of the vent and the under tail coverts; the remaining upperparts, including the wings and tail, slaty blue, the feathers of the upper mantle with darker centers, the majority of the remiges with a white area along the inner web near the base; the under wing coverts slaty gray with broad white tips; the axillaries white with broad slaty-gray tips. The adult female differs from the male in having the orange-rufous of the head and underparts rather duller and in having the slaty blue of the upperparts replaced by olivaceous-brown (changing to slaty on the rump, upper tail coverts, and tail).

Considerable doubt has been cast by authors upon the distinctness of *innotata* from *citrina*, in view of the fact that, *in winter*, the two forms, together with intermediates, occur together in the Malay Peninsula. I submit that, in so strongly migratory a species, only breeding populations may properly be used as evidence for or against the validity of a given race. Suffice it to say that (1) in the Peninsula we find both *citrina* and *innotata* in winter but neither one in summer; (2) all summer-taken birds from any part of Thailand have been *innotata*. Winter specimens that fall between the two may well have had their origin in geographically intermediate areas.

The individual from Khun Tan listed (1938) as *citrina* by Riley has faintly indicated paler tips to the median upper wing coverts and may be considered a slightly aberrant example of *innotata* from a locality probably near the periphery of the subspecies' range.

GEOKICHLA SIBIRICA SIBIRICA (Pallas)

SIBERIAN SLATE-COLORED GROUND THRUSH

Turdus sibiricus PALLAS, Reise durch verschiedene Provinzen des russischen Reichs, vol. 3, 1776, p. 694 ("in syluis alpinis et borealioribus Sibiriae . . ."; type specimen from the Konda river, *fide* Pallas, *ibid.*, p. 186 [where called *T. alpinus, nomen nudum*]).

Geocichla sibirica sibirica, ROGERS and DEIGNAN, Proc. Biol. Soc. Washington. 1934, p. 91 (Doi Ang Ka).

The slate-colored ground thrush is known in our area only from Doi Ang Ka, 4,400 feet, where two or three individuals were seen by me in April, 1931; one which was collected proved to be an immature male of the present race.

This shy species of the dense evergreen is likely to occur in winter at suitable localities throughout the northern provinces.

The adult male has a broad and conspicuous white supercilium; the rest of the upperparts and underparts slaty gray, changing to white on the center of the abdomen; the remiges marked with white as in the preceding species; the two central pairs of rectrices slaty gray, the remaining pairs with outwardly increasingly broad white tips; the under tail coverts slaty gray with broad white tips; the under wing coverts and axillaries as in the preceding species. The adult female has the upperparts olivaceous-brown, changing to rufescent on the wings and tail, the upper wing coverts tipped with rufescent-buff; a narrow buffy-white supercilium; the lores and a narrow mustachial streak blackish brown; the remaining underparts white (strongly suffused on the breast and upper flanks with rufescent-buff), the feathers tipped with dark brown but the throat, center of the belly, and the under tail coverts almost immaculate; the under wing coverts and axillaries as in the male but with the slaty gray replaced by blackish brown.

ZOOTHERA DIXONI (Seebohm)

LONG-TAILED PLAIN-BACKED MOUNTAIN THRUSH

Geocichla dixoni SEEBOHM, Catalogue of the birds in the British Museum, vol. 5, 1881, p. 161 (Nepal).

Oreocincla dixoni, DE SCHAUENSEE, Proc. Acad. Nat. Sci. Philadelphia, 1938, p. 30 (Doi Pha Hom Pok).

A female, taken by de Schauensee's collectors on Doi Pha Hom Pok, 6,400 feet, February 10, 1938, is the sole example of this rare thrush yet known from Thailand.

It has the entire upperparts olivaceous-brown, sometimes tinged rufescent; the wings olivaceous-brown, most of the remiges with a buffy-white area along the inner web toward the base, the upper coverts with flabelliform buff tips; the two central pairs of rectrices olivaceous-brown, the next two pairs blackish brown with very narrow white tips, the fifth pair blackish brown with a broader white tip, the outermost pair olivaceous-brown (blackish brown at the base) with a broad white tip and central streak; the underparts white, more or less strongly washed with buff on the breast and flanks, most of the feathers with a conspicuous semicircular black tip; the under tail coverts white, many of them edged at the sides with olivaceous-brown; the axillaries white, broadly tipped with black; the under wing coverts black, broadly tipped with white.

ZOOTHERA DAUMA DAUMA (Latham)

HIMALAYAN LUNULATED-BACKED MOUNTAIN THRUSH

[*Turdus*] *Dauma* LATHAM, Index ornithologicus, vol. 1, 1790, pp. 362–363 (India; type locality restricted to Kashmir, by Stuart Baker, Journ. Bombay Nat. Hist. Soc., vol. 27, 1921, p. 720).

Oreocincla dauma, GYLDENSTOLPE, Journ. Nat. Hist. Soc. Siam, 1915, p. 170 (listed).

Turdus aureus angustirostris GYLDENSTOLPE, Orn. Monatsb., vol. 24, 1916, p. 28 (Khun Tan, North Thailand).

Turdus aureus angustirostris, GYLDENSTOLPE, Kungl. Svenska Vet.-Akad. Handl., 1916, p. 47 (Khun Tan); Ibis, 1920, p. 477 (Khun Tan).

Oreocincla dauma socius [*sic*], DE SCHAUENSEE, Proc. Acad. Nat. Sci. Philadelphia, 1929, p. 543 (Doi Suthep).

Oreocincla dauma socia, DEIGNAN, Journ. Siam Soc. Nat. Hist. Suppl., 1931, p. 143 (Doi Suthep); 1936, p. 113 (Doi Suthep).—DE SCHAUENSEE, Proc. Acad. Nat. Sci. Philadelphia, 1934, p. 211 (Doi Suthep, Doi Chiang Dao).—RILEY, U. S. Nat. Mus. Bull. 172, 1938, p. 413 (Doi Langka).

Turdus dauma subsp., CHASEN and BODEN KLOSS, Journ. Siam Soc. Nat. Hist. Suppl., 1932, p. 245 (Doi Suthep).

Oreocincla dauma dauma, RILEY, U. S. Nat. Mus. Bull. 172, 1938, p. 413 (Khun Tan, Doi Hua Mot).

Oreocincla horsfieldi affinis, RILEY, U. S. Nat. Mus. Bull. 172, 1938, p. 414 (Doi Langka).

This thrush, which occurs throughout the year in the dense, moist evergreen of the provinces west of (and including) the Khun Tan chain, is probably fairly common, although, owing to the nature of its haunts, it is seldom seen. It has been taken on Doi Khun Tan at 3,000 feet; on Doi Ang Ka, at 4,400 feet; on Doi Suthep, between 4,500 and 5,500 feet; however, I have collected, December 26, a specimen at the very foot of Doi Pha Hom Pok, which indicates that it may occur in suitable forest at whatever elevation, at least during the cold weather.

It is a shy bird of the heaviest cover, ranging in pairs through damp ravines and along small streams, keeping normally to the ground but, when alarmed, flying onto some low branch, whence after a moment, it disappears silently into the darkness of the jungle. An example from Doi Ang Ka had been feeding on large, hard fruits.

Smith had the good fortune to take a breeding female, with her nest and young, on Doi Hua Mot, August 28, 1934. Riley (1938) has commented on them as follows: "A nest with three nestlings with the eyes unopened was taken. It is a large flat nest composed entirely of pine needles, except for a narrow rim of mud mixed with a little moss around the base to fasten it to the limb it was on. It was 10 feet from the ground in a tree. The nest cavity is very shallow, and the nest is very unthrushlike in appearance. The outside diameter of the nest is 8 inches; the egg cavity 4 inches wide and about 1 inch deep."

A male from Doi Ang Ka had the irides dark brown; the maxilla blackish brown; the mandible yellowish horn, dark at the tip; the interior of the mouth yellow; the feet and toes horny yellow; the claws pale horny.

The present species somewhat resembles *Z. dixoni* but may at once be known by its having all the feathers of the upperparts with conspicuous, crescentic black tips, instead of uniform olivaceous-brown.

I have already shown (Journ. Siam Soc. Nat. Hist. Suppl., 1938, pp. 119–122) that, in our provinces, *Zoothera dauma* may have either 12 or 14 rectrices; examination of 18 Thai specimens has indicated that those with 12 are a little more than twice as frequent as those with 14 and that none is separable from Himalayan birds by color characters.

It is well known that the general color of the upperparts in this species becomes duller and grayer with wear and Riley's recognition of no less than three races among the seven examples collected by Smith is due to failure to allow for such seasonal variation. I believe that *Zoothera dauma socia* (Thayer and Bangs) will likewise prove to be nothing but *Zd. dauma* in fine, fresh plumage; the type specimen was taken September 28. If eastern birds prove to be indeed separable from those of Kashmir, Thayer and Bangs's name will, of course, take precedence over Gyldenstolpe's *angustirostris.*

ZOOTHERA DAUMA AUREA (Holandre)

JAPANESE LUNULATED-BACKED MOUNTAIN THRUSH

Turdus aureus HOLANDRE, Fauna du Département de la Moselle . . . Les Oiseaux, *in* Annuaire de la Moselle, 1825, p. 60 [in reprint, pp. 11–12] ("à quelques lieues de Metz, dans les bois de Rezonville" [a straggler]).

Oreocincla aurea aurea [*partim*], DE SCHAUENSEE, Proc. Acad. Nat. Sci. Philadelphia, 1934, p. 211 (Khun Tan).

Oreocincla aurea aurea, DEIGNAN, Journ. Siam Soc. Nat. Hist. Suppl., 1936, p. 113 (Chiang Mai).

The present race seems to be a very rare winter visitor to northern Thailand, where it has been found only four times: De Schauensee took a female at Khun Tan, January 2, 1933; at Chiang Mai, I collected a female, January 12, 1936, and a male, March 7, 1936; on Doi Pha Hom Pok, de Schauensee's men shot a female, February 8, 1938, at 6,400 feet.

In view of the habitat of our resident form of the species, it is noteworthy that my female was shot in a city garden, where it was feeding in the open on a newly spaded flowerbed, while the male was discovered in dry, deciduous jungle on the plain a few miles northeast of the town.

Z. d. aurea seems always to possess 14 rectrices. From the preceding subspecies it is not separable by color but may be known by its longer wing tip and generally greater dimensions: whereas the wing length of *dauma* ranges from 138 to 146 mm., that of *aurea* ranges from 152.6 to 168.5 mm. (8 specimens of the former, against 26 of the latter).

The male from Kengtung Town, recorded (1934) by de Schauensee as *aurea*, is, in my opinion, an example of *dauma* with 14 rectrices.

ZOOTHERA MARGINATA PARVA Delacour and Jabouille

INDO-CHINESE LESSER LONG-BILLED THRUSH

Zoothera marginata parva DELACOUR and JABOUILLE, L'Oiseau et la Revue Française d'Ornithologie, vol. 11, 1930, p. 397 (Long-Phinh, Pakha, Tongking).

Zoothera marginata, DEIGNAN, Journ. Siam Soc. Nat. Hist. Suppl., 1935, p. 65 (Doi Ang Ka).

Zoothera marginata marginata, DEIGNAN, Journ. Siam Soc. Nat. Hist. Suppl., 1936, p. 113 (Doi Suthep).

Zoothera marginata parva, GREENWAY, Bull. Mus. Comp. Zool., 1940, p. 181 (Doi Ang Ka, Doi Nang Kaeo).

This long-billed thrush is apparently, if not actually, a very rare bird in northern Thailand: it has been taken on Doi Nang Kaeo at 2,800 feet; on Doi Suthep (once) at 3,500 feet; on Doi Ang Ka at various elevations between 4,600 and 8,400 feet on Doi Pha Hom Pok at 6,400 feet.

It is a shy species of dense, moist evergreen forest, where it keeps to the ground and probably is often overlooked in the darkness of the undergrowth. A clew to its real numbers is given by the fact that, on Doi Ang Ka, 4,600 to 4,800 feet, between September 4 and 7, 1935, I saw no less than six juveniles, four of which were easily collected; these examples drew attention to themselves by their reiterated alarm note: *pit-pit-pit*.

In three of my specimens postjuvenal molt is just beginning, while in the fourth it is far advanced.

The adult has the crown and nape deep olivaceous-brown, the feathers indistinctly edged darker; the mantle rufous-brown, the feathers similarly margined; the wings rufous-brown, most of the remiges with a buffy-white area along the inner web toward the base, the upper coverts narrowly tipped with rufous-buff; the tail rufous-brown; the sides of the head and neck mixed buffy white and deep olivaceous-brown; the chin and throat white, many of the feathers with blackish-brown tips, these tips larger at each side of the throat to form a poorly defined mustachial line; the feathers of the breast buffy white, broadly margined (especially at the sides) with olivaceous-brown, those of the flanks olivaceous-brown with buffy-white shaft streaks, those of the belly white with posteriorly obsolescent olivaceous-brown crescentic tips; the under tail coverts olivaceous-brown, with buffy-white margins and central streaks; the under wing coverts blackish brown, broadly tipped with buffy white; the axillaries buffy white, broadly tipped with deep brown. The juvenile differs chiefly in having the upperparts deep slaty brown (many of the feathers with buffy shaft streaks) and the dark markings of the sides of head, neck, throat, and breast almost black.

The birds of all Thailand seem to belong to this southern race, which is perhaps separable from *marginata* only by its rather shorter and weaker bill.

COCHOA VIRIDIS Hodgson

Green Cochoa

Co[*choa*] **Viridis** Hodgson, Journ. Asiat. Soc. Bengal, vol. 5, 1836, pp. 359–360 (Nepal).

Cochoa viridis, Riley, Journ. Siam Soc. Nat. Hist. Suppl., 1933, p. 157 (Khun Tan).—Deignan, Journ. Siam Soc. Nat. Hist. Suppl., 1936, p. 114 (Doi Suthep).—de Schauensee, Proc. Acad. Nat. Sci. Philadelphia, 1934, p. 212 (Doi Suthep).—Riley, U. S. Nat. Mus. Bull. 172, 1938, p. 420 (Khun Tan).

The green cochoa is a rare permanent resident of the higher mountains of all our provinces, occurring in the evergreen from about 4,500 to 5,500 feet. In addition to the localities named above, it is known from Doi Ang Ka and Phu Kha.

At Doi Ang Ka, on the slopes of Pha Mon, I collected one from the top of a tree in dry open hill-forest on the ridge between two moist ravines, but all other specimens taken by me were found in dense evergreen, watered by small streams. An example obtained by de Schauensee was seen "flying out after insects from the top of a tall tree."

A bird from Doi Suthep, 5,400 feet, July 16, is in the initial stages of postjuvenal molt, while Smith's specimens from Khun Tan, October 23 and 26, are nearing completion of this molt.

An adult male had the irides brown; the eyelids edged pinkish horn; the naked skin behind the eye pale pink; the interior of the mouth pink; the bill black; the tarsi dark brown; the toes and claws horny brown; the soles pale tan-yellow.

The adult male has the lores and a narrow supercilium black; the forehead, crown, and nape shining violet-blue; the sides of the head and neck (below and behind the eye) purple-blue; the upperparts shining deep green (the feathers of the mantle often with indistinct black shaft streaks and tips), changing in certain lights to burnished copper; the central pair of rectrices violet-blue, broadly tipped with black, the next four pairs similar but with the inner webs black, the outermost pair all black; most of the remiges and the greater and median coverts black, each with the outer web pale blue toward the base to form two conspicuous wing bands, the lesser coverts deep green with black tips;

the underparts shining green (rather paler than the mantle but with a similar coppery sheen), more or less strongly suffused with blue on the chin, upper throat, and center of the abdomen. The adult female seems to differ chiefly in having most of the pale blue in the wing replaced by a curious brownish-green color. The juvenile has the feathers of the forehead and crown bluish white with a black subterminal bar and light blue tip; a broad supercilium and narrow nuchal collar connected with it black; the feathers of the sides of the neck white tipped with black; the wings and tail as in the adult of corresponding sex; the rest of the plumage rufous-buff, each feather broadly tipped with black.

COCHOA PURPUREA Hodgson

PURPLE COCHOA

Cochoa purpurea HODGSON, Journ. Asiat. Soc. Bengal, vol. 5, 1836, p. 359 (Nepal).
Cochoa purpurea, GREENWAY, Bull. Mus. Comp. Zool., 1940, p. 182 (Doi Saket [Doi Lan]).

The purple cochoa seems to be an extremely rare bird in Thailand, until now known by only two records: An adult female collected by the Asiatic Primate Expedition at Doi Saket, 1,280 feet, February 23, 1937; an adult female taken by me on Doi Suthep, 3,300 feet, March 23, 1937.

I have noted that my specimen had the naked skin behind the eye of "exactly the same color as the feathers of the crown."

I have never seen a male of this form, and copy the following description from Stuart Baker (Fauna of British India, Birds, ed. 2): "Lores, a narrow line next the bill, supercilium, sides of head and a narrow line round the crown black; crown lavender-blue; wing-coverts and bars of secondaries lavender-purple; primary-coverts black; first two primaries all black; other primaries with a patch of lavender-grey on the base of the outer webs; tips of secondaries black; tail lavender-purple with a black tip; remainder of plumage brownish purple, darkest on the throat and breast." The adult female differs chiefly in having the purple portions of the plumage and most of the lavender in the wings replaced by rufescent-brown above, brownish rufous below.

Family MUSCICAPIDAE

MUSCICAPA SIBIRICA SIBIRICA Gmelin

SIBERIAN SOOTY FLYCATCHER

[*Muscicapa*] *sibirica* GMELIN, Systema naturae, vol. 1, pt. 2, 1789, pp. 936–937 ("circa lacum Baikal, et in orientali Sibiria ad Camtschatcam usque").
Hemichelidon sibirica sibirica, RILEY, U. S. Nat. Mus. Bull. 172, 1938, p. 444 (Doi Hua Mot).

This race of the sooty flycatcher is probably a mere straggler to our provinces: it has been found only by Smith, who collected an adult female at Doi Hua Mot, August 20, 1934.

The adult has the entire upperparts brownish gray, the feathers of the forehead and crown with indistinct blackish centers, the wings and tail darker; the remiges margined with pale rufous-buff along the inner web toward the base, the upper coverts and secondaries narrowly tipped and margined along the outer web with white or buffy white; the lores and a narrow eye ring white; the underparts (including the sides of the neck) white, indistinctly streaked with brownish gray on the sides of the throat, across the breast, along the flanks, and on the under tail coverts; the under wing coverts and axillaries pale rufous-buff (this color sometimes suffusing the breast and flanks).

MUSCICAPA SIBIRICA CACABATA Penard

Nepalese Sooty Flycatcher

Muscicapa sibirica cacabata Penard, Proc. New England Zool. Club, vol. 7, 1919, p. 22. New name for *H*[*emichelidon*] *fuliginosa* Hodgson, Proc. Zool. Soc. London, pt. 13, 1845, p. 32 (Nepal), not [*Muscicapa*] *fuliginosa* Gmelin 1789, nor *Musicapa fuliginosa* Sparrman 1787.

Hemichelidon sibirica subsp., Deignan, Journ. Siam Soc. Nat. Hist. Suppl., 1935, p. 66 (Doi Ang Ka); 1936, p. 118 (Doi Suthep).

I have collected six specimens of the present form in the Thanon Thong Chai range: An adult male and an adult female on Doi Ang Ka, 5,000 feet, September 2 and 4, 1935; a pair of juveniles on Doi Suthep, 5,200 and 5,300 feet, September 26, 1936; two juvenile males on Doi Mae Lai, October 4, 1936. Its status in Thailand is uncertain.

The examples from Doi Ang Ka were found perched on scattered small trees growing in an extensive area of lalang; those from Doi Suthep, in parklike pine-forest.

An adult female had the irides brown; the bill black, with the basal half of the mandible fleshy horn; the interior of the mouth bright yellow; the feet, toes, and claws brownish black.

From *M. s. sibirica*, *cacabata* differs in its darker coloration throughout (with much heavier streaking below and consequent reduction in extent of the pure white areas), and also in its smaller dimensions (the wing length ranging from 70 to 75 mm., against 75 to 83 mm.). The juvenile of either race has the general color still deeper in tone than the corresponding adult, the feathers of the upperparts with white or buffy-white streaks and the wing feathers margined with pale rufous-buff.

Thai examples agree perfectly with summer-taken birds from Szechwan and northwestern Yunnan, which have been named *rothschildi*, but I have been unable to separate this race from the Himalayan *cacabata* and am more than skeptical of its validity. See Bangs and Peters, Bull. Mus. Comp. Zool., vol. 68, 1928, p. 336.

MUSCICAPA CINEREICEPS (Bowdler Sharpe)

FERRUGINOUS FLYCATCHER

Hemichelidon cinereiceps BOWDLER SHARPE, Ibis, 1887, p. 441 (Mount Kinabalu, British North Borneo).

Hemichelidon cinereiceps, ROGERS and DEIGNAN, Proc. Biol. Soc. Washington, 1934, p. 92 (Doi Ang Ka).

Hemichelidon ferruginea, DEIGNAN, Journ. Siam Soc. Nat. Hist. Suppl., 1935, p. 65 (Doi Ang Ka).

The status of this flycatcher in our provinces is uncertain. In 1931 I found it not uncommon in the evergreen of Doi Ang Ka at 4,400 feet and collected an adult male, April 13; on the same mountain, at 4,600 feet, I took an adult female, September 1, 1935. The only other example known from the area is a juvenile male from Doi Mae Kong Ka, October 23, 1936.

The adult male had the irides dark brown; the maxilla blackish brown; the mandible with the anterior half blackish brown, the basal half dull fleshy orange; the rictus and interior of the mouth yellow; the feet and toes dull orange-horny; the claws horny.

The adult of either sex has the crown and nape brownish slate, changing to dark rufescent-brown on the mantle and to deep ferruginous on the rump and upper tail coverts; the wing feathers blackish, margined with buffy-rufous; the central pair of rectrices blackish brown, the others ferruginous margined blackish along the outer web near the tip; the lores buffy rufous; a conspicuous white eye ring; the sides of the head and throat mixed slate and buffy rufous; the chin and a broad area down the center of the throat white; the remaining underparts orange-rufous, sullied with brown across the breast and along the upper flanks and changing to white on the center of the abdomen. The juvenile is similar to the adult but has the crown and mantle streaked with buffy rufous.

MUSCICAPA MUTTUI MUTTUI (Layard)

INDIAN BROWN-BREASTED FLYCATCHER

Butalis Muttui LAYARD, Ann. Mag. Nat. Hist., ser. 2, vol. 13, 1854, p. 127 (Point Pedro, Ceylon).

Alseonax siamensis GYLDENSTOLPE, Orn. Monatsb., vol. 24, 1916, p. 27 (Pang Hua Phong, northern Thailand).

Alseonax siamensis, GYLDENSTOLPE, Kungl. Svenska Vet.-Akad. Handl., 1916, p. 74 (Pang Hua Phong).

Alseonax latirostris siamensis, GYLDENSTOLPE, Ibis, 1920, p. 572 (Pang Hua Phong).

The inclusion of the brown-breasted flycatcher in our list is based upon the two males from Pang Hua Phong, May 27, 1914, after which Gyldenstolpe described his "*Alseonax siamensis.*" Judged by the late date of collection, the author may be quite correct in his statement that it is "probably a resident in Northern Siam where it inhabits the higher mountains"; it must, in any event, be a bird of great rarity in our provinces.

Gyldenstolpe (1916, b) notes that his specimens had "iris brownish black; bill horn colour and with the lower mandible dirty yellow; legs black."

The full English description of "*Alseonax siamensis*" (Kungl. Svenska Vet.-Akad. Handl., 1916, pp. 74–75) is as follows:

General colour above "Saccardo's Umber" (Ridgway, Nomencl. Colours, plate 39 [= plate 29]); upper tail-coverts washed with ferruginous; wing-coverts dusky brown, margined with "Saccardo's Umber"; primaries and secondaries dusky brown, the latter edged with isabelline on the inner webs; tail dusky brown with pale brown shafts; lores and a narrow line round the eye greyish white; ear-coverts "Saccardo's Umber"; chin and upper throat greyish white slightly washed with brown; lower throat, breast and flanks ashy brown; middle of abdomen, vent and under tail-coverts white; thighs brown; under wing-coverts and axillaries light fawn colour; quills dusky brown below and fawn colour along the inner webs; tail-feathers brownish white below with white shafts to the feathers; wing lining light fawn colour.

Gyldenstolpe described "*Alseonax siamensis*" as "related to *Alseonax latirostris* Raffl. from which it is, however, clearly distinguished by being umber brown . . . above instead of ashy brown." In 1920, he made it a race of *latirostris* and, in 1926 (Ark. för Zool., vol. 19A, No. 1, pp. 61–62), he synonymized it with *Alseonax latirostris latirostris*, while changing his *A. l. latirostris* of 1920 to *A. l. poonensis* (Sykes). Uncritically accepting his disposition as correct, I did not avail myself of the opportunity of examining the type specimen in 1939.

As has been shown by Whistler and Kinnear (Journ. Bombay Nat. Hist. Soc., vol. 36, 1932, pp. 85–86) and confirmed by my own studies, continental birds must all be placed under the name *latirostris*. Among them we find a certain amount of color variation, both seasonal and individual, but it is noteworthy that, in a series of 89 specimens (17 of them collected in northern Thailand between September 26 and May 3), not one agrees with the diagnosis of "*Alseonax siamensis*," while, on the other hand, *Butalis muttui* Layard ("common above 5,000 feet" in the Southern Shan States, *fide* Rippon, Ibis, 1901, p. 541) agrees with it in every important character. I am forced to believe, then, that "*Alseonax siamensis*" is a renaming of *Muscicapa muttui*.

The measurements given by Gyldenstolpe for his examples (wing length: 68, 69 mm.) indicate that they belong with the smaller race, *Muscicapa muttui muttui*, and that the name *Muscicapa* (*Alseonax*) *muttui stötzneri* Weigold for the larger birds of Szechwan will probably not be invalidated by the designation given Thai specimens.

MUSCICAPA LATIROSTRIS LATIROSTRIS Raffles

CONTINENTAL GRAY-BREASTED FLYCATCHER

Muscicapa latirostris RAFFLES, Trans. Linn. Soc. London, vol. 13, 1822, p. 312 (Sumatra; type locality, restricted to Benkulan, by Kinnear and Robinson, Bull. Brit. Orn. Club, vol. 47, 1927, p. 130).

Alseonax latirostris, GYLDENSTOLPE, Journ. Nat. Hist. Soc. Siam, 1915, p. 169 (listed); Kungl. Svenska Vet.-Akad. Handl., 1916, p. 74 (Khun Tan, Tha Chomphu).

Alseonax latirostris latirostris, GYLDENSTOLPE, Ibis, 1920, p. 572 ("Various parts of the country").—GREENWAY, Bull. Mus. Comp. Zool., 1940, p. 183 (listed).

Alseonax latirostris latirostris [*partim*], DEIGNAN, Journ. Siam Soc., Nat. Hist. Suppl., 1931, p. 144 (Doi Suthep [*partim*]).

Arizelomyia latirostris latirostris, RILEY, U. S. Nat. Mus. Bull. 172, 1938, p. 446 (Chiang Mai, Ban Nam Khian).

In this flycatcher we have a case, analogous to that of *Saxicola t. stejnegeri*, in which our birds arrive and depart in two distinct migratory waves, which may well be connected with separate northern breeding grounds. The species first appears in small numbers on the mountains of the western provinces, where it has been recorded in autumn only between September 21 (Khun Tan) and October 3 (Doi Suthep), at elevations from 2,000 to 4,800 feet; dates for the return movement in spring are not yet available. The main body reach the plains, throughout the area, somewhat later (earliest known date at Chiang Mai, November 25) and are present at least until May 3 (savannas of the Mae Nam Ing). There is no reason to believe with Gyldenstolpe (1916) that the bird breeds in Thailand; it is merely, with *Phragamaticola a. rufescens* and *Lanius c. cristatus*, one of the very last of the northern visitors to depart.

This is a bird of uninhabited but rather open country, occurring at clearings in the evergreen and in the mixed-deciduous forest. Its habits are quite like those of its congeners; it is normally seen alone, making aërial sallies after its insect prey and, between flights, perching quietly on one of several favored perches.

Gyldenstolpe notes that his specimens had the irides dark brown; the bill black, with the base of the mandible dirty yellow; the feet and toes black. The dark apex of the mandible may perhaps be a useful field mark in distinguishing between *M. latirostris* and *M. muttui*.

In the hand, *M. l. latirostris* may readily be known from *M. s. sibirica* by its different proportions, the shape of its bill, and other minor points; in life, it appears to differ only in having the sides of the throat, the breast, and the flanks strongly overlaid with brownish ashy, wholly or almost *without* streaking.

SIPHIA PARVA ALBICILLA (Pallas)

EASTERN ORANGE-THROATED FLYCATCHER

Muscicapa Albicilla PALLAS, Zoographia Rosso-asiatica, vol. 1, 1811, p. 462, Aves, pl. 1 (Davuria).

Siphia albicilla, GYLDENSTOLPE, Kungl. Svenska Vet.-Akad. Handl., 1913, p. 36 (Ban Huai Hom, Denchai); Journ. Nat. Hist. Soc. Siam, 1915, p. 169 (listed).

Siphia parva albicilla, GYLDENSTOLPE, Ibis, 1920, p. 572 (Ban Huai Hom, Denchai).—DE SCHAUENSEE, Proc. Acad. Nat. Sci. Philadelphia, 1928, p. 570 (Chiang Mai); 1929, p. 545 (between Ban Chong and Ban Mae Sai, Chiang Saen, Chiang Mai); 1934, p. 213 (Chiang Dao, Chiang Mai, Khun Tan).—DEIGNAN, Journ. Siam Soc. Nat. Hist. Suppl., 1931, p. 144 (Chiang Mai); 1936, p. 118 (Chiang Mai, Doi Suthep).—RILEY, U. S. Nat. Mus. Bull. 172, 1938, p. 446 (Bang Mae Klang, Doi Ang Ka, Phrae).

The orange-throated flycatcher is a very common winter visitor to the lowlands of all our provinces, occurring also in small numbers on the hills as high as 5,500 feet. The extreme dates for its stay at Chiang Mai are September 20 (1930) and April 15 (1937); a solitary female observed by me on Doi Suthep at 4,600 feet, May 30, 1931, should probably be considered a belated migrant.

This species may be seen at clearings in the evergreen, in deciduous or semideciduous forest, and especially in gardens where the trees are not too densely planted. Upon its first arrival in autumn, each individual stakes out for itself a territory in which it may be found day after day throughout the cold weather, employing any one of several optional perches—a dead twig on a low branch, the coping of a well, a telephone wire—from which it makes sallies after flying insects or stoops to terrestrial prey; I have noted that the same perches are utilized each year. The bird has a pretty habit of erecting the tail above the line of the back, at the same time spreading it to show the white bases of the outer feathers and uttering a characteristic *chur-r-r*.

Smith took a female in prenuptial molt at Phrae, April 11, 1930.

A male had the irides deep brown; the bill dark brown, with the base of the mandible horny brown; the feet, toes, and claws brownish black.

The adult male (rarely seen with us) has the crown and mantle ashy brown; the upper tail coverts black; the rectrices black, all except the two central pairs with the basal two-thirds wholly or largely white; the lores and eye ring ashy white; the chin and throat orange; the sides of the head, the breast, and the upper flanks ashy (sometimes washed with pale orange); the remaining underparts white, often more or less strongly suffused with pale orange; the under wing coverts and axillaries creamy or pale orange. The female and the first-winter male are similar to the adult male but differ in having the chin and throat white.

SIPHIA STROPHIATA STROPHIATA Hodgson

HIMALAYAN ORANGE-GORGETED FLYCATCHER

Siphia Strophiata HODGSON, India Rev., vol. 1, 1837, pp. 651–652 (Nepal).
Siphia strophiata strophiata [*partim*], DE SCHAUENSEE, Proc. Acad. Nat. Sci. Philadelphia, 1929, p. 545 (Doi Suthep [*partim*]) ; 1934, p. 213 (Doi Suthep, Doi Chiang Dao).—DEIGNAN, Journ. Siam Soc. Nat. Hist. Suppl., 1931, p. 144 (Doi Suthep [*partim*]) ; 1936, p. 118 (Doi Suthep [*partim*]).
Siphia strophiata strophiata, CHASEN and BODEN KLOSS, Journ. Siam Soc. Nat. Hist. Suppl., 1932, p. 239 (Doi Suthep).—RILEY, U. S. Nat. Mus. Bull 172, 1938, p. 447 (Khun Tan, Doi Ang Ka).

This race of the orange-gorgeted flycatcher is a fairly common winter visitor to the higher peaks of the provinces west of (and including) the Khun Tan chain, at elevations ranging from 4,000 feet (Doi Khun Tan) to 6,000 feet (Doi Ang Ka). On Doi Suthep it has been recorded between November 7 (1936) and March 1 (1933).

Except that it confines itself to the edge of the evergreen at high altitudes, the present form differs little in habits from *S. p. albicilla.*

De Schauensee has noted (1929) that his specimens had the irides brown; the bill black; the feet and toes fleshy horn.

The adult male has the forehead and a narrow line above either lore white, edged above with slaty gray, which is continued beyond the eye as a supercilium; the crown and mantle olivaceous-brown, posteriorly suffused with rufescent; the remiges blackish, narrowly margined along the outer web with rufescent; the upper tail coverts black; the rectrices black, all except the central pair with the basal half wholly or largely white; an orange-rufous or chestnut-orange gorget across the lower throat, the feathers with more or less visible white bases; the lores, chin, and upper throat deep slate or dull black, changing to slaty gray on the sides of the head and neck and on the breast below the gorget, this latter color changing to olivaceous-buff along the flanks and the sides of the abdomen, to ashy white on the center of the abdomen, and to white on the under tail coverts; the under wing coverts and axillaries pale orange. The adult female *frequently* wears a plumage identical with that of the male; in true female dress she has the gorget pale orange and much reduced in size; the lores, chin, throat, sides of the head and neck, and the breast below the gorget uniformly slaty gray.

SIPHIA STROPHIATA ASEMA Deignan

SHAN ORANGE-GORGETED FLYCATCHER

Siphia strophiata asema DEIGNAN, Smithsonian Misc. Coll., vol. 99, No. 18, 1940, pp. 1–2 (Doi Suthep, Chiang Mai Province, North Thailand).
Siphia strophiata strophiata [*partim*], DE SCHAUENSEE, Proc. Acad. Nat. Sci. Philadelphia, 1929, p. 545 (Doi Suthep [*partim*]).—DEIGNAN, Journ. Siam

Soc. Nat. Hist. Suppl., 1931, p. 144 (Doi Suthep [*partim*]); 1936, p. 118 (Doi Suthep [*partim*]).

This putative race is based upon a unique adult female taken by me on Doi Suthep, 5,500 feet, November 7, 1936; with it I have provisionally placed three adult males collected by de Schauensee on Doi Suthep (December), Doi Pha Hom Pok (February), and Kiu Loi, Kengtung State (February). It is assumed to be a form which breeds in the Southern Shan States and reaches Thailand only during the cold weather.

"The type specimen differs most strikingly from the corresponding sex of both *strophiata* and *fuscogularis* (Annam) in wholly lacking a gorget. The chin, throat, and center of the upper breast are uniformly of a color which lies between buckthorn brown (Ridgway) and isabella color (Ridgway) and which changes imperceptibly into the olivaceous-brown of the sides of the breast and the flanks; all the feathers of the throat and breast have the concealed bases dark slate-gray and the concealed portion of the shaft white; the lores, supercilia, ear-coverts, and sides of the neck are dark brownish slate, not pure slate-gray as in the other races. . . .

"The three adult males which presumably belong here differ from the corresponding sex of *strophiata* and *fuscogularis* in having the gorget so much reduced in area, both the orange and the white portions, but especially the former, that it is almost or entirely invisible until the feathers of the breast are raised" (*ex* original description).

SIPHIA HODGSONII Verreaux

SLATY-BACKED FLYCATCHER

Siphia hodgsonii VERREAUX, Nouv. Arch. Mus. [Paris], vol. 6, 1870 [= 1871], Bull., p. 34 (Mu-pin, Chinese Tibet).

Alseonax latirostris latirostris [*partim*], DEIGNAN, Journ. Siam Soc. Nat. Hist. Suppl., 1931, p. 144 (Doi Suthep [*partim*]).

Siphia hodgsonii, CHASEN and BODEN KLOSS, Journ. Siam Soc. Nat. Hist. Suppl., 1932, p. 239 (Doi Suthep).

Muscicapula hodgsonii, DE SCHAUENSEE, Proc. Acad. Nat. Sci. Philadelphia, 1934, p. 213 (Doi Suthep).—DEIGNAN, Journ. Siam Soc. Nat. Hist. Suppl., 1936, p. 118 (Doi Suthep).—GREENWAY, Bull. Mus. Comp. Zool., 1940, p. 182 (Doi Ang Ka).

The slaty-backed flycatcher is a rare winter visitor to the higher peaks of the Thanon Thong Chai range, recorded until now only between January 9 (Doi Suthep) and March 31 (Doi Ang Ka). On Doi Suthep it has been found from 4,600 to 5,500 feet; on Doi Ang Ka, from 4,300 feet to the summit.

This species occurs in the same places as *Siphia strophiata* and seems to have quite the same habits.

An adult female had the irides brown; the bill, feet, toes, and claws blackish brown. A bird sexed by me as a female (but wearing an anomalous dress combining characters of both male and female plumage) had the irides brown; the bill black, with the rictus horny white; the feet, toes, and claws horny brown.

The adult male, in full plumage, has the entire upperparts slate, slightly paler on the rump, but changing to black on the upper tail coverts; occasionally a few scattered white feathers at the sides of the posterior crown; the remiges blackish brown, narrowly margined along the outer web with dull rufous; the rectrices black, all except the central pair with the basal third wholly or largely white; the lores (and often the sides of the head and neck as well) blackish; the chin, throat, breast, upper abdomen, under wing coverts, and axillaries bright orange-rufous; the remaining underparts (including the under tail coverts) pale rufous-buff, becoming white on the center of the lower abdomen. The adult female (and some adult males) have the entire upperparts olivaceous-brown, changing to rufous-buff on the rump and upper tail coverts; the wings and tail dull dark brown, the greater upper wing coverts narrowly tipped with pale buffy to form a single wing bar; a pale buffy eye ring; the underparts grayish buff, changing to white on the center of the abdomen. Some of the curious aberrations of plumage shown by this species are discussed by Ticehurst (Ibis, 1939, p. 754).

Bingham's *Cyornis brevirostris* (Ann. Mag. Nat. Hist., 1900, p. 359) seems to be a mere renaming of *Siphia hodgsonii*.

SIPHIA MELANOLEUCA MELANOLEUCA (Blyth)

HIMALAYAN BLACK-AND-WHITE FLYCATCHER

M[uscicapula] melanoleuca BLYTH, Journ. Asiat. Soc. Bengal, vol. 12, 1843, p. 940 (Nepal, Darjiling).

Muscicapula melanoleuca westermanni, DE SCHAUENSEE, Proc. Acad. Nat. Sci. Philadelphia, 1929, p. 545 (Doi Suthep).—DEIGNAN, Journ. Siam Soc. Nat. Hist. Suppl., 1931, p. 144 (Doi Suthep).

Muscicapula melanoleuca melanoleuca, CHASEN and BODEN KLOSS, Journ. Siam Soc. Nat. Hist. Suppl., 1932, p. 239 (Doi Suthep).—DEIGNAN, Journ. Siam Soc. Nat. Hist. Suppl., 1936, p. 119 (Doi Suthep).—DE SCHAUENSEE, Proc. Acad. Nat. Sci. Philadelphia, 1934, p. 214 (Doi Suthep, Doi Chiang Dao).—RILEY, U. S. Nat. Mus. Bull. 172, 1938, p. 459 (Doi Hua Mot, Doi Langka).—GREENWAY, Bull. Mus. Comp. Zool., 1940, p. 182 (Doi Ang Ka).

The little pied flycatcher is a common permanent resident on those mountains of the Thanon Thong Chai and Khun Tan ranges that rise to elevations in excess of 4,500 feet; on Doi Suthep it occurred from that altitude to the summit (5,500 feet). A unique specimen from the Chiang Mai plain, November 21, 1936, must be considered merely a wanderer.

This delightful bird, which is conspicuous in the open hill-forest and at clearings in the evergreen, keeps to the lower branches, where it investigates the epiphytes and makes sallies after insects in the manner characteristic of the family. It is extraordinarily tame, and I have had one, after bathing in a tiny spring, perch upon my foot to preen itself.

A specimen from Doi Suthep, March 12, had the gonads greatly enlarged. Examples in postnuptial molt have been taken July 15 and August 17.

An adult male had the irides dark brown; the bill black; the feet, toes, and claws dark brown.

The old male has a broad white supercilium; the upper half of the head and neck and the remaining upperparts black; the wings black, the inner greater upper coverts and the outer web of the inner secondaries white to form a conspicuous longitudinal bar; the rectrices black, all except the central pair with the basal half wholly or largely white; the entire underparts white. The adult female has the upperparts light grayish brown, changing to dull rufous on the rump and upper tail coverts (the crown and mantle as well more or less strongly suffused with this color); the wings blackish brown, the greater upper coverts and the inner secondaries narrowly margined with white or buffy white; the rectrices brown, narrowly edged along the outer web with dull rufous; the entire underparts white, washed with sooty gray (especially across the breast and along the flanks).

An aberrant female from Doi Suthep agrees perfectly with specimens of *S. m. langbianis* (South Annam).

SIPHIA NARCISSINA ZANTHOPYGIA (Hay)

WHITE-BROWED NARCISSINE FLYCATCHER

Muscicapa Zanthopygia HAY, Madras Journ. Lit. Sci., vol. 13, pt. 2, 1844 [=1845], pp. 162–163 (Malacca).

Zanthopygia narcissina zanthopygia, DEIGNAN, Journ. Siam Soc. Nat. Hist. Suppl., 1936, p. 170 (Ban Na Ko).

The charming black-and-yellow flycatcher is known from our area thus far only as a rare spring migrant through Nan Province: I took an adult male at Ban Na Ko (near Muang Pua), April 2, 1936, and saw a second at the edge of the Mae Nan near Uttaradit, April 10, 1937.

The bird from Na Ko was found flitting about a vinery on the outskirts of lowland evergreen forest; the one from the river's edge was working its way along a thicket of *takrai nam* (*Homonoia riparia*).

The adult male has a conspicuous white supercilium; the lower back and the rump golden-yellow; the remaining upperparts, including the tail, black; the wings black, with a conspicuous longitudinal white stripe; the underparts golden-yellow (the throat and breast often suffused in spring with orange); the under tail coverts, under wing coverts, and axillaries pure white. The adult female has the lores and eye ring buffy or buffy white; the upperparts olive-green, except for the yellow rump and olive-tipped black tail coverts; the remiges and rectrices blackish, the white markings on the former washed with buff; the underparts (except for the white under tail coverts, under wing coverts, and axillaries) pale yellow or yellowish white, the feathers of the chin, throat, and breast indistinctly edged olivaceous.

SIPHIA SUPERCILIARIS AESTIGMA (G. R. Gray)

EASTERN WHITE-BROWED FLYCATCHER

Muscicapa aestigma G. R. GRAY, Catalogue of . . . Mammalia and birds of Nepal and Thibet . . . British Museum, 1846, pp. 90, 155 (Nepal).

Muscicapula superciliaris astigma, ROGERS and DEIGNAN, Proc. Biol. Soc. Washington, 1934, p. 91 (Doi Suthep).

Muscicapula superciliaris aestigma, DEIGNAN, Journ. Siam Soc. Nat. Hist. Suppl., 1936, p. 118 (Doi Suthep).

I found this charming little flycatcher to be a rare winter visitor to the hills of the Thanon Thong Chai range. The only records are: An adult male shot on Doi Suthep at 4,200 feet, February 26, 1932; another taken on the same mountain at 1,700 feet, December 5, 1936, and a third observed at 1,500 feet, January 9, 1937; an adult male (one of several seen) collected on Doi Chiang Dao at 5,000 feet, March 20, 1937.

The two examples from lower elevations were in deciduous jungle, those from the heights in pine-forest. The specimen from Doi Chiang Dao, loosely accompanied by others of the same species, was probably bound for the northern breeding ground.

My birds had the irides dark brown; the bill, feet, toes, and claws black.

The adult male has the entire upperparts ultramarine, brighter on the front and forecrown, the secondaries narrowly margined along the outer web with bluish white; a supercilium occasionally indicated by a few scattered bluish-white feathers; the *sides* of the head, neck, and breast deep ultramarine; the remaining underparts white, this color extending from the upper abdomen to the chin as a broad central streak. The adult female has the entire upperparts ashy gray, more or less suffused with brown on the front, forecrown, and upper tail coverts; the sides of the head, neck, and breast ashy gray; the remaining underparts white, as in the male.

SIPHIA HYPERYTHRA HYPERYTHRA (Blyth)

HIMALAYAN WHITE-FRONTED FLYCATCHER

[*Muscicapa*] *hyperythra* BLYTH, Journ. Asiat. Soc. Bengal, vol. 11, 1842, p. 885. New name for *D*[*imorpha*] *supercilaris* BLYTH, *ibid.*, 1842, p. 190 (Nepal, Darjiling), not *Muscicapa superciliaris* Jerdon 1840.

Cyornis hyperythra subsp., DE SCHAUENSEE, Proc. Acad. Nat. Sci. Philadelphia, 1929, p. 545 (Doi Suthep).

Muscicapula hyperythra hyperythra, DEIGNAN, Journ. Siam Soc. Nat. Hist. Suppl., 1931, p. 144 (Doi Suthep); 1936, p. 118 (Doi Suthep).—GREENWAY, Bull. Mus. Comp. Zool., 1940, p. 182 (Doi Ang Ka).

This small flycatcher has been found only on Doi Ang Ka (5,500 feet to the summit), on Doi Suthep (once, at 4,600 feet), and on Doi Chiang Dao (5,500 feet). Although seldom seen, it is probably a permanent resident on many of the higher mountains of the more western provinces.

De Schauensee has noted (1929) that he shot a specimen out of a tall tree, but all seen by me were perched within 2 or 3 feet of the ground along narrow tracks through dense, moist evergreen forest; it is a quiet little bird, and this fact, in conjunction with its choice of habitat, may account for the paucity of records in our area.

My specimens had the irides dark brown; the bill black; the tarsi horny flesh; the toes horn brown; the claws horny.

The adult male has a white frontal band (usually broken just at the center) continued over either eye as a short supercilium; the entire upperparts slaty blue; the remiges blackish brown, narrowly edged along the outer web with dull rufous; the rectrices slaty blue, all except the two central pairs with the extreme base wholly or largely white; the lores, chin, and sides of the throat blackish, changing to slaty blue on the sides of the head, neck, and breast and along the flanks; the center of the throat and breast orange-rufous, this color changing gradually to olivaceous-brown on the sides of the abdomen and to white on the center of the abdomen and the under tail coverts. The adult female has the forehead and supraloral line rufous-buff; the remaining upperparts olivaceous-brown, the remiges and rectrices narrowly edged with rufescent along the outer web; the underparts rufous-buff, more brownish along the flanks, albescent on the center of the throat and abdomen.

SIPHIA SOLITARIS LEUCOPS (Bowdler Sharpe)

UPPER BURMESE WHITE-THROATED FLYCATCHER

Digenea leucops BOWDLER SHARPE, Proc. Zool. Soc. London, 1888, p. 246 (Shillong; Karen-ni).

Anthipes moniliger leucops, RILEY, Journ. Siam Soc. Nat. Hist. Suppl., 1933, p. 158 (Doi Langka).—DEIGNAN, Journ. Siam Soc. Nat Hist. Suppl., 1933, p. 119 (Doi Suthep).—DE SCHAUENSEE, Proc. Acad. Nat. Sci. Philadelphia, 1934, p. 216 (Doi Suthep).—RILEY, U. S. Nat. Mus. Bull. 172, 1938, p. 455 (Doi Langka).

The white-throated flycatcher has been found in our provinces only on Doi Pha Hom Pok, Doi Langka, Doi Suthep (twice), Doi Ang Ka, and Phu Kha; it is probably a rare permanent resident wherever dense, humid evergreen grows at elevations in excess of 4,500 feet.

The few examples seen by me were perched within a foot or two of the ground at the heart of heavy thickets, where they were almost as well protected from gunshot as from observation; thus, like *Siphia hyperythra*, the species is perhaps commoner than the records would indicate.

A specimen from Phu Kha, April 11, had the ovaries slightly enlarged.

The adult of either sex has the frontal band and short, broad supercilium white or ashy white; the remaining upperparts olivaceous-brown, becoming rufescent on the upper tail coverts; the remiges and rectrices dark brown, edged along the outer webs with rufous; the lores olivaceous-gray; the chin and throat covered by a pure white triangular patch, completely outlined by a narrow black edging; the remaining underparts dark olivaceous-buff, albescent on the abdomen.

SIPHIA SAPPHIRA LAOTIANA (Delacour and Greenway)

INDO-CHINESE SAPPHIRE-BLUE FLYCATCHER

Muscicapula sapphira laotiana DELACOUR and GREENWAY, Bull. Brit. Orn. Club, vol. 59, 1939, p. 132 ("Col de Taloun, 25 km. east of Luang Prabang, Laos").

Muscicapula sapphira, RILEY, Journ. Siam Soc. Nat. Hist. Suppl., 1933, p. 158 (Khun Tan); U. S. Nat. Mus. Bull. 172, 1938, p. 458 (Khun Tan).

Smith collected an adult male on Doi Khun Tan, 4,000 feet, November 21, 1928, and de Schauensee's men took another on Doi Pha Hom Pok, 6,400 feet, February 11, 1938; the species is otherwise unknown from Thailand, to which country it is probably a very rare winter visitor.

The adult male, as seen in our provinces, has the upper half of the head and neck and the greater part of the back olivaceous-brown (the forehead and the sides of the forecrown suffused with orange-rufous); the remaining upperparts shining sapphire blue, deepest on the upper wing coverts and brightest on the upper tail coverts; the chin, throat, and center of the breast bright orange, changing to orange-suffused olivaceous-brown on the sides of the breast; the remaining underparts ashy, changing to white on the center of the abdomen and the under tail coverts; the under wing coverts and axillaries pure white. The adult female (not examined by me) is said to have the entire upperparts olivaceous-brown; the chin, throat, and breast pale brown; the abdomen sullied brown and whitish.

CYORNIS HAINANA (Ogilvie Grant)

BLUE-BREASTED CYORNIS

Siphia hainana OGILVIE GRANT, Bull. Brit. Orn. Club, vol. 10, 1900, p. 36 (Five-finger Mountains, Hainan).

Cyornis pallidipes, GYLDENSTOLPE, Kungl. Svenska Vet.-Akad. Handl., 1916, p. 77 (Khun Tan, Pha Kho).

Cyornis pallidipes hainana, GYLDENSTOLPE, Ibis, 1920, p. 577 (Khun Tan, Pha Kho).

Muscicapula pallipes hainana, DE SCHAUENSEE, Proc. Acad. Nat. Sci. Philadelphia, 1934, p. 214 (Chiang Mai).

Muscicapula hainana, DEIGNAN, Journ. Siam Soc. Nat. Hist. Suppl., 1936, p. 119 (Chiang Mai).

Cyornis hainana [*partim*], RILEY, U. S. Nat. Mus. Bull. 172, 1938, p. 448 (Khun Tan [*partim*]).

Muscucapula [*sic*] *hainana*, GREENWAY, Bull. Mus. Comp. Zool., 1940, p. 183 (Doi Nang Kaeo).

The blue-breasted flycatcher is local and uncommon in the northern provinces, from most places known by a single specimen and not yet recorded at all from Mae Hong Son and Chiang Rai. In addition to localities named above, I have it from Ban Samoeng, Ban Huai Chang Tai, Doi San Huai Wai, Ban Huai Ki, and Ban Nam Puat (in the French Enclave).

This species occurs in uninhabited and broken country at the foot of the mountains, haunting light evergreen, mixed-deciduous forest, and bamboo, rarely reaching such high elevations as 2,800 (Doi Nang Kaeo) or 3,000 feet (Doi Khun Tan).

A juvenile (sexed as a male but probably a female) was taken at Phu Het, in the southern part of Nan Province, June 9, 1936. From equaeval examples of *Cyornis t. sumatrensis*, collected at the same time and place, it is clearly separable only by its brown rectrices without the least trace of blue.

Gyldenstolpe notes (1916) that his specimens had the irides dark brown; the bill black; the feet and toes pale brown.

The adult male has the forehead, supercilium, and shoulder patch shining blue; the lores black; the remaining upperparts deep blue; the chin, throat, and breast indigo-blue, gradually changing to smoky along the flanks and to white on the abdomen, under tail coverts and under wing coverts (this last color often encroaching boldly on the center of the breast and throat); the thighs slaty blue. The adult female has the upperparts olivaceous-brown, grayer on the crown and nape, rufescent on the upper tail coverts and tail; the lores and orbital region grayish white or rusty white; the underparts dull orange, strongly infuscated on the sides of the throat and breast, changing to white on the abdomen and under tail coverts.

CYORNIS RUBECULOÏDES DIALILAEMA Salvadori

KAREN BLUE-THROATED CYORNIS

Cyornis dialilaema SALVADORI, Ann. Mus. Civ. Stor. Nat. Genova, ser. 2, vol. 7, 1889, pp. 387–388 (Taho, Karen-ni).

Cyornis dialilaema, GYLDENSTOLPE, Journ. Nat Hist. Soc. Siam, 1915, p. 169 (listed); Kungl. Svenska Vet.-Akad. Handl., 1916, p. 75 (Khun Tan, Pang Hua Phong); Ibis, 1920, p. 576 ("Northern Siam").

Cyornis rubeculoïdes, GYLDENSTOLPE, Kungl. Svenska Vet.-Akad. Handl., 1916, p. 76 (Khun Tan); Ibis, 1920, p. 576 (Khun Tan).
Cyornis banyumas tickelliae, GYLDENSTOPLE, Kungl. Svenska Vet.-Akad. Handl., 1916, p. 77 (Khun Tan).
Cyornis banyumas tickelliae [*partim*], GYLDENSTOLPE, Ibis, 1920, p. 576 (Khun Tan).
Muscicapula rubeculoïdes rubeculoïdes, DE SCHAUENSEE, Proc. Acad. Nat. Sci. Philadelphia, 1934, p. 214 (Khun Tan).
Cyornis hainana [*partim*], RILEY, U. S. Nat. Mus. Bull. 172, 1938, p. 448 (Khun Tan [*partim*]).
Cyornis rubeculoïdes dialilaema, RILEY, U. S. Nat. Mus. Bull. 172, 1938, p. 451 (Khun Tan, Mae Kong Ka valley).

In addition to specimens recorded under the references given above, I have examined (in Hannover) two males and one female taken by Eisenhofer in "Siam" and (in Stockholm) 12 males and about 7 females obtained by the same collector at Khun Tan (one of them dated June 9, 1913). The species is evidently abundant at Khun Tan and is at least not rare in the neighborhood of Doi Mae Kong Ka, but is otherwise unknown from any part of our provinces.

Examples listed (1916) by Gyldenstolpe as *rubeculoïdes* "were all shot on the summits of the highest hills among the Koon Tan range where they occurred either in pairs or in small flocks among the pine-trees." Smith's specimens from Khun Tan were taken at 3,000 and 4,000 feet.

The adult male has the forehead, supercilium, and shoulder patch shining blue; the lores black; the remaining upperparts bright, deep blue; the chin, upper throat, and sides of the lower throat, neck and breast deep blue; the center of the lower throat and breast bright orange-rufous, this color gradually fading away along the flanks and changing to white on the abdomen and under tail coverts; the thighs deep blue. The adult female has the upperparts rufescent-brown (more olivaceous on the crown and nape), becoming rufous on the upper tail coverts and rectrices; the underparts dull orange, changing to white on the lower abdomen and the under tail coverts.

CYORNIS BANYUMAS WHITEI Harington

SHAN RUFOUS-THROATED CYORNIS

Cyornis whitei HARINGTON, Ann. Mag. Nat. Hist., ser. 8, vol. 2, 1908, pp. 245–246 (Watan, Bhamo district, Burma).
Cyornis banyumas dialilaema, DE SCHAUENSEE, Proc. Acad. Nat. Sci. Philadelphia, 1929, p. 545 (Doi Suthep, "8 Kls. S. of Shan States Border," Chiang Saen).
Muscicapula rubeculoïdes dialilaema [*partim*], DEIGNAN, Journ. Siam Soc. Nat. Hist. Suppl., 1931, p. 144 (Doi Suthep).
Cyornis banyumas whitei, CHASEN and BODEN KLOSS, Journ. Siam Soc. Nat. Hist. Suppl., 1932, p. 239 (Doi Suthep).
Muscicapula banyumas dialilaema, DE SCHAUENSEE, Proc. Acad. Nat. Sci. Philadelphia, 1934, p. 215 (Doi Suthep, Doi Chiang Dao, Khun Tan).

Muscicapula banyumas whitei, DEIGNAN, Journ. Siam Soc. Nat. Hist. Suppl., 1936, p. 119 (Doi Suthep).—GREENWAY, Bull. Mus. Comp. Zool., 1940, p. 183 (Doi Nang Kaeo).

Cyornis whitei whitei, RILEY, U. S. Nat. Mus. Bull. 172, 1938, p. 451 (Khun Tan, Ban Mae Khan).

The rufous-throated cyornis is a common permanent resident on most of the hills of the provinces west of (and including) the Khun Tan chain, at elevations between 2,100 and 4,600 feet; it occurs also on the high peaks of northern Nan (Phu Kha). Between October 13 and February 27, odd specimens have been taken at numerous lowland localities (Thattafang, Mae Khan, Chiang Mai [once], Ban Pang An, Chiang Saen, etc.); such birds may be true migrants from farther north but more probably are merely wanderers from the neighboring hills.

This flycatcher is found (usually in pairs) in tall bamboo jungle and in the evergreen along streams. Its habits seem to be precisely those of *C. r. dialilaema* and *C. t. sumatrensis*, and it is noteworthy that, on Doi Khun Tan, where alone *whitei* is definitely known to dwell side by side with *dialilaema*, the former is a distinctly rare bird.

A male from Phu Kha, April 4, had the gonads enlarged; another from Doi Suthep, March 5, had them greatly enlarged.

A male had the irides brown; the bill black; the feet and toes violet-gray; the claws horn.

The adult male differs from that of *C. r. dialilaema* only in having the upperparts of a rather duller, grayer blue; the point of the chin black and the entire throat bright orange-rufous like the breast. The adult female differs from that of *dialilaema* in having the upperparts olivaceous-brown, becoming dark rufescent-brown on the tail; from that of *hainana*, in lacking infuscation on the sides of the throat and breast.

CYORNIS TICKELLIAE SUMATRENSIS (Bowdler Sharpe)

SUMATRAN WHITE-BELLIED CYORNIS

Siphia sumatrensis BOWDLER SHARPE, Catalogue of the birds in the British Museum, vol. 4, 1879, p. 451 (Sumatra).

Cyornis tickelli, GYLDENSTOLPE, Kungl. Svenska Vet.-Akad. Handl., 1913, p. 37 (Den Chai, Ban Huai Hom).

Cyornis banyumas tickelliae [*partim*], GYLDENSTOLPE, Ibis, 1920, p. 576 (Ban Huai Hom, Den Chai).

Muscicapula rubeculoides dialilaema [*partim*] DEIGNAN, Journ. Siam. Soc. Nat. Hist. Suppl., 1931, p. 144 (Chiang Mai).

Muscicapula tickelliae indochina [*partim*], DE SCHAUENSEE, Proc. Acad. Nat. Sci. Philadelphia, 1934, p. 215 (Chiang Mai).

Muscicapula tickelliae indochina, DEIGNAN, Journ. Siam. Soc. Nat. Hist. Suppl., 1936, p. 119 (Chiang Mai).

Cyornis tickelliae sumatrensis, RILEY, U. S. Nat. Mus. Bull. 172, 1938, p. 449 (Chom Thong).

The range of this flycatcher extends into the southern portions of our area along the drainage systems of the Mae Ping (Ban Sop Mae Chaem, Chom Thong, Chiang Mai), the Mae Wang (Ban Mae Mo), the Mae Yom (Ban Huai Hom, Den Chai), and the Mae Nan (Doi San Huai Wai, Doi San Pa Bong, Phu Het).

The white-bellied cyornis is a fairly common permanent resident of the lowlands (not yet recorded at elevations above 1,000 feet), likely to be found wherever a heavy stand of tall bamboo overarches some quiet stream or pool. It may occur in temple precincts and village gardens as well as in wild bamboo brakes far from human habitation. It has a soft, whistled song of five or six notes, the first and fifth or the second and sixth notes higher than the others.

A male from Chiang Mai, May 19, had the gonads greatly enlarged. Examples in postjuvenal molt have been taken June 4 (Doi San Huai Wai), June 11 (Phu Het), August 21 and 25 (Ban Mae Mo); a bird in postnuptial molt, October 10 (Chiang Mai).

Adults had the irides brown; the bill black; the feet, toes, and claws violet-gray; the soles whitish.

The old male differs from that of *C. b. whitei* only in having the bright orange-rufous of the throat and breast sharply divided (in a straight line) from the white of the remaining underparts (the under wing coverts and the flanks but slightly, if at all, washed with orange-rufous). The adult female differs from those of all the closely related forms of our provinces in having the upperparts olivaceous-brown, more or less strongly overlaid with bluish ashy, and changing to grayish blue on the upper tail coverts and tail; the orange of the throat and breast sharply divided from the white of the remaining underparts, as in the male.

CYORNIS UNICOLOR UNICOLOR Blyth

HIMALAYAN PALE-BLUE CYORNIS

C[yornis] unicolor BLYTH, Journ. Asiat. Soc. Bengal, vol. 12, 1843, pp. 1007–1008 (Darjiling).

Cyornis unicolor harterti, DE SCHAUENSEE, Proc. Acad. Nat. Sci. Philadelphia, 1928, p. 571 (Doi Suthep).

Cyornis unicolor unicolor, CHASEN and BODEN KLOSS, Journ. Siam Soc. Nat. Hist. Suppl., 1932, p. 239 (Doi Suthep). — RILEY, U. S. Nat. Mus. Bull. 172, 1938, p. 453 (Khun Tan, Doi Langka, Doi Hua Mot, "Doi Kiew Koh Ma").

Muscicapula unicolor unicolor, DE SCHAUENSEE, Proc. Acad. Nat. Sci. Philadelphia, 1934, p. 214 (Doi Suthep, Doi Chiang Dao). — DEIGNAN, Journ. Siam Soc. Nat. Hist. Suppl., 1936, p. 119 (Doi Suthep).

The pale-blue flycatcher is an uncommon permanent resident on the higher hills of the Thanon Thong Chai and Khun Tan ranges; it has been recorded at elevations between 3,000 feet (Doi Khun Tan) and 5,500 feet (Doi Suthep).

I have found this species usually in humid evergreen jungle but occasionally in the pines adjacent to such forest.

Specimens with the gonads greatly enlarged were taken March 12 and May 13. De Schauensee has recorded (1934) an example in post-juvenal molt, July 21; Smith collected birds in postnuptial molt, August 28 and September 2.

A breeding male had the irides brown; the bill black; the feet and toes brown; the claws horny brown.

The adult male has the forehead, supercilium, and shoulder patch shining blue; the remaining upperparts a beautiful soft blue; the chin, throat, and breast a similar but paler blue, changing to bluish ashy on the remaining underparts (albescent on the center of the abdomen); the under tail coverts bluish ashy (often washed with buff), broadly tipped with bluish white; the under wing coverts and axillaries buffy white. The adult female has the upperparts olivaceous-brown, suffused with rufescent on the mantle and changing to rufous along the outer webs of the remiges and on the upper tail coverts; the rectrices rufous-brown; a conspicuous buffy-white eye ring; the underparts sooty gray, more or less strongly suffused with buff, especially at the sides of the throat, along the flanks, and on the under tail coverts (albescent on the chin, center of the throat, and center of the abdomen); the under wing coverts and axillaries buffy white.

EUMYIAS THALASSINA THALASSINA (Swainson)

INDIAN VERDITER-BLUE FLYCATCHER

Muscicapa thalassina SWAINSON, *in* The Naturalist's Library, vol. 21 [Ornithology, vol. 10], Flycatchers, 1838, p. 252 (India).

Stoparola melanops, GYLDENSTOLPE, Kungl. Svenska Vet.-Akda. Handl., 1913, p. 37 (Den Chai, Khao Phlung); Journ. Nat. Hist. Soc. Siam, 1915, p. 169 (listed).

Stoparola melanops melanops, GYLDENSTOLPE, Ibis, 1920, p. 575 ("Throughout Siam proper").—DE SCHAUENSEE, Proc. Acad. Nat. Sci. Philadelphia, 1928, p. 570 (Doi Suthep).

Stoporola thalassina thalassina, DE SCHAUENSEE, Proc. Acad. Nat. Sci. Philadelphia, 1929, p. 545 (Doi Suthep, Chiang Rai, Chiang Saen).

Stoporala thalassina thalassina, CHASEN and BODEN KLOSS, Journ. Siam Soc. Nat. Hist. Suppl., 1932, p. 240 (Doi Suthep).

Eumyias thalassina thalassina, DEIGNAN, Journ. Siam Soc. Nat. Hist. Suppl., 1931, p. 144 (Doi Suthep, Chiang Mai); 1936, p. 119 (Doi Suthep, Chiang Mai).—DE SCHAUENSEE, Proc. Acad. Nat. Sci. Philadelphia, 1934, p. 216 (Doi Suthep, Doi Chiang Dao, Khun Tan). — RILEY, U. S. Nat. Mus. Bull. 172, 1938, p. 470 (Khun Tan, Doi Langka).

The verditer-blue flycatcher is a fairly common resident of the more open evergreen on the mountains of the Thanon Thong Chai and Khun Tan ranges and on Phu Kha, at elevations between 3,500 (rarely 2,700) and 5,500 feet. During the cold weather it also occurs sparingly in lowland bamboo throughout our area; whether these birds of the plains are visitors from the North or merely wanderers from the neighboring hills is not yet known.

The present species, which superficially resembles the rarer *Cyornis u. unicolor*, is frequently seen along the forest tracks on Doi Suthep.

A male from Doi Ang Ka, April 16, had the gonads greatly enlarged.

My specimens had the irides dark brown; the bill, feet, toes, and claws black.

The adult male has the lores conspicuously black; the plumage generally verditer blue, the exposed portions of the remiges and rectrices of a brighter and purer blue; the under tail coverts broadly edged with bluish white. The adult female is similar but has the lores merely dusky and the general color duller and grayer.

NILTAVA CYANOMELANA CUMATILIS (Thayer and Bangs)

CHINESE BLUE-AND-WHITE NILTAVA

Cyanoptila cumatilis THAYER and BANGS, Bull. Mus. Comp. Zool., vol. 52, No. 8, 1909, p. 141 (Ma-fu-ling, Hupeh, China).

Cyanoptila cyanomelana cumatilis, GREENWAY, Bull. Mus. Comp. Zool., 1940, p. 185 (Doi Nang Kaeo).

Evidently a very rare winter visitor, this race is known from Thailand by only two specimens: a male shot by de Schauensee's collectors in the mountains near Ban Chong (Chiang Rai Province), March 30, 1935, and another taken by the Asiatic Primate Expedition on Doi Nang Kaeo, 2,800 feet, April 8, 1937.

An adult male paratype of *N. c. cumatilis* has the lores, a narrow frontal band, and the point of the chin black; the crown bright, shining blue, this color changing gradually on the nape into the duller blue of the remaining upperparts; the sides of the head, the throat, and the breast dull blue, the breast margined posteriorly by an indistinct, narrow black or blackish band, interrupted at the center; the remaining underparts white, washed with smoky gray along the flanks (the abdomen irregularly sullied with the same color); the under wing coverts and axillaries smoky gray. The adult female has not been seen but in other races has the upperparts light olivaceous-brown, changing to dull rufous-brown on the rump, upper tail coverts, and tail; the chin and center of the throat white or pale buff, to form a patch which flares somewhat where it meets the breast; the remaining underparts light buffy brown, changing to white on the abdomen and under tail coverts. Some females have the brown portions of the plumage overlaid with gray.

Greenway (*loc. cit.*) refers his specimen only provisionally to *cumatilis*.

NILTAVA VIVIDA OATESI Salvadori

INDO-CHINESE RUFOUS-BELLIED NILTAVA

Niltava Oatesi SALVADORI, Ann. Mus. Civ. Stor. Nat. Genova, ser. 2, vol. 5, 1887, p. 514 (Mount Muleyit, Tenasserim).

Niltava smithi RILEY, Proc. Biol. Soc. Washington, vol. 42, May 3, 1929, p. 162 (Doi Suthep, North Thailand).

Niltava williaminae DE SCHAUENSEE, Proc. Acad. Nat. Sci. Philadelphia, vol. 81, August 12, 1929, p. 469 (Doi Suthep, North Thailand).

Niltava williaminae, DE SCHAUENSEE, Proc. Acad. Nat. Sci. Philadelphia, 1929, p. 546 (Doi Suthep).—DEIGNAN, Journ. Siam Soc. Nat. Hist. Suppl., 1931, p. 145 (Doi Suthep).

Muscicapula rivida oatesi, DEIGNAN, Journ. Siam Soc. Nat. Hist. Suppl., 1931, p. 144 (Doi Suthep).

Niltava smithi, DEIGNAN, Journ. Siam Soc. Nat. Hist. Suppl., 1931, p. 145 (Doi Suthep).

Cyornis vivida oatesi, CHASEN and BODEN KLOSS, Journ. Siam Soc. Nat. Hist. Suppl., 1932, p. 239 (Doi Suthep).

Niltava vivida oatesi, DE SCHAUENSEE, Proc. Acad. Nat. Sci. Philadelphia, 1934, p. 218 (Doi Suthep, Doi Chiang Dao).—DEIGNAN, Journ. Siam Soc. Nat. Hist. Suppl., 1936, p. 120 (Doi Suthep).—RILEY, U. S. Nat. Mus. Bull. 172, 1938, p. 456 (Doi Suthep, Khun Tan).

This rather large flycatcher is known in Thailand chiefly from Doi Suthep, 4,600 to 5,500 feet, where it is decidedly uncommon and possibly present only in winter (December 15 to March 12).

I have seen it, usually in pairs, only in dense, damp evergreen forest. It is a quiet bird, with habits quite like those of its relatives.

My specimens had the irides dark brown; the bill black; the feet and toes dark brown; the claws dark horny brown or black.

The adult male has the crown, nape, sides of the neck, the shoulder patch, rump, and upper tail coverts shining ultramarine; the remaining upperparts deep, shining purplish blue; the lores and sides of the head black; the chin, throat, and sides of the upper breast black, overlaid with purplish blue; the remaining underparts dull orange-rufous, this color encroaching in an irregular point onto the center of the lower throat. The adult female has the crown, nape, and sides of the neck olivaceous-gray (each feather of the crown margined paler to give a squamate appearance), changing to olivaceous-brown on the mantle, this color strongly suffused with rufescent on the rump and upper tail coverts; the rectrices and the margins of the outer webs of the remiges rufous-brown; a conspicuous eye ring rich buff; the feathers of the lores, sides of the head, the chin, and upper throat rich buff, faintly barred with blackish; those of the center of the lower throat unmarked buff, forming a patch that flares somewhat where it meets the breast; the breast brownish gray, changing to ashy on the flanks and abdomen, all of these parts often more or less strongly washed with buff; the under tail coverts, under wing coverts, and axillaries rich buff or buffy white.

NILTAVA SUNDARA DENOTATA Bangs and Phillips

YUNNANESE ORANGE-BELLIED NILTAVA

Niltava sundara denotata BANGS and PHILLIPS, Bull. Mus. Comp. Zool., vol. 58, 1914, p. 280 (Mengtze, southeastern Yunnan).

Cyornis oatesi, GYLDENSTOLPE, Journ. Nat. Hist. Soc. Siam, 1915, p. 169 (listed); Ibis, 1920, p. 577 (Khun Tan).

Niltava sundara denotata, DE SCHAUENSEE, Proc. Acad. Nat. Sci. Philadelphia, 1929, p. 546 (Doi Suthep); 1934, p. 218 ("N. Siam").—DEIGNAN, Journ. Siam. Soc. Nat. Hist. Suppl., 1931, p. 145 (Doi Suthep).—CHASEN and BODEN KLOSS, Journ. Siam Soc. Nat. Hist. Suppl., 1932, p. 239 (Doi Suthep).—DEIGNAN, Journ. Siam Soc. Nat. Hist. Suppl., 1936, p. 120 (Doi Suthep).—RILEY, U. S. Nat. Mus. Bull. 172, 1938, p. 455 (Doi Suthep).

This species is a not uncommon winter visitor to the higher peaks of the Thanon Thong Chai and Khun Tan chains between October 31 (Doi Suthep) and April 14 (Doi Ang Ka). On Doi Suthep it is most frequent from 4,500 feet to the summit, occasionally seen as low as 3,500 feet, casual at 2,500 feet; where the evergreen extends down to the foothills, as at the base of Doi Pha Hom Pok, it has been taken almost at the level of the plains.

The orange-bellied niltava is restricted in range to the humid evergreen and occurs not only at clearings and along the trails but also in the deepest parts of the forest, haunting the lower branches, brushy thickets, and the tangles of fallen trees.

A male had the irides dark brown; the bill black; the feet and toes dark horny brown; the claws blackish brown.

The adult male has the forehead, lores, and eye ring black; the crown and nape, a transverse mark at each side of the neck, the shoulder patch, rump, and upper tail coverts shining violet-blue; the mantle deep purple-blue; the remiges black, edged along the outer web with deep purple-blue; the central pair of rectrices purple-blue, the remaining pairs black with the outer web purple-blue; the chin, throat, and ear coverts black, overlaid with deep purple-blue; the remaining underparts (including the under wing coverts, axillaries, and under tail coverts) bright rufous-orange. The adult female has the crown and nape olivaceous-brown (suffused with buff on the forehead), changing to rufescent-brown on the mantle, to rufous on the upper tail coverts and the outer webs of the remiges, and to chestnut-rufous on the rectrices; the eye ring, chin, and throat deep olivaceous-buff; a shining violet-blue transverse mark at either side of the throat, the two connected by a conspicuous gorget of pure white; the remaining underparts pale olivaceous-brown, cinerescent on the center of the abdomen and the under tail coverts; the under wing coverts and axillaries olivaceous-buff.

NILTAVA GRANDIS GRANDIS (Blyth)

HIMALAYAN GREATER BLACK-BREASTED NILTAVA

[*Chaïtaris*] *grandis* BLYTH, Journ. Asiat. Soc. Bengal, vol. 11, 1842, p. 189 (Darjiling).

Niltava grandis nobilis RILEY, Proc. Biol. Soc. Washington, vol. 42, 1929, pp. 161–162 (Doi Ang Ka, North Thailand).

Niltava grandis nobilis, DE SCHAUENSEE, Proc. Acad. Nat. Sci. Philadelphia, 1929, p. 546 (Doi Suthep).—DEIGNAN, Journ. Siam Soc. Nat. Hist. Suppl., 1931, p. 145 (Doi Suthep).—CHASEN and BORDEN KLOSS, Journ. Siam Soc. Nat. Hist. Suppl., 1932, p. 239 (Doi Suthep).—RILEY, U. S. Nat. Mus. Bull. 172, 1938, p. 456 (Doi Ang Ka, Doi Langka).

Niltava grandis grandis, DE SCHAUENSEE, Proc. Acad. Nat. Sci. Philadelphia, 1934, p. 217 (Doi Suthep)—DEIGNAN, Journ. Siam Soc. Nat. Hist. Suppl., 1936, p. 119 (Doi Suthep).—GREENWAY, Bull. Mus. Comp. Zool., 1940, p. 184 (Doi Ang Ka).

This large and robust flycatcher is a common or *very* common permanent resident on the higher hills of the Thanon Thong Chai and Khun Tan chains and also on Phu Kha; on Doi Suthep it ranges through the evergreen from 3,500 to 5,500 feet and on Doi Ang Ka from 4,500 to 8,400 feet.

It occurs in much the same places as the preceding species but, as befits its greater size, keeps to rather higher levels of the forest. The unmistakable song is a soft, rising *one-two-three . . . one-two-three.*

Specimens with the gonads enlarged or greatly enlarged were taken April 10 (Phu Kha) and April 13 (Doi Ang Ka) and, at the latter locality, a juvenile just out of the nest was collected April 8. Postnuptial molt is shown by a bird of September 4 and postjuvenal molt by others of October 25 and 29.

A breeding male had the irides dark brown; the bill black; the feet, toes, and claws brownish black. An adult female differed only in having the feet and toes plumbeous and the claws blackish brown. The very young juvenile mentioned above had the irides brown; the bill blackish brown; the rictus and interior of the mouth light yellow; the tarsi and toes wood brown; the posterior part of the tibiotarsal joint and the soles bright yellow; the claws dark brown above, yellow beneath.

The adult male has the forehead, lores, and eye ring deep black; the remaining upperparts, including the remiges and rectrices, as in the adult male of *N. s. denotata* (but with the shining portions rather more violet, less blue); the underparts black, overlaid from the lower breast on with deep purple-blue, canescent on the lower abdomen, lower flanks, under tail coverts, under wing coverts, and axillaries. The adult female differs from that of *N. s. denotata* chiefly in having the crown and nape more or less strongly suffused with dark ashy; the transverse marks at the sides of the neck shining azure blue; the chin and center of the throat to the uppermost breast pale buff or buffy white; the remaining underparts olivaceous-brown (often suffused with rich buff), cinerescent on the center of the abdomen; the under tail coverts, under wing coverts, and axillaries rich buff (occasionally washed with ashy).

NILTAVA MACGRIGORIAE (Burton)

LESSER BLACK-BREASTED NILTAVA

Phoenicura MacGrigoriae BURTON, Proc. Zool. Soc. London, pt. 3, 1835 [=1836], p. 152 ("Montes Himalayenses").

Niltava macgregoriae, DE SCHAUENSEE, Proc. Acad. Nat. Sci. Philadelphia, 1934, p. 3 (Doi Suthep).

Niltava macgrigoriae, ROGERS and DEIGNAN, Proc. Biol. Soc. Washington, 1934, p. 91 (Doi Ang Ka).—DE SCHAUENSEE, Proc. Acad. Nat. Sci. Philadelphia, 1934, p. 219 (Doi Suthep).—DEIGNAN, Journ. Siam Soc. Nat. Hist. Suppl., 1936, p. 120 (Doi Suthep).—RILEY, U. S. Nat. Mus. Bull. 172, 1938, p. 457 (Doi Hua Mot).

The only examples of this little flycatcher yet known from Thailand are a male and a female from Doi Hua Mot, August 17 and 22, 1934 (Smith), a male from Doi Suthep, 4,500 feet, July 18, 1933 (de Schauensee), and a male from Doi Ang Ka, April 6, 1931 (Deignan); at the last-named locality, however, I found it common between 4,400 and 5,500 feet throughout the month of April, 1931.

On Doi Ang Ka it was seen on the lower branches of the trees in dense, humid evergreen forest where small streams flowed among moss-covered rocks and boulders; so deep was the shade that this small, dark-colored bird might have been overlooked had not its loud song drawn attention to the singer.

The species is said ordinarily to breed in rock crevices along streams, but a nest found by me on Doi Ang Ka, 4,900 feet, April 15, 1931, was placed in a sapling about 8 feet above ground; the nest was loosely constructed, and, standing beneath it, one could easily make out two reddish eggs.

De Schauensee's specimen from Doi Suthep and Smith's male from Doi Hua Mot are in postjuvenal molt, while the latter's female (August 22) is in postnuptial molt.

My adult male had the irides brown; the bill black; the feet, toes, and claws dark horny brown.

The old male has the forehead and lores black; the forecrown, supercilium, a transverse mark at each side of the neck, the rump, and upper tail coverts shining violet-blue; the remaining upperparts, including the wings and tail, deep purple-blue; the ear coverts, chin, throat, and upper breast black, strongly overlaid with deep purple-blue, changing to slaty gray on the remaining underparts (paling posteriorly); the under wing coverts and axillaries pure white. The adult female has the entire upperparts as in the adult female of *N. s. denotata*; the transverse mark at either side of the neck azure blue; the lores, eye ring, chin, and throat rufous-buff; the remaining underparts olivaceous-brown, washed with rich buff along the upper flanks, albescent on the center of the abdomen and almost white along the lower flanks; the under tail coverts rich buff; the under wing coverts and the axillaries pure white.

MUSCICAPELLA HODGSONI HODGSONI (Moore)

NEPALESE PYGMY FLYCATCHER

Nemura hodgsoni MOORE, *in* Horsfield and Moore, Catalogue of the birds in the Museum of The Hon. East-India Co., vol. 1, 1854, p. 300 (Nepal).

Muscicapella hodgsoni hodgsoni, RILEY, Journ. Siam Soc. Nat. Hist. Suppl., 1933, p. 159 (Doi Langka); U. S. Nat. Mus. Bull. 172, 1938, p. 454 (Doi Langka).

Two males, taken by Smith on Doi Langka, November 10, 1930, and April 27, 1931, are the only examples of this apparently rare form yet known from Thailand.

Smith records that one of his specimens had the irides dark brown; the maxilla black; the mandible "dark blue"; the feet and toes "light blue."

The adult male has the extreme forehead blackish; the remaining upperparts deep ultramarine, brighter and glistening on the crown; the lores black; the sides of the head and neck black; overlaid with deep ultramarine; the underparts light golden-orange, albescent on the center of the abdomen; the under tail coverts, under wing coverts, and axillaries pure white. The adult female (not seen by me) is described by Stuart Baker as having the "whole upper plumage olive-brown, more rufous on the lower back, rump and upper tail-coverts; tail and wing-feathers brown edged with rufous-brown; lores and cheek fulvous-yellow mottled with brown; whole lower plumage pale saffron-yellow, albescent on centre of abdomen, vent and under tail-coverts."

CULICICAPA CEYLONENSIS PERCNOCARA Oberholser

INDO-CHINESE GRAY-HEADED FLYCATCHER

Culicicapa ceylonensis percnocara OBERHOLSER, Smithsonian Misc. Coll., vol. 60, No. 7, 1912, p. 12 (Simalur Island, West Sumatra).

Culicicapa ceylonensis, GYLDENSTOLPE, Kungl. Svenska Vet.-Akad. Handl., 1913, p. 37 (Mae Raem river); 1916, p. 81 (Khun Tan); Journ. Nat. Hist. Soc. Siam, 1915, p. 169 (listed); Ibis, 1920, p. 575 ("Northern Siam").

Culicicapa ceylonensis ceylonensis, DE SCHAUENSEE, Proc. Acad. Nat. Sci. Philadelphia, 1929, p. 546 (Doi Suthep, Chiang Saen); 1934, p. 216 (Doi Suthep, Doi Chiang Dao).—DEIGNAN, Journ. Siam Soc. Nat. Hist. Suppl., 1931, p. 145 (Doi Suthep, Chiang Mai).—CHASEN and BODEN KLOSS, Journ. Siam Soc. Nat. Hist. Suppl., 1932, p. 241 (Doi Suthep).—DEIGNAN, Journ. Siam Soc. Nat. Hist. Suppl., 1936, p. 119 (Doi Suthep, Chiang Mai).

Culicicapa ceylonensis calochrysea, RILEY, U. S. Nat. Mus. Bull. 172, 1938, p. 469 (Doi Ang Ka, Doi Hua Mot, Khun Tan, Lampang).

The gray-headed flycatcher is a very common or even abundant permanent resident in the evergreen of the Thanon Thong Chai and Khun Tan ranges and on Phu Kha, at elevations in excess of 2,500 feet; during the cold weather, examples of this species, whether from the neighboring hills or from a more northern breeding range, appear also in small numbers in lowland bamboo.

On Doi Suthep this active little bird may be seen, solitary or in pairs, at every clearing and along all the trails and watercourses.

I collected a male with enlarged gonads on Phu Kha, April 13. Gyldenstolpe has recorded (1916) a juvenile male from Khun Tan, May 14; one of Smith's specimens from the same locality, September 6, is in postjuvenal molt.

An adult male had the irides brown; the maxilla black; the mandible horn, browner on the apical half; the feet and toes fleshy brown; the claws light horny brown.

The adult of either sex has the entire head, neck, and breast gray, more slaty on the crown and nape, more ashy on the throat and breast; the remaining upperparts bright golden-olive, becoming olive-golden on the rump; the remiges and rectrices blackish brown, edged along the outer web with olive-golden; the remaining underparts bright yellow, strongly suffused with olivaceous on the upper abdomen and along the flanks.

It appears that this flycatcher breaks up into only two recognizable forms, one of which is restricted to the island of Ceylon. For the non-Ceylonese race, many names are available; the oldest are three on the same page of a single paper by Oberholser, and I here employ the first of the three.

In 1923 Oberholser named *Culicicapa ceylonensis calochrysea* from "Quaymos, Choung, Thoungyin River, Tenasserim." This is a fitting place to point out that the original label on the type specimen reads "Quaymoo Choung, Thoungyin Rr." The "Quaymoo choung," *fide* Bingham (Stray Feathers, vol. 9, 1880, p. 156) is "a small feeder of the Thoungyeen, entering a little below the rapids of Kamaukla." The type locality of *calochrysea*, then, is the Tenasserimese side of the Mae Moei or Thaungyin river, at about latitude 17°15′ N.

CHELIDORYNX HYPOXANTHA (Blyth)

YELLOW-BROWED FLYCATCHER

Rhipidura hypoxantha BLYTH, Journ. Asiat. Soc. Bengal, vol. 12, 1843, p. 935 (Darjiling).

Chelidorhynx hypoxanthum, ROGERS and DEIGNAN, Proc. Biol. Soc. Washington, 1934, p. 91 (Doi Ang Ka).—DE SCHAUENSEE, Proc. Acad. Nat. Sci. Philadelphia, 1934, pp. 3, 220 (Doi Chiang Dao).—RILEY, U. S. Nat. Mus. Bull. 172, 1938, p. 463 (Doi Ang Ka).

583136—45——30

This pretty flycatcher is recorded in Thailand only from Doi Ang Ka, 5,000–8,400 feet, and from Doi Chiang Dao at about 5,000 feet.

In the *Rhododendra* which fringe the sphagnum-bog at the summit of Ang Ka, I found this to be the commonest bird in April and May 1931; at that season its weak but pleasing song was heard on every side and it was probably breeding in the neighborhood. It is a most active species, even when at rest constantly quivering the wings and spreading the tail like a fan to exhibit the conspicuous white pattern.

An adult female had the irides brown; the maxilla dark brown; the mandible fleshy horn; the feet and toes fleshy yellow; the claws horny.

The adult male has the forehead and broad supercilium bright yellow; the remaining upperparts dark olive-green, brighter on the crown and nape and suffused with gray on the mantle; the remiges and rectrices dull blackish, each of the latter with a pure white shaft streak and all but the central pair with a broad, transverse white terminal patch; the lores and orbital region black, this colo rwashed with olive-green on the ear coverts; the entire underparts bright yellow. The adult female differs from the male only in having the lores and sides of the head dull blackish, suffused with olive-green.

RHIPIDURA AUREOLA BURMANICA (Hume)

Burmese White-browed Fantail Flycatcher

[*Leucocerca*] *burmanica* Hume, Stray Feathers, vol. 9, 1880, p. 175 (Thaungyin valley, Tenasserim).

I have 10 specimens of this flycatcher from six widely separated localities in Mae Hong Son, Chiang Mai, and Phrae Provinces; it seems to occur more frequently in Mae Hong Son, and east of the Khun Tan chain it has been found only at Ban Mae Ten but, for the reason discussed below, will probably eventually be shown to have a range in our area exactly coincident with that of *Tephrodornis pondiceriana thai.*

The white-browed fantail, not hitherto recorded from the North, was discovered to be a rare and local resident of our provinces in consequence of my observation in central Thailand of a pair in company with a band of the lesser wood-shrike. When, some six months later, a flock of this wood-shrike was seen in Chiang Mai Province, a few moments' search again disclosed the presence of a pair of fantails; thereafter, all such parties were carefully scrutinized and so close did the association prove to be (at least during the nonbreeding period) that all my subsequent specimens of the flycatcher were obtained as a direct result of it.

This particular companionship seems not yet to have been consciously noted elsewhere and may probably be explained as an operation of the same simple impulse as induces other pairs or groups of more or less sociable and noncompeting species to consort together (e. g., *Sitta f. corallina* and *Erpornis*, etc.). The rather striking similarity in color pattern exhibited by wood-shrike and flycatcher is of greater interest than importance.

Outside of the fact that the white-browed fantail is wholly restricted in range to parklike, deciduous forest in the lowlands, a description of its habits would apply equally well to the following species. No greater contrast can be imagined than that between the deliberate movements of the wood-shrike and the incessant dancing and tail-flirting of the flycatcher.

A nest of this bird (apparently completed but still without eggs) was found by my collector at Ban San Pa Sak, February 25, 1937. It was constructed on the upper surface of a small branch just at a horizontal fork and stands a little more than two inches high, although the cuplike depression has a depth of only one inch. It is woven almost entirely of very fine grass stems and thinly faced everywhere on the outside with cobwebs, some strands of which have been drawn down one side of the supporting branch and up the other so as to anchor the structure in a most efficient manner.

A specimen from Nong Phung (along the Chiang Dao road, about 46 km. north of Chiang Mai), June 20, 1936, is in postnuptial molt.

The adult in fresh plumage has the forehead and a broad supercilium white; the lores, sides of the head, the crown, and nape deep brownish slate; the mantle brownish slate, strongly overlaid with ashy; the remiges slaty brown, their upper coverts with small, indistinct whitish tips; the central pair of rectrices wholly blackish brown, the next pair likewise or narrowly tipped with white, the remaining pairs with an outwardly increasingly broad white tip (the outermost pair with only the basal half of the inner web not white); the feathers of the chin and throat slaty gray, more or less broadly fringed with white; the sides of the breast and abdomen slaty gray; the remaining underparts (including the sides of the neck behind the ear coverts) white. With wear, the dark portions of the plumage become browner and the pale tips of the upper wing coverts disappear.

RHIPIDURA ALBICOLLIS ALBICOLLIS (Vieillot)

INDIAN WHITE-THROATED FANTAIL FLYCATCHER

Platyrhynchos albicollis VIEILLOT, Nouveau dictionnaire d'histoire naturelle, nouv éd., vol. 27, 1818, p. 13 (Bengal).

Rhipidura albicollis, GYLDENSTOLPE, Kungl. Svenska Vet.-Akad. Handl., 1916, p. 80 (Khun Tan); Ibis, 1920, p. 574 (Khun Tan).—CHASEN and BODEN KLOSS, Journ. Siam Soc. Nat. Hist. Suppl., 1932, p. 240 (Doi Suthep).

Rhipidura albicollis celsa RILEY, Proc. Biol. Soc. Washington, vol. 42, 1929, p. 166 (Khun Tan, North Thailand).

Rhipidura albicollis albicollis, DE SCHAUENSEE, Proc. Acad. Nat. Sci. Philadelphia, 1929, p. 547 (Doi Suthep); 1934, p. 220 (Doi Suthep, Doi Chiang Dao).—RILEY, U. S. Nat. Mus. Bull. 172, 1938, p. 463 (Khun Tan, Doi Langka).—GREENWAY, Bull. Mus. Comp. Zool., 1940, p. 185 (Doi Ang Ka, Doi Nang Kaeo).

Leucocirca albicollis albicollis, DEIGNAN, Journ. Siam Soc. Nat. Hist. Suppl., 1931, p. 145 (Doi Suthep); 1936, p. 120 (Doi Suthep).

The white-throated fantail is a very common or even abundant permanent resident in the heavy evergreen of the provinces west of (and including) the Khun Tan chain; on such mountains as Doi Suthep and Doi Ang Ka it is unknown below 3,200 and 4,300 feet respectively, but where the evergreen reaches the bases of the hills, as in western Chiang Rai, it occurs almost at the level of the plains.

In suitable forest this is one of the most conspicuous and unmistakable birds; a pair may be found with almost any mixed band of small babblers, and it is sure to be seen at the edge of old clearings and along the tracks and stream courses. Like its congener of the plains, it is in constant motion, dashing from branch to branch, swooping and diving through the air with snapping bill, and forever spreading and folding the flabelliform tail. On Doi Suthep and other peaks of the Thanon Thong Chai range, only *Culicicapa*, of all the family, is equally numerous.

Smith collected a full-plumaged juvenile on Doi Langka, May 2, and Gyldenstolpe (1916) took juveniles on Doi Khun Tan, May 24 and 30. A specimen from Doi Suthep, July 15, is in postnuptial molt.

The adult has a short, narrow supercilium white; the lores, eye ring, and forehead black, this color changing to slaty black on the crown and ear coverts and to deep slaty gray on the mantle; the remiges blackish brown; the rectrices brownish black, the central pair wholly of this color, the next pair narrowly tipped with ashy white, and the remaining pairs broadly tipped with the same; the feathers of the chin deep slaty gray, those of the throat similar but more or less broadly fringed with white; the remaining underparts slaty gray (paler than the mantle), the feathers at the center of the abdomen often tipped or fringed with ashy ("*celsa*"); the under wing coverts and axillaries mixed slaty gray and ashy white. The juvenile differs from the adult only in having the upper wing coverts, the inner secondaries, and the feathers of mantle and abdomen fringed with ferruginous.

HYPOTHYMIS AZUREA STYANI (Hartlaub)

INDO-CHINESE BLACK-NAPED FLYCATCHER

Siphia Styani HARTLAUB, Abh. Naturw. Ver. Bremen, vol. 16, 1899, pp. 248–249 (Hainan).

Hypothymis azurea prophata, GYLDENSTOLPE, Kungl. Svenska Vet.-Akad. Handl., 1913, p. 37 (Ban Huai Hom, Den Chai).

Hypothymis azurea, GYLDENSTOLPE, Journ. Nat. Hist. Soc. Siam, 1915, p. 169 (listed).

Hypothymis azurea styani, GYLDENSTOLPE, Kungl. Svenska Vet.-Akad. Handl., 1916, p. 79 (Khun Tan, Pang Hua Phong, Pha Kho, Tha Chomphu, Doi Pha Sakaeng); Ibis, 1920, p. 573 ("Throughout Siam proper").—DEIGNAN, Journ. Siam Soc. Nat. Hist. Suppl., 1931, p. 145 (Chiang Mai, Doi Suthep); 1936, p. 120 (Chiang Mai, Doi Suthep). — DE SCHAUENSEE, Proc. Acad. Nat. Sci. Philadelphia, 1934, p. 220 (Chiang Mai, Khun Tan). — RILEY, U. S. Nat. Mus. Bull. 172, 1938, p. 461 (Mae Hong Son, Chiang Mai, Doi Hua Mot, Khun Tan, Lampang, Ban Nam Khian).

Hypothymis azurea montana RILEY, Proc. Biol. Soc. Washington, vol. 42, 1929, p. 165 (Chiang Mai, North Thailand).

Hypothymis azurea stayani, DE SCHAUENSEE, Proc. Acad. Nat. Sci. Philadelphia, 1929, p. 548 (Chiang Mai, Doi Suthep, Chiang Saen).

Hypothymis azurea montana, CHASEN and BODEN KLOSS, Journ. Siam Soc. Nat. Hist. Suppl., 1932, p. 240 (Doi Suthep).

Throughout the northern provinces, this is the commonest resident flycatcher of the plains and lower hills: it may be found in the lowlands wherever some small stream or pool is shaded by bamboo and other dense growth, in fruit gardens, and in the precincts of monasteries; on Doi Suthep and certain other mountains it appears again in the mixed-deciduous and light evergreen forest between 2,000 and 3,500 feet.

In the neighborhood of Chiang Mai, one pair or more of this beautiful species may be seen in every outvillage, and the harsh call note is not infrequently heard from groves of trees in the very heart of the city. It differs from other resident members of the family chiefly by its tameness and familiarity with man.

Examples taken in the Khun Tan range, August 27 and 30, are in postnuptial molt.

An adult male had the irides dark brown; the bill plumbeous-blue, with the apical half of the maxilla black; the feet, toes, and claws brownish slate. De Schauensee has noted (1929) that his specimens had the irides dark brown; the bill dark plumbeous, tipped black; the interior of the mouth olive-green; the feet and toes dark plumbeous.

The adult male has a narrow frontal line, the extreme point of the chin, a large patch on the nape, and a narrow gorget across the uppermost breast velvety black; the rest of the plumage violet-blue, brightest on the head and neck, dullest on the wings and tail (the rectrices narrowly tipped with white), this color fading gradually to pure white on the lower abdomen, the under tail coverts, axillaries, and under wing coverts. The adult female differs from the adult male in the absence of the black nuchal patch and gorget; in having the mantle dull pinkish brown, the remiges and rectrices similar but overlaid with blue; the blue of the head, neck, and breast paler and duller.

TERPSIPHONE PARADISI INDOCHINENSIS (Salomonsen)

INDO-CHINESE PARADISE FLYCATCHER

Tchitrea affinis indochinensis SALOMONSEN, Ibis, 1933, pp. 734–736 (Angkor, Cambodia).

Terpsiphone affinis, GYLDENSTOLPE, Kungl. Svenska Vet.-Akad. Handl., 1916, p. 81 (Khun Tan).

Tchitrea paradisi affinis [*partim*], GYLDENSTOLPE, Ibis, 1920, p. 574 ("Throughout the whole country").

Tchitrea paradisi, DEIGNAN, Journ. Siam Soc. Nat. Hist. Suppl., 1931, p. 145 (Doi Suthep).

Tchitrea paradisi indochinensis, DEIGNAN, Journ. Siam. Soc. Nat. Hist. Suppl., 1936, p. 120 (Doi Suthep).

The breeding race of the paradise flycatcher is a very local and rather uncommon seasonal visitor to our provinces: Gyldenstolpe collected four specimens at Khun Tan between May 6 and September 22, 1914; I found it in small numbers between February 13 (1936) and August 23 (1930) on Doi Suthep, 2,700 to 3,500 feet (a bird of the year taken November 21, 1936, is the only exceptional record); an example from Ban Huai Som, March 28, 1937, is the sole proof of its occurrence east of the Khun Tan chain.

This is a bird of moist and fairly dense evergreen; judged from my experience, it is most likely to be observed where, along some forest stream, the shrubs and trees are bound together by a profusion of vines. It is intolerant of intrusion and soon attracts attention to itself by harsh, scolding notes, not unlike those of the black-naped flycatcher.

A male from Doi Suthep, February 29, had the gonads enlarged; the one from Ban Huai Som, March 28, had them greatly enlarged. It is interesting to note that, of the nine northern Thai specimens known to me, no less than eight are males.

An example from Doi Suthep, July 25, is in postnuptial molt.

An adult female had the irides brown; the eye ring smalt blue; the maxilla with the basal half horny black, the tip black, the edges of the commissure horny, the rest (including the basal half of the culmen) smalt blue; the mandible blackish brown with the edges of the commissure horny; the feet and toes smalt blue; the claws horny brown. Birds of the year have the entire bill, at least in the dried skin, horn color.

The adult male has the erectile feathers of the crown glossy blue-black; the nape deep ashy gray; the remaining upperparts bright rufous; the rectrices graduated and the central pair enormously elongated; the lores, sides of the head, chin, throat, and upper breast deep ashy gray (like the nape), changing on the lower breast to the pure white of the abdomen; the under tail coverts rufous-buff. The adult female and the younger male differ from the adult male only in the lack of the elongated central tail feathers.

No one has ever recorded a white-phased paradise flycatcher from any part of our area; if such be seen, especially in the more eastern provinces, it is likely to be an example of the Chinese race.

TERPSIPHONE PARADISI INCEI (Gould)

Chinese Paradise Flycatcher

Muscipeta Incei Gould, The birds of Asia, vol. 2, pt. 4, Nov. 1852, pl. 19 and text ("Neighbourhood of Shanghai in China").

Terpsiphone affinis, Gyldenstolpe, Journ. Nat. Hist. Soc. Siam, 1915, p. 169 (listed).

Tchitrea paradisi affinis [*partim*], Gyldenstolpe, Ibis, 1920, p. 574 ("Throughout the whole country").

Terpsiphone incei incei, Riley, U. S. Nat. Mus. Bull. 172, 1938, p. 466 (Nan, Ban Nam Khian).

The Chinese paradise flycatcher is probably a regular and not uncommon bird of passage through the provinces east of the Khun Tan range; the definite records are: a female and a male taken by Eisenhofer at Pha Hing, April 29 and May 5, 1912 (specimens listed by Gyldenstolpe and now deposited in Stockholm); two males collected by Smith in Nan Province, April 15 and 19, 1930; a male shot by me at Ban Nam Puat (French Enclave), April 26, 1936, and a young female from Ban Sa-iap (Phrae Province), September 9, 1936.

The adult male, in the white phase, has the whole head and neck (including the throat) glossy blue-black; the rest of the plumage white, all the feathers of the upperparts with more or less distinct black shaft streaks and the rectrices with narrow black margins as well. The adult male in the brown phase differs from that of *indochinensis* in having the entire head and neck (including the nape and throat) glossy blue-black; the upperparts chestnut-rufous, distinctly glossed with violet on the mantle; the gray of the breast continued over the greater part of the abdomen, with resultant restriction of the area of pure white. The adult female resembles the brown male but has the chin and throat deep gray, slightly glossed with steel blue, and lacks the elongated central rectrices.

T. p. indochinensis of either sex has a decidedly larger and heavier bill than *incei;* in the rare event of the occurrence of *indochinensis* in a white phase, it could probably be distinguished from the Chinese bird only by comparison of bills.

Family SYLVIIDAE

SEICERCUS BURKII TEPHROCEPHALA (Anderson)

Burmese Golden-spectacled Flycatcher Warbler

Culicipeta tephrocephalus Anderson, Proc. Zool. Soc. London, 1871, p. 213 (Bhamo, Upper Burma).

Cryptolopha burkii tephrocephalus, Gyldenstolpe, Kungl. Svenska Vet.-Akad. Handl., 1913, p. 30 (Khao Phlung); 1916, p. 82 (Khun Tan).

Cryptolopha burki tephrocephala, GYLDENSTOLPE, Journ. Nat. Hist. Soc. Siam, 1915, p. 167 (listed); Ibis, 1920, p. 575 (Khao Phlung, Khun Tan).
Seicercus burkei tephrocephalus [*partim*], DE SCHAUENSEE, Proc. Acad. Nat. Sci. Philadelphia, 1929, p. 546 (Doi Suthep [*partim*], Chiang Saen).
Seicercus burkii tephrocephalus [*partim*], DEIGNAN, Journ. Siam Soc. Nat Hist. Suppl., 1931, p. 150 (Doi Suthep [*partim*]); 1936, p. 117 (Doi Suthep [*partim*]).—DE SCHAUENSEE, Proc. Acad. Nat. Sci. Philadelphia, 1934, p. 231 ("Chiengmai"=Doi Suthep [*partim*], Khun Tan, Doi Chiang Dao).—RILEY, U. S. Nat. Mus. Bull. 172, 1938, p. 437 (Khun Tan).

The present race is a common winter visitor to northern Thailand, where it has been noted from September 12 (1936) at Ban Tha Fa to April 13 (1936) on Phu Kha. It seems to be restricted to the more open evergreen forest but in that type of growth ranges from the plains (Chiang Saen) to an elevation of 6,400 feet (Doi Pha Hom Pok).

This form travels through the lower trees in company with such birds as *Culicicapa*, *Hypothymis*, *Erpornis*, and the various species of *Phylloscopus*. Like its near relatives, it is more or less constantly in motion, whether foraging among the leaves or darting through the air in pursuit of flies and other small game.

A male had the irides dark brown; the maxilla dark horny brown; the mandible horny yellow; the feet and toes horny yellow; the claws yellow.

The adult has a broad coronal streak ashy gray, more or less strongly suffused with olive-green, and bordered at each side by a broad band of dull black; the lores, ocular region, ear coverts, and entire upperparts olive-green; a conspicuous and unbroken eye ring of yellow feathers; the two outermost pairs of rectrices with the inner web white; the entire underparts yellow, more olivaceous along the sides of the body.

SEICERCUS BURKII DISTINCTA (La Touche)

YUNNANESE GOLDEN-SPECTACLED FLYCATCHER WARBLER

Cryptolopha burkii distincta LA TOUCHE, Bull. Brit. Orn. Club, vol. 43, 1922, p. 41 (Mengtz, southeastern Yunnan).
Cryptolopha burkei tephrocephala, DE SCHAUENSEE, Proc. Acad. Nat. Sci. Philadelphia, 1928, p. 570 (Chiang Mai).
Seicercus burkei tephrocephalus [*partim*], DE SCHAUENSEE, Proc. Acad. Nat. Sci. Philadelphia, 1929, p. 546 (Doi Suthep [*partim*]).
Seicercus burkii tephrocephalus [*partim*], DEIGNAN, Journ. Siam Soc. Nat. Hist. Suppl., 1931, p. 150 (Chiang Mai, Doi Suthep [*partim*]); 1936, p. 117 (Chiang Mai, Doi Suthep [*partim*]).—DE SCHAUENSEE, Proc. Acad. Nat. Sci. Philadelphia, 1934, p. 231 ("Chiengmai"=Doi Suthep [*partim*]).—RILEY, U. S. Nat. Mus. Bull. 172, 1938, p. 437 (Muang Pai).

This flycatcher warbler winters in small numbers in the provinces of Chiang Mai and Mae Hong Son, whence it is now known by nine specimens collected between November 25 (1931) and March 23 (1936, 1937).

Six of these examples were shot in lowland bamboo brakes, which must be considered the normal habitat of the bird. I have seen, however, in Philadelphia, a perfectly typical specimen from Doi Suthep, 3,000 feet, December 20, 1932; a second (with damaged head but probably correctly determined) from the same hill at 4,500 feet, December 7, 1928; and I have myself taken one there at 3,200 feet, March 23, 1937. Thus, while *tephrocephala* has not yet been found in lowland bamboo, *distincta* occasionally appears in the mountain evergreen and field identifications based upon altitudinal range must be considered untrustworthy.

An unsexed adult had the irides dark brown; the maxilla black; the mandible horny yellow, tipped horny; the feet and toes yellowish horny brown; the claws horn.

S. b. distincta differs from *tephrocephala* in having the broad coronal streak pure ashy gray, the lateral bands a rather deeper black and outwardly edged (above the ear coverts) by a narrower streak of pure ashy gray; the upperparts a rather more golden olive-green; the underparts a more golden-yellow.

SEICERCUS POLIOGENYS (Blyth)

Gray-cheeked Flycatcher Warbler

C[ulicipeta] poliogenys Blyth, Journ. Asiat. Soc. Bengal, vol. 16, 1847, p. 441 (Darjiling, India).

Seicercus affinis, Deignan, Journ. Siam Soc. Nat. Hist. Suppl., 1936, p. 170 (Phu Kha).

The gray-cheeked flycatcher warbler is known from Thailand by a single specimen: an adult female, collected by me at the summit of Phu Kha, 5,500 feet, April 10, 1936.

This species has a broad coronal streak (extending over the nape) ashy gray, bordered at either side by a broad band of black; the lores, ocular region, ear coverts, and sides of the nape ashy gray; a conspicuous eye ring of pure white feathers, interrupted above the eye by an ashy-gray portion; the remaining upperparts golden olive-green; the greater upper wing coverts tipped with yellow to form a narrow bar; the three outermost pairs of rectrices with the inner web white; the chin (and sometimes the upper throat) pale ashy; the remaining underparts golden-yellow.

SEICERCUS SUPERCILIARIS SUPERCILIARIS (Blyth)

Indo-Chinese White-throated Flycatcher Warbler

Abrornis superciliaris "Tickell" Blyth, Journ. Asiat. Soc. Bengal, vol. 28, 1859, p. 414 (mountainous interior of the Tenasserim provinces).

Abrornis superciliaris, Gyldenstolpe, Kungl. Svenska Vet.-Akad. Handl., 1913, p. 30 (Mae Raem river); 1916, p. 82 (Khun Tan, Doi Pha Sakaeng, Pha Kho); Journ. Nat. Hist. Soc. Siam, 1915, p. 167 (listed).

Abrornis superciliaris superciliaris, GYLDENSTOLPE, Ibis, 1920, p. 575 (Khun Tan, Pha Kho, Mae Raem, Doi Pha Sakaeng).
Abroscopus superciliaris salwinensis, DEIGNAN, Journ. Siam Soc. Nat. Hist. Suppl., 1931, p. 150 (Doi Suthep).
Abroscopus superciliaris superciliaris, DEIGNAN, Journ. Siam Soc. Nat. Hist. Suppl., 1936, p. 117 (Doi Suthep).—RILEY, U. S. Nat. Mus. Bull. 172, 1938, p. 438 (Khun Tan).

The white-throated flycatcher warbler has been found in all the northern provinces except Mae Hong Son, where it is almost certain to occur. It is restricted in range to districts with extensive bamboo-brakes but, at suitable places, is common from the level of the plains to about 3,500 feet. The sole record for the vicinity of Chiang Mai is a solitary bird observed by me on Doi Suthep, 3,500 feet, July 12, 1930 (in a clump of bamboo at the edge of the evergreen); on the lower slopes of Doi Mon Khwam Long, the next mountain to the North, where bamboo is plentiful, the species is almost abundant.

Along small streams and trails through the bamboo forest, this is a most lively and conspicuous little bird, taking its insect food on the wing and, during the breeding season, constantly rendering a sweet, but very shrill, whistled song.

A specimen of August 29 (Ban Mae Mo) is in postjuvenal molt; postnuptial molt is shown by another of July 20 (Doi Mon Khwam Long).

An adult male had the irides brown; the bill black, with the base of the mandible plumbeous; the feet, toes, and claws horn.

The adult of either sex has the front and crown brownish gray; the remaining upperparts golden olive-green, with a narrow band of yellow across the rump; the lores and postocular streak slaty; the supercilium white; the chin and throat ashy white, changing on the upper breast to the bright yellow of the remaining underparts.

SEICERCUS CASTANICEPS COLLINSI Deignan

THAI CHESTNUT-CROWNED FLYCATCHER WARBLER

Seicercus castaniceps collinsi DEIGNAN, Proc. Biol. Soc. Washington, vol. 56, 1943, pp. 29–30 (Doi Langka, Northern Thailand).
Seicercus castaneoceps castaneoceps, RILEY, Journ. Siam Soc. Nat. Hist. Suppl., 1933, p. 157 (Doi Langka).
Seicercus castaniceps castaniceps, RILEY, U. S. Nat. Mus. Bull. 172, 1938, p. 438 (Doi Langka).

An adult male (the holotype of the race), collected by Smith on Doi Langka, April 22, 1931, is the sole example of the species now known from Thailand. Since I myself saw a small party on Doi Ang Ka at 5,500 feet in April 1931, we may expect it to occur on yet others of our higher peaks.

Those observed by me were near the ground, moving rapidly through a dense tangle of vines and other vegetation growing on the steep slope of a ravine at the edge of moist evergreen forest.

The type has the front and crown chestnut-rufous, with a band of black beginning above each eye and extending to the nape; the rest of the nape ashy white; the dorsum ashy gray, suffused with olive-green posteriorly and on the scapulars; the rump yellow; the upper tail coverts olive-green; the wings blackish, the exposed parts of the feathers edged with olive-green, the median and greater upper coverts also broadly tipped with yellow to form two bars; the rectrices blackish, their exposed parts edged with olive-green, the two outermost pairs wholly white on the inner webs; an eye ring of tiny ashy-white feathers; the lores, sides of the head and neck, the chin, throat, and entire breast ashy gray; the center of the abdomen white; the remaining underparts yellow.

SEICERCUS ALBOGULARIS HUGONIS (Deignan)

Thai Black-throated Flycatcher Warbler

Abroscopus albogularis hugonis Deignan, Auk, 1938, p. 510 (Pang Mae Ton, Doi Langka, northern Thailand).

Abroscopus albogularis albogularis, Riley, Journ. Siam Soc. Nat. Hist. Suppl., 1933, p. 158 (Doi Langka) ; U. S. Nat. Mus. Bull. 172, 1938, p. 439 (Doi Langka, Doi Hua Mot).

Abroscopus albogularis hugonis, Greenway, Bull. Mus. Comp. Zool., 1940, p. 190 (Doi Nang Kaeo).

Like other diminutive flycatcher warblers of the mountain evergreen, this species is seldom seen and appears to be very rare. The only specimens known from our area are a male from Doi Langka, May 2, 1931, and a female from Doi Hua Mot, August 14, 1934, both collected by Smith; a mummified example from Doi Ang Ka, April 1931, sent by me to the Princeton Museum of Zoology; a female taken by Griswold on Doi Nang Kaeo, 2,800 feet, April 9, 1937. On Doi Suthep I saw one or two at 4,500 feet, October 10, 1936.

The few observed by me were in dense forest and, on Doi Ang Ka, accompanied a flock of *Alcippe castaneceps exul*.

Griswold's bird of April 9 is listed by Greenway (*loc. cit*) as a nestling; Smith's example of August 14 is in postnuptial molt.

The adult has the forehead, crown, and nape light rufous-brown, the crown and nape bordered at each side by a black streak; the remaining upperparts dark olive-green, with a broad yellowish-white band across the rump; the sides of the head and neck (including the superciliary region) light rufous; the feathers of the chin white, those of the throat, black with white tips; the breast, upper flanks, and under tail coverts yellow; the remaining underparts white.

PHYLLOSCOPUS SUBAFFINIS Ogilvie Grant

BUFF-BELLIED WILLOW WARBLER

Phylloscopus subaffinis OGILVIE GRANT, Bull. Brit. Orn. Club, vol. 10, 1900, pp. 37–38 (Pu-an-ting, southwestern Kweichow, China).

Phaeoradina subaffinis, RILEY, U. S. Nat. Mus. Bull. 172, 1938, p. 432 (Doi Langka).

The buff-bellied willow warbler, known from Thailand by a single female collected by Smith at Doi Langka, November 13, 1930, is evidently very rare in our provinces.

The specimen is in rather worn plumage but is undergoing molt of the feathers of throat and upper back.

This plain-colored but distinctive species has the entire upperparts olive-green, strongly suffused with buff; the lores and postocular streak olivaceous-brown; the supercilium and underparts yellow, strongly suffused with buff, especially along the flanks and on the under tail coverts.

PHYLLOSCOPUS FUSCATUS FUSCATUS (Blyth)

SIBERIAN DUSKY WILLOW WARBLER

Phyllopneuste fuscata BLYTH, Journ. Asiat. Soc. Bengal, vol. 11, 1842, p. 113 ("Shot in the neighbourhood" [=Calcutta, Bengal]).

Phylloscopus fuscata fuscata, GYLDENSTOLPE, Kungl. Svenska Vet.-Akad. Handl., 1916, p. 45 (Khun Tan, Sop Tui); Ibis, 1920, p. 474 (Khun Tan, Sop Tui).

Phylloscopus fuscatus fuscatus, DEIGNAN, Journ. Siam Soc. Nat. Hist. Suppl., 1931, p. 149 (Chiang Mai); 1936, p. 116 (Chiang Mai).

Phaeoradina fuscata fuscata, RILEY, U. S. Nat. Mus. Bull. 172, 1938, p. 432 (Ban Nam Khian).

The dusky willow warbler is a very common winter visitor to the lowlands of every part of our area, where it has been recorded from September 30 (Chiang Mai) to May 6 (Chiang Rai).

Of all the many willow warblers that visit Thailand during the cold weather, only *P. i. inornatus* occurs in greater numbers than this one. Strictly confined to the plains, *fuscatus* is never found high in the trees but haunts hedges and bushes, in gardens or wastelands, and especially the great clumps of bamboo overhanging ponds and streams.

Specimens taken between April 22 and May 6 are in prenuptial molt.

A male had the irides dark brown; the maxilla horny brown; the mandible yellowish, dusky flesh at the tip; the feet and toes fleshy horn; the soles yellow; the claws horn.

Another plain-colored form, this bird has the entire upperparts dark olivaceous-brown; the lores and a streak behind the eye blackish brown; the supercilium and underparts pale rusty buff, albescent on the chin, throat, and center of the abdomen, usually more grayish on the breast (the center of the abdomen sometimes lightly washed with cream).

PHYLLOSCOPUS ARMANDII ARMANDII (Milne Edwards)

NORTHERN STREAKED-BREASTED WILLOW WARBLER

Abrornis Armandii MILNE EDWARDS, Nouv. Arch. Mus. [Paris], vol. 1, 1865, Bull., pp. 22–23, col. pl. 2, fig. 1 (no locality given; type specimen "from mountains W. and N. W. of Pekin," *fide* Ticehurst, Systematic review of the genus *Phylloscopus*, 1938, p. 91).

The nominate race of *P. armandii* finds a place in our list on the basis of a male from the vicinity of Chiang Mai (at the foot of Doi Suthep, near Doi Kham), March 20, 1936, identified as of this form by my late friend Dr. Claud B. Ticehurst, and an unsexed specimen from the other side of Chiang Mai (Ban Pa Muat), March 19, 1936, provisionally placed here by the same authority.

Both of these examples were collected by me from low undergrowth in dry, deciduous forest at about 1,000 feet elevation.

The bird of March 20 is beginning prenuptial molt.

Typical *armandii*, according to Ticehurst (*loc. cit.*), "resembles *Phylloscopus armandii perplexus*, but is a little paler and greyer above; the yellow and buff on the under parts is paler. Differences can be seen in a series, but not easily on single, worn or poor skins."

PHYLLOSCOPUS ARMANDII PERPLEXUS Ticehurst

SOUTHERN STREAKED-BREASTED WILLOW WARBLER

Phylloscopus armandii perplexus TICEHURST, Bull. Brit. Orn. Club, vol. 54, 1934, pp. 96–97 (Chien-chuan valley, lat. 26° 40′ N., northwestern Yunnan).

Phylloscopus armandii armandii, DE SCHAUENSEE, Proc. Acad. Nat. Sci. Philadelphia, 1934, pp. 3, 230 (Chiang Mai).—DEIGNAN, Journ. Siam. Soc. Nat. Hist. Suppl., 1936, p. 116 (Chiang Mai).

Dr. Ticehurst identified as *P. a. perplexus* a female taken by me on Doi Suthep, 1,800 feet, January 25, 1936; a male from Chiang Mai (Ban Pa Muat), March 19, 1936; and a female from Ban San Pa Pao, December 20, 1936. The male collected by de Schauensee at Chiang Mai, January 28, 1933, is evidently the example which first led Ticehurst to include "N. W. Siam" in the winter range of the race (Systematic review of the genus *Phylloscopus*, 1938, p. 93).

P. a. perplexus occurs in precisely the same arid forests as *armandii* and the species seems not to ascend the hills at all beyond the upper limit of this type of vegetation.

The bird of March 19 is in prenuptial molt.

My specimens have the entire upperparts olivaceous-brown; the lores and postocular streak similar but darker; the supercilium buffy white; the underparts pale yellow, becoming ashy on the chin and throat, yellowish buff along the flanks and on the under tail coverts, the throat, breast, and belly very indistinctly streaked with a deeper yellow.

PHYLLOSCOPUS SCHWARZI (Radde)

THICK-BILLED WILLOW WARBLER

Sylvia (*Phyllopneuste*) *Schwarzi* RADDE, Reisen im Süden von Ost-Sibirien, vol. 2, 1863, pp. 260–263, pl. 9, fig. 1 (Tarai-nor, Davuria, East Siberia).

Herbivocula schwarzi, DE SCHAUENSEE, Proc. Acad. Nat. Sci. Philadelphia, 1929, p. 555 (Mae Rim); 1934, p. 229 (Doi Suthep, Doi Chiang Dao).—DEIGNAN, Journ. Siam Soc. Nat. Hist. Suppl., 1931, p. 149 (Mae Rim); 1936, p. 116 (Chiang Mai. Doi Suthep).—RILEY, U. S. Nat. Mus. Bull. 172, 1938, p. 431 (Doi Suthep, Doi Langka, Lampang).

Phylloscopus affinis, DE SCHAUENSEE, Proc. Acad. Nat. Sci. Philadelphia, 1934, p. 229 (Doi Suthep).—DEIGNAN, Journ. Siam Soc. Nat. Hist. Suppl., 1936, p. 116 (Doi Suthep).

The thick-billed willow warbler is a not uncommon winter visitor to our area, where it has been noted from November 5 (Doi Mae Lai) to April 2 (Doi Suthep); it occurs in the lowlands and also at suitable places on the mountains to 5,400 feet. Two females taken by Smith at Lampang, November 17, 1928, are the only examples yet known from the districts east of the Khun Tan chain but the species is almost certain to turn up in every one of our provinces.

This is a bird of the dry jungle, on the plains and lower slopes of the hills haunting the same places as the forms of *Phylloscopus armandii*, at higher elevations keeping to the grass and undergrowth of the oak and pine forests.

Prenuptial molt is shown by a skin from the vicinity of Chiang Mai, March 20.

A male had the irides dark brown; the maxilla dark brown; the mandible fleshy, yellow at the base; the interior of the mouth yellow; the feet and toes fleshy yellow; the claws horny brown.

The present species appears with us in two types of plumage. One has the entire upperparts olivaceous-brown; the lores and postocular streak blackish brown; the supercilium pale buffy; the underparts whitish, sullied with pale buffy brown (especially on the breast) and becoming pale rufous-buff along the flanks and on the under tail coverts. The second, which probably represents the first-winter dress, is similar but has the olivaceous-brown of the upperparts more or less strongly suffused with rufescent; the underparts as in the other type but with the ground-color pale yellow instead of whitish.

P. schwarzi, in the latter livery, is likely to be confused with *P. armandii*. Ticehurst says (Systematic review of the genus *Phylloscopus*, 1938, p. 96): "Immediately recognisable from *armandii* by the fact that if there is yellow in the underparts this is uniform and *never streaked with brighter yellow*."

PHYLLOSCOPUS PULCHER PULCHER Blyth

NEPALESE ORANGE-BARRED WILLOW WARBLER

Ph[ylloscopus] pulcher "(Hodgson)" BLYTH, Journ. Asiat. Soc. Bengal, vol. 14, 1845 [=1846], pp. 592–593 (Nepal).

Phylloscopus pulcher pulcher, RILEY, U. S. Nat. Mus. Bull. 172, 1938, p. 432 (Doi Suthep).—GREENWAY, Bull. Mus. Comp. Zool., 1940, p. 190 (Doi Ang Ka).

A female was collected by Smith on Doi Suthep, 5,500 feet, December 15, 1928, while five males and one female were taken by Griswold (Asiatic Primate Expedition) at the summit of Doi Ang Ka between March 24 and 30, 1937; the species is probably an uncommon winter visitor, restricted to the tops of our highest mountains.

P. p. pulcher has the forehead, crown, and nape dark olive-green, with an ill-defined paler median streak; the mantle rufescent olive-green; the rump pale yellow; the three outermost pairs of rectrices largely white; the wings like the mantle but with the innermost secondaries tipped buffy yellow, the median coverts tipped yellowish olive to form an indistinct bar, and the greater coverts broadly tipped orange to form a conspicuous bar; the lores and postocular streak blackish; the supercilium buffy yellow; the underparts dull pale yellow, sullied (especially anteriorly) with gray.

PHYLLOSCOPUS INORNATUS INORNATUS (Blyth)

SIBERIAN INORNATE WILLOW WARBLER

Regulus inornatus BLYTH, Journ. Asiat. Soc. Bengal, vol. 11, 1842, pp. 191–192 (India; type specimens from Calcutta, *fide* Ticehurst, Systematic review of the genus *Phylloscopus*, 1938, p. 100).

Phylloscopus superciliosa, GYLDENSTOLPE, Kungl. Svenska Vet.-Akad. Handl., 1913, p. 29 (Den Chai).

Phylloscopus superciliosa superciliosa, GYLDENSTOLPE, Ibis, 1920, p. 474 ("Throughout the whole country").

Phylloscopus superciliosus superciliosus, DE SCHAUENSEE, Proc. Acad. Nat. Sci. Philadelphia, 1928, p. 563 (Doi Suthep).

Phylloscopus humii praemium, DE SCHAUENSEE, Proc. Acad. Nat. Sci. Philadelphia, 1929, p. 555 (Chiang Mai, Doi Suthep, Chiang Rai).—DEIGNAN, Journ. Siam Soc. Nat. Hist. Suppl., 1931, p. 149 (Chiang Mai, Doi Suthep).

P[hylloscopus] i[nornatus] inornatus, CHASEN and BODEN KLOSS, Journ. Siam Soc. Nat. Hist. Suppl., 1932, p. 245, footnote (Doi Suthep).

Phylloscopus inornatus inornatus, DE SCHAUENSEE, Proc. Acad. Nat. Sci. Philadelphia, 1934, p. 230 (Doi Suthep, Chiang Mai, Khun Tan, Doi Chiang Dao, Mae Taeng).—DEIGNAN, Journ. Siam Soc. Nat. Hist. Suppl., 1936, p. 116 (Chiang Mai, Doi Suthep).—RILEY, U. S. Nat. Mus. Bull. 172, 1938, p. 433 (Doi Ang Ka, Doi Suthep, Doi Langka, Khun Tan).

The inornate willow warbler is a very common, or even abundant, winter visitor to every part of northern Thailand, ranging from the level of the plains to the summits of the mountains. The extreme dates for its occurrence with us are September 26 (1936) on Doi Suthep and April 18 (1936) on Phu Kha.

This willow warbler may be seen in almost any sort of arboreal cover except bamboo and the denser evergreen forest; it is the *Phylloscopus* oftenest observed in gardens and orchards.

A male had the irides dark brown; the maxilla dark horny-brown; the mandible horny yellow, tipped dark horny brown; the feet, toes, and claws horny brown.

P. i. inornatus, in fresh autumn dress, has the upperparts bright olive-green, the forehead, crown, and nape with an ill-defined paler median streak; the wings with the coverts broadly tipped yellowish white to form two conspicuous bars, the inner primaries and outer secondaries narrowly tipped white, the inner secondaries broadly edged apically with greenish white; the lores and postocular streak dark olive-green; the broad supercilium pale yellow; the underparts white, more or less strongly washed everywhere with greenish yellow; the under wing coverts and axillaries pale yellow.

Ticehurst records (*loc. cit.*, p. 105) an example of *P. i. mandellii* (Brooks) from "Siam"; the specimen very probably came from some locality in northern Thailand.

PHYLLOSCOPUS PROREGULUS CHLORONOTUS (G. R. Gray)

Nepalese Yellow-rumped Willow Warbler

Abrornis chloronotus G. R. Gray, Catalogue of . . . Mammalia and birds of Nepal and Thibet . . . British Museum, 1846, pp. 66, 152 (Nepal).

P[hylloscopus] proregutus [*sic*] *forresti*, Chasen and Boden Kloss, Journ. Siam Soc. Nat. Hist. Suppl., 1932, p. 245, footnote (Doi Suthep).

Phylloscopus proregulus forresti, Deignan, Journ. Siam Soc. Nat. Hist. Suppl., 1936, p. 116 (Doi Suthep).

The yellow-rumped willow warbler is a rare winter visitor to northern Thailand, known thence by only three specimens: Two males collected by Aagaard on Doi Suthep, 5,500 feet, in February or March, 1931; a female taken by me on Phu Kha, 4,500 feet, April 6, 1936.

The Phu Kha bird was found only a few feet above the ground in a dense tangle of coarse grass and *Rubus* sp. at an abandoned *hai*.

This species has the forehead, crown, and nape deep, almost blackish, olive-green, with a broad yellowish olive-green median line; the remaining upperparts, except for the pale yellow rump, buffy olive-green; the wing coverts tipped with yellowish white to form two conspicuous bars; the lores and postocular streak blackish olive-green; the supercilium olivaceous-yellow; the underparts white, more or less strongly washed everywhere with pale olivaceous-buff; the under wing coverts and axillaries pale yellow.

PHYLLOSCOPUS MACULIPENNIS MACULIPENNIS (Blyth)

EASTERN ASHY-THROATED WILLOW WARBLER

Abrornis maculipennis BLYTH, Ibis, 1867, p. 27 (Nepal or Sikkim).
Phylloscopus maculipennis maculipennis, GREENWAY, Bull. Mus. Comp. Zool., 1940, p. 189 (Doi Ang Ka).

The ashy-throated willow warbler has been found in Thailand only by Griswold (Asiatic Primate Expedition), who collected two males and two females at the summit of Doi Ang Ka, March 22 and 30, 1937. It is probably only a winter visitor, restricted to our highest mountains.

This distinctively marked form has the forehead, crown, and nape dark brownish gray, with a broken ashy-white median streak; the remaining upperparts, except for the yellow rump, bright deep olive-green; the wings like the mantle but with the inner secondaries tipped yellowish white on the outer web and the median coverts narrowly, the greater coverts broadly, tipped yellow to form two conspicuous bars; the three outermost pairs of rectrices with the inner web pure white; the lores and postocular streak dark brownish gray; the long supercilium ashy white; the chin and throat ashy gray; the remaining underparts yellow.

PHYLLOSCOPUS BOREALIS BOREALIS (Blasius)

SIBERIAN ARCTIC WILLOW WARBLER

Phyllopneuste borealis BLASIUS, Naumannia, 1858, pp. 313–314 (Okhotsk Sea).

A female collected by me at Ban Tha Fa (Phrae Province), September 11, 1936, has been determined by Ticehurst to belong to the present race, which is otherwise not recorded from northern Thailand.

The bird was shot from a tall clump of bamboo in a district of low hills covered with mixed-deciduous forest.

This robust species has the entire upperparts grayish olive-green; the wing like the mantle but with the outer greater coverts narrowly tipped yellowish white to form a fairly conspicuous bar (the median coverts often tipped slightly paler olive-green to form an obsolescent bar); the lores and postocular streak dark olive-green; the conspicuous supercilium yellowish white; the entire underparts white, sullied with gray, and more or less strongly washed with pale yellow.

PHYLLOSCOPUS BOREALIS EXAMINANDUS Stresemann

KAMCHATKAN ARCTIC WILLOW WARBLER

Phylloscopus borealis examinandus STRESEMANN, Nov. Zool., vol. 20, 1913, pp. 353–354 (Bali, Lesser Sunda Islands).
Acanthopneuste borealis xanthodryas, DEIGNAN, Journ. Siam Soc. Nat. Hist. Suppl., 1936, p. 116 (Chiang Mai).

A unique female from Chiang Mai, 1,000 feet, October 27, 1935, has been studied by Dr. Ticehurst, whose comment is: "*examinandus*, if sex is right." The specimen, evidently not mutilated by shot, was skinned by me and, since nothing in my field-catalogue indicates that I was then doubtful of the sex, I leave it under this name.

"In spring dress like *borealis* but a little greener, less grey green on upper parts and a little yellower on the under parts. Averages larger in size. Less green and less yellow than is usual in *xanthodryas*" (Ticehurst, Systematic review of the genus *Phylloscopus*, 1938, p. 128).

PHYLLOSCOPUS TROCHILOIDES TROCHILOIDES (Sundevall)

Eastern Himalayan Dull-green Willow Warbler

Acanthiza trochiloides Sundevall, Physiogr. Sällsk. Tidskr. [Lund], vol. 1, 1837, p. 76 (Calcutta, Bengal).

Phylloscopus trochiloides trochiloides, Greenway, Bull. Mus. Comp. Zool., 1940, p. 190 (Doi Nang Kaeo).

A male and a female of the nominate race of the dull-green willow warbler were collected by Griswold (Asiatic Primate Expedition) on Doi Nang Kaeo, 2,800 feet, April 8 and 18, 1937.

Both specimens are in prenuptial molt.

Another large species, this bird has the entire upperparts dark olive-green; the wing like the mantle but with the greater coverts tipped pale yellow or yellowish white to form a conspicuous bar (the median coverts often similarly tipped to form a more or less distinct bar); the lores and postocular streak blackish olive-green; the conspicuous supercilium yellowish white; the entire underparts yellowish white sullied with gray. In life, the races of *P. trochiloides* cannot be distinguished from those of *P. borealis;* in the hand, they may be most easily recognized by their having the sixth primary emarginate on the outer web.

Greenway observes (*loc. cit.*) that these examples "are assigned with some doubt to this species [= subspecies], though they are closest to it." I have been privileged to examine the birds in question and, having compared them with series of *trochiloides*, *obscuratus*, and *plumbeitarsus* (all determined by Ticehurst), wholly concur with Greenway's identification. The form is already known to winter in all the areas adjacent to northern Thailand.

PHYLLOSCOPUS TROCHILOIDES OBSCURATUS Stresemann

Kansu Dull-green Willow Warbler

Phylloscopus trochiloides obscuratus Stresemann, Orn. Monatsb., vol. 37, 1929, pp. 74–75 (South Tetung Mountains, North Kansu).

A female in fine plumage, shot by me at Chiang Mai, 1,000 feet, May

15, 1936, has been identified by Dr. Ticehurst as an example of *P. t. obscuratus.*

"Like *trochiloides*, but somewhat paler, brighter and greener on the upper parts and edges of wings and tail, but a little darker than *plumbeitarsus.* The upper wing bar is usually indicated, in some markedly so, and the lower one is broader than in *plumbeitarsus*, both bars yellowish in fresh dress as in *trochiloides.* Under parts a little more yellow than in *plumbeitarsus.* . . ." (Ticehurst, Systematic review of the genus *Phylloscopus*, 1938, p. 147).

PHYLLOSCOPUS TROCHILOIDES PLUMBEITARSUS Swinhoe

SIBERIAN DULL-GREEN WILLOW WARBLER

Phylloscopus plumbeitarsus SWINHOE, Ibis, 1861, pp. 330–331 ("between Takoo and Peking, in the neighbourhood of the Peiho River, Province of Chelee, North China").

Phylloscopus nitidus plumbeitarsus, GYLDENSTOLPE, Kungl. Svenska Vet.-Akad. Handl., 1913, p. 29 ("Northern Siam"); Ibis, 1920, p. 474 (Den Chai).—DE SCHAUENSEE, Proc. Acad. Nat. Sci. Philadelphia, 1934, p. 230 (Chiang Mai, "Tung Sio").—RILEY, U. S. Nat. Mus. Bull. 172, 1938, p. 434 (Mae Hong Son, Muang Pai, Chiang Mai, Phrae, Ban Nam Khian).

Acanthopneuste nitidus plumbeitarsus, DEIGNAN, Journ. Siam Soc. Nat. Hist. Suppl., 1936, p. 116 (Chiang Mai).

The Siberian dull-green willow warbler is a common winter visitor to the lowlands of all the northern provinces, where it has been recorded from November 8 (1935) at Chom Thong to April 26 (1930) at Phrae.

This bird seems to be strictly confined to the plains and, in my experience, is only found in the great clumps of garden bamboo, which are so important a feature of our landscapes.

Prenuptial molt is shown by specimens taken between March 30 and April 26.

A male had the irides dark brown; the maxilla dark horny brown; the mandible horny yellow; the tarsi plumbeous-brown; the toes and claws horny brown.

Distinguished "from *trochiloides* by the greener, less olive brown upper parts and whiter under parts; supercilium less yellow and sharper defined; streak behind eye paler, neck less ashy; wing bars narrower; and by wing formula and smaller size and shorter first primary. In skins the upper mandible in winter is brown and in *trochiloides* nearly black. . . ." (Ticehurst, Systematic review of the genus *Phylloscopus*, 1938, p. 151).

PHYLLOSCOPUS TENELLIPES Swinhoe

PALE-LEGGED WILLOW WARBLER

Phylloscopus tenellipes SWINHOE, Ibis, 1860, p. 53 (Amoy, China).

Phylloscopus tennellipes [*sic*], GYLDENSTOLPE, Kungl. Svenska Vet.-Akad. Handl., 1916, p. 46 (Den Chai).

Phylloscopus tenellipes, GYLDENSTOLPE, Ibis, 1920, p. 473 ("Different parts of Siam").—DE SCHAUENSEE, Proc. Acad. Nat. Sci. Philadelphia, 1934, p. 230 (Doi Suthep).

Acanthopneuste tenellipes, DEIGNAN, Journ. Siam Soc. Nat. Hist. Suppl., 1936, p. 117 (Doi Suthep).

The pale-legged willow warbler is known from our area by only two specimens: A male collected by Gyldenstolpe at Den Chai, February 8, 1912, and an unsexed bird taken by de Schauensee on Doi Suthep, 5,000 feet, February 27, 1933.

Gyldenstolpe notes that his example had the irides dark brown; the bill horn color; the feet and toes pale brownish yellow.

This species has the upperparts olivaceous-brown, dark and dull on the head but bright on the mantle and strongly suffused with ochraceous on the rump, upper tail coverts, and rectrices; the wing like the mantle but with the greater and median coverts tipped buffy yellow or yellowish white to form two indistinct bars; the lores and postocular streak blackish olivaceous-brown; the long, broad supercilium pale buff or buffy white; the underparts white, more or less strongly washed with brownish buff along the flanks; the under tail coverts pale buff or pale buffy yellow; the bend of the wing and the axillaries pale buffy yellow; the under wing coverts white (sometimes tinged with pale buffy yellow).

PHYLLOSCOPUS CORONATUS CORONATUS (Temminck and Schlegel)

JAPANESE CROWNED WILLOW WARBLER

Ficedula coronata TEMMINCK and SCHLEGEL, *in* Siebold, Fauna Japonica, Aves, 1847, pp. 48–50, col. pl. 18 (Japan).

Phylloscopus occipitalis coronatus, DE SCHAUENSEE, Proc. Acad. Nat. Sci. Philadelphia, 1934, p. 230 (Doi Suthep, Doi Chiang Dao).

Acanthopneuste occipitalis coronatus, DEIGNAN, Journ. Siam Soc. Nat. Hist. Suppl., 1936, p. 117 (Doi Suthep, Chiang Mai).

At one time I believed the crowned willow warbler to be a common winter visitor to all the northern provinces, from the level of the plains to at least 5,500 feet and, at Chiang Mai, occurring from September 26 (1936) to March 1 (1933). It now appears that I have confused *coronatus* in the field with the various forms of *reguloides*, and the true status of the former must for the present remain in doubt. I have collected a specimen of *coronatus* at Ban Sa-iap (Phrae Province) as early as September 8 (1936).

This is probably the willow warbler with conspicuous coronal bands frequently encountered in gardens and orchards, associated with *P. i. inornatus*.

A male had the irides brown; the maxilla dark brown; the mandible horny yellow; the feet and toes horny brown; the claws horn.

P. c. coronatus has the forehead, crown, and nape deep olive-green (almost blackish on the nape), with a broad yellowish olive-gray median band; the remaining upperparts olive-green; the wing like the mantle but with the greater coverts narrowly tipped pale yellow or yellowish white to form an indistinct bar; the lores and postocular streak blackish olive-green; the long supercilium yellowish white, yellower anteriorly; the underparts white, faintly streaked with pale yellow; the under tail coverts, under wing coverts, and axillaries pale yellow.

PHYLLOSCOPUS REGULOIDES ASSAMENSIS Hartert

Assamese Greater White-tailed Willow Warbler

Phylloscopus trochiloides assamensis Hartert, Vögel der paläarktischen Fauna, vol. 3, 1921, p. 2139. New name for *Acanthopneuste trochiloides harterti* Stuart Baker 1913 (Assam Hills [=Khasya Hills, Assam]), not *Phylloscopus bonelli harterti* Zedlitz, 1912.

Phylloscopus reguloides reguloides [*partim*], Riley, U. S. Nat. Mus. Bull. 172, 1938, p. 435 (Khun Tan [*partim*]).

Phylloscopus reguloides assamensis, Greenway, Bull. Mus. Comp. Zool., 1940, p. 189 (Doi Ang Ka).

A specimen taken by Smith at Khun Tan, October 27, 1929, has been examined by Dr. Ticehurst, who writes: "Seems to be (small ♂) *assamensis*." Nine males and one female (all in poor condition), collected by Griswold at the summit of Doi Ang Ka, March 22–30, 1937, are also called *assamensis* by Ticehurst, with the qualifying remark: "I cannot make anything else of them." In addition, a male from Doi Suthep, 2,700 feet, January 18, 1936, and a female from Chiang Saen Kao, January 12, 1937, are identified by the same authority as *P. r. assamensis* ⋚ *claudiae*.

This willow warbler has the forehead, crown, and nape deep olive-green (almost blackish on the nape), with a broad yellowish olive-gray median band; the remaining upperparts olive-green; the wing like the mantle but with the greater coverts broadly tipped, the median coverts less distinctly tipped, with pale yellow to form two bars; the two outermost pairs of rectrices narrowly edged with white along the inner web; the lores and postocular streak blackish olive-green; the long supercilium pale yellow; the underparts white, suffused and indistinctly streaked with pale yellow; the under tail coverts white, tinged with pale yellow; the under wing coverts and axillaries bright pale yellow.

PHYLLOSCOPUS REGULOIDES CLAUDIAE (La Touche)

Szechwanese Greater White-tailed Willow Warbler

Acanthopneuste trochiloides claudiae La Touche, Bull. Brit. Orn. Club, vol. 43, 1922, p. 22 (Mengtz, southeastern Yunnan).

Phylloscopus reguloides reguloides [*partim*], RILEY, U. S. Nat. Mus. Bull. 172, 1938, p. 435 (Khun Tan [*partim*]).

Phylloscopus reguloides claudiae, RILEY, U. S. Nat. Mus. Bull. 172, 1938, p. 435 (Khun Tan).

Dr. Ticehurst has identified as *claudiae* two males taken by Smith on Doi Khun Tan, 3,000 and 4,000 feet, February 22, 1932; a male from Ban Samoeng, November 23, 1935; and a female from Ban Muang Sum, December 25, 1936. Two specimens considered by him intermediate between *claudiae* and *assamensis* have already been listed under the latter name.

P. r. claudiae "resembles *assamensis*, but the upper parts slightly brighter, not so yellowish-green; cheeks and mesial coronal streaks greyer yellow and paler; under parts whiter, any yellow being confined to streaks on the breast, no wash of yellow; two outer pairs of tail feathers only very narrowly and sharply edged with white . . . Intergrades with *assamensis*, and not every specimen can be placed" (Ticehurst, Systematic review of the genus *Phylloscopus*, 1938, p. 171).

PHYLLOSCOPUS DAVISONI DAVISONI (Oates)

TENASSERIMESE LESSER WHITE-TAILED WILLOW WARBLER

Acanthopneuste davisoni OATES, Fauna of British India, Birds, vol. 1, 1889, pp. 420–421 (Mount Muleyit, Tenasserim).

Acanthopneuste trochiloides davisoni DE SCHAUENSEE, Proc. Acad. Nat. Sci. Philadelphia, 1929, p. 555 (Doi Suthep).

Acanthopneuste reguloides davisoni, DEIGNAN, Jour. Siam Soc. Nat. Hist. Suppl., 1931, p. 149 (Doi Suthep).

P[*hylloscopus*] *reguloides* subsp., CHASEN and BODEN KLOSS, Journ. Siam Soc. Nat. Hist. Suppl., 1932, p. 245, footnote (Doi Suthep).

Phylloscopus trochiloides davisoni, DE SCHAUENSEE, Proc. Acad. Nat. Sci. Philadelphia, 1934, p. 231 (Doi Suthep, Doi Chiang Dao).

Acanthopneuste reguloides harterti, DEIGNAN, Journ. Siam Soc. Nat. Hist. Suppl., 1936, p. 117 (Doi Suthep).

Acanthopneuste davisoni, DEIGNAN, Journ. Siam Soc. Nat. Hist. Suppl., 1936, p. 117 (Doi Suthep).

Phylloscopus flavo-olivaceus flavo-olivaceus, RILEY, U. S. Nat. Mus. Bull. 172, 1938, p. 436 (Doi Suthep, Doi Langka, Doi Hua Mot).

Phylloscopus davisoni davisoni, GREENWAY, Bull. Mus. Comp. Zool., 1940, p. 189 (Doi Ang Ka).

This bird is a common permanent resident in the more open evergreen at altitudes in excess of 4,500 feet, occurring on all the northern mountains of sufficiently high elevation (Doi Ang Ka, Doi Suthep, Doi Chiang Dao, Doi Pha Hom Pok, Doi Langka, Doi Hua Mot, and Phu Kha). It is the only species of *Phylloscopus* likely to be found in summer in Thailand.

A male from Phu Kha, April 15, had the gonads enlarged. Postnuptial molt is shown by a long series of examples taken between June 22 and November 3. The period of prenuptial molt is still unknown; no sign of it appears in three specimens collected between February 1 and 10.

P. d. davisoni "resembles *Ph. reguloides assamensis*, but sex for sex is smaller, upper parts and edges of wings more vivid green; typically the two outer pairs of tail feathers are pure white on the inner webs . . ." (Ticehurst, Systematic review of the genus *Phylloscopus*, 1938, pp. 175–176).

PHYLLOSCOPUS DAVISONI DISTURBANS (La Touche)

Szechwanese Lesser White-tailed Willow Warbler

Acanthopneuste trochiloides disturbans La Touche, Bull. Brit. Orn. Club, vol. 43, 1922, pp. 22–23 (Mengtz, southeastern Yunnan).

An unsexed specimen from Doi Chiang Dao, 5,200 feet, March 18, 1937, has been seen by Dr. Ticehurst, who writes: "Possibly *disturbans* . . . tail right for that . . ." The bird was taken in an area of freshly burned forest and has the plumage distinctly darkened by soot, which may account for his use of the word "possibly."

"In coloration there is little, if any, difference on the upper parts compared with *davisoni;* on the under parts *disturbans* . . . is whiter, *davisoni* more sullied with and streaked with yellow.

"In size *disturbans* may be a trifle larger, but too few have been examined to be sure of this. The only other difference lies in the tail; instead of having the inner web of the outer feather and most of the inner web of the penultimate feather white as in *davisoni*, the white is confined to the edges of the webs" (Ticehurst, Systematic review of the genus *Phylloscopus*, 1938, pp. 178–179).

PHYLLOSCOPUS CANTATOR RICKETTI (Slater)

Chinese Yellow-breasted Willow Warbler

Cryptolopha ricketti Slater, Ibis, 1897, pp. 174–175, col. pl. 4, fig. 2 (Kuatun, northwestern Fuhkien, China).

During my last winter in Thailand I took two specimens of this beautiful bird: A female on Doi Suthep, 2,700 feet, November 7, 1936, and a male on Doi Chiang Dao, November 26, 1936. The species, although not previously recorded from Thailand, was quite to be expected there, and these examples were the result of a purposeful search which led me to examine carefully every individual of what appeared to be the common *Seicercus b. tephrocephala.* I suspect that *ricketti* is a regular winter visitor to our mountains, but has been mistaken again and again for the more abundant flycatcher warbler.

My specimens were shot in light evergreen forest, where they were associated with mixed flocks of such small birds as *Erpornis*, *Seicercus*, and other species of *Phylloscopus.*

P. c. ricketti has the forehead, crown, and nape olivaceous-yellow, edged at each side by a broad, black band; the remaining upperparts bright olive-green; the wings like the mantle but with the greater coverts narrowly tipped yellow to form a bar (the median coverts tipped pale olive-green to form a less distinct bar); the lores and postocular streak olive-washed black; the long supercilium and entire underparts lemon yellow.

PHRAGAMATICOLA AEDON RUFESCENS Stegmann

AMUR THICK-BILLED REED WARBLER

Phragamaticola aedon rufescens STEGMANN, Journ. für Orn., vol. 77, 1929, pp. 250–251 (Amur-land).

Lusciniola aedon, GYLDENSTOLPE, Kungl. Svenska Vet.-Akad. Handl., 1913, p. 29 (Den Chai); Journ. Nat. Hist. Soc. Siam, 1915, p. 167 (listed).

Arundinax aedon, GYLDENSTOLPE, Kungl. Svenska Vet.-Akad. Handl., 1916, p. 43 (Khun Tan); Ibis, 1920, p. 473 ("Siam").

Phragmaticola aedon, DEIGNAN, Journ. Siam Soc. Nat. Hist. Suppl., 1931, p. 149 (Chiang Mai).—DE SCHAUENSEE, Proc. Acad. Nat. Sci. Philadelphia, 1934, p. 229 (Chiang Mai).—RILEY, U. S. Nat. Mus. Bull. 172, 1938, p. 430 (Nan).

Phragamaticola aedon rufescens, DEIGNAN, Journ. Siam Soc. Nat. Hist. Suppl., 1936, p. 115 (Chiang Mai, Doi Suthep).

The thick-billed reed warbler is a common winter visitor to the lowlands of all the northern provinces; the extreme dates for its stay with us are November 21 (1936) at Chiang Mai and May 10 (1936) at Ban Mae Chai. I have once found it on Doi Suthep at 2,200 feet, March 12, 1932.

While this species is not likely to be found at any great distance from water, it is by no means so paludicolous as the birds of the genus *Acrocephalus:* I have constantly observed it, not in the actual reed beds, but among the bushes and low trees growing on rising ground at the edge of a marsh and in the thickets and tall grass covering the banks of canals and irrigation ditches. It is one of the latest of our winter visitors to depart for the northern breeding grounds; early in May 1936, on the great marsh at Mae Chai, I found it still present in considerable numbers and in full voice—the elaborate and melodious song being rendered from the very top of some tree or shrub, whence, when alarmed, the bird dived precipitately into the safer cover of grass and sedge. The ordinary call note, heard from the depths of the thickets, is a loud *chuck-chuck.*

Four males had the irides brown or gray-brown; the maxilla dark horny brown or horny black; the mandible flesh; the rictus fleshy, tinged orange; the interior of the mouth bright orange; the feet and toes greenish gray or plumbeous; the soles yellowish; the claws horn.

The present form differs from the great reed warbler in having the bill proportionately much shorter and thus apparently thicker; the olivaceous-brown of the upperparts more strongly washed with rufescent, especially on the crown and nape; in the lack of a pale supercilium; and in having the rectrices more strongly graduated.

ACROCEPHALUS ARUNDINACEUS BRUNNESCENS (Jerdon)

INDIAN GREAT REED WARBLER

A[grobates] brunnescens JERDON, Madras Journ. Lit. Sci., vol. 10, 1839, p. 269 (The Carnatic, near Trichinopoly, southern India).

Acrocephalus stentoreus amyae, DEIGNAN, Journ. Siam Soc. Nat. Hist. Suppl., 1936, p. 114 (Chiang Mai).

The present form is known in northern Thailand only as an apparently rare winter visitor to the Chiang Mai plain, where I have taken three examples: a female, January 19, 1932 (skin at Princeton); a male, November 29, 1935; and a female, January 16, 1937.

In habits and appearance it is nowise distinguishable in life from the commoner Japanese race, with which it shares the same reed beds.

A female had the irides yellowish brown; the maxilla blackish brown, with the edges of the commissure fleshy; the mandible plumbeous-flesh; the rictus, interior of the mouth, and the skin of the chin salmon; the feet and toes horny violet; the claws dark horny brown.

This is a large, strong-billed reed warbler without conspicuous markings. It has the upperparts olivaceous-brown, suffused with rufescent on the mantle and upper tail coverts and with rufescent-buff on the rump; a short, indistinct brownish-white or buffy-white supercilium; the lores and a small spot behind the eye blackish brown; the underparts buff (this color richest on the under tail coverts, region of the vent, the flanks, and under wing coverts), the center of the abdomen albescent, the chin and throat almost white. *A. a. brunnescens* has the second primary shorter than the fifth; in the two specimens before me, it is equal to the sixth.

ACROCEPHALUS ARUNDINACEUS ORIENTALIS (Temminck and Schlegel)

JAPANESE GREAT REED WARBLER

Salicaria turdina orientalis TEMMINCK and SCHLEGEL, *in* Siebold, Fauna Japonica, Aves, 1847, pp. 50–51, pl. 21 B [=20 B] (Japan).

Acrocephalus arundinaceus orientalis, DEIGNAN, Journ. Siam Soc. Nat. Hist. Suppl., 1931, p. 148 (Chiang Mai); 1936, p. 114 (Chiang Mai).

The Japanese great reed warbler is a locally common winter visitor at Chiang Mai, where I have found it between December 2 (1935) and April 3 (1931).

At small, marshy areas in the fields, where tall, dense vegetation retards evaporation of moisture during the months of drought and rails and bluethroats congregate, the rasping *chur-r-r* of the various reed warblers is heard from the sedges and coarse grasses, but only rarely will the soberly dressed birds be seen clambering about the stems or flitting across an open spot where the rank growth has been trampled down by cattle.

A female had the irides light brown; the maxilla brownish black; the mandible fleshy, with the apical half tinged horny; the interior of the mouth bright orange; the feet and toes plumbeous; the claws horny brown.

In the hand, *orientalis* may be known from *brunnescens* by its having the second primary longer than the fifth; five Thai specimens before me have it between the fourth and fifth in length.

ACROCEPHALUS AGRICOLA CONCINENS (Swinhoe)

CHINESE PADDY-FIELD WARBLER

Calamoherpe concinens SWINHOE, Proc. Zool. Soc. London, 1870, pp. 432–433 (Peking, China).

Acrocephalus concinens concinens, DEIGNAN, Journ. Siam Soc. Nat. Hist. Suppl., 1931, p. 148 (Chiang Mai).—CHASEN and BODEN KLOSS, Journ. Siam Soc. Nat. Hist. Suppl., 1932, p. 246 (Doi Suthep).—DEIGNAN, Journ. Siam Soc. Nat. Hist. Suppl., 1936, p. 114 (Chiang Mai, Doi Suthep).

The paddy-field warbler is a locally common winter visitor to the Chiang Mai plain, where I have found it between November 29 (1935) and February 14 (1931); it occurs rarely also on Doi Suthep, where I shot an example at 2,300 feet, December 30, 1931, and where Aagaard collected one at 4,600 feet in February or March 1931.

This species is normally an inhabitant of the same marshes as its congeners but, not infrequently, especially toward the end of its stay, may be found in quite dry locations, such as wastelands where the grass has been almost entirely burned off.

A male had the irides brown; the maxilla horny black; the mandible with the basal half flesh, the apical half plumbeous; the interior of the mouth deep yellow; the tarsi horny flesh, the toes browner; the soles yellow; the claws horn brown. A female differed only in having the whole of the mandible fleshy.

A. a. concinens may be described roughly as a much smaller edition of the great reed warbler. As seen with us in winter, it has the entire upperparts olivaceous-brown, suffused (especially on the mantle, rump, and upper tail coverts) with rufescent; a poorly defined buffy-white supercilium; the underparts rufous-buff, brighter posteriorly, the chin, throat, and center of the abdomen almost white.

ACROCEPHALUS BISTRIGICEPS Swinhoe

BLACK-BROWED REED WARBLER

Acrocephalus bistrigiceps SWINHOE, Ibis, 1860, pp. 51–52 (Amoy, China).
Acrocephalus bistrigiceps, DEIGNAN, Journ. Siam Soc. Nat. Hist. Suppl., 1931, p. 148 (Chiang Mai) ; 1936, p. 114 (Chiang Mai).

The black-browed reed warbler is a locally common winter visitor to our area, recorded until now only from Mae Hong Son, Chiang Mai, and Nan Provinces but almost certain to occur also in the remaining three. I have found it at Chiang Mai between November 2 (1935) and April 3 (1931) but have collected it at Thattafang as early as October 13 (1936) and at Ban Huai Pa Khan as late as April 8 (1937).

This species haunts exactly the same marshes as the other reed warblers.

It has the irides brown; the maxilla brownish black; the mandible with the basal half fleshy or yellow, the apical half plumbeous or horny; the rictus and interior of the mouth yellow; the tarsi dusky flesh or fleshy horn; the toes light horny brown or plumbeous; the soles yellow; the claws light horny brown.

The present form is very near to the paddy-field warbler in size and coloration but may always be recognized by its having a conspicuous buff supercilium, edged above by a broad black or blackish-brown band.

LOCUSTELLA LANCEOLATA (Temminck)

LANCEOLATED GRASSHOPPER WARBLER

Sylvia lanceolata TEMMINCK, Manuel d'ornithologie, ed. 2, vol. 4, 1840, pp. 614–615 (Mayence, error; type locality corrected to Russia, by Hartert, Vögel der paläarktischen Fauna, vol. 1, 1910, p. 553).
Locustella lanceolata, GYLDENSTOLPE, Journ. Nat. Hist. Soc. Siam, 1915, p. 167 (listed) ; Ibis, 1920, p. 471 ("Northern Siam").—CHASEN and BODEN KLOSS, Journ. Siam Soc. Nat. Hist. Suppl., 1932, p. 245 (Doi Suthep).
Locustella lanceolata [*partim*], DEIGNAN, Journ. Siam Soc. Nat. Hist. Suppl., 1936, p. 114 (Chiang Mai [*partim*]).

This secretive little bird is known from northern Thailand by only four specimens: An unsexed example taken by Eisenhofer at Khun Tan in 1914 and now deposited in Stockholm; a female shot by Aagaard on Doi Suthep, 4,600 feet, in February or March 1931; a female collected by me at Chiang Mai, November 26, 1931, and another from Nong Phung (along the Chiang Dao road, some 46 or 48 km. north of Chiang Mai), March 25, 1936.

The lanceolated warbler keeps to the ground beneath the sedge tussocks and, if seen at all, resembles nothing so much as a small mouse; if made to fly, it drops almost immediately back into the marsh vegetation. With such habits, it may well be a not uncommon winter visitor to our area, despite the paucity of definite records.

My specimens had the irides bright brown; the maxilla brownish black or blackish brown, with the edges of the commissure fleshy; the mandible fleshy; the feet and toes fleshy; the claws horn or horny flesh.

This species has the entire upperparts rufescent olivaceous-brown, most of the feathers with broad black central streaks; a very indistinct buffy supercilium; the underparts white, washed with buff (most strongly along the flanks, sides of the abdomen, and on the under tail coverts), the feathers of the breast, flanks, and under tail coverts with lanceolate black central streaks.

LOCUSTELLA CERTHIOLA MINOR David and Oustalet

Amur Gray-naped Grasshopper Warbler

Locustella minor David and Oustalet, Oiseaux de la Chine, 1877, pp. 250–251 (Peking, China).

Locustella lanceolata, Deignan, Journ. Siam Soc. Nat. Hist. Suppl., 1931, p. 148 (Chiang Mai).

Locustella certhiola minor, Deignan, Journ. Siam Soc. Nat. Hist. Suppl., 1936, p. 114 (Chiang Mai).

Locustella lanceolata [*partim*], Deignan, Journ. Siam Soc. Nat. Hist. Suppl., 1936, p. 114 (Chiang Mai [*partim*]).

The gray-naped grasshopper warbler is an apparently rare winter visitor to the northern provinces, where I have collected three specimens: a female from the Chiang Mai plain, February 17, 1931; a male from the same locality, November 28, 1935; and an unsexed bird from Ban Na Noi (Nan Province), April 2, 1937.

The Chiang Mai examples were found at a small marsh but that from Na Noi, obviously a migrant, was shot beside a small, drying river (the Nam Haeng), on a beach of sand and gravel almost covered by a dense growth of *takrai nam* (*Homonoia riparia*). The habits of this species seem to be quite like those of the lanceolated warbler.

A male had the irides brown; the maxilla dark horny brown; the mandible flesh; the feet and toes dark flesh; the claws horn. A female differed in having the maxilla brownish black; the mandible horny brown, fleshy at the base; the feet and toes pale flesh; the soles whitish.

This bird superficially resembles its congener but has the ground color of the occiput and nape more or less strongly overlaid with ashy; a fairly conspicuous buffy supercilium; the rectrices olivaceous-brown with an outwardly increasingly broad ashy tip and a black subterminal bar (these markings more evident beneath, where the pale tips are ashy white); the underparts usually immaculate (the sides of the lower throat and breast occasionally with tiny, obsolescent blackish spots).

MEGALURUS PALUSTRIS ANDREWSI Bangs

Continental Striated Marsh Warbler

Megalurus palustris andrewsi Bangs, Bull. Amer. Mus. Nat. Hist., vol. 44, 1921, pp. 592–593 (Meng-ting, Yunnan-Burma border).

Megalurus palustris, Deignan, Journ. Siam Soc. Nat. Hist. Suppl., 1931, p. 149 (Chiang Mai) ; 1936, p. 115 (Chiang Mai).

This large and unmistakable grass warbler, which is resident in districts both north and south of us, has been found solely as a rare and irregular cold-weather visitor to the Chiang Mai plain, between October 28 (1936) and February 17 (1931).

I have seen it only in the immediate vicinity of the marshes, where it may be observed flying for long distances above the reeds, with tail violently pumped, or perched at the top of some isolated bush or tree. Its song, which I have heard in April in the State of Kengtung, is a notable performance of loud, chattery, bubbling notes, rendered in the air as the bird glides from an altitude of as much as 40 feet back down to a favored arboreal perch.

A female had the irides light brown; the maxilla dark horny brown; the mandible horny flesh; the feet and toes fleshy horn; the soles yellowish; the claws horn.

The species has the upperparts buffy, suffused (especially on the crown and nape) with rufous, the feathers with black central streaks which are narrow on the crown, nape, and upper tail coverts, broad on the back, scapulars, upper wing coverts, and inner secondaries, virtually absent on the rump; the strongly graduated and sharply pointed rectrices buffy brown with dark brown shafts; an indistinct whitish supercilium; the underparts brownish white, more buffy along the flanks and on the under tail coverts, albescent on the throat and center of the abdomen, the feathers of the breast, flanks, and under tail coverts with narrow blackish-brown shaft streaks.

ORTHOTOMUS SUTORIUS INEXPECTATUS La Touche

Indo-Chinese Long-tailed Tailorbird

Orthotomus sutorius inexpectatus La Touche, Bull. Brit. Orn. Club, vol. 43, 1922, p. 42 (Mengtz, southeastern Yunnan).

Sutoria sutoria, Gyldenstolpe, Kungl. Svenska Vet.-Akad. Handl., 1916, p. 44 (Khun Tan, Doi Pha Sakaeng).

Sutoria sutoria phyllorrapheus, Gyldenstolpe, Ibis, 1920, p. 471 ("Throughout Siam").

Sutoria sutoria patia, de Schauensee, Proc. Acad. Nat. Sci. Philadelphia, 1928, p. 562 (Chiang Mai).

Orthotomus sutorius patia, de Schauensee, Proc. Acad. Nat. Sci. Philadelphia, 1929, p. 554 (Doi Suthep).—Deignan, Journ. Siam Soc. Nat. Hist. Suppl., 1931, p. 148 (Chiang Mai, Doi Suthep) ; 1936, p. 115 (Chiang Mai, Doi Suthep).

Orthotomus sutorius maculicollis, RILEY, U. S. Nat. Mus. Bull. 172, 1938, p. 423 (Ban Nam Khian).

[*Orthotomus sutorius*] *inexpectatus*, GREENWAY, Bull. Mus. Comp. Zool., 1940, p. 188 (Doi Nang Kaeo).

The long-tailed tailorbird is very common or even abundant throughout the northern lowlands; on Doi Suthep, and without doubt on other mountains as well, it occurs in small numbers at inhabited clearings as high as 3,500 feet.

This little warbler, one of the best-known birds of our provinces, occurs impartially in gardens, hedgerows, thickets, bamboo groves, and even the *pa daeng*. It is a thoroughly domesticated species and regularly explores the vines that shade one's veranda or hops about on the floor without regard for human occupants, the tail carried cocked forward above the back or, in flight, pumped energetically up and down in a most ludicrous fashion. It has a number of shrill, monotonous, and rather annoying calls, which are heard constantly, during even the hottest hours of the day, throughout the seasons of heat and rain: *weet-weet-weet; whee-whee-whee; tŭ-wheet′*, *tŭ-wheet′*, *tŭ-wheet′; pee′-to*, *pee′-to*, *pee′-to;* etc., etc. The male, while vocalizing, swells the lower throat in such a way as to disclose at each side an area of naked blackish skin, which is normally concealed by the adjacent feathers.

The breeding season probably embraces the whole period from April to August, at which time the males are wearing the greatly elongated central rectrices. At Chiang Mai I took females with the gonads slightly enlarged, May 3, and greatly enlarged, June 1. Gyldenstolpe has reported (1916) finding a nest with two fresh eggs near Doi Pha Sakaeng, July 22, 1914; in my garden at Chiang Mai I discovered a nest with three apparently fresh eggs as late as August 19, 1930. The remarkable nest has been often described but I may mention that, at Chiang Mai, all examined by me were formed from mango leaves sewn together. A male collected at Chiang Mai, July 6, is just beginning the postnuptial molt.

An adult male had the irides tan; the edges of the eyelids brownish yellow; the maxilla brownish horn, darker on the culmen, the commissure edged pale fleshy; the mandible pale fleshy; the feet and toes fleshy pink; the claws horn.

This species has the forehead and forecrown dull orange-rufous, changing to dull olivaceous-brown on the occiput and nape; the remaining upperparts bright olive-green; the lores and an indistinct supercilium buffy white; the underparts buffy white, the dark gray bases of the feathers often showing irregularly to give a broadly streaked appearance; the thighs rufous-buff.

ORTHOTOMUS ATROGULARIS NITIDUS Hume

INDO-CHINESE BLACK-THROATED TAILORBIRD

Orthotomus nitidus HUME, Stray Feathers, vol. 2, 1874, pp. 507–508 (Tenasserim).

Orthotomus atrigularis, GYLDENSTOLPE, Kungl. Svenska Vet.-Akad. Handl., 1913, p. 29 (Den Chai).

Orthotomus atrigularis nitidus, DE SCHAUENSEE, Proc. Acad. Nat. Sci. Philadelphia, 1929, p. 554 (Chiang Rai).

Orthotomus atrogularis nitidus, RILEY, U. S. Nat. Mus. Bull. 172, 1938, p. 424 (Chiang Dao, Muang Pai).

The black-throated tailorbird is restricted in range to the districts of lowland evergreen, with the result that, while it is known from all our provinces, it is of necessarily local distribution.

This form, unlike its congener, avoids proximity to man and his cultivation, preferring overgrown abandoned clearings, the thickets beside jungle roads, or even the uncut forest. Its habits seem to differ in no important particular from those of *O. s. inexpectatus*, a fact that may well explain its withdrawal into the one type of environment not yet occupied by its more aggressive relative.

A male taken along the Chiang Mai-Chiang Dao road, about 9 km. south of the latter town, August 17, 1935, had the gonads enlarged.

The same specimen had the irides tan; the maxilla horny brown; the mandible horny flesh; the feet and toes flesh; the claws light horny brown.

The adult male has the lores, superciliary region, forehead, crown, and nape bright orange-rufous; the remaining upperparts bright olive-green; the feathers of chin and throat ashy with slaty-black bases, the dark portion increasing in extent on the lower throat so as to form a conspicuous, irregular patch of ashy-streaked black; the remaining underparts buffy white, with gray bases of the feathers showing through irregularly to give a broadly streaked appearance, the flanks strongly washed with olive-yellow; the thighs bright rufous, suffused with yellow; the under tail coverts, under wing coverts, and axillaries yellow. The adult female closely resembles the long-tailed tailorbird but may always be known by the yellow-washed flanks, the yellowish-rufous thighs, and the yellow under tail coverts, under wing coverts, and axillaries.

ORTHOTOMUS CUCULLATUS CORONATUS Blyth

HIMALAYAN YELLOW-BELLIED TAILORBIRD

Orthotomus coronatus "Jerd. & Blyth" BLYTH, Proc. Zool. Soc. London, 1861, p. 200 (Sikkim; type specimen from Darjiling, *fide* Bowdler Sharpe, Catalogue of the birds in the British Museum, vol. 7, 1883, p. 230).

Phyllergates coronatus coronatus, DEIGNAN, Journ. Siam Soc. Nat. Hist. Suppl., 1935, p. 65 (Doi Ang Ka, Doi Chiang Dao).

The yellow-bellied tailorbird, until now recorded in northern Thailand only from Doi Ang Ka, Doi Chiang Dao, and Phu Kha, is an uncommon resident of the evergreen between 4,400 and 5,500 feet.

I have found it singly or in pairs on the steep slopes of ravines, in the lalang of abandoned *hai*, and along the trails in deep, damp forest. In all its actions it is quite like the species of the lowlands.

A bird taken September 4 on Doi Ang Ka is in postnuptial molt; another collected two days later at the same locality is in postjuvenal molt.

An adult female had the irides brown; the maxilla dark horny brown; the mandible with the basal half horny yellow, the apical half dark horny brown; the feet and toes fleshy yellow; the claws brownish horn.

The adult has the forehead and crown bright orange-rufous, changing to dark olive-green on the occiput; a broad nuchal band slaty gray; the remaining upperparts dark olive-green; the remiges and rectrices brown, edged along the outer web with olive-green, the two outer pairs of tail feathers with the whole inner web white; a narrow supercilium ashy white (bright yellow immediately above the eye); the lores and an indistinct postocular streak blackish; the sides of the head and neck otherwise slaty gray, like the nape; the chin, throat, breast, and center of the upper abdomen ashy white, the gray bases of the feathers showing through in places; the remaining underparts bright yellow; the thighs dark olive-green. The juvenile differs from the adult in having the crown and nape dark olive-green, like the remaining upperparts; a narrow olive-yellow supercilium; the white of the chin, throat, and breast washed with pale olive-green.

PRINIA HODGSONII ERRO Deignan

Thai Gray-breasted Prinia

Prinia hodgsonii erro Deignan, Smithsonian Misc. Coll., vol. 103, No. 3, 1942, pp. 6–7 (Chiang Mai, North Thailand).

Franklinia gracilis, de Schauensee, Proc. Acad. Nat. Sci. Philadelphia, 1928, p. 563 (Chiang Mai).—Deignan, Journ. Siam Soc. Nat. Hist. Suppl., 1931, p. 149 (Chiang Mai); 1936, p. 115 (Chiang Mai).

Franklinia gracilis [*partim*], de Schauensee, Proc. Acad. Nat. Sci. Philadelphia, 1934, p. 229 (Chiang Mai [*partim*], Doi Chiang Dao).—Riley, U. S. Nat. Mus. Bull. 172, 1938, p. 427 (Chiang Mai, Doi Langka).

Owing to the difficulty attendant upon distinguishing in the field between the nearly allied *P. r. rufescens* and the present species in *winter* dress, the ranges of the two must be defined from actual museum specimens. These indicate that *erro* is common on the Chiang Mai plain but is otherwise found only on a few of the higher mountains: on Doi Ang Ka at 4,400 feet, on Phu Kha at 4,500 feet, and on Doi

Chiang Dao at 4,600 feet. The bird's complete absence from Doi Suthep, which rises directly from the Chiang Mai lowlands, is worthy of mention.

The gray-breasted prinia is conspicuous at Chiang Mai, where, in flocks of as many as twenty or thirty individuals, it travels through the lower growth of brushy wastelands and the thickets bordering canals and ditches; on the hills it is necessarily restricted to extensive stands of lalang. Its behavior is quite like that of the related species, the members of the flock making short flights, with pumping tail, from bush to bush and keeping together by an endless twittering.

Specimens from Chiang Mai had the gonads enlarged, May 26, and greatly enlarged, July 3 and September 7. The picture of the molts presented by the material before me agrees well with that detailed by Ticehurst and Whistler (Ibis, 1939, p. 763) from Indian series: a bird of January 24 (Chiang Mai) wears full winter dress; one of April 6 (Phu Kha) is in complete prenuptial molt; examples taken between May 2 and September 7 (Doi Langka, Chiang Mai) are in full summer dress; one of November 26 (Chiang Mai) is in complete postnuptial molt. Two skins from Chiang Mai, June 29 and September 1, show respectively postnatal molt and full juvenal plumage.

Males in breeding dress had the irides bright brown or yellow-brown; the swollen edges of the eyelids orange; the bill black; the feet and toes light orange-brown or brownish flesh; the claws horn. A winter-taken male (November 19) differed in having the edges of the eyelids neither swollen nor brightly colored; the bill horny yellow, with the culmen dark horny brown; the feet and toes horny yellow (with the fore part of the tarsus horny pink).

In the breeding season, the adult of either sex has the upperparts chaetura-black (Ridgway), this color almost pure on the front, crown, and nape, faintly tinged with rufescent on the mantle, rump, and upper tail coverts; the wing feathers dark brown, edged along the outer web with dark rufescent; the graduated rectrices brownish ashy, with an ashy-white tip and a black subterminal spot (more conspicuous beneath); the supraloral region concolorous with the crown; the tiny feathers of both eyelids slaty; the underparts white, with a broad pectoral band and the flanks deep ashy gray (the throat and center of the abdomen faintly tinged with cream). In winter, it differs in having the front, crown, and nape slaty brown or brownish slate, changing gradually to dark olivaceous-brown, suffused with rufescent on the lower back, rump, and upper tail coverts; the supraloral streak dark ashy, very rarely ashy white; the tiny feathers of the upper eyelid ashy gray, those of the lower eyelid ashy gray or mixed ashy gray and white; the underparts white (more or less sullied with ashy gray on the breast and upper flanks), washed with cream, which posteriorly changes to rufous-cream. The characters of the rectrices serve to separate this species, at any age or season, from *P. r. rufescens.*

PRINIA RUFESCENS RUFESCENS Blyth

BURMESE RUFESCENT PRINIA

Pr[inia] rufescens BLYTH, Journ. Asiat. Soc. Bengal, vol. 16, 1847, p. 456 (Arakan).

Prinia blanfordi, GYLDENSTOLPE, Kungl. Svenska Vet.-Akad. Handl., 1913, p. 30 (Pak Pan).

Franklinia rufescens poliocephala, GYLDENSTOLPE, Kungl. Svenska Vet.-Akad. Handl., 1916, p. 44 (Khun Tan); Ibis, 1920, p. 473 (Khun Tan).

Franklinia rufescens beavani, GYLDENSTOLPE, Kungl. Svenska Vet.-Akad. Handl., 1916, p. 44 (Sop Tui, Khun Tan); Ibis, 1920, p. 473 (Pak Pan, Khun Tan, Sop Tui).

Franklinia rufescens rufescens, DE SCHAUENSEE, Proc. Acad. Nat. Sci. Philadelphia, 1929, p. 555 (Doi Suthep, Chiang Mai, Mae Rim); 1934, p. 229 (Doi Suthep, Chiang Mai, Doi Chiang Dao).—DEIGNAN, Journ. Siam Soc. Nat. Hist. Suppl., 1931, p. 149 (Doi Suthep, Chiang Mai).—CHASEN and BODEN KLOSS, Journ. Siam Soc. Nat. Hist. Suppl., 1932, p. 246 (Doi Suthep).—DEIGNAN, Journ. Siam Soc. Nat. Hist. Suppl., 1936, p. 115 (Doi Suthep, Chiang Mai).

Franklinia gracilis [*partim*], DE SCHAUENSEE, Proc. Acad. Nat. Sci. Philadelphia, 1934, p. 229 (Chiang Mai [*partim*,]=Doi Suthep).—RILEY, U. S. Nat. Mus. Bull. 172, 1938, p. 427 (Khun Tan).

Franklinia rufescens rufescens [*partim*], RILEY, U. S. Nat. Mus. Bull. 172, 1938, p. 428 (Doi Hua Mot, Khun Tan).

The rufescent prinia is common in all the northern provinces, where specimens have been taken from the level of the plains to about 5,500 feet.

It is difficult to understand why, at a few localities (Chiang Mai, 1,000 feet, and Doi Chiang Dao, 4,600 feet), *Prinia r. rufescens* and *P. h. erro* are cohabitant, while at all other places, to judge from collected material, either one or the other exists alone. This impression is perhaps partly the result of simple failure to collect such common birds, but it is nevertheless true that, during years of work on Doi Suthep, I never once saw *erro* on that mountain and that the bird never came to the attention of Eisenhofer and Gyldenstolpe on Doi Khun Tan; on the other hand, during six weeks on Doi Ang Ka, where *erro*, in nuptial dress, was very common, I failed completely to find *rufescens.*

At Chiang Mai, the two species, so similar in actions and requirements, occurred at exactly the same localities, so that I have sometimes had a flock of each in view at the same time. On the hills, *erro* is apparently restricted to areas of almost pure lalang, but *rufescens* ranges also through the grass under oak and pine and the bushes beside the tracks in mixed-deciduous forest.

Examples with the gonads enlarged were taken at Chiang Mai, May 21, and at Ban Mae Klang, August 30. Birds in full winter dress have been collected between January 18 and February 20 (Doi Suthep, Doi Khun Tan); in complete prenuptial molt, between February 25 and June 8 (Phu Het, Doi Ta Kong, Doi Khun Tan); in full summer dress, between May 21 and August 30 (Chiang Mai, Ban Mae Klang, Ban Mae Mo); in complete postnuptial molt, between August 29 and November 25 (Doi Hua Mot, Doi Khun Tan, Chom Thong, Doi Chiang Dao). A specimen from Doi Hua Mot, August 20, shows postnatal molt; another from Ban Mae Mo, August 25, wears full juvenal plumage.

A breeding male, May 21, had the irides bright brown; the bill blackish; the feet and toes fleshy yellow. Winter-taken examples differ in having the bill horn color.

In nuptial plumage, the adult of either sex has the front, crown, and nape brownish slate; the mantle dark rufous-brown; the wings dark rufous; the graduated rectrices dark rufous above, ashy brown beneath, with a rufous-gray tip and a black subterminal spot; the well-marked supraloral streak (often continued beyond the eye as a short supercilium) and the tiny feathers of both eyelids white; the underparts white, washed with buff, most strongly along the flanks and on the thighs and under tail coverts. In winter, it differs in having the front, crown, and nape rufous-brown, tinged with slate; the mantle bright rufous-brown; the underparts white, washed with rufous-buff, most strongly along the flanks, over the greater part of the abdomen, and on the thighs and under tail coverts. Juveniles have the posterior underparts strongly washed with creamy yellow.

PRINIA INORNATA BLANFORDI (Walden)

Burmese Plain-colored Prinia

Drymoeca blanfordi Walden, *in* Blyth, Catalogue of the mammals and birds of Burma, Journ. Asiat. Soc. Bengal, vol. 43, pt. 2, extra no., 1875, p. 118 (Toungoo, Burma).

Prinia inornata burmanica, Deignan, Journ. Siam Soc. Nat. Hist. Suppl., 1931, p. 150 (Chiang Mai); 1936, p. 118 (Chiang Mai).—de Schauensee, Proc. Acad. Nat. Sci. Philadelphia, 1934, p. 232 (Chiang Mai).

Prinia exter, Riley, U. S. Nat. Mus. Bull. 172, 1938, p. 443 (Ban Nam Khian).

A form of the plain-colored prinia that, on the basis of fine-plumaged January specimens, may quite safely be called *blanfordi*, is a very common permanent resident of the rice plain at Chiang Mai. The species is otherwise known from our area only by two summer examples from Muang Fang (Mae Khong drainage) and one from Ban Nam Khian, which cannot, at this time, be subspecifically identified with any degree of certainty.

In the vicinity of Chiang Mai, the bands of this prinia frequent the high grass at the borders of the marshes, the lush growth of sedges lining the irrigation ditches, and, before the harvest, the far-flung stands of rice. The species is probably common, in similar terrain, throughout the northern provinces.

A specimen from Chiang Mai, May 15, had the gonads enlarged. Both the postnuptial and the postjuvenal molts are shown by the two birds from Muang Fang, July 18. Examples from Chiang Mai, January 23 and 24, are just beginning prenuptial molt, and this molt is far advanced in the one from Ban Nam Khian, April 13.

The adult, in winter dress, has the upperparts olivaceous-brown, faintly suffused with rufescent, the feathers of the crown and mantle with obsolescent darker central streaks; the elongated tail light brown, each feather showing beneath a narrow pale tip and an ill-defined blackish subterminal bar; the lores and a short supercilium pale buffy; the entire underparts buff, more rufescent on the flanks, thighs, and under tail coverts, albescent on the throat and center of the abdomen. In summer, it differs in having the upperparts dull grayish brown; the underparts pale buff or even buffy white; the tail shorter.

I have discussed the specimens from Muang Fang and Ban Nam Khian in my "Revision of the Indo-Chinese Forms of the Avian Genus *Prinia*" (Smithsonian Misc. Coll., vol. 103, No. 3, 1942, p. 8).

PRINIA FLAVIVENTRIS DELACOURI Deignan

INDO-CHINESE YELLOW-BELLIED PRINIA

Prinia flaviventris delacouri DEIGNAN, Smithsonian Misc. Coll., vol. 103, No. 3, 1942, pp. 8–9 (Chiang Mai, North Thailand).

Prinia flaviventris flaviventris, DEIGNAN, Journ. Siam Soc. Nat. Hist. Suppl., 1931, p. 150 (Chiang Mai); 1936, p. 118 (Chiang Mai).

This distinctively colored prinia is apparently a very rare form in northern Thailand, where I have observed only four examples: One at Chiang Mai, February 18, 1931; one on the marshes between Chiang Mai and Lamphun, July 25, 1931; another at the same locality, January 30, 1932; and one at Ban Hong Khaeo (Chiang Rai Province), May 5, 1936.

The few seen by me were all in tall, dense marsh vegetation at decidedly wet places.

A male (January 30) had the irides tan-brown; the edges of the eyelids tan; the bill black, with the extreme tip and a narrow edging to the commissure horny; the feet and toes fleshy orange; the claws horny yellow.

An adult male before me (collected May 5) has the lores slaty, with an ill-defined whitish superior edging; the forehead, forecrown, and sides of the head and neck dark ashy gray, changing to dark olive-green on the rest of the crown, the nape, and the remaining upperparts (the wings tinged with rufescent); the long tail light rufescent olive-green; the chin, throat, and breast white, slightly washed with buffy; the remaining underparts bright yellow, suffused with buff along the flanks; the thighs rufous-buff.

PRINIA ATROGULARIS ERYTHROPLEURA (Walden)

PEGUAN WHITE-BROWED HILL PRINIA

Suya erythropleura WALDEN, *in* Blyth, Catalogue of the mammals and birds of Burma, Journ. Asiat. Soc. Bengal, vol. 43, pt. 2, extra no., 1875, p. 116 (Toungoo, Burma).

Suya superciliaris superciliaris, DE SCHAUENSEE, Proc. Acad. Nat. Sci. Philadelphia, 1929, p. 556 (Doi Suthep); 1934, p. 231 (Doi Suthep, Doi Chiang Dao).—DEIGNAN, Journ. Siam Soc. Nat. Hist. Suppl., 1931, p. 150 (Doi Suthep); 1936, p. 118 (Doi Suthep).—RILEY, U. S. Nat. Mus. Bull. 172, 1938, p. 440 (Doi Langka, Doi Hua Mot).

The hill prinia occurs from 4,400 to 5,500 feet in stands of lalang, and its numbers vary from one locality to another directly with the extent of such growth at sufficiently high elevations. Thus, while it is very common on Doi Suthep and only slightly less so on Doi Ang Ka, it is wholly unknown from Doi Khun Tan and in the provinces east of the Khun Tan chain has been found only on Phu Kha.

Along the topmost ridge of Doi Suthep the small bands of this species are a familiar sight, thanks to the curiosity that induces them to come to the edge of a trail or the tops of the grass to scold the passerby. Its habits seem to differ in no important particular from those of its congeners.

Postjuvenal molt is shown by specimens of April 25 (Doi Langka) and July 14 (Doi Suthep); postnuptial molt, by birds of August 12 (Doi Hua Mot) and October 26 (Doi Suthep).

An adult male had the irides olive-gray; the maxilla dark horny brown, fleshy along the edges of the commissure; the mandible fleshy; the rictus bright yellow; the feet, toes, and claws fleshy. There seems to be no seasonal change in the color of the bill in this form.

The adult in winter dress has the entire upperparts olivaceous-brown, suffused with rufescent on the mantle, wings, and tail; the lores black; a conspicuous superciliary stripe white; the chin, throat, breast, and center of the abdomen buffy white (the feathers of the breast with narrow black lateral edgings, which give an irregularly streaked appearance), changing to rufous-buff along the flanks and on the thighs and under tail coverts. In summer it differs in having the upperparts almost free of rufescent tinge; the rufous-buff of the underparts paler; the tail shorter.

CISTICOLA JUNCIDIS MALAYA Lynes

MALAYAN COMMON FANTAIL WARBLER

Cisticola juncidis malaya LYNES, Review of the genus *Cisticola*, Ibis, suppl. no., 1930, pp. 92–94, pl. 2, figs. a–c (Klang, Malay Peninsula).

Cisticola juncidis cursitans, DEIGNAN, Journ. Siam Soc. Nat. Hist. Suppl., 1931, p. 149 (Chiang Mai).

Cisticola juncidis malaya, DEIGNAN, Journ. Siam. Soc. Nat. Hist. Suppl., 1936, p. 115 (Chiang Mai).

Cisticola exilis equicaudata, DEIGNAN, Journ. Siam. Soc. Nat. Hist. Suppl., 1936, p. 115 (Chiang Mai).

The common fantail warbler is definitely known within our area only from the provinces of Chiang Mai (Chiang Mai, Ban Sop Mae Chaem) and Chiang Rai (Ban Mae Chai). At Chiang Mai, where it may be found in the ricefields at any time of the year, it is rather common during the rains but rare and local at other seasons.

This little bird keeps to open country, haunting the growing rice and the moist, grassy borders of marshes, large or small. It is a skulker, outside of the breeding season not likely to be observed until accidentally flushed, when it makes a short, low flight before dropping again into cover. During the rains, however, the male may be very conspicuous by his song, a series of sharp notes uttered as the bird circles with undulating flight high above his mate—*tsit* . . . *tsit* . . . *tsit*, each *tsit* synchronized with a dip in the flight.

Thanks to the nuptial performance, I have collected males with the gonads enlarged or greatly enlarged between May 9 (Ban Mae Chai) and August 26 (Chiang Mai). A specimen taken by me at Chiang Mai, January 14, 1936 (erroneously recorded as *Cisticola exilis equicaudata*), is in an advanced stage of postjuvenal molt.

A breeding male had the irides tan; the maxilla horny brown, blackish at the base; the mandible fleshy plumbeous; the rictus and interior of the mouth black; the feet and toes flesh; the claws pale horny flesh. A winter example of the same sex had the irides light brown; the maxilla dark horny brown; the mandible fleshy, horny at the tip; the feet and toes yellowish fleshy; the claws horn.

The adult male, in summer, has the feathers of the forehead, crown, and nape dark brown with narrow light brown margins; those of the upper back black with light brown margins; the lower back and rump ferruginous; each feather of the fan-shaped tail brown, with a conspicuous white tip and a black subterminal bar; a buffy-white supercilium; the underparts white, washed with buffy rufous, most heavily along the flanks and on the thighs. The adult male in winter is similar but differs in having the forehead and crown like the upper back and the underparts with a rather stronger buffy-rufous wash. The plumages of the female vary only in minor points from those of the male.

CISTICOLA EXILIS TYTLERI Jerdon

BENGALESE EXILED FANTAIL WARBLER

Cisticola Tytleri "BLYTH" JERDON, Birds of India, vol. 2, pt. 1, 1863, p. 176 (Dacca, Bengal).

The species is known from northern Thailand by a single adult female (in fresh, complete summer dress), collected by me at Ban Hong Khaeo (Chiang Rai Province), May 5, 1936; in the absence of a breeding male, the subspecific identification is provisional and based solely on geographical probabilities.

This example was shot on one of the bush-clad "islands" that arise here and there from the vast, marshy plains of Chiang Rai. Said to be a bird of uncultivated lands, especially such as are covered with tall grass, the "exile" may well prove to be common in those uninhabited wastes, although it is not likely to occur in other portions of our area.

Cisticola exilis is with difficulty distinguished from *C. juncidis* at most times but, in any plumage, has the rectrices tipped with dull rufous-white, *not* pure white. The male in summer, however, is unmistakable, the color of the crown ranging from orange-red to pale yellow according to subspecies.

The late Rear-Admiral Hubert Lynes, who kindly gave me determinations for all my Cisticolae, wrote of this bird: "350295 is about average *equicaudata* ≷ *tytleri* ♀ S[ummer dress] in coloration—but it may be just a rather darkish individual of a Samkok aggregate ♀ S[ummer dress]—??".

TESIA OLIVEA (McClelland)

GOLDEN-HEADED TESIA

Saxicola? olivea MCCLELLAND, Proc. Zool. Soc. London, pt. 7, 1839 [=1840], p. 161 (Assam).

Tesia cyaniventer, DEIGNAN, Journ. Siam Soc. Nat. Hist. Suppl., 1931, p. 141 (Doi Suthep, Doi Ang Ka).

Tesia cyaniventer cyaniventer, CHASEN and BODEN KLOSS, Journ. Siam Soc. Nat. Hist. Suppl., 1932, p. 247 (Doi Suthep).—DEIGNAN, Journ. Siam Soc. Nat. Hist. Suppl., 1936, p. 110 (Doi Suthep).

The tesia is until now recorded only from certain of the higher peaks of the more western provinces. On Doi Ang Ka I found it very common from 4,900 to 6,800 feet, but it has been met with on the nearby Doi Suthep only by Aagaard, who took a pair at 4,600 feet, March 1931; one example is known from Doi Chiang Dao, 5,000 feet (Deignan) and one other from Doi Pha Hom Pok, 6,000 feet (de Schauensee). To complete the roster of Thai localities, it may be added that Lowe reports (Ibis, 1933, p. 269) a pair collected 50 miles southeast of Um Phang (south of our limits) at 3,400 feet.

This curious little bird, with no visible tail, on Doi Ang Ka inhabited the deepest and dampest evergreen, where, in company with *Alcippe m. laotiana*, it kept to the lower undergrowth. It is so intensely inquisitive, coming to the edge of the trail to scold the intruder with shrill, piping notes, that, where numerous, it can scarcely be overlooked.

A female from Doi Ang Ka, September 5, is in postnuptial molt.

Adults collected by me had the irides brown; the maxilla blackish brown; the mandible orange; the rictus and interior of the mouth orange; the feet and toes horny brown; the claws horny yellow.

The adult of either sex has the entire upperparts olive-green, this color, on the crown and nape, strongly suffused with golden; a postocular streak black; the sides of the head and neck and the entire underparts slaty gray, albescent on the center of the abdomen; the thighs and under tail coverts olive-green.

A series of 52 adults of this genus from the Asiatic mainland wholly support the views expressed by Ludlow and Kinnear (Ibis, 1937, pp. 257–261) as to the probable existence of two continental species, *T. cyaniventer* Hodgson and *T. olivea* (McClelland), which, in certain areas (Sikkim, Upper Assam, Upper Burma), are cohabitant. I discover no trace of intergradation, and so each individual may without hesitation be placed with one or the other form.

I have examined six of the nine or ten examples so far taken in Thailand and find all to be *T. olivea*. Since only *cyaniventer* is known from Annam, it is noteworthy that Chasen and Boden Kloss assert (*loc. cit.*) that their two birds from Doi Suthep (not seen by me) "like specimens from Annam . . . have the top of the head green and not golden brown . . ." I suggest that these authors have been misled by published descriptions and by their lack of suitable comparative material and that the examples in question, like all the others, will prove to be *T. olivea*.

CETTIA SQUAMEICEPS (Swinhoe)

Scaly-headed Bush Warbler

Tribura squameiceps Swinhoe, Proc. Zool. Soc. London, 1863, p. 292 (Canton, China).

Urophlexis squameiceps, Rogers and Deignan, Proc. Biol. Soc. Washington, 1934, p. 92 (Doi Suthep).

Urosphena squameiceps squameiceps, Deignan, Journ. Siam Soc. Nat. Hist. Suppl., 1936, p. 117 (Doi Suthep).

I have found the scaly-headed warbler only seven times, on Doi Chiang Dao and on Doi Suthep, at 2,700 and 3,500 feet; the extreme dates for its stay are November 24 (1936) and March 5 (1932).

This short-tailed little bird is probably a commoner winter visitor than my field experience with it would indicate. It seems always to occur on or near the ground in dense, swampy evergreen forest and would perhaps never be noted at all if it did not attract attention by its low *chip-chip*, *chip-chip*.

My specimens had the irides dark brown; the maxilla dark horny brown; the mandible with the apical half dark horny brown, the basal half yellowish flesh; the feet and toes yellowish white; the claws white.

The adult has the entire upperparts rich brown, suffused with rufescent, the feathers of the crown edged slightly darker to give a scaly appearance; the lores and a postocular streak to the nape brownish black, edged above by an equally long and conspicuous pale buff supercilium; the feathers of the sides of the head and neck pale buff, edged darker to give a scaly appearance; the underparts pale buff, almost white on the chin, throat, and center of the abdomen, more brownish along the flanks.

CETTIA PALLIDIPES LAURENTEI (La Touche)

YUNNANESE PALE-FOOTED BUSH WARBLER

Urosphena laurentei LA TOUCHE, Bull. Brit. Orn. Club, vol. 42, 1921, pp. 30–31 (Poutoutsing, southeastern Yunnan).

Two males, one taken by my collectors at Chiang Saen Kao, January 15, 1937, and the other by me at Ban Pa Muat (near Chiang Mai) just one day later, are the only examples of this species yet known from Thailand.

Soft chipping notes from the heart of a dense growth of coarse grass (3 feet high) led to my discovery of the pale-footed bush warbler. Since the birds, of which two were present, kept to the ground and darted among the culms like small, dark mice, it was not possible to see them at all from a distance of a few feet, yet they were too small to shoot from a point nearer at hand and only after hours of effort was I able to collect a specimen by a lucky shot to one side.

It had the irides dark brown; the maxilla horny brown; the mandible fleshy white, tipped horny brown; the feet, toes, and claws fleshy white.

The adult has the entire upperparts olivaceous-brown, darker on the rather broad rectrices; the lores and a postocular streak brownish black, edged above by an equally long pale brownish-buff supercilium; the sides of the head otherwise pale brownish buff; the underparts white, washed with dull buffy brown or brownish buff on the sides of the breast, along the flanks, and on the under tail coverts; the under wing coverts and axillaries white.

Thai specimens agree perfectly with an example from Laos, where only *laurentei* is likely to occur. Lack of suitable material has, however, prevented me from verifying the putative distinctions between *laurentei* and the Sikkimese *pallidipes*.

CETTIA DIPHONE CANTURIANS (Swinhoe)

CHINESE SINGING BUSH WARBLER

Arundinax canturians SWINHOE, Ibis, 1860, p. 52 (Amoy, China).

The only specimen yet known from Thailand is a male taken by my collector at Chiang Saen Kao, January 15, 1937, but the species is likely to occur in winter anywhere within our provinces.

This large bush warbler is superficially very similar to *Phragamaticola aëdon rufescens*, a much commoner bird. In winter, it has the entire upperparts rufescent-brown, this color much intensified on the forehead and crown; a poorly defined supercilium pale buff; an indistinct transocular streak blackish brown; the underparts buffy, paler (almost white) on the chin, throat, and center of the abdomen, deeper along the flanks and on the under tail coverts (the slaty bases of the feathers often showing through on the breast); the thighs mixed brownish slate and ashy. The female is colored like the male but is strikingly smaller.

BRADYPTERUS THORACICUS PRZEVALSKII (Sushkin)

KANSU GRAY-BREASTED BUSH WARBLER

[*Dumeticola thoracica*] *przevalskii* SUSHKIN, Proc. Boston Soc. Nat. Hist., vol. 38, 1925, pp. 41–42 ("Dshachar Mts., upper Hwang-ho").

A female in complete prenuptial molt, collected by me on Phu Kha, 4,500 feet, April 5, 1936, may be placed provisionally with this form, which is otherwise not recorded from Thailand.

The bird was shot from a dense tangle of lalang and *Rubus* sp. at an abandoned *hai*.

It has the entire upperparts dark rufescent-brown; a narrow ashy supercilium; the underparts ashy, fading to white on the chin and abdomen and changing to rufescent-brown along the flanks, each feather of the throat with a distinct blackish subapical spot; the under tail coverts rufescent-brown with broad white tips.

This unique example does not match any one of a series of thirteen from northwestern Yunnan and southwestern Szechwan (which may be taken to represent *thoracicus*) but agrees well with my single specimen from Sungpan, northwestern Szechwan (which is either *przevalskii* or intermediate between *przevalskii* and *thoracicus*).

B. t. saturatus of Kwangsi has been separated from *thoracicus* on grounds of lesser wing length and the former name possibly should be applied to the Thai specimen; its condition of molt, however, renders measurement of the wing meaningless. The validity of *saturatus* is, in any case, not yet established.

BRADYPTERUS THORACICUS THORACICUS (Blyth)

HIMALAYAN GRAY-BREASTED BUSH WARBLER

D[umeticola] thoracica BLYTH, Journ. Asiat. Soc. Bengal, vol. 14, 1845, p. 584 (Nepal).

Tribura thoracica thoracica, GREENWAY, Bull. Mus. Comp. Zool. 1940, p. 187 (Doi Ang Ka).

The sole Thai record for the present race is based upon a female taken by the Asiatic Primate Expedition on Doi Ang Ka, 4,300 feet, March 3, 1937.

Griswold, the collector, has noted that his specimen had the irides light brown; the maxilla gray; the mandible flesh; the feet and toes flesh.

According to Yen (Orn. Monatsb., vol. 41, 1933, p. 17), this subspecies is differentiated from *B. t. przevalskii* only by having the rufescent-brown of the crown concolorous with that of the mantle, rather than darker.

Griswold's bird, which I have examined, matches extraordinarily well a female of *thoracicus* from Mount Omei in southwestern Szechwan.

BRADYPTERUS THORACICUS SHANENSIS (Ticehurst)

SHAN GRAY-BREASTED BUSH WARBLER

Tribura thoracica shanensis TICEHURST, Ibis, 1941, p. 318 (Maymyo, Upper Burma).

Dumeticola thoracica thoracica, RILEY, U. S. Nat. Mus. Bull. 172, 1938, p. 422 (Doi Langka).

A male collected by Smith on Doi Langka, May 2, 1931, and an unsexed bird taken by me on Doi Suthep, 3,300 feet, March 23, 1937, are unquestionably of Ticehurst's race, with the description of which they agree in every particular.

On my last visit to Doi Suthep, at the boggy area below the Phrathat (which had been explored by me periodically over a number of years), I found for the first time, March 23, 1937, a gathering of small brown warblers concealing themselves among the entangled sedges. It proved to be impossible to shoot them from a reasonable distance, and the two specimens obtained were too badly injured to be preserved otherwise than as mummies. One of these examples is listed above, while the second belongs to the next following species; both are probably merely rare winter visitors to northern Thailand.

Smith's bird of May 2 is in prenuptial molt.

B. t. shanensis differs from the preceding form in having the rufescent-brown portions of the plumage replaced by olivaceous-brown; the ashy-gray portions replaced by ashy white; the dark spots on the throat fewer and rather less conspicuous.

BRADYPTERUS LUTEOVENTRIS TICEHURSTI Deignan

Burmese Buff-breasted Bush Warbler

Bradypterus luteoventris ticehursti Deignan, Proc. Biol. Soc. Washington, vol. 56, 1943, pp. 70–71. New name for *Tribura luteoventris saturatus* [*sic*] Ticehurst, Ibis, 1941, pp. 318–319 ("Thayetmyo-Minbu border, 5000 feet, Southern Chin Hills"), not *Tribura thoracica saturata* Yen, 1933.

The one imperfect specimen of *Bradypterus luteoventris* known from Thailand is an unsexed example from Doi Suthep, 3,300 feet, March 23, 1937; the circumstances surrounding its discovery have been fully related in the account of *Bradypterus t. shanensis.*

It has the entire upperparts chestnut-brown; the indistinct supercilium buff; the underparts (including the under tail coverts) brownish buff, becoming white on the chin, throat, and center of the abdomen (unspotted, but with the slaty bases of the feathers sometimes showing through on the throat and breast).

My bird is so distinct from one specimen of *luteoventris* and seventeen of *russulus* and agrees so well with Ticehurst's description of his *saturatus* that I have no choice but to place it with this putative Burmese race, which probably has a more southerly distribution than *luteoventris.*

Family MOTACILLIDAE

MOTACILLA ALBA LEUCOPSIS Gould

Amur Pied Wagtail

Motacilla leucopsis Gould, Proc. Zool. Soc. London, pt. 5, 1837 [=1838], p. 78 (India).

Motacilla alba leucopsis, Gyldenstolpe, Kungl. Svenska Vet.-Akad. Handl., 1913, p. 41 (Den Chai); 1916, p. 31 (Mae Ping river); Journ. Nat. Hist. Soc. Siam, 1915, p. 171 (listed); Ibis, 1920, p. 459 ("Siam").

Motacilla lugubris leucopsis, de Schauensee, Proc. Acad. Nat. Sci. Philadelphia, 1929, p. 561 (Chiang Mai).—Riley, U. S. Nat. Mus. Bull. 172, 1938, p. 471 (Muang Pai).

Motacilla leucopsis [*partim*], Deignan, Journ. Siam Soc. Nat. Hist. Suppl., 1931, p. 153 (Chiang Mai [*partim*]); 1936, p. 121 (Chiang Mai [*partim*]).—de Schauensee, Proc. Acad. Nat. Sci. Philadelphia, 1934, p. 238 (Chiang Mai [*partim*]).

The pied wagtail, represented in our provinces by at least four forms, is an abundant winter visitor throughout the northern lowlands except in forested areas. Specimens of the present race (which is certainly the commonest with us) have been taken in the provinces of Mae Hong

Son, Chiang Mai, and Chiang Rai; at Chiang Mai Town it has been found between September 19 (1930) and March 29 (1929). The only mountain record is based upon a male collected by de Schauensee's men at 6,400 feet on Doi Pha Hom Pok, February 16, 1938.

Among the earliest of the winter birds to arrive, these wagtails appear with us in a spectacular manner: where, one day, none is to be seen, the next morning finds them everywhere in town and country, dancing at the margins of pools and streams, strutting across the lawns, parading on the rooftrees, and sweeping in loose bands along the metaled highways. Their numbers fall off somewhat during the cold weather, but locally they become even more numerous just before the northward flight, when suitably moist places are difficult to find; at this season they may be observed with other species of wagtails. All agree in being long, slim birds which walk or run with bobbing head and constantly moving tail; all have a characteristic, undulating flight. At Chiang Mai the pied forms are fancifully known as *nok um bat*, the black pectoral crescent being compared to the begging-bowl (*bat*) carried (*um*) before the breast by Buddhist monks.

No Thai specimen at hand is in molt. Certain individuals, at the postnuptial molt, assume a plumage differing from full nuptial dress only in having the black feathers of the pectoral band very narrowly fringed with white; such birds are of not infrequent occurrence in Thailand.

A male had the irides brown; the bill black; the feet and toes dull black; the soles gray; the claws horny black. A female differed in having the basal half of the mandible gray; the feet and toes dark brown.

The exceptional examples noted above have the sinciput, lores, ocular region, ear coverts, sides of the neck, the chin, and throat pure white; the remaining upperparts black; the upper wing coverts pure white to form a conspicuous shoulder patch; the remiges black, all with a large patch of white toward the base of the inner web, the primaries narrowly, the outer secondaries broadly, edged with white along the outer web; the two outermost pairs of rectrices white except for a narrow black edging toward the base of the inner web, the remaining pairs black; a broad crescentic band of black across the upper breast (the feathers in winter with narrow white fringes); the remaining underparts pure white. Birds in normal winter dress are similar but have the black of the upperparts restricted to the crown, nape, and upper tail coverts; the mantle gray (sharply defined from the black of the nape and upper tail coverts), irregularly sullied with blackish.

This race is evidently tending toward the complete elimination of a winter plumage distinct in coloration from that of summer. As I have already observed, some individuals acquire the full nuptial dress at the postnuptial molt; other winter specimens wear a livery variably intermediate between those of summer and winter; even what I have for convenience called the "normal" winter plumage is characterized by pure black crown, nape, and upper tail coverts, while the gray of the mantle seems never to be wholly free of blackish sullies.

MOTACILLA ALBA BAICALENSIS Swinhoe

DAVURIAN PIED WAGTAIL

Motacilla baicalensis SWINHOE, Proc. Zool. Soc. London, 1871, p. 363 ("Eastern Asia").

Motacilla alba leucopsis, DE SCHAUENSEE, Proc. Acad. Nat. Sci. Philadelphia, 1928, p. 560 (Chiang Mai).

Motacilla leucopsis [*partim*], DEIGNAN, Journ. Siam Soc. Nat. Hist. Suppl., 1931, p. 153 (Chiang Mai [*partim*]); 1936, p. 121 (Chiang Mai [*partim*]).—DE SCHAUENSEE, Proc. Acad. Nat. Sci. Philadelphia, 1934, p. 238 (Chiang Mai [*partim*]).

Motacilla alba baicalensis, RILEY, U. S. Nat. Mus. Bull. 172, 1938, p. 470 (Lampang).

In addition to the specimen from Lampang reported (1938) by Riley, I place here two examples collected by de Schauensee at Chiang Mai and five others taken by me at Chom Thong and Ban Thung Ma Num. The extreme dates for its stay in Chiang Mai Province are September 26 (1936) and March 9 (1928).

It is worthy of note that the five birds secured by me were all shot on extensive sandbars along the Mae Ping; it may be found that this race confines itself to the immediate vicinity of the larger streams.

Two specimens of November 5 and 12 are wearing what seems to be the nuptial dress; this plumage differs from what I have called the "normal winter dress" of *M. a. leucopsis* in having the mantle a rather paler gray without any trace of blackish suffusion, this gray gradually deepening posteriorly to become black or blackish only on the longest upper tail coverts; the sides of the breast and the flanks strongly washed with gray. The normal winter plumage of *baicalensis* differs from that just described in having the crown and nape concolorous with the mantle or, at the most, merely sullied with blackish.

MOTACILLA ALBA OCULARIS Swinhoe

CHUKOTSK PIED WAGTAIL

Motacilla ocularis SWINHOE, Ibis, 1860, p. 55 (Amoy, China).

Motacilla leucopsis [*partim*], DEIGNAN, Journ. Siam Soc. Nat. Hist. Suppl., 1931, p. 153 (Chiang Mai [*partim*]).

Motacilla ocularis, DEIGNAN, Journ. Siam Soc. Nat. Hist. Suppl., 1936, p. 120 (Chiang Mai).

Motacilla alba ocularis, DE SCHAUENSEE, Proc. Acad. Nat. Sci. Philadelphia, 1934, p. 238 (Chiang Mai).—RILEY, U. S. Nat. Mus. Bull. 172, 1938, p. 470 (Chiang Mai, Lampang).

This wagtail is probably common in every part of the northern lowlands although it is still definitely known only from Chiang Mai, Lampang, and Chiang Rai Provinces; specimens have been taken between October 28 (1936) and April 5 (1935).

The present form associates with *M. a. leucopsis* in the fields and along the highways but is not often seen in the streets and gardens of towns.

M. a. ocularis is readily identifiable, even in life, by having a narrow black transocular streak from the base of the bill to the nape; otherwise its plumages seem to be identical with the corresponding ones of *M. a. baicalensis*.

MOTACILLA ALBA ALBOIDES Hodgson

HIMALAYAN PIED WAGTAIL

[*Motacilla*] *Alboides* HODGSON, Asiatic Researches, vol. 19, 1836, p. 191 (no locality given=Nepal).

Motacilla alboides, DE SCHAUENSEE, Proc. Acad. Nat. Sci. Philadelphia, 1934, p. 238 (Chiang Saen Kao).

A male collected by me at Thattafang on the Salwin, October 11, 1936, and another taken by de Schauensee at Chiang Saen Kao on the Mae Khong, February 12, 1933, are still the only specimens of this race known from Thailand, although it probably occurs regularly on the sand bars of these two great streams.

In full breeding dress, *alboides* resembles *M. a. leucopsis*, but, while having the sinciput, lores, and ocular region pure white, it has the entire chin, throat, upper breast, sides of the neck, and the ear coverts black. Examples in winter plumage vary individually much as do those of *leucopsis*, having the mantle black or black-sullied gray, the chin and throat white, black, or a mixture of the two. The white-throated specimens may easily be known from *leucopsis*, however, by always having, from the base of the bill, a narrow black streak which passes *below* the lore and the ocular region and broadens posteriorly to cover the whole of the ear coverts.

MOTACILLA CINEREA MELANOPE Pallas

EASTERN GRAY WAGTAIL

Motacilla Melanope PALLAS, Reise durch verschiedene Provinzen des russischen Reichs, vol. 3, 1776, p. 696 ("In Dauuria . . . occurrit . . .").

Motacilla boarula melanope, GYLDENSTOLPE, Kungl. Svenska Vet.-Akad. Handl., 1913, p. 41 (Pak Pan); 1916, p. 31 (Pha Kho); Journ. Nat. Hist. Soc. Siam, 1915, p. 171 (listed); Ibis, 1920, p. 460 ("Various parts of Siam").—DE SCHAUENSEE, Proc. Acad. Nat. Sci. Philadelphia, 1928, p. 560 (Chiang Mai); 1929, p. 561 (Chiang Saen).

Motacilla cinerea caspica, DEIGNAN, Journ. Siam Soc. Nat. Hist. Suppl., 1931, p. 153 (Chiang Mai, Doi Suthep).—DE SCHAUENSEE, Proc. Acad. Nat. Sci.

Philadelphia, 1934, p. 238 (Doi Chiang Dao).—RILEY, U. S. Nat. Mus. Bull. 172, 1938, p. 472 (Chiang Mai, Nan).

Motacilla cinerea melanope, DEIGNAN, Journ. Siam Soc. Nat. Hist. Suppl., 1936, p. 121 (Chiang Mai, Doi Suthep).

The gray wagtail is a very common winter visitor to all the northern provinces, occurring chiefly on the plains but ascending the hills in small numbers along the larger streams, to 2,700 feet on Doi Suthep and to 4,300 feet on Doi Ang Ka. At Chiang Mai it is regularly present from September 5 (1931) to April 23 (1935) but it sometimes appears extraordinarily early: I have found a pair on Doi Suthep at 1,800 feet, July 25, 1936, and a solitary bird at the base of the same mountain, August 3, 1929; it is not to be supposed, however, that the species ever breeds in Thailand.

This wagtail haunts chiefly the shingle and stony shallows of streams, and on the lower slopes of the hills a pair may be seen almost wherever a brook falls over broad shelves of rock or flows among tumbled boulders. Its manner of feeding and its sweet calls are much like those of its congeners.

Postnuptial molt seems to be completed before the bird arrives in Thailand, and even the specimen of July 25 is in full winter dress; prenuptial molt is shown by examples taken February 26 and later but the species disappears before acquiring full summer plumage. Some individuals, however, don summer dress at the postnuptial molt so that an occasional black-throated specimen is seen even in midwinter.

A male had the irides brown; the bill dull blackish, with the basal half of the mandible plumbeous; the feet, toes, and claws horny brown.

The gray wagtail, in winter, has the forehead, crown, and mantle gray (faintly suffused with olive-green), changing on the rump and upper tail coverts to bright olive-yellow; the wings black, the secondaries edged buffy white along the outer web and with white bases which show as a band in flight; the three outermost pairs of rectrices almost wholly white, the remaining pairs black; a narrow but conspicuous supercilium white; the chin and throat white (sometimes tinged with yellow or buff); the remaining underparts yellow, brighter posteriorly, fading to yellowish ashy along the sides of the body under the wings. In summer dress, it differs chiefly in having the chin and throat black (the feathers narrowly tipped with white), bordered at either side by a long white mustachial streak.

MOTACILLA FLAVA MACRONYX (Stresemann)

AMUR YELLOW WAGTAIL

Budytes flavus macronyx STRESEMANN, Avifauna Macedonica, 1920, p. 76 (Vladivostok, eastern Siberia).

Motacilla flava thunbergi, DE SCHAUENSEE, Proc. Acad. Nat. Sci. Philadelphia, 1929, p. 561 (Chiang Rai).—DEIGNAN, Journ. Siam Soc. Nat. Hist. Suppl., 1931, p. 154 (Chiang Mai) ; 1936, p. 121 (Chiang Mai).

Budytes thunbergi plexus, RILEY, U. S. Nat. Mus. Bull. 172, 1938, p. 473 (Ban Nam Khian).

This race of the yellow wagtail is a common winter visitor throughout the northern lowlands; at Chiang Mai it has been recorded from October 27 (1936) to March 14 (1930), but I have collected it at Mae Sariang as early as October 6 (1936) and at Ban Tong Yang as late as May 4 (1936).

The present species occurs in wet fields and at grassy areas beside ponds and marshes; at the period of the northward migration, when the countryside is largely desiccated, it gathers at such places in great numbers and appears to be more abundant than it really is.

Prenuptial molt is to be seen in examples from Nan Province, collected April 2 and 13.

A male had the irides brown; the bill black, with the base of the mandible plumbeous; the feet and toes dark brown; the claws brownish black.

The adult male has the forehead, crown, and nape bluish slate; the remaining upperparts olive-green; the wings blackish brown, the feathers edged with creamy yellow along the outer web; the two outermost pairs of rectrices largely white, the remaining pairs black; the lores and ear coverts blackish or slaty; the entire underparts bright yellow (often whitish at the point of the chin); the thighs brownish ashy. The adult female differs from the male in having the forehead, crown, and nape duller and suffused with olive-green and in having the underparts less bright yellow. The young in first-winter plumage (seen very commonly in autumn) has the entire upperparts brownish ashy; the wing feathers edged with creamy white; a narrow white supercilium; the lores and ear coverts brownish ashy; the underparts white, more or less strongly washed with buff, especially on the breast and lower throat; the under wing coverts and axillaries buffy white or buffy cream.

The male from Ban Nam Khian recorded by Riley (*loc. cit.*) as *plexa* is in such worn and discolored plumage as scarcely to be racially identifiable; to my eye, it agrees best with *macronyx*.

MOTACILLA FLAVA ANGARENSIS (Sushkin)

BAIKAL YELLOW WAGTAIL

[*Budytes flava*] *angarensis* SUSHKIN, Proc. Boston Soc. Nat. Hist., vol. 38, 1925, pp. 33–34 ("Village Sharagolskaia, Transbaikalia").

Motacilla borealis, GYLDENSTOLPE, Journ. Nat. Hist. Soc. Siam, 1915, p. 171 (listed).

Motacilla flava borealis [*partim*], GYLDENSTOLPE, Ibis, 1920, p. 460 ("Northern Siam").

A single unsexed and undated example of the yellow wagtail, collected by Eisenhofer at Khun Tan and now deposited in Stockholm (under the name *simillima*), is without doubt the bird listed by Gyldenstolpe in 1915 as *borealis;* it is probably a representative of *angarensis.* The race is otherwise known from our provinces by an adult female taken at Ban Tong Yang, May 4, 1936, and a first-winter female from Thattafang, October 16, 1936. Its status with us is still uncertain but collecting may prove it to be as common a winter visitor as *M. f. macronyx*, with which it associates.

Adults of the present form may be separated from those of *macronyx* by their having a narrow white superciliary streak from the base of the bill to the posterior ear coverts. The young in first-winter dress differs from that of *macronyx* in having the under wing coverts and axillaries olivaceous-yellow or creamy yellow and the posterior flanks more or less strongly washed with yellow or cream.

The specimens mentioned above and many others from Bangkok do not agree with any of the yellow wagtails previously recorded from Thailand. From *plexa* they differ in having the pileum sharply demarcated from the mantle; from *macronyx*, in having a distinct supercilium; from *simillima*, in having the supercilium less clearly defined and narrower (particularly behind the eye). In the circumstances, I have no choice but to place them with Sushkin's race, which has not otherwise been taken in winter quarters.

It is highly unlikely that a form that breeds in Kamchatka and winters chiefly in the more eastern Malaysian islands should ever appear in the central and western portions of Indo-China, and records for the occurrence of *simillima* in Burma and Thailand should be viewed with skepticism.

MOTACILLA CITREOLA CITREOLA Pallas

AMUR YELLOW-HEADED WAGTAIL

Motacilla citreola PALLAS, Reise durch verschiedene Provinzen des russischen Reichs, vol. 3, 1776, p. 696 ("In Sibiria orientaliore").

Motacilla citreola calcarata, DEIGNAN, Journ. Siam Soc. Nat. Hist. Suppl., 1931, p. 154 (Chiang Mai).

Motacilla citreola citreola, DE SCHAUENSEE, Proc. Acad. Nat. Sci. Philadelphia, 1934, p. 238 (Chiang Mai).—DEIGNAN, Journ. Siam Soc. Nat. Hist. Suppl., 1936, p. 121 (Chiang Mai).

The yellow-headed wagtail is very locally common at Chiang Mai from November 3 (1936) to February 10 (1936), after which date the countryside becomes too dry for its taste; it is otherwise recorded only from Chiang Rai, where, along the Mae Kok, I found it in some numbers as late as May 7, 1936.

This species is even more partial to wet, grassy areas than *Motacilla flava* and is never likely to be observed away from them. Its choice of habitat is, in fact, exactly that of *Anthus cervinus* and, in the vicinity of Chiang Mai, the two forms regularly occur together.

The adult male, in breeding dress, has the head, neck, and entire underparts bright yellow; a narrow nuchal collar black; the mantle ashy gray, more or less suffused with olive-green; the wings black, most of the feathers conspicuously margined with white along the outer web; the two outermost pairs of rectrices largely white, the remaining pairs black. The adult female, at the same season, differs in having the forehead, supercilium, and sides of the head dull yellow (mixed with dull olive-green on the ear coverts); the crown and nape dull olive-green; the underparts dull yellow, changing to white on the longer under tail coverts. In winter plumage, adults of either sex are much like the summer female. Many examples seen in Thailand wear first-winter dress; they have the underparts wholly or partly ashy white and, in life, resemble the immature of *M. flava* but, toward the end of their stay, are easily recognized by their having the forehead and supercilium yellow.

DENDRONANTHUS INDICUS (Gmelin)

FOREST WAGTAIL

[*Motacilla*] *indica* GMELIN, Systema naturae, vol. 1, pt. 2, 1789, p. 962 (India).

Limonidromus indicus, GYLDENSTOLPE, Kungl. Svenska Vet.-Akad. Handl., 1913, p. 42 (Pak Pan); 1916, p. 32 ("Three days march north of Chieng Mai"); Journ. Nat. Hist. Soc. Siam, 1915, p. 171 (listed); Ibis, 1920, p. 460 (Pak Pan, Chiang Rai).

Dendronanthus indicus, DEIGNAN, Journ. Siam Soc. Nat. Hist. Suppl., 1931, p. 154 (Doi Suthep); 1936, p. 121 (Chiang Mai, Doi Suthep).—RILEY, U. S. Nat. Mus. Bull. 172, 1938, p. 474 (Mae Khan, Doi Langka, Mae Kong Ka valley, Ban Nam Khian).

Although the forest wagtail has been recorded from all our provinces, it seems to be a decidedly uncommon winter visitor to northern Thailand. In the neighborhood of Chiang Mai it has been found only three times: one on Doi Suthep, 3,300 feet, August 31, 1929; one at the foot of the same mountain, November 21, 1935; one on the plain, March 19, 1936. The extreme dates for its stay are *ca.* August 23 (1914) between Wiang Pa Pao and Chiang Mai (Gyldenstolpe, 1916) and May 2 (1931) at Doi Langka. Robinson's assertion (Birds of the Malay Peninsula, vol. 1, 1927, p. 294) that it breeds "in Siberia and North China, occasionally in Northern Burma and Siam" is merely a careless copying of Stuart Baker's statement (Fauna of British India, Birds, ed. 2, vol. 3, 1926, p. 276) that it breeds "in Eastern Siberia, the hills of Northern China, Burma and Assam."

This aberrant wagtail is truly an inhabitant of the jungle, whether evergreen or bamboo, where it occurs, singly or in pairs, along the forest tracks or at the edge of tiny streams. In such places it runs about the cleared ground and leaps into the air after insects in the manner of the preceding species, constantly wagging the tail from side to side; occasionally it takes refuge on a bough above the trail.

A specimen from Chiang Mai, March 19, is undergoing prenuptial molt.

A female had the irides dark brown; the maxilla dark horny brown; the mandible flesh, with the apical half light horn brown; the feet and toes fleshy brown (the toes darker); the claws horny brown.

The present form has the upperparts grayish olive, becoming blackish on the upper tail coverts; the wings black, crossed by three conspicuous, equidistant creamy-white bands; the outermost pair of rectrices almost wholly white, the next pair with the basal half black and the apical half white, the following three pairs black, the shorter central pair colored like the mantle; a conspicuous supercilium creamy white; the lores, ear coverts, and sides of the lower throat grayish olive; the underparts creamy white, the upper breast crossed by a bold black gorget, the lower breast by a dull black gorget (often interrupted in the middle), the two usually connected by a short black central streak. Worn examples tend to be grayer above and whiter below.

ANTHUS HODGSONI HODGSONI Richmond

SIBERIAN OLIVE-BACKED TREE PIPIT

Anthus hodgsoni RICHMOND, *in* Blackwelder, Report on Zoology, Carnegie Inst. Washington Publ. No. 54, Research in China, vol. 1, pt. 2, 1907, p. 493. New name for *A* [*nthus*] *maculatus* "Hodgson" Jerdon 1864 (". . . all India . . . at Calcutta, and elsewhere in Bengal . . . "), not *Motacilla maculata* Gmelin, 1789.

Anthus trivialis maculatus, GYLDENSTOLPE, Kungl. Svenska Vet.-Akad. Handl., 1913, p. 42 (Den Chai); Journ. Nat. Hist. Soc. Siam, 1915, p. 171 (listed).

Anthus maculatus, GYLDENSTOLPE, Ibis, 1920, p. 461 ("Throughout the country").

Anthus trivialis hodgsoni, DE SCHAUENSEE, Proc. Acad. Nat. Sci. Philadelphia, 1928, p. 560 (Chiang Mai, Doi Suthep).

Anthus trivialis yunnanensis, DE SCHAUENSEE, Proc. Acad. Nat. Sci. Philadelphia, 1929, p. 562 (Doi Suthep, Chiang Rai).

Anthus hodgsoni, CHASEN and BODEN KLOSS, Journ. Siam Soc. Nat. Hist. Suppl., 1932, p. 248 (Doi Suthep).—RILEY, U. S. Nat. Mus. Bull. 172, 1938, p. 475 (Chiang Mai, Doi Langka, Khun Tan, Mae Hong Son, Muang Pai).

Anthus hodgsoni yunnanensis, DEIGNAN, Journ. Siam Soc. Nat. Hist. Suppl., 1931, p. 154 (Chiang Mai, Doi Suthep); 1936, p. 121 (Chiang Mai, Doi Suthep).—DE SCHAUENSEE, Proc. Acad. Nat. Sci. Philadelphia, 1934, p. 238 (Chiang Mai, Doi Chiang Dao, Chiang Saen).

The tree pipit is a very common, even abundant, winter visitor to every part of northern Thailand, ranging, wherever it finds a suitable environment, from the plains to the summits of the mountains; in the vicinity of Chiang Mai it was absent only from the dry, deciduous forest which extends from the foot of Doi Suthep to about 2,700 feet. The extreme dates for its stay at Chiang Mai are October 21 (1930) and April 14 (1937) but on Doi Suthep it regularly appears much earlier (about October 10) and probably leaves later; it is, however, almost certain that the racially inseparable populations of mountain and plain have their origins in widely separated breeding grounds.

This familiar form avoids the open country inhabited by our other pipits, haunting, in the lowlands, orchards and shaded gardens, bamboo brakes and copses, on the hills, trails and park-like clearings in the evergreen and forests of oak or pine. The flocks are sedentary and spend the entire cold weather within a very limited area: a band of about twenty which appeared each winter in my compound at Chiang Mai scarcely left the densely shaded ground beneath a large tamarind except to seek shelter in its foliage at night or to escape some passing danger. The members of the flock spend their time walking about with bobbing tail in search of small seeds and insects and, in the trees, have a habit of walking along the boughs.

A female had the irides dark brown; the maxilla horny black; the mandible fleshy, horny black at the tip; the feet and toes fleshy; the soles livid white; the claws fleshy horn.

The tree pipit has the entire upperparts brownish olive-green, the crown and mantle with black central streaks which are obsolescent posteriorly and disappear on the rump; the upper wing coverts black, tipped with buff or buffy white to form two more or less conspicuous bars; the outermost pair of rectrices largely brownish white, the next pair black with a small brownish-white tip, the succeeding three pairs black, the shorter central pair colored like the mantle; the buff or buffy-white supercilium edged above by a narrow black line; the underparts more or less rich buff, albescent on the lower breast and abdomen, boldly streaked with black at the sides of the throat, on the breast and upper abdomen, and along the flanks.

I am in complete agreement with Whistler and Kinnear (Journ. Bombay Nat. Hist. Soc., vol. 37, 1934, pp. 97–98) and with Ticehurst (Ibis, 1938, pp. 627–628) in the view that Hartert and Steinbacher's *inopinatus* is a quite unnecessary renaming of Richmond's *hodgsoni*.

A series of about 40 examples from Thailand are without exception of the paler, lightly streaked Siberian race; it is not likely that any other form of the species will be found to occur with us.

ANTHUS RICHARDI RUFULUS Vieillot

INDIAN PADDY-FIELD PIPIT

Anthus rufulus VIEILLOT, Nouveau dictionnaire d'histoire naturelle, nouv. éd., vol. 26, 1818, p. 494 (Bengal).

Anthus rufulus [*partim*], GYLDENSTOLPE, Journ. Nat. Hist. Soc. Siam, 1915, p. 171 (listed).

Anthus rufulus, DE SCHAUENSEE, Proc. Acad. Nat. Sci. Philadelphia, 1928, p. 560 (Chiang Mai).

Anthus richardi rufulus, DE SCHAUENSEE, Proc. Acad. Nat. Sci. Philadelphia, 1929, p. 561 (Chiang Mai).

Anthus richardi rufulus [*partim*], DEIGNAN, Journ. Siam Soc. Nat. Hist. Suppl., 1931, p. 154 (Chiang Mai [*partim*]).—DE SCHAUENSEE, Proc. Acad. Nat. Sci. Philadelphia, 1934, p. 239 (Chiang Mai).

Anthus novae-seelandiae rufulus, DEIGNAN, Journ. Siam Soc. Nat. Hist. Suppl., 1936, p. 121 (Chiang Mai).

Anthus richardi malayensis, RILEY, U. S. Nat. Mus. Bull. 172, 1938, p. 476 (Chom Thong).

This small resident form is very common or even abundant in the cultivated areas of all the six northern provinces.

The paddy-field pipit occurs in the same places as the collared bushlark, to which it bears a strong superficial resemblance, but it may be readily distinguished by its slimmer body and longer tail, by the absence of rufous in the wings, and the presence of white in the outer rectrices. It has the habit, when alarmed, of running rapidly, then stopping with neck stretched up and bill raised above the horizontal (in an attitude of listening), before running on again. The call note is a *tch-tch-tch*, and the song, heard during the hot weather, a repetition of the syllables *tiss'-yip*, *tiss'-yip*, *tiss'-yip*, rendered as the singer makes a little soaring flight.

A male with the gonads greatly enlarged was taken at Ban Bu (Nan Province), April 21; another with them enlarged at Ban Mae Chai (Chiang Rai Province), May 10. Postnuptial molt begins remarkably early and is already shown by the breeding bird of April 21, as well as by all collected between May 26 and November 14; postjuvenal molt, by an example of August 2.

An adult had the irides brown; the maxilla dark horn brown, with the edges of the commissure fleshy; the mandible fleshy, with the tip dark horn brown; the rictus and interior of the mouth yellow; the feet and toes fleshy; the claws fleshy horn.

In fresh winter dress, this pipit has the entire upperparts brown, suffused with buff, the feathers with brownish-black centers (obsolescent or absent on the rump and shorter upper tail coverts) to give a strongly streaked appearance; the wing feathers brownish black, broadly margined along the outer web with buff (the buff tips to the coverts forming two indistinct bars); the two outermost pairs of rectrices largely white, the remaining pairs brownish black; a broad buff superciliary streak; the underparts buff (albescent on the chin, throat, and center of the abdomen), with a band of short, narrow brownish-black streaks across the upper breast, these streaks continued up the sides of the throat to form a pair of narrow and broken mustachial streaks. With wear, the feathers of the upperparts and wings tend to lose their light edgings, while the buffy wash disappears both above and below, so that the plumage becomes generally duller and darker.

Anthus r. malayensis, the race resident in Peninsular Thailand, is separable from *rufulus* at any season by its stronger bill and, in fresh plumage, by its heavier pectoral streaking and the darker upperparts, which result from a lesser amount of buffy suffusion.

ANTHUS RICHARDI SINENSIS (Bonaparte)

CHINESE PADDY-FIELD PIPIT

C[orydalla] sinensis BONAPARTE, Conspectus generum avium, vol. 1, 1850, p. 247 ("China mer[idionalis]").
Anthus richardi striolatus, GYLDENSTOPLE, Kungl. Svenska vet.-Akad. Handl., 1913, p. 42 (Den Chai).
Anthus richardi striolatus [*partim*], GYLDENSTOLPE, Ibis, 1920, p. 461 (Den Chai).

I place under this name only the female reported (1913) by Gyldenstolpe from Den Chai, February 15, 1912 (wing length: 88.5 mm., not 87 as published), and a second female collected by me at Ban Pong Fa (Chiang Rai Province), May 4, 1936 (wing length: 88.8 mm.). The race winters commonly in eastern Thailand and it is perhaps significant that the two northern specimens are both from districts *east* of the Khun Tan chain.

A. r. sinensis is merely a rather larger edition of *rufulus*. For comparative wing lengths of the three forms of paddy-field pipit occurring in northern Thailand, see under *A. r. richardi*.

ANTHUS RICHARDI RICHARDI Vieillot

SIBERIAN PADDY-FIELD PIPIT

Anthus Richardi VIEILLOT, Nouveau dictionnaire d'histoire naturelle, nouv. éd., vol. 26, 1818, pp. 491–493 (France).
Anthus rufulus [*partim*], GYLDENSTOLPE, Journ. Nat. Hist. Soc. Siam, 1915, p. 171 (listed).
Anthus richardi striolatus, GYLDENSTOLPE, Kungl. Svenska Vet.-Akad. Handl., 1916, p. 32 (Khun Tan).
Anthus richardi striolatus [*partim*], GYLDENSTOLPE, Ibis, 1920, p. 461 (Khun Tan).
Anthus richardi rufulus [*partim*], DEIGNAN, Journ. Siam Soc. Nat. Hist. Suppl., 1931, p. 154 (Chiang Mai [*partim*]).
Anthus richardi richardi, DE SCHAUENSEE, Proc. Acad. Nat. Sci. Philadelphia, 1934, p. 239 (Chiang Mai).—RILEY, U. S. Nat. Mus. Bull. 172, 1938, p. 476 (Ban Nam Khian).
Anthus novae-seelandiae richardi, DEIGNAN, Journ. Siam Soc. Nat. Hist. Suppl., 1936, p. 121 (Chiang Mai).
Anthus campestris godlewskii, DEIGNAN, Journ. Siam Soc. Nat. Hist. Suppl., 1936, p. 122 (Chiang Mai).

The Siberian subspecies of the paddy-field pipit is a common winter visitor to the lowlands of all our provinces from October 1 (1936) at Ban Mae Wen to April 16 (1930) at Ban Nam Khian.

This form haunts the same places as *Anthus r. rufulus*, from which it is usually separable at a glance by its greater proportions.

A specimen from Chiang Mai Province, March 25, 1936, is in prenuptial molt.

A female had the irides brown; the maxilla horny brown; the mandible yellow, horny at the tip; the rictus and interior of the mouth yellow; the feet and toes fleshy; the claws horny brown.

The present bird is like *A. r. rufulus* in plumage but is *very* much larger.

Whistler and Kinnear (Journ. Bombay Nat. Hist. Soc., vol. 37, 1934, p. 100) keep *Anthus richardi* specifically distinct from *A. rufulus*. Since the gaps between the two, both geographical and dimensional, are completely bridged by *A. sinensis*, the recognition of more than one species is quite unnecessary. The wing lengths of 11 northern Thai examples of *richardi* range from 90.4 to 98.3 mm.; of 2 of *sinensis*, from 88.5 to 88.8 mm.; of 21 of *rufulus*, from 73 to 85 mm.

The tarsal length of my 11 specimens of *A. r. richardi* ranges from 29.5 to 32.5 mm.; there is still no evidence for the occurrence in northern Thailand of *Anthus campestries* "*thermophilus*" Jerdon, said to have the length of tarsus from 25 to 28.5 mm.

ANTHUS CERVINUS (Pallas)

Red-throated Pipit

Motacilla Cervina Pallas, Zoographia Rosso-asiatica, vol. 1, 1811, p. 511 (Siberia).
Anthus rufogularis, Deignan, Journ. Siam Soc. Nat. Hist. Suppl., 1931, p. 154 (Chiang Mai); 1936, p. 122 (Chiang Mai).

The red-throated pipit has been taken in northern Thailand only at Thattafang, Chiang Mai, and Ban Na Noi (Nan Province), but it is quite certain to occur, at least during the migrations, at suitable localities throughout our area. At Chiang Mai it is a locally common visitor from November 9 (1931) to January 30 (1932); the extreme dates for the entire North are October 13 (1936) at Thattafang and April 2 (1937) at Ban Na Noi.

I have already noted that the present species and the yellow-headed wagtail regularly occur together at very wet, grassy places; both forms leave the vicinity of Chiang Mai, owing to the increasing aridity of the countryside, long before their final departure from Thailand for the northern breeding grounds.

Two males had the irides dark brown; the maxilla with the basal half brown and the apical half horny black; the mandible with the basal half yellow and the apical half horny black (or dusky flesh, with the base yellow and the tip horny black); the rictus yellow; the feet and toes yellowish fleshy; the soles yellow; the claws horn.

Thai examples in autumn have the entire upperparts grayish olivaceous-brown, everywhere (including the rump and upper tail coverts) boldly and broadly streaked with black; the wing feathers brownish black, broadly margined with grayish buff; the rectrices brownish black, the two outermost pairs tipped grayish white; a broad but rather indistinct supercilium pale buff; the underparts pale buff or buffy white, boldly streaked with black at the sides of the throat, on the breast and upper abdomen, and along the flanks. Many spring birds differ in having the entire upperparts lightly suffused with buff; the supercilium, chin, throat, and upper breast cinnamon-pink; the remaining underparts pale pinkish buff; the black streaks few beneath and restricted to the breast and flanks. All types of intermediates between these two plumages may be seen in winter and spring.

Family ARTAMIDAE

ARTAMUS FUSCUS Vieillot

Ashy Swallow-shrike

Artamus fuscus Vieillot, Nouveau dictionnaire d'histoire naturelle, nouv. éd., vol. 17, 1817, p. 297 (Bengal).

Artamus fuscus, Gyldenstolpe, Kungl. Svenska Vet.-Akad. Handl., 1916, p. 43 (Chiang Saen); Ibis, 1920, p. 471 ("Throughout the whole country").—de Schauensee, Proc. Acad. Nat. Sci. Philadelphia, 1929, p. 551 (Chiang Mai); 1934, p. 225 (Chiang Mai).—Deignan, Journ. Siam Soc. Nat. Hist. Suppl., 1931, p. 147 (Chiang Mai); 1936, p. 122 (Chiang Mai, Doi Suthep).

The swallow-shrike is a very common permanent resident in deforested lowland districts throughout the northern provinces; I have found it above the level of the plains only on Doi Suthep, where, during the cold weather and since the construction of a road, it occurs occasionally as high as 2,700 feet.

Outside the breeding season, this familiar species may be seen in bands of many dozen individuals, which wheel in wide circles above the ricefields like so many huge, gray swallows. Each flock has some central point—an isolated *Dipterocarpus* or sugar-palm or clump of giant bamboo—to which the members repair between flights and at the top of which, huddled close together along the branches, they settle for the night. The unmistakable call is a sharp, nasal *mă-ă-ă*, *mă-ă-ă*, *mă-ă-ă*, endlessly repeated in flight or at rest and heard from the sky even when the birds are almost at the limit of vision.

I have taken juveniles, newly on the wing, at Ban Pang Ai, July 23. Adults collected at various localities between July 6 and 30 are in postnuptial molt.

An adult female had the irides dark brown; the bill light blue, with extreme tip black; the feet and toes plumbeous; the claws slaty.

The adult of either sex has the lores black; the rest of the head and neck (including the chin and throat) slaty gray, changing on the nape to the dark vinaceous-brown of the remaining upperparts; the longer upper tail coverts white or smoky gray; the wings slaty gray; the rectrices blackish slate, narrowly tipped with white or smoky gray; the remaining underparts light vinaceous-brown, paling posteriorly and often becoming vinaceous-white on the under tail coverts; the lining of the underwing ashy gray. With wear the vinaceous coloring changes to a dull rufous-brown. Juveniles are similar to the adults but have the feathers of the upperparts brownish and narrowly fringed on the mantle with rufescent-white; the upper wing coverts narrowly tipped with pale rufous and the remiges similarly tipped with white; the underparts pale rufous, the feathers of the breast with faint, dusky cross bars.

Family LANIIDAE

LANIUS SCHACH TRICOLOR Hodgson

HIMALAYAN BLACK-HEADED SHRIKE

[*Lanius*] *Tricolor* HODGSON, India Rev., vol. 1, 1837 [=1836], p. 446 (no locality given=Nepal).

Lanius nigriceps nigriceps, DEIGNAN, Journ. Siam Soc. Nat. Hist. Suppl., 1931, p. 145 (Chiang Mai); 1936, p. 122 (Chiang Mai).—DE SCHAUENSEE, Proc. Acad. Nat. Sci. Philadelphia, 1934, p. 221 (Chiang Mai).—GREENWAY, Bull. Mus. Comp. Zool., 1940, p. 186 (Doi Ang Ka).

The black-headed shrike is fairly common on the Chiang Mai plain at all seasons *except* during the period between March 3 (1931) and July 13 (1935); then it is presumably breeding at extensive deforested areas on our higher mountains, for I found it numerous, April and May 1931, in the open valley below Pha Mon on Doi Ang Ka, and Griswold (Asiatic Primate Expedition) took two females there at 4,300 feet, March 3 and 9, 1937. It is otherwise known from our provinces only by specimens which I collected at Chiang Saen Kao, January 13 and 15, 1937, and by a single straggler observed on Doi Suthep, 3,300 feet, February 13, 1937.

At Chiang Mai, this large shrike is a bird of the cultivated districts but usually keeps to such wastelands as cremation grounds and the vicinity of ruined *phrachedi*, where dense thickets of bamboo and thorny shrubs afford it suitable habitat; when vegetation of this type grows near a highway, a telegraph wire is often utilized as a perch. Stomachs examined by me have contained ants, beetles, flies, and grasshoppers, but small birds and rodents are probably taken as well. Prey too large to be swallowed on the spot or at the lookout post is carried to some thorny bush and there impaled upon a spine to facilitate butchering and eating. I have found no cases of impalement for storage but this habit is not likely to appear outside the breeding period, at which season the bird is not readily observable in Thailand.

It is perhaps noteworthy that, of the 11 specimens so far taken by various collectors in our provinces, *all* have been adult or subadult females. The small series before me fails to clarify the picture of the molts: one taken at Chiang Mai, August 29, has evidently completed postjuvenal molt but retains scattered juvenal feathers on the crown and mantle and the worn brownish remiges and rectrices of immaturity; the two January examples from Chiang Saen are similar but have the head and mantle colored as in the adult. A bird from Chiang Mai, November 23, is in molt, having still to lose the brownish outer secondaries and having the outer pairs of fresh rectrices not yet fully grown.

Two females had the irides dark brown; the bill black, with the base of the mandible dusky flesh or light horny brown; the feet and toes brownish black or dark brown; the soles light brownish; the claws black. Breeding individuals are said to have the bill wholly black.

The adult has the entire upper half of the head and neck black; the mantle rufous, suffused with ashy next to the black nape and with chestnut on the upper tail coverts; the wings black, the inner primaries with the basal portion of the outer web white, to form a conspicuous patch, the secondaries narrowly edged along the outer web with dull, pale rufous; the rectrices black, all narrowly tipped and the two outermost pairs also outwardly edged, with dull, pale rufous; the underparts white, changing along the flanks and on the under tail coverts to buffy rufous. Birds in the barred juvenal dress have not yet been found in northern Thailand and would be, in any case, highly difficult to distinguish from similar examples of *Lanius c. collurioïdes*.

Thai specimens of the black-headed shrike differ in no important particular from topotypes of Hodgson's *tricolor*.

I find no evidence of integradation between *tricolor* and *schomburgki* and, in fact, one may doubt whether the ranges of the two forms meet at any point: whereas, in Thailand, the former is recorded only from the provinces of Chiang Mai and Chiang Rai, the latter (a well-marked resident race) seems to be restricted to the Great Plain of Central Thailand, where it is known to occur no farther north than the neighborhood of Sawankhalok.

LANIUS SCHACH SCHACH Linnaeus

Chinese Gray-headed Shrike

[*Lanius*] *Schach* Linnaeus, Systema naturae, ed. 10, vol. 1, 1758, p. 94 (China; type locality here restricted to Canton).

An anomalous shrike (female) shot by me at Pang Makham Phong, December 30, 1936, is neither *tricolor* nor *schach* but is so near the latter that it may conveniently be placed with this race, which is otherwise not recorded from Thailand. It should be sought as a rare winter visitor to our provinces.

My specimen, which has the brown rectrices of immaturity, is evidently a bird of the year.

Typical *schach* resembles *tricolor* but differs in having only the forehead, lores, ocular region, and ear coverts black; the crown, nape, and upper back ashy gray, this color changing imperceptibly into the rufous of the remaining upperparts.

This example differs from true *schach* by having the predominantly gray crown and nape irregularly overlaid with a blackish tinge. We have here either a case of atavism in the resident *Lanius schach tricolor* or, more probably, one of the hybrids between *tricolor* and *schach* discussed at some length by Dunajewski in his revision of the species (Journ. für Orn., vol. 87, 1939, p. 45). I have examined a very similar specimen from the neighborhood of Laokay, Tongking, taken April 28, 1924.

LANIUS SCHACH NIPALENSIS Hodgson

TIBETAN GRAY-BACKED SHRIKE

[*Lanius*] *Nipalensis* HODGSON, India Rev., vol. 1, 1837, pp. 445–446 (no locality given=Nepal).

Lanius schach tephronotus, GYLDENSTOLPE, Kungl. Svenska Vet.-Akad. Handl., 1913, p. 32 (Ban Huai Hom); Ibis, 1920, p. 469 (Ban Huai Hom).—DE SCHAUENSEE, Proc. Acad. Nat. Sci. Philadelphia, 1929, p. 549 (Chiang Rai, Chiang Saen, Doi Suthep).

Lanius tephronotus, DEIGNAN, Journ. Siam. Soc. Nat. Hist. Suppl., 1931, p. 146 (Doi Suthep); 1936, p. 122 (Doi Suthep).—DE SCHAUENSEE, Proc. Acad. Nat. Sci. Philadelphia, 1934, p. 222 (Doi Suthep).

The gray-backed shrike is only a winter visitor to northern Thailand, where I have found it from December 5 (Doi Chiang Dao) to April 6 (on the mountains between Wiang Pa Pao and Muang Phan). While rather common in Chiang Rai Province, it is rare and local farther south; Gyldenstolpe's bird from Ban Huai Hom and mine from Doi Suthep seem to be the most southerly yet recorded from the Kingdom.

At Chiang Mai, solitary birds are occasionally seen in bushy clearings on Doi Suthep from 3,300 to 5,500 feet but never at lower elevations; in the Mae Khong drainage, however, the form occurs throughout the plains and, about Muang Fang, may be observed at almost any overgrown *hai* in the lowland evergreen, even in close proximity to human habitation.

The adult of either sex differs from those of the preceding forms in having the crown, nape, and entire mantle soft slaty gray, changing to dull rufous on the rump and upper tail coverts; the white patch at the base of the inner secondaries wholly or virtually absent. Perhaps the majority of our examples are immature; they have the gray of the upperparts more or less suffused with rufous and the feathers of the breast and flanks crossed by narrow, wavy bars.

LANIUS COLLURIOIDES COLLURIOIDES Lesson

BURMESE CHESTNUT-BACKED SHRIKE

Lanius collurioides LESSON, *in* Bélanger, Voyage aux Indes-Orientales, Zoologie, 1834 [=1832], pp. 250–251 (Pegu).

Lanius collurioides, GYLDENSTOLPE, Journ. Nat. Hist. Soc. Siam, 1915, p. 167 (listed).—DE SCHAUENSEE, Proc. Acad. Nat. Sci. Philadelphia, 1929, p. 549 (Chiang Mai, Chiang Rai, Chiang Saen).—RILEY, U. S. Nat. Mus. Bull. 172, 1938, p. 478 (Chiang Mai).

Lanius hypoleucus siamensis, GYLDENSTOLPE, Kungl. Svenska Vet.-Akad. Handl., 1916, p. 40 (Pong Pa O, Khun Tan).

Lanius collurioides collurioides, GYLDENSTOLPE, Ibis, 1920, p. 469 ("Throughout Siam").—DEIGNAN, Journ. Siam Soc. Nat. Hist. Suppl., 1931, p. 145 (Chiang Mai); 1936, p. 122 (Chiang Mai).—DE SCHAUENSEE, Proc. Acad. Nat Sci. Philadelphia, 1934, p. 221 (Chiang Mai, "Tung Sio", Chiang Saen).

Otomela collurioides, DE SCHAUENSEE, Proc. Acad. Nat. Sci. Philadelphia, 1928, p. 562 (Chiang Mai).

At Chiang Mai the chestnut-backed shrike is quite absent during the period between March 14 (1930, 1931) and May 25 (1935) and decidedly rare from the latter date to the beginning of July; throughout the rest of the year it is one of the commonest lowland birds. Not yet recorded from Nan and Mae Hong Son Provinces, observations and specimens from the remaining districts indicate that its status at a given season is much the same throughout our area. A solitary female collected by me on the Chiang Dao road, 48 km. north of Chiang Mai, March 25, 1936, had the gonads inactive and was evidently a sterile individual that had failed to migrate with others of the species.

This shrike is a more confiding species than *Lanius schach tricolor* and is constantly seen along the highways, casting itself upon grasshoppers and other insect prey from hedges, fences, and telegraph wires. It is not known to impale for storage during its stay with us.

Postjuvenal molt is shown by specimens taken between July 10 and September 9; postnuptial molt, by a series collected between July 2 and November 26.

An adult female (January 6) had the irides brown; the bill dull black, fleshy plumbeous at the base of the mandible; the rictus fleshy plumbeous; the feet and toes brownish black; the soles gray; the claws black.

The fresh-plumaged adult has the upper half of the head and neck slate, this color paling posteriorly but deepening into black on the forehead, lores, ocular region, and ear coverts (the lores sometimes gray or whitish); the mantle, rump, and upper tail coverts chestnut. the wings black, the coverts and the secondaries tipped and outwardly edged with chestnut, the inner primaries white at the base to form a conspicuous patch; the central pair of rectrices black, narrowly tipped with chestnut or rufous-white, the next three pairs black with increasingly broad white tips, the two outermost pairs almost wholly white; the entire underparts white, more or less strongly washed with vinaceous-buff. There is considerable variation in the depth of colors of head and mantle and Delacour has named certain pale examples from Laos "*griseicapillus*"; similar birds may occur anywhere in Thailand. Young birds, as seen with us, have the ear coverts blackish brown and the crown and nape narrowly barred blackish brown and dull rufous; the mantle rufous, with wavy blackish cross bars; the rectrices rufous-brown, with obsolescent darker cross bars; the underparts white, more or less strongly washed with rufous-buff, the feathers of the breast and flanks crossed by narrow, wavy blackish-brown bars.

LANIUS CRISTATUS CRISTATUS Linnaeus

SIBERIAN BROWN SHRIKE

[*Lanius*] *cristatus* LINNAEUS, Systema naturae, ed. 10, vol. 1, 1758, p. 93 (Bengal).
Lanius cristatus, GYLDENSTOLPE, Kungl. Svenska Vet.-Akad. Handl., 1913, p. 31 (Ban Huai Hom); Journ. Nat. Hist. Soc. Siam, 1915, p. 167 (listed).
Otomela cristata, GYLDENSTOLPE, Kungl. Svenska Vet.-Akad. Handl., 1916, p. 41 (Tha Chomphu).—DE SCHAUENSEE, Proc. Acad. Nat. Sci. Philadelphia, 1928, p. 562 (Chiang Mai).
Otomela cristata cristata, GYLDENSTOLPE, Ibis, 1920, p. 469 ("Several parts of the country").
Lanius cristatus cristatus, DE SCHAUENSEE, Proc. Acad. Nat. Sci. Philadelphia, 1929, p. 459 (Chiang Mai); 1934, p. 221 (Chiang Mai).—DEIGNAN, Journ. Siam Soc. Nat. Hist. Suppl., 1931, p. 146 (Chiang Mai); 1936, p. 123 (Chiang Mai).

The Siberian brown shrike is a very common winter visitor to the lowlands of Chiang Mai, where I have observed it from August 29 (1936) to May 4 (1935), but has been found elsewhere in our area only at Ban Huai Hom, February 23, 1912 (Gyldenstolpe) and at Chiang Rai, January 26, 1937 (Deignan). This apparently anomalous distribution may be at least partially explained by the fact that the principal winter quarters of the race are in the countries to the west of Thailand.

At Chiang Mai, this little shrike not only haunted roadside hedges and the clumps of bushes bordering marshes and irrigation ditches but often entered open spaces in parks and gardens where it would employ as a lookout the coping of a well or the posts and backstops of a tennis court.

A female had the irides dark brown; the maxilla horny black, with the edges of the commissure bluish white; the mandible bluish white, tipped horny black; the feet and toes slaty brown; the claws black.

The adult, as seen in April and May after the complete prenuptial molt, has the lores, ocular region, and ear coverts black, edged above by a pure white supercilium; the crown soft reddish brown, fading to white on the forehead; the remaining upperparts brown, suffused with rufous on the upper tail coverts and rectrices; the wings blackish brown, the coverts and secondaries narrowly margined with rufous-brown, the primaries usually with no sign of a speculum; the chin and throat white, changing to rich buff on the remaining underparts. Winter birds have the upperparts similar but duller throughout and the forehead concolorous with the crown; the underparts wholly buffy white. Most Thai examples are immature; they have narrow, wavy blackish bars more or less conspicuous on the upperparts and similar blackish-brown bars on the breast and flanks.

LANIUS CRISTATUS LUCIONENSIS Linnaeus

CHINESE BROWN SHRIKE

[*Lanius*] *lucionensis* LINNAEUS, Systema naturae, ed. 12, vol. 1, 1766, p. 135 (Luzón, P. I.).

Lanius lucionensis, GYLDENSTOLPE, Journ. Nat. Hist. Soc. Siam, 1915, p. 167 (listed).

Otomela cristata lucionensis, GYLDENSTOLPE, Ibis, 1920, p. 469 ("Northern Siam").

I have examined in Stockholm the only specimen of the Chinese brown strike yet known from our area; it is a female, collected by Eisenhofer at Khun Tan sometime in 1913. The race is scarcely more than a straggler to Thailand, and is not likely to occur at all west of the Khun Tan range.

From *cristatus*, *lucionensis* differs strikingly in having the forehead and forecrown ashy, this color changing gradually on the hindcrown and nape to the cold gray-brown of the mantle; the wing feathers with paler edgings (almost white on the secondaries); the rufous of the upper tail coverts and rectrices duller and grayer.

LANIUS TIGRINUS Drapiez

TIGRINE SHRIKE

Lanius tigrinus DRAPIEZ, *in* Dictionnaire classique d'histoire naturelle, éd. Bory de Saint-Vincent, vol. 13, 1828, p. 523 (Java).

Lanius tigrinus, GYLDENSTOLPE, Kungl. Svenska Vet.-Akad. Handl., 1916, p. 39 (Khun Tan); Ibis, 1920, p. 468 (Khun Tan).—RILEY, U. S. Nat. Mus. Bull. 172, 1938, p. 481 (Phrae).

The present species is evidently a rather rare migrant through the provinces east of (and including) the Khun Tan chain. Gyldenstolpe mentions (1916) having seen several in the mountainous regions of northern Thailand and he collected an adult male at Khun

Tan, May 4, 1914; Smith took an adult male at Phrae, April 27, 1930; I myself shot an adult female at Ban Din Tok in Laos (a few miles north of the Nan border), April 25, 1936.

My specimen was found in dense undergrowth at the edge of a clearing in lowland evergreen forest.

Smith's specimen had the irides dark brown and the bill, feet, and toes bluish slate. Gyldenstolpe's differed in having the bill black and the feet and toes brownish gray.

The adult male has the forehead, lores, ocular region, and ear coverts black; the crown, nape, and upper back plumbeous-gray; the remaining upperparts deep rufous, the feathers of the mantle, rump, and upper tail coverts with wavy black cross bars; the entire underparts white, only the feathers of the lower flanks with wavy blackish bars. The adult female differs in having a short white bar above the black ear coverts; the lores white, very narrowly edged above with black; the barring beneath heavier and extending forward to the sides of the breast. The immature bird resembles the juvenile of *Lanius c. cristatus* but is more richly colored and more strongly barred above and below; it is usually distinguishable from *cristatus* by having the lores and ear coverts black-barred rufous-brown like the crown instead of plain black or blackish brown.

Family STURNIDAE

GRACULA RELIGIOSA INTERMEDIA Hay

INDO-CHINESE GRACKLE

[*Gracula*] *intermedius* [*sic*] HAY, Madras Journ. Lit. Sci., vol. 13, pt. 2, 1844 [1845], pp. 156–157 ("Northern India and Arracan"; type locality restricted to Cachar, *fide* Stuart Baker, Journ. Bombay Nat. Hist. Soc., vol. 27, 1921, p. 698).

Eulabes intermedia, GYLDENSTOLPE, Kungl. Svenska Vet.-Akad. Handl., 1913, p. 34 (Ban Huai Hom, Pak Pan, Den Chai).

Gracula javana intermedia, GYLDENSTOLPE, Journ. Nat. Hist. Soc. Siam, 1915, p. 168 (listed); Kungl. Svenska Vet.-Akad. Handl., 1916, p. 23 (Pha Kho, Khun Tan); Ibis, 1920, p. 453 ("Throughout the whole of Siam").

Eulabes javana intermedia, DE SCHAUENSEE, Proc. Acad. Nat. Sci. Philadelphia, 1929, p. 558 (Chiang Mai).

Gracula religiosa intermedia, DEIGNAN, Journ. Siam Soc. Nat. Hist. Suppl., 1931, p. 151 (Chiang Mai, Doi Suthep); 1936, p. 123 (Chiang Mai, Doi Suthep).—DE SCHAUENSEE, Proc. Acad. Nat. Sci. Philadelphia, 1934, p. 233 (Chiang Mai, Doi Suthep).—RILEY, U. S. Nat. Mus. Bull. 172, 1938, p. 487 (Doi Langka, Khun Tan, Mae Khan, Huai Mae Sae).

The grackle, or hill myna, occurs throughout the wooded districts of the northern provinces, from the plains to about 4,500 feet, but, at a given locality, varies in numbers from rare to abundant in accordance with the supply of fruit available at a particular season.

The *nok iang kham* or "golden starling" is usually seen in small bands not exceeding a dozen individuals but may appear in great numbers, together with other frugivorous species, where figs or similarly fleshy fruits are ripening. It is a noisy bird, with an enormous variety of notes which range from low, hoarse clucks and chuckles to loud, ringing whistles; its talent for mimicry and its ability to pronounce words and phrases with a distinctly human quality in the voice make it a favorite cagebird of the Lao.

Postjuvenal molt is shown by a specimen taken August 5; postnuptial molt appears in a series collected between August 27 and September 7.

Adults have the irides dark brown; the bill deep orange, tipped bright yellow; the wattles and the bare skin on the sides of the head bright yellow; the feet and toes bright yellow; the claws horny brown.

This unmistakable form has a broad white band across the central portion of the primaries; the rest of the plumage black, highly glossed with purple (crown, mantle, and breast), blue-green (rump and upper tail coverts), and deep blue (remaining parts); a bright yellow fleshy lappet at each side of the nape, connected with an extensive area of bright yellow bare skin on either side of the head below and behind the eye. Young birds are less glossy and have the lappets undeveloped.

MINO CORONATUS (Blyth)

GOLDEN-CRESTED MYNA

A[mpeliceps] coronatus BLYTH, Journ. Asiat. Soc. Bengal, vol. 11, 1842, p. 194 (Tenasserim).

Ampeliceps coronatus, GYLDENSTOLPE, Kungl. Svenska Vet.-Akad. Handl., 1913, p. 35 (Ban Huai Hom); 1916, p. 24 (Pha Kho); Journ. Nat. Hist. Soc. Siam, 1915, p. 168 (listed); Ibis, 1920, p. 454 ("Northern Siam").

This interesting starling seems to be common and widely distributed in the provinces east and north of (and including) the Khun Tan range. Eisenhofer sent to Hannover five examples from "Siam," one from Ban Huai Hom, and two from Huai Pu; to Stockholm, 12 from Khun Tan and three from Pha Hing. I myself have found it in Nan Province at Ban Hai Huai Som and in Chiang Rai on the savannas of the Nam Ing, as well as in the neighborhood of Wiang Pa Pao.

In Lampang, Phrae, and Nan it is a bird of the treetops in dense lowland evergreen, but on the Nam Ing savannas I discovered it in the rather stunted trees that form a parklike jungle on the islands of slightly higher land rising from the great marshes.

A pair observed near Wiang Pa Pao, April 6, were evidently about to nest in a hole about 40 feet above ground in one of several gigantic trees left standing at an abandoned *hai*. Specimens taken near the Nam Ing, May 3, had the gonads slightly to greatly enlarged. Eisenhofer collected juveniles at Pha Hing, April 23 and 25, and at Khun Tan, June 8.

Adults have the irides dark brown; the orbital skin orange or yellow; the bill with the basal half plumbeous-blue, the apical half orange-yellow; the feet and toes orange; the claws horny brown.

Old birds have the crested forehead and crown, the chin, and throat golden-yellow; the primaries with a broad band near their base, golden-yellow on the outer web and white on the inner web; the rest of the plumage black, highly glossed with deep blue. Juveniles probably have the entire head glossy blue-black; the golden feathers are acquired only gradually and over a long period.

ACRIDOTHERES TRISTIS TRISTIS (Linnaeus)

INDIAN HOUSE MYNA

[*Paradisea*] *tristis* LINNAEUS, Systema naturae, ed. 12, vol. 1, 1766, p. 167 ("in Philippinis," error; type locality corrected to Calcutta, Bengal, by Stuart Baker, Fauna of British India, Birds, ed. 2, vol. 3, 1926, p. 53).

Acridotheres tristis, GYLDENSTOLPE, Journ. Nat. Hist. Soc. Siam, 1915, p. 168 (listed); Kungl. Svenska Vet.-Akad. Handl., 1916, p. 27 (Khun Tan); Ibis, 1920, p. 454 ("Throughout the whole country").

Acridotheres tristis tristis, DEIGNAN, Journ. Siam Soc. Nat. Hist. Suppl., 1931, p. 151 (Chiang Mai); 1936, pp. 124, 134 (Chiang Mai, Chom Thong, Ban Tha Than, Ban Wang Lung).

The house myna seems to have appeared in northern Thailand, whether through human agency or as an adventurous immigrant, not earlier (and possibly much later) than the beginning of the twentieth century. During the thirties, old residents of Chiang Mai, both Thai and European, informed me that it was rare or unknown 30 years before; by 1914, however, Gyldenstolpe (1916) found it "rather abundant in or near villages especially in the northern parts of the country." Now (as of 1937) it is widely dispersed in our provinces but will not be found beyond sight of human habitation; its numbers vary from place to place directly with the size of the towns and it is still absent from many of the smaller settlements, especially when these are in forested districts.

The present species is the most familiar of all birds at Chiang Mai, where it is as much a part of the dooryard scene as the dogs and domestic fowls, among which it struts, head bobbing and plump body swinging, with complete unconcern. It is always noisy but especially so at evening, when the pairs gather together in flocks to roost in the bamboos and coconut crowns; its calls range from the most melodious notes through squeaks and chattering to harsh grating sounds and may even be heard in the middle of the night if the sleepers be disturbed by moonlight or a passing owl. The house myna is the nemesis of snakes, gathering around and following a victim with excited outcries and not infrequently directly leading to its dispatch at human hands. I have observed it feeding, at various times, on vegetable matter, earthworms, and insects, and it must be considered, despite a bad habit of damaging tiled roofs during the long breeding period, an interesting and generally beneficial resident of any compound.

An adult male had the irides dull brown with white flecks; the orbital region yellow; the bill wax yellow, with the base of the mandible blackish; the rictus and interior of the mouth yellow; the feet and toes wax yellow; the claws yellowish horn. An unsexed juvenile (August 16) differed in having the irides dark gray and the naked orbital skin white.

Old birds have the lanceolate feathers of the forehead, crown, and nape glossy black; the remaining upperparts rich vinaceous-brown; the primaries black, crossed by a broad white band at the base, the secondaries brown, glossed with bronze; the rectrices brownish black, with outwardly increasingly broad white tips; the chin, throat, and uppermost breast blackish slate; the remaining underparts rich vinaceous-brown, becoming vinaceous-white on the center of the abdomen; the under tail coverts, under wing coverts, and axillaries pure white.

Of *Acridotheres t. tristis* in its homeland, Stuart Baker observes (Fauna of British India, Birds, ed. 2, vol. 3, 1926, p. 54): "This Myna is one of the most universally common birds in India and is rapidly becoming more common in areas where it was but recently unknown or merely a rare straggler. This is especially the case in the hills, where these birds have followed mankind to higher elevations and into places where the country is being opened up."

Discussing its status in Central Thailand prior to April 1920, Herbert (Journ. Nat. Hist. Soc. Siam, vol. 6, 1923, p. 111) writes that it "does not occur in Bangkok, though possibly a stray bird might be seen there, as it is found in very small numbers on the Petriu side and sometimes at Klong Rangsit or Ayuthia, as well as on the Tachin side. In 1919 I sent my collector to all these places on several occasions but he only found it breeding at Hua Takhae on the Petriu line, where there were five or six pairs nesting in some old temples." An editor's footnote (May 1923) adds: "This remark was true up to a few years ago, but the bird has now established itself as one of the common species of the Capital, where it breeds from March onwards in suitable nesting-holes in buildings, etc." Aagaard concurs with these remarks (The common birds of Bangkok, 1930, p. 52): "Not more than 12 to 15 years ago this bird was a rare visitor to Bangkok; but is now very abundant, and getting more and more numerous year by year."

Of the house myna in the French territories, Delacour says (Les Oiseaux de l'Indochine Française, vol. 4, 1931, p. 249): "En Indochine, il est encore local. Il est probable qu'il n'y est venu, naturellement d'ailleurs, que depuis peu, et il s'y étend graduellement. . . En Indochine il a été obtenu à Siemreap (Cambodge), Kontoum, Huê, Haïlang, Laobao (Annam), Paksé et Muongyo (Laos)."

ACRIDOTHERES CRISTATELLUS GRANDIS Moore

Thai Crested Myna

A[cridotheres] grandis Moore, *in* Horsfield and Moore, Catalogue of the birds in the Museum of the Hon. East-India Co., vol. 2, 1858, p. 537 (Sumatra, error; type locality here corrected to Bangkok, Thailand).

AEthiopsar grandis, Gyldenstolpe, Journ. Nat. Hist. Soc. Siam, 1915, p. 168 (listed); Kungl. Svenska Vet.-Akad. Handl., 1916, p. 26 (Khun Tan).

AEthiopsar fuscus grandis, Gyldenstolpe, Ibis, 1920, p. 455 ("Throughout the whole country").

AEthiopsar grandis grandis, de Schauensee, Proc. Acad. Nat. Sci. Philadelphia, 1928, p. 558 (Chiang Mai); 1929, p. 559 (Chiang Mai); 1934, p. 234 (Chiang Mai).—Deignan, Journ. Siam Soc. Nat. Hist. Suppl., 1931, p. 152 (Chiang Mai); 1936, p. 124 (Chiang Mai).—Riley, U. S. Nat. Mus. Bull. 172, 1938, p. 494 (Ban Nam Khian.)

The crested myna is an abundant permanent resident in suitable territory throughout the northern lowlands.

Wherever cultivation and pasture have superseded the jungle and man has raised his home, the present species is one of the tamest and most familiar birds. Together with other terrestrial starlings, it is commonly seen about the feet and on the backs of grazing cattle, where it captures insects frightened from the grass; after the harvest it may be found gleaning grains of rice from the dry fields; during rainy periods it is a regular visitor to the lawns of parks and gardens, where it feeds on earthworms driven to the surface of the ground. It is almost fearless and will walk within arm's length of an observer; when pursued, it begins to hop and only at the last moment, with a soft nasal grunt, flies low over the grass to alight again a short distance ahead. The song is a harsh *queeter*, *queeter*, *queeter*, *queeter*, *queeter*.

Specimens taken at Chiang Mai, April 30 and June 3, had the gonads enlarged. A nest found May 19 was in a tree cavity about 15 feet above ground; another, discovered on July 1 (with crying young), was built in the crown of a coconut palm. In towns it occasionally breeds under roof tiles but this is properly the preserve of *Acridotheres t. tristis*.

Old birds have the irides bright red-brown; the bill bright chrome yellow, paler at the tip; the feet and toes chrome yellow; the claws horn.

The species is unmistakable among our mynas by having the elongated, lanceolate feathers of the forehead permanently erected to form a bushy crest. Adults have the plumage generally black, glossy on the crest, crown, and nape, duller elsewhere; the wings black, overlaid with bronze on the exposed portions and with a broad white band at the bases of the primaries; the rectrices black, with an outwardly increasingly broad white tip; the shortest under tail coverts black, the others white with the concealed bases black.

Stuart Baker has "corrected" the type locality of *Acridotheres grandis* Moore to Tenasserim (Journ. Bombay Nat. Hist. Soc., vol. 27, 1921, p. 702); since there is still no good evidence for the occurrence of the race in any part of that province, his fixation cannot stand. The facts seem to be that Baker, in 1921, confused *grandis* with *torquatus* and that his *grandis* of 1921 from Tenasserim is equivalent to his *torquatus* of 1926 from Pahang (Fauna of British India, Birds, ed. 2, vol. 3, 1926, p. 58), which was not mentioned at all in 1921. In any case, the type locality of the true *Acridotheres grandis* Moore must be altered, and I now establish it as Bangkok; at the same time, clearly to place it in synonymy with *grandis*, I restrict to Bangkok the type locality of *Acridotheres siamensis* Swinhoe (Proc. Zool. Soc. London, 1863, p. 303).

STURNUS MALABARICUS NEMORICOLA (Jerdon)

INDO-CHINESE ASHY-HEADED MYNA

Sturnia nemoricola JERDON, Ibis, 1862, p. 22 (Thayetmyo, Burma).

Sturnia malabarica, GYLDENSTOLPE, Journ. Nat. Hist. Soc. Siam, 1915, p. 168 (listed).

Spodiopsar malabaricus nemoriculus [*sic*], GYLDENSTOLPE, Kungl. Svenska Vet.-Akad. Handl., 1916, p. 25 (Khun Tan).

Spodiopsar malabaricus nemoricolus, GYLDENSTOLPE, Ibis, 1920, p. 454 (Khun Tan).

Sturnia malabarica malabarica, DE SCHAUENSEE, Proc. Acad. Nat. Sci. Philadelphia, 1929, p. 558 (Doi Suthep, Chiang Maï, Chiang Saen); 1934, p. 233 (Chiang Mai).—DEIGNAN, Journ. Siam Soc. Nat. Hist. Suppl., 1931, p. 151 (Doi Suthep, Chiang Mai).

Sturnia malabarica nemoricola, DEIGNAN, Journ. Siam Soc. Nat. Hist. Suppl., 1931, p. 151 (Chiang Mai); 1936, p. 123 (Doi Suthep, Chiang Mai).—DE SCHAUENSEE, Proc. Acad. Nat. Sci. Philadelphia, 1934, p. 233 (Chiang Mai).—RILEY, U. S. Nat. Mus. Bull. 172, 1938, p. 490 ("Doi Tin Pata" [= Foot of Doi Pata?]).

The ashy-headed myna is a rare and locally distributed permanent resident but an abundant winter visitor in the provinces of Chiang Rai, Chiang Mai, and Mae Hong Son; from the remaining parts of the North it has not yet been recorded at all. At Chiang Mai Town it was a most conspicuous bird, chiefly on the plain but occasionally on Doi Suthep to 3,300 feet, from November 19 (1931) to February 14 (1936).

The movements of this small starling, which, making its appearance in great numbers overnight, vanishes as suddenly at the end of its stay, are largely governed by the antheses of the *mai kwao* (*Butea frondosa*) and the silk-cotton (*Bombax malabaricum*), which, in the cold weather, are leafless but ablaze with scarlet ornithophilous flowers. Among the various birds that visit these two trees, the present species draws attention by its numbers, its eager crowding over the blossom-laden branches, and its continual, not unpleasing, churring and chatter. It is probable that insects, rather than nectar, are the lure, especially since the attraction of the *mai kwao* for the myna continues beyond the period of bloom; those few individuals which stay throughout the year are, in my experience, never seen away from the groves of that tree.

A male collected at Chiang Mai, May 18, had the gonads greatly enlarged and was evidently one of a pair breeding in a hole in a *mai kwao*, about ten feet above the ground. A male from the same locality, September 1, is in postjuvenal molt.

Adults have the irides white, blue-gray, or pale blue; the bill slaty blue at the base, green at the center, and bright yellow at the tip; the interior of the mouth blue; the feet and toes pinkish yellow or fleshy brown; the claws yellowish horn. Juveniles differ in having the bill wholly yellow.

This is an extraordinarily variable form, subject both to erythrism and to albinism; curiously enough, the two conditions often appear in the same individual! A more or less normal adult in fresh plumage (October) has the elongated, lanceolate feathers of the crown and nape soft gray, with silvery-gray shaft streaks; the remaining upperparts soft gray, faintly washed with rufous (more strongly on the upper tail coverts); the primaries black, the inner ones narrowly tipped with silvery gray; the secondaries black with an inwardly increasingly broad margin of silvery gray until the innermost are wholly of this color; the two central pairs of rectrices silvery gray, the remaining pairs dull black, with an outwardly increasingly broad chestnut-rufous tip: the underparts pale gray, almost white on the chin and throat (the feathers of the breast with white shaft streaks), washed with dull rufous along the flanks and on the under tail coverts; the bend of the wing, the under wing coverts, and the axillaries pure white. There is considerable individual variation in the amount and degree of rufous (or even chestnut) suffusion above and below; albinism appears usually symmetrically in the wing. With wear the feathers of the crown and nape tend to lose the darker margins and these parts may become partly or wholly silvery gray or silvery white. The juvenile is similar to the adult but has the upperparts generally dull brownish gray, the head and nape paler and without the specialized feathers.

STURNUS CONTRA FLOWERI (Bowdler Sharpe)

Thai Pied Myna

Sturnopastor floweri Bowdler Sharpe, Bull. Brit. Orn. Club, vol. 7, 1897, p. 17 ("Pachim [=Prachinburi] and Tahkamen," Central Thailand).

Sturnopastor superciliaris, Gyldenstolpe, Journ. Nat. Hist. Soc. Siam, 1915, p. 168 (listed).

Sturnopastor superciliaris superciliaris, Gyldenstolpe, Ibis, 1920, p. 455 (Khun Tan).

Sturnopastor capensis floweri, de Schauensee, Proc. Acad. Nat. Sci. Philadelphia, 1928, p. 558 (Chiang Mai).

Sturnopastor contra floweri, Deignan, Journ. Siam Soc. Nat. Hist. Suppl., 1931, p. 152 (Chiang Mai); 1936, p. 124 (Chiang Mai).—Riley, U. S. Nat. Mus. Bull. 172, 1938, p. 495 (Phrae, Ban Nam Khian).

Sturnopastor contra superciliaris, Deignan, Journ. Siam Soc. Nat. Hist. Suppl., 1936, p. 124 ("Some parts of North Siam").

The pied myna, while rather less abundant than the other terrestrial starlings, is still one of the commonest birds in the cultivated lowland districts of all the northern provinces.

This species seems to be somewhat more gregarious during the daylight hours than its relatives and is less often observed in the immediate proximity of houses, but otherwise has habits much like theirs.

A specimen from Ban Khana (Nan Province), April 21, was carrying an oviduct egg, and two from Chiang Mai, June 5 and 20, had the gonads enlarged. An example of September 19 is in postnuptial molt. Postnatal molt appears in a bird of April 22 (Chiang Mai) and the full juvenal dress in one of June 27 from the same locality.

Old birds taken by me had the irides pale yellow, creamy yellow, or cream; the orbital skin bright orange, becoming orange-yellow posteriorly (above the ear coverts); the skin of the chin and throat (beneath the feathers) bright orange; the bill with the basal half red-orange and the apical half ivory white or fleshy white; the feet and toes pale yellow or yellowish flesh; the claws horny or fleshy horn. The juvenile of June 27 differed in having the irides grayish white; the orbital skin yellowish; the culmen brown (darker on the basal half) and the rest of the bill fleshy horn; the feet and toes brown; the claws dark brown.

The fresh-plumaged adult has the lanceolate feathers of the front and forecrown white, with black bases which posteriorly show through to give a streaked appearance; the supercilium and ear coverts pure white; the chin, throat, upper breast, sides of the neck, the hindcrown, nape, and back black, more or less glossed with green; the rump pure white; the wings black (the ends of the secondaries somewhat glossed with bronze), with a longitudinal bar formed by the pure white lesser coverts and the white external edging of the median coverts; the rectrices black; the remaining underparts white (with a faint vinaceous suffusion), mixed with dull black along the lower flanks. In a short time the feathers of the front and forecrown lose much of the white portion (with resultant increase in the amount of black visible), the black parts become an unglossed brownish black, and the white become very stained. The juvenile is similar but lacks white on the front and crown and has the black replaced by dark brown.

Specimens formerly believed by me to represent *S. c. superciliaris* are nothing but *floweri* in worn plumage. This race seems to have originated on the plain of Central Thailand and to have entered the northern provinces along the valleys of the larger rivers.

STURNUS NIGRICOLLIS (Paykull)

BLACK-COLLARED MYNA

Gracula nigricollis PAYKULL, Kongl. [Svenska] Vet.-Akad. Nya Handl., vol. 28, 1807, pp. 291–293, pl. 9 (Canton, China).

Graculipica nigricollis, GYLDENSTOLPE, Kungl. Svenska Vet.-Akad. Handl., 1913, p. 35 (Pak Pan, Den Chai); 1916, p. 26 (Khun Tan); Journ. Nat. Hist. Soc. Siam, 1915, p. 168 (listed); Ibis, 1920, p. 455 ("Throughout the whole country").—DE SCHAUENSEE, Proc. Acad. Nat. Sci. Philadelphia, 1928, p. 558 (Chiang Mai); 1929, p. 559 (Chiang Mai).

Gracupica nigricollis, DEIGNAN, Journ. Siam Soc. Nat. Hist. Suppl., 1931, p. 151 (Chiang Mai, Doi Suthep); 1936, p. 123 (Chiang Mai, Doi Suthep).—DE SCHAUENSEE, Proc. Acad. Nat. Sci. Philadelphia, 1934, p. 234 (Chiang Mai).

The *nok iang hua lan* or "bald-headed myna" is an abundant and familiar species wherever, in the North, it finds cultivated lands and human habitation. Although characteristically a bird of the plains, I have occasionally found it in the dry, stunted forest at the base of Doi Suthep as high as 1,500 feet (whither it had accompanied grazing cattle), and a small colony is resident near the Karen village on Doi Ang Ka at 3,500 feet.

This starling is a strong walker and feeds almost entirely on the ground, where it collects seeds, earthworms, and other small creatures. Although it is most commonly seen in pastures or among the rice stubbles, it regularly appears, especially at the end of the rains, on the lawns of gardens and parks. Like other mynas, it is very vocal, and its calls range from loud, shrill rattles to relatively melodious notes.

The breeding season runs throughout the hot, dry season: specimens with active gonads have been taken from February 19 at Pak Pan

(Gyldenstolpe) to May 27 at Chiang Mai (Deignan). The nest is an enormous and untidy globular structure of grass, leaves, and sticks, placed near the top of a tree in or at the edge of a field. During May and June one sees everywhere young birds just out of the nest, following the parents and pleading for food with vibrating wings and a shrill *kh-kh-kh-kh-kh.*

Adults have the irides creamy gray; the orbital skin yellow; the bill brownish black; the feet and toes pale yellow; the claws horn brown.

The adult in fresh plumage has the entire head white, followed by a black collar, which covers the nape, sides of the neck, the lower throat, and upper breast; the back brownish black (the feathers just behind the collar with broad ashy tips); the rump white; the primary coverts white, all the remaining feathers of the wing brownish black with narrow white tips (these tips broader on the outer secondaries); the rectrices brownish black, with outwardly increasingly broad white tips; the remaining underparts white, mixed with deep brown along the lower flanks. The upperparts soon change to a dark brown and the white portions of the plumage become much soiled with mud, dust, etc. Juveniles wholly lack the black collar and have the head, neck, throat, breast, and belly brownish gray, the feathers with whitish edgings to give an indistinctly streaked appearance.

Family NECTARINIIDAE

CHALCOPARIA SINGALENSIS ASSAMENSIS Boden Kloss

ASSAMESE RUBYCHEEK

Chalcoparia singalensis assamensis BODEN KLOSS, Bull. Brit. Orn. Club, vol. 50, May 7, 1930, pp. 69–70. New name for "*Chalcoparia singalensis lepida* (Latham)" Stuart Baker, Fauna of British India, Birds, ed. 2, vol. 3, 1926, p. 370 ("India, now restricted to Cachar"), not [*Certhia*] *lepida* Latham, 1790, nor *Certhia lepida* Sparrman, 1787, each of which =*Certhia* (*malacensis*) Scopoli, 1786.

Chalcoparia singalensis rubinigentis STUART BAKER, Fauna of British India, Birds, ed. 2, vol. 7, March [=May 14], 1930, p. 282. New name for "*Chalcoparia singalensis lepida* (Latham)" Stuart Baker, Fauna of British India, Birds, ed. 2, vol. 3, 1926, p. 370 ("India, now restricted to Cachar"), not [*Certhia*] *lepida* Latham, 1790, nor *Certhia lepida* Sparrman, 1787, each of which =*Certhia* (*malacensis*) Scopoli, 1786.

Chalcoparia phaenicotis [*partim*], GYLDENSTOLPE, Kungl. Svenska Vet.-Akad. Handl., 1913, p. 45 (Ban Huai Hom, Den Chai).

Chalcoparia phaenicotis, GYLDENSTOLPE, Kungl. Svenska Vet.-Akad. Handl., 1916, p. 34 (Pha Kho, Tha Chomphu).

Chalcoparia singalensis koratensis [*partim*], GYLDENSTOLPE, Ibis, 1920, p. 464 ("Throughout the whole country" [*partim*]).

Chalcoparia singalensis singalensis, DE SCHAUENSEE, Proc. Acad. Nat. Sci. Philadelphia, 1929, p. 563 (Chiang Rai).—DEIGNAN, Journ. Siam Soc. Nat. Hist. Suppl., 1931, p. 154 (Chiang Mai, Doi Suthep).

Chalcoparia singalensis interposita [*partim*], DE SCHAUENSEE, Proc. Acad. Nat. Sci. Philadelphia, 1934, p. 240 (Chiang Mai, Chiang Dao).—RILEY, U. S. Nat. Mus. Bull. 172, 1938, p. 512 (Doi Ang Ka, Chiang Mai, Muang Pai).

Chalcoparia singalensis interposita, DEIGNAN, Journ. Siam Soc. Nat. Hist. Suppl., 1936, p. 125 (Chiang Mai, Doi Suthep).—GREENWAY, Bull. Mus. Comp. Zool., 1940, p. 191 (Chiang Dao).

The northern race of the rubycheek, not previously recognized from Thailand, occurs as an uncommon and rather local permanent resident in every one of our provinces: in addition to localities listed above, I have it from Ban Hai Huai Som, Doi San Pa Bong, Ban Mae Mo, and Wiang Pa Pao. It is normally a species of the plains, but Smith took it at 2,000 feet on Doi Ang Ka and I have found it in small numbers on Doi Suthep between 2,000 and 3,300 feet.

In the lowlands, although this bird is sometimes seen in fruit gardens, its real home is the dense growth of bamboos, brambles, and creepers that succeeds the cleared forest or springs up along the secondary roads; on Doi Suthep it was noted in similar vegetation beside the broader trails. I have never observed it in flocks of its own kind, perhaps because it is not a very common bird with us, but it regularly accompanies such forms as *Mixornis* and *Erpornis*. In notes and actions, it resembles these species and the white-eyes, rather than the other sunbirds.

Postnuptial molt is shown by specimens taken between June 6 and October 25. I have collected examples in full juvenal dress July 24 and 25 and August 29, while young males acquiring the first nuptial plumage were found December 27 (Smith) and February 10 (Gyldenstolpe).

An adult male had the irides crimson; the bill black, whitish at the base of the mandible; the interior of the mouth orange-yellow; the feet and toes yellowish green; the claws greenish horn.

The old male has the entire upperparts metallic green, with bronzy reflections; the lesser wing coverts metallic green, the median and greater coverts black, outwardly edged with metallic peacock blue, the remiges black, faintly and narrowly edged with metallic blue; the rectrices black, narrowly edged with metallic peacock blue; the ear coverts metallic copper red, posteriorly edged below by a streak of metallic violet; the chin, throat, and breast ferruginous, this color (on the lower breast) passing into bright greenish yellow. Certain specimens appear to be adult, but younger, males: their plumage differs from that just described in having the rump unglossed olive-green and the remiges very narrowly edged along the outer web with rufescent-yellow. The adult female has the entire upperparts dull olive-green; the remiges and rectrices blackish, edged rufescent olive-green; the ear coverts grayish olive-green; the chin, throat, and breast pale rufescent, this color passing into the greenish yellow of the remaining underparts. The juvenile male is like the adult female but has merely a rufescent wash over the throat and breast; from him the juvenile female differs in having the entire underparts dull olive-yellow.

Chalcoparia s. assamensis is nearest *C. s. interposita*, differing in having the rather paler ferruginous of throat and breast usually not extending so far onto the lower breast and the remaining underparts a rather purer, less greenish, yellow. *C. s. koratensis* is a very distinct form, in which the deep ferruginous breast is sharply defined from the almost pure yellow abdomen.

AETHOPYGA SIPARAJA SEHERIAE (Tickell)

INDIAN SCARLET-THROATED SUNBIRD

Necterinia [*sic*] *Seheriae* TICKELL, Journ. Asiat. Soc. Bengal, vol. 2, 1833, p. 577 (Seheria, Borabham).

AEthopyga siparaja, DEIGNAN, Journ. Siam Soc. Nat. Hist. Suppl., 1931, p. 155 (Chiang Mai).

AEthopyga siparaja seheriae, DEIGNAN, Journ. Siam Soc. Nat. Hist. Suppl., 1936, p. 124 (Chiang Mai).

I found this lovely sunbird to be rather rare in the *town* of Chiang Mai between November 30 (1936) and June 29 (1929) and apparently quite absent at other seasons; it is otherwise known from our area by a specimen taken at Muang Fang, July 9, 1936, and a small series collected at Wiang Pa Pao between July 27 and August 3, 1935.

Owing to its small size and its habit of keeping to the tops of the trees in shady fruit gardens, the present form is probably often overlooked, especially since its only note seems to be a shrill *tsit*, *tsit*. My eight examples from Chiang Mai were all brought me by small boys.

The gonads were slightly enlarged in a bird of February 23, more enlarged in one of March 9, and greatly enlarged in a third of May 15. A male in full juvenal dress was shot at Wiang Pa Pao, July 30; four others taken at Chiang Mai between November 30 and March 16 show progressive stages of the complete molt from juvenal to first-nuptial plumage.

A breeding male had the irides brown; the maxilla blackish brown; the mandible light brown; the feet and toes brown; the claws horny brown.

The adult male has the front and most of the crown metallic peacock green (sometimes with violet reflections); the extreme hind-crown and the nape brownish olive; the sides of the head and neck, the back, scapulars, lesser and median wing coverts deep crimson; the rump golden-yellow, more or less concealed by long brownish-olive feathers growing from the sides of the lower back; the upper tail coverts and the central pair of rectrices (greatly elongated and narrowed on the terminal third) metallic peacock green, the remaining rectrices blackish (some narrowly edged with metallic peacock green); the remiges blackish brown, edged along the outer web with rufescent olive-green; a long mustachial streak at each side of the throat metallic blue; the chin, throat, and entire breast bright crimson; the remaining underparts yellowish olive-green. The female has the entire upperparts olive-green (the edgings of the remiges and the central pair of rectrices more rufescent); the entire underparts yellowish olive-green; the rectrices indistinctly tipped creamy white beneath. The juvenile male resembles the female but has the chin and most of the throat crimson-pink.

Delacour does not admit *A. s. seheriae* to the avifauna of Indochine, although specimens from Haut-Laos and eastern Tongking are of this race, as has been correctly reported long since by Bangs and Van Tyne (Publ. Field Mus. Nat. Hist., zool. ser., vol. 18, No. 3, 1931, p. 115).

AETHOPYGA SIPARAJA CARA Hume

TENASSERIMESE SCARLET-THROATED SUNBIRD

AE[thopyga] cara HUME, Stray Feathers, vol. 2, 1874, p. 473 (Tenasserim, south of Moulmein).

AEthopyga cara, GYLDENSTOLPE, Kungl. Svenska Vet.-Akad. Handl., 1913, p. 42 (Ban Huai Hom); Journ. Nat. Hist. Soc. Siam, 1915, p. 171 (listed).

AEthopyga siparaja cara, GYLDENSTOLPE, Ibis, 1920, p. 462 ("Northern districts").

AEthopyga siparaja seheriae, RILEY, U. S. Nat. Mus. Bull. 172, 1938, p. 497 (Ban Nam Khian).

The Tenasserimese scarlet-throated sunbird is common in the lowlands of Phrae and Nan Provinces; Gyldenstolpe has noted (1913) that "near Bang Hue Hom it was the most common of all Sun-birds . . ."

Both Gyldenstolpe and I found it in second-growth evergreen and at forest clearings, rather than in villages and towns.

At Ban Huai Hom, Gyldenstolpe collected a male assuming the first-nuptial plumage, February 23, and, the following day, a pair with gonads greatly enlarged. I took a bird with enlarged testes at Ban San Tha, April 1. A specimen from Ban Hai Huai Som, June 20, wears full juvenal dress.

From the full-plumaged male of *seheriae*, that of *cara* differs in having the feathers of the hindcrown and nape broadly tipped with deep crimson and the brownish-olive color absent or reduced to a narrow subterminal band; the central pair of tail feathers but slightly elongated and scarcely narrowed toward the tip; the visible portions of the rectrices glossed wholly or in part with metallic peacock blue rather than metallic peacock green; the abdomen and under tail coverts gray, sometimes with the lightest wash of olive-green. Females and juveniles of the two forms are probably inseparable.

The birds of Nan and Phrae and the provinces of eastern Thailand show no constant character by which they may be distinguished from topotypical *cara*.

AETHOPYGA SATURATA SANGUINIPECTUS Walden

INDO-CHINESE BLACK-THROATED SUNBIRD

AEthopyga sanguinipectus WALDEN, Ann. Mag. Nat. Hist., ser. 4, vol. 15, 1875, pp. 400–401 ("Tonghoo hills [Karen-hee]," error; type locality corrected to "the Tonghoo and Karen-nee hills," by Wardlaw Ramsay, *in* The ornithological works of Arthur, Ninth Marquis of Tweeddale, 1881, p. 414).

AEthopyga dabryi, GYLDENSTOLPE, Kungl. Svenska Vet.-Akad. Handl., 1916, p. 33 (Khun Tan) ; Ibis, 1920, p. 462 (Khun Tan).

AEthopyga sanguinipectus, WILLIAMSON, Journ. Nat. Hist. Soc. Siam, 1918, p. 23 (Muang Wang).

AEthopyga sanguinipectus [*partim*], GYLDENSTOLPE, Ibis, 1920, p. 462 (Muang Wang).

AEthopyga sanguinipecta sanguinipecta, DE SCHAUENSEE, Proc. Acad. Nat. Sci. Philadelphia, 1929, p. 563 (Doi Suthep, Chiang Saen).—DEIGNAN, Journ. Siam Soc. Nat. Hist. Suppl., 1931, p. 155 (Doi Suthep).—CHASEN and BODEN KLOSS, Journ. Siam Soc. Nat. Hist. Suppl., 1932, p. 248 (Doi Suthep).—RILEY, U. S. Nat. Mus. Bull. 172, 1938, p. 499 (Doi Suthep, Doi Khun Tan, Doi Langka, Doi Hua Mot).

AEthopya saturata sanguinipecta, DE SCHAUENSEE, Proc. Acad. Nat. Sci. Philadelphia, 1934, p. 241 (Doi Suthep, Doi Khun Tan, Doi Chiang Dao).—DEIGNAN, Journ. Siam Soc. Nat. Hist. Suppl., 1936, p. 124 (Doi Suthep).

Aethopyga dabryii dabryii [*partim*], RILEY, U. S. Nat. Mus. Bull. 172, 1938, p. 498 (Khun Tan).

On Phu Kha and on all the higher peaks of the Thanon Thong Chai and Khun Tan ranges, the black-throated sunbird is a common resident of the evergreen, at elevations between 3,300 and 5,500 feet. Two males taken by de Schauensee at Chiang Saen, January 9 and 14, 1929, probably represent winter wanderers from the hills.

This species keeps to the lower trees, in clearings or at the edge of the forest, and especially those which are heavily laden with blooming epiphytes. Like all of the genus, it flutters before the flowers to probe into them for nectar and the minute insects entrapped therein.

A bird of April 27 (Doi Ang Ka) had the testes greatly enlarged. Postnuptial molt is shown by examples collected between July 22 and September 8.

Two males had the irides brown; the bill black; the feet and toes dark brown; the claws horny brown.

The adult male has the front, crown, and nape metallic blue or violet-blue; the sides of the breast and neck, the back, and scapulars deep crimson-maroon; the rump with a narrow band of bright light yellow, more or less concealed by long yellowish-gray feathers growing from the sides of the lower back; the upper tail coverts and the basal two-thirds of the greatly elongated central pair of rectrices metallic blue, their apical third and the remaining rectrices dull black (some narrowly edged with metallic blue); the wings dull black; a long mustachial streak (extending to the upper breast) at each side of the throat metallic blue or violet-blue; the sides of the head, the chin, throat, and center of the upper breast black; the lower breast and upper abdomen bright light yellow, irregularly and finely streaked with blood-red, changing to uniform olivaceous-yellow on the remaining underparts. The adult female has the rump band light yellow; the remaining upperparts olive-green, grayer on the head and nape (the remiges edged rufescent); the chin, throat, and upper breast olivaceous-gray, changing to pale olivaceous-yellow on the remaining underparts; the rectrices indistinctly tipped white beneath.

AETHOPYGA GOULDIAE DABRYII (Verreaux)

SZECHWANESE BLUE-THROATED SUNBIRD

Nectarinia Dabryii VERREAUX, Rev. Mag. Zool., ser. 2, vol. 19, 1867, pp. 173–174, pl. 15 ("le nord de la Chine"; type locality corrected to "the hills above Ta-tsien-leou, which border the eastern [*sic*] boundary of the Chinese province of Sechnen [*sic*]," by Sclater, Ibis, 1870, p. 297; see Deignan, Auk, 1944, pp. 133–135).

AEthopyga dabryi, DE SCHAUENSEE, Proc. Acad. Nat. Sci. Philadelphia, 1928, p. 561 (Doi Suthep); 1929, p. 563 (Doi Suthep).—DEIGNAN, Journ. Siam Soc. Nat. Hist. Suppl., 1931, p. 155 (Doi Suthep).

AEthopyga gouldiae dabryi, DE SCHAUENSEE, Proc. Acad. Nat. Sci. Philadelphia, 1934, p. 241 (Doi Chiang Dao).—DEIGNAN, Journ. Siam Soc. Nat. Hist. Suppl., 1936, p. 124 (Doi Suthep).

AEthopyga dabryii dabryii [*partim*], RILEY, U. S. Nat. Mus. Bull. 172, 1938, p. 498 (Doi Suthep, Doi Langka).

AEthopyga gouldiae harrietae, DELACOUR and GREENWAY, L'Oiseau et la Revue Française d'Ornithologie, 1940, p. 69 (Doi Ang Ka).

The blue-throated sunbird is an uncommon winter visitor to the higher mountains of the provinces west of (and including) the Khun Tan range, from 4,500 to 5,500 feet; a male collected by de Schauensee on Doi Suthep at 1,500 feet (March 11, 1928) must be considered a straggler from the top of the mountain. The extreme dates for its occurrence with us are November 4 (1930) on Doi Langka and March 18 (1937) on Doi Chiang Dao.

At suitable elevations, this species may be seen at the same places as *A. s. sanguinipectus*, although, of course, always in inferior numbers.

The sequence of molts in this form is difficult to understand. A young male of November 4 is already beginning to acquire the first-nuptial plumage; an apparently adult male of November 11 is near completion of what must be the postnuptial molt; two females of February 5 are presumably in prenuptial molt; a male of March 18 is nearing completion of molt into first-nuptial dress. I find no evidence for the existence of an eclipse plumage, although such may exist: specimens in female dress are much less likely to be collected than full-colored males.

The male has the forehead, crown, and center of the nape, the posterior ear coverts, the chin, center of the throat, and an isolated patch at each side of the upper breast metallic blue (more or less strongly glossed with violet); the supercilium, sides of the head, throat, and neck, the back, scapulars, and lesser wing coverts deep crimson; the rump golden-yellow (sometimes partly concealed by long yellowish-gray feathers growing from the sides of the lower back), the posterior feathers tipped with black (or black and red) to form a narrow band; the upper tail coverts and basal two-thirds of the greatly elongated central pair of rectrices metallic blue, their apical third and the remaining rectrices black (some narrowly edged with metallic blue), all but the central pair with outwardly increasingly broad ashy tips; the remiges blackish, outwardly edged with rufescent olive-green; the breast and upper abdomen scarlet-crimson, this color paling posteriorly and changing through bright yellow to greenish yellow on the remaining underparts. The female is inseparable in the field from that of *sanguinipectus;* direct comparison in the hand will show that *dabryii* has the light tips of the rectrices bolder and whiter.

AEthopyga gouldiae harrietae Delacour and Greenway, with type from Laos but based in part upon material from Doi Ang Ka, seems to me inseparable from a topotype of *dabryii.* I suspect that the richness of the reds and the purity of the metallic blue vary directly with the freshness of the feathers in question.

AETHOPYGA NIPALENSIS ANGKANENSIS Riley

DOI ANG KA GREEN-THROATED SUNBIRD

AEthopyga nipalensis angkanensis RILEY, Proc. Biol. Soc. Washington, vol. 42, 1929, pp. 162–163 (Doi Ang Ka, North Thailand).

AEthopyga nipalensis angkanensis, RILEY, U. S. Nat. Mus. Bull. 172, 1938, p. 500 (Doi Ang Ka).—GREENWAY, Bull. Mus. Comp. Zool., 1940, p. 192 (Doi Ang Ka).

This beautiful sunbird, known only from the top of the highest peak of Doi Ang Ka, was discovered by Smith, who took a pair at 8,400 feet, December 5, 1928, and a second male the following day at 8,000 feet. In April, 1931, I found it decidedly uncommon at 8,400 feet and, in September, 1935, failed to see it at all. Its home was next visited by members of the Asiatic Primate Expedition, who on the five days March 23, 24, 25, 28, and 31, 1937, shot no less than 34 males and 15 females, all at 8,400 feet.

I observed it only in the gnarled and epiphyte-covered rhododendron trees, which make an almost impenetrable barrier around the open bog at the summit of the mountain.

Griswold (of the Asiatic Primate Expedition), at the end of March, collected a pair "with their nest which had no eggs in it. The nest was about 20 feet from the ground at the end of a small branch." He notes further that "in [the case of] the two nests which I observed being built the female did all the work."

The male has the forehead, crown, nape, and center of the upper back metallic peacock green; the sides of the neck and upper back and the middle back crimson-maroon; the upper wing coverts, scapulars, and lower back deep olive-green; the rump bright yellow (sometimes partly concealed by long yellowish-olive feathers growing from each side of the lower back); the upper tail coverts and basal three-fourths of the greatly elongated central pair of rectrices metallic peacock green, the apical fourth and the remaining rectrices black (some narrowly edged with metallic peacock green), all but the two central pairs with outwardly increasingly broad yellowish-ashy tips; the remiges black, outwardly edged with rufescent olive-green; the sides of the head black, slightly glossed (especially on the ear coverts) with metallic peacock green; the chin and throat metallic peacock green; the uppermost breast bright yellow, changing into scarlet on the lower breast and upper abdomen, this color, in turn, changing into bright yellow on the remaining underparts (more greenish along the lower flanks). The female closely resembles those of *A. g. dabryii* and *A. s. sanguinipectus* but has the rump olive-green like the rest of the upperparts and the bold white tips of the rectrices suffused with pale yellow.

Robinson and Boden Kloss state (Journ. Nat. Hist. Soc. Siam, vol. 5, No. 3, 1924, p. 375) that "Mr. W. J. F. Williamson has specimens [of *A. nipalensis*] from North Siam which have not yet been critically examined . . ." They presumably here refer to Williamson's record (1918) of *A. s. sanguinipectus* from Muang Wang; Robinson himself had earlier (Journ. Federated Malay States Mus., vol. 5, 1915, p. 109) mistaken the still undescribed *A. n. australis* for *sanguinipectus* and may have supposed that Williamson had made a similar misidentification.

NECTARINIA ASIATICA INTERMEDIA (Hume)

INDO-CHINESE PURPLE SUNBIRD

A[rachnechthra] intermedia HUME, Ibis, 1870, pp. 436–437 (Tipperah, eastern Bengal).

Arachnechthra asiatica, GYLDENSTOLPE, Kungl. Svenska Vet.-Akad. Handl., 1913, p. 43 (Den Chai) ; Ibis, 1920, p. 462 ("Throughout the country").

Leptocoma asiatica intermedia, DE SCHAUENSEE, Proc. Acad. Nat. Sci. Philadelphia, 1929, p. 563 (Chiang Mai, Chiang Saen) ; 1934, p. 241 (Chiang Mai).—DEIGNAN, Journ. Siam Soc. Nat. Hist. Suppl., 1931, p. 155 (Chiang Mai) ; 1936, p. 124 (Chiang Mai).

The purple sunbird is a very common permanent resident of the North, recorded from all the provinces except Nan (where it is almost certain to occur). Although the species was inadvertently omitted from his list by Riley (1938), Dr. Smith's collection included specimens from Mae Hong Son, Mae Sariang, and Phrae. I have never noted it at an elevation in excess of 1,500 feet (Doi Ang Ka).

This is a familiar and widely distributed bird, abounding equally in orchards and gardens, coconut groves, and the dry, deciduous forest. The call note is *sweet, sweet;* the song, rendered with the gold and orange pectoral tufts exposed, a hoarse *swee-e, swee-e, swee-e.*

The extreme dates for males in full nuptial dress are (at Chiang Mai) December 12 and June 10. Examples in various stages of prenuptial molt may be observed throughout December and the first half of January; similar examples in postnuptial molt, from the middle of May to the end of June. The adjective "purple" is highly misleading when applied to old males in nonbreeding (eclipse) plumage, when they are inseparable from the dull-colored juveniles of the same sex.

The present form has the irides dark brown; the bill, feet, and toes black; the claws black or dark brown.

The full-plumaged male, in the field, may appear to be wholly black. In fact, he has the forehead, crown, sides of the head and neck, the mantle, scapulars, lesser wing coverts, rump, and upper tail coverts metallic blue, more or less glossed with violet (or with green toward the end of the season); the rectrices black, overlaid with deep blue (often narrowly tipped beneath with ashy); the feathers of the wings blackish, narrowly edged with grayish brown; the throat and breast metallic blue (the chin and center of the throat more bronzy purple); a narrow band of chestnut-maroon separating the breast from the abdomen (sometimes wholly or partly lacking); at either side of the upper abdomen a tuft of elongated feathers, the shorter orange, the longer golden-yellow (usually concealed beneath the wing); the remaining underparts black, overlaid with deep blue. In eclipse plumage, he has the wings and tail as described above, but the remaining upperparts dull olive-green; the underparts wholly yellow, except for a broad purple-glossed black stripe down the center of the throat to the upper breast. The female differs from the postnuptial male chiefly in having the throat all yellow, without a gular stripe.

NECTARINIA JUGULARIS FLAMMAXILLARIS Blyth

INDO-CHINESE PURPLE-THROATED SUNBIRD

N[ectarinia] flammaxillaris BLYTH, Journ. Asiat. Soc. Bengal, vol. 14, 1845, p. 557. New name for "*N[ectarinia] jugularis* Vieillot, apud Jardine" Blyth, Journ. Asiat. Soc. Bengal, vol. 12, 1843, p. 979 ("the Tenasserim provinces"), not [*Certhia*] *jugularis* Linnaeus 1766.

Arachnechthra flammaxillaris, GYLDENSTOLPE, Journ. Nat. Hist. Soc. Siam, 1915, p. 171 (listed).

Cyrtostomus flammaxillaris, GYLDENSTOLPE, Kungl. Svenska Vet.-Akad. Handl., 1916, p. 33 (Khun Tan, Pang Hua Phong); Ibis, 1920, p. 463 ("Throughout Siam proper").

Chrysostomus jugularis flammaxillaris, DE SCHAUENSEE, Proc. Acad. Nat. Sci. Philadelphia, 1928, p. 561 (Chiang Mai).

Leptocoma jugularis flammaxillaris, DE SCHAUENSEE, Proc. Acad. Nat. Sci. Philadelphia, 1929, p. 564 (Chiang Mai, Doi Suthep); 1934, p. 242 (Chiang Mai, Doi Suthep, Chiang Saen).—DEIGNAN, Journ. Siam Soc. Nat. Hist. Suppl., 1936, p. 124 (Chiang Mai, Doi Suthep).

Leptocoma flammaxillaris flammaxillaris, DEIGNAN, Journ. Siam Soc. Nat. Hist. Suppl., 1931, p. 155 (Chiang Mai, Doi Suthep).

Cyrtostomus flammaxillaris flammaxillaris, RILEY, U. S. Nat. Mus. Bull. 172, 1938, p. 502 (Ban Nam Khian, Phrae).

The present species is a very common permanent resident, recorded from all the northern provinces except Mae Hong Son. I have never noted it on the hills above 1,500 feet, but de Schauensee states (1934) that a single specimen was taken by him on Doi Suthep at 3,000 feet.

Like its congener, the purple-throated sunbird is an inhabitant of orchards and gardens, coconut plantations, and (less frequently) the *pa daeng*. In all these places it occurs in equal numbers with the nearly related species and the two may often be seen harmoniously feeding together in the same trees. The mutual tolerance shown by so evidently competitory forms can perhaps be explained by the abundance of nectariferous flowers available throughout the year in our inhabited districts.

As is the case with *Nectarinia a. intermedia*, the breeding season is of long duration: I have collected examples with the gonads slightly enlarged November 26, greatly enlarged February 25, and enlarged May 18 and 28.

A nest containing young was discovered in a Chiang Mai compound, January 28, 1929. It was a pensile, pyriform structure, attached by cobweb to a mango branch about 12 feet above ground, and composed of fine grass and vegetable fiber; a side entrance disclosed an inner lining of feathers. The whole was loosely overlaid with strands of cobweb which hung down as much as three inches below the chamber to form a "tail" and were everywhere adorned with bits of dry leaves, thin pieces of bark, and (especially on the "tail") with the woody frass of cossid larvae.

My daily observation of this species over a period of years showed no evident falling-off in numbers of full-plumaged males at any season, and I am convinced that an eclipse dress is assumed only very exceptionally or not at all in our area; birds similar to eclipsed adult males of *N. a. intermedia* are probably nothing but ordinary juveniles of *flammaxillaris*. If this surmise be correct, postjuvenal molt is just beginning in a male of July 6 and near completion in others of July 5 and 25. Postnuptial molt is shown by two females of May 6 and 24 and a male of August 13, prenuptial molt by a male of November 26.

My specimens had the irides dark brown; the bill black; the rictus and interior of the mouth deep yellow; the feet, toes, and claws black.

The nuptial male has the entire upperparts olive-green, rather brighter on the upper tail coverts; the remiges blackish brown, outwardly edged with olive-green; the rectrices black, slightly glossed with deep blue, and beneath with outwardly increasingly broad white tips; the throat and upper half of the breast metallic blue (the chin and center of the throat metallic purple); the lower half of the breast completely covered by two bands, the first orange-chestnut, the second black or dusky; the remaining underparts bright yellow; at either side of the lower breast a tuft of elongated feathers, golden-orange with bright yellow bases (usually concealed beneath the wing). The female and the juvenile male are separable from those of the purple sunbird only by having the rectrices broadly tipped beneath with white, not narrowly tipped with ashy.

ANTHREPTES HYPOGRAMMICUS LISETTAE Delacour

INDO-CHINESE PURPLE-NAPED SUNBIRD

Anthreptes hypogrammica lisettae DELACOUR, Bull. Brit. Orn. Club, vol. 47, 1926, p. 22 (Col des Nuages, Annam).

Anthreptes macularia macularia, DE SCHAUENSEE, Proc. Acad. Nat. Sci. Philadelphia, 1929, p. 564 (Chiang Saen).

This apparently rare form is known from Thailand by only five specimens, four of which are in my collection: a female from Chiang Saen, January 12, 1929 (de Schauensee); a male from Doi Mae Kong Ka, October 20, 1936; a male from Doi Chiang Dao, December 2, 1936; two females from Ban Huai Som and Ban Huai Ki, March 28, 1937. I have, in addition, taken a male at Ban Nam Puat, in Laos, just north of the province of Nan.

The purple-naped sunbird is a species of the lowland evergreen, ascending the mountains for a short distance only where their bases are clothed with that type of vegetation. It seems to have an especial liking for wet ravines in which grow profuse stands of palms and wild bananas.

The two examples of March 28 had the gonads greatly enlarged. The bird of October 20 is in postnuptial molt.

De Schauensee notes (1929) that his specimen had the irides dark brown; the bill black; the feet and toes olive-brown.

The male has the front and crown grayish olive-green; a narrow nuchal band and the rump and upper tail coverts metallic purple; the remaining upperparts, including the exposed portions of the wings and tail, golden olive-green (a patch of feathers at either side of the lower back with concealed white bases); the underparts creamy white, gradually deepening posteriorly to become bright yellow on the under tail coverts, the feathers of the chin, throat, breast, belly, and flanks with broad dark olive-green central streaks; all but the central pair of rectrices narrowly tipped beneath with creamy white. The female differs in having the nape, rump, and upper tail coverts golden olive-green like the mantle and in lacking the concealed patches of white at the sides of the lower back.

ARACHNOTHERA LONGIROSTRA LONGIROSTRA (Latham)

ASSAMESE WHITE-THROATED SPIDER-HUNTER

[*Certhia*] *longirostra* LATHAM, Index ornithologicus, vol. 1, 1790, pp. 299–300 ("Bengala"; type locality restricted to Sylhet, Assam, by Stuart Baker, Journ. Bombay Nat. Hist. Soc., vol. 28, 1921, p. 90).

Arachnothera longirostris, GYLDENSTOLPE, Kungl. Svenska Vet.-Akad. Handl., 1913, p. 45 (Ban Huai Hom); Journ. Nat. Hist. Soc. Siam, 1915, p. 171 (listed).

Arachnothera longirostris longirostris, GYLDENSTOLPE, Ibis, 1920, p. 464 ("Northern Siam").—GREENWAY, Bull. Mus. Comp. Zool., 1940, p. 191 (Doi Ang Ka, Doi Nang Kaeo).

Aracnothera longirostra longirostra, DE SCHAUENSEE, Proc. Acad. Nat. Sci. Philadelphia, 1929, p. 564 (Chiang Saen, Chiang Rai).

Arachnothera longirostra longirostra, DEIGNAN, Journ. Siam. Soc. Nat. Hist. Suppl., 1931, p. 155 (Chiang Mai); 1936, p. 125 (Chiang Mai).

The white-throated spider-hunter is generally distributed in the lowlands of the Mae Khong drainage basin but occurs only locally in other parts of our area: thus, while it is rather common on Doi Ang Ka at 4,400 feet, it is quite unknown from precisely similar territory on Doi Suthep and has been found at Chiang Mai only once as a straggler (July 10, 1930). It has not yet been reported at all from the provinces of Mae Hong Son and Lampang.

This bird is primarily a species of the evergreen and, like *Anthreptes h. lisettae*, has a strong predilection for the dense groves of palms and wild bananas that often occupy the ravines. In Chiang Rai Province, however, perhaps as a result of its greater numbers, it is seen, not infrequently, in the coconut plantations of towns and villages.

The breeding season must begin very early in the year, for a male from Ban Ton Phung, December 22, had the gonads already greatly enlarged and an adult observed at Muang Phan, April 7, was accompanied by a well-grown juvenile. An example of June 4 is in postnuptial molt.

Adults have the irides dark brown; the maxilla blackish slate; the mandible slaty, paling to plumbeous toward the base; the feet and toes dark plumbeous; the claws horny brown. The juvenile at Muang Phan was not collected but seemed to have the bill fleshy pink.

The adult of either sex has the upperparts olive-green, more grayish on the crown (where the feathers have blackish centers) and strongly suffused with golden on the mantle; the remiges blackish, outwardly edged with golden olive-green; the rectrices blackish, tipped beneath with ashy white; the ear coverts and sides of the head ashy; the lores ashy white, edged below by a narrow slaty streak from the rictus; the chin and throat ashy white, this color gradually changing to bright yellow on the remaining underparts; the pectoral tufts mixed bright yellow and golden-orange.

ARACHNOTHERA MAGNA MAGNA (Hodgson)

HIMALAYAN STREAKED SPIDER-HUNTER

[*Cinnyris*] *Magna* HODGSON, India Rev., vol. 1, 1836, p. 272 (Nepal).

Arachnothera magna, GYLDENSTOLPE, Kungl. Svenska Vet.-Akad. Handl., 1913, p. 44 (Ban Huai Hom); 1916, p. 34 (Chiang Rai).

Arachnothera magna aurata, GYLDENSTOLPE, Kungl. Svenska Vet.-Akad. Handl., 1916, p. 34 (Khun Tan, Doi Pha Sakaeng); Ibis, 1920, p. 464 ("Northern Siam").—DEIGNAN, Journ. Siam Soc. Nat. Hist. Suppl., 1931, p. 155 (Doi Suthep); 1936, p. 125 (Doi Suthep).—DE SCHAUENSEE, Proc. Acad. Nat. Sci. Philadelphia, 1934, p. 242 (Doi Suthep, Doi Chiang Dao).

Arachnothera magna magna, GYLDENSTOLPE, Ibis, 1920 p. 464 (Chiang Rai).—RILEY, U. S. Nat. Mus. Bull. 172, 1938, p. 507 (Khun Tan, Doi Langka, Doi Hua Mot).

Aracnothera magna, DE SCHAUENSEE, Proc. Acad. Nat. Sci. Philadelphia, 1929, p. 564 (Doi Suthep).

This large spider-hunter is a very common or even abundant species of the northern mountains (including Phu Kha), haunting the heavy evergreen, at whatever elevation it be found, from the foothills to about 5,500 feet. It necessarily reaches its lower limit of range on Doi Suthep at 3,300 feet and on Doi Ang Ka at 4,400 feet.

The present form, like other sunbirds of the dense forest, is particularly fond of the wild banana but is by no means restricted to its neighborhood. It is an unmistakable bird by its long, robust, curved bill, its stout body, and its relatively short tail, whether seen flying overhead with strong but undulating flight and a characteristic trilling note or perched upon a bough craning its neck and twisting the head from side to side.

Unfortunately, despite the large number of specimens known from our area, in no case has the condition of the gonads been noted. I suspect that breeding takes place throughout both the hot weather and the rains for, while Gyldenstolpe (1916) captured two young from a nest at Khun Tan, September 11, 1914, I have myself collected a bird already in postjuvenal molt on Doi Ang Ka, September 6, 1935, and find postnuptial molt in an example obtained as early as May 4. Postnuptial molt appears in others of June 4 and 13, September 6, and November 20, but not in specimens of August 19 and 20, September 9, and October 4.

Adults have the irides brown; the bill black; the interior of the mouth and the concealed mandibular edges of the commissure yellow; the feet, toes, and claws orange-yellow.

The streaked spider-hunter has the entire upperparts bright golden olive-green, the feathers with black central spots which posteriorly change to streaks; the rectrices olive-green, each with a broad black subterminal band; the underparts creamy white, each feather with a black central streak; the under tail coverts dark olive-green, broadly tipped with pale yellow.

I formerly believed that *Arachnothera magna* could not be divided into subspecies. Specimens shown me by Ticehurst have convinced me that the population of a limited portion of eastern Burma may properly be separated as *aurata*, and a reexamination of Riley's *remota* (South Annam) indicates that it also is distinguishable, at least in series, from *magna*.

Family DICAEIDAE

DICAEUM CRUENTATUM SIAMENSE Boden Kloss

INDO-CHINESE SCARLET-BACKED FLOWERPECKER

Dicaeum cruentatum siamensis [*sic*] BODEN KLOSS, Ibis, 1918, pp. 216–217 (Lat Bua Khao, East Thailand).

Dicaeum cruentatum, GYLDENSTOLPE, Journ. Nat. Hist. Soc. Siam, 1915, p. 171 (listed).

Dicaeum cruentatum coccinea, GYLDENSTOLPE, Kungl. Svenska Vet.-Akad. Handl., 1916, p. 35 (Tha Chomphu).

Dicaeum cruentatum siamensis, GYLDENSTOLPE, Ibis, 1920, p. 465 ("Siam proper").—DE SCHAUENSEE, Proc. Acad. Nat. Sci. Philadelphia, 1934, p. 243 (Chiang Mai).

Dicaeum cruentatum ignitum, DE SCHAUENSEE, Proc. Acad. Nat. Sci. Philadelphia, 1929, p. 564 (Doi Suthep, Chiang Mai, Chiang Saen).—DEIGNAN, Journ. Siam Soc. Nat. Hist. Suppl., 1931, p. 155 (Chiang Mai).

Dicaeum cruentatum siamense, DEIGNAN, Journ. Siam. Soc. Nat. Hist. Suppl., 1936, p. 125 (Doi Suthep, Chiang Mai).

Dicaeum cruentatum ignitum [*partim*], RILEY, U. S. Nat. Mus. Bull. 172, 1938, p. 513 (Mae Hong Son, Ban Nam Khian).

The scarlet-backed flowerpecker is very common throughout the lowlands of all the northern provinces, occurring both in gardens and in the dry, deciduous forest; in the latter type of growth it ascends the hills to about 1,800 feet.

Sharing with the sunbirds the name *nok kin pli* ("bird that eats the banana flower"), this diminutive species of the treetops is well known to all residents of our area through its rapid flight, sharp notes, and striking color pattern. In the deciduous jungle it is seldom seen away from the clumps of mistletoe.

Specimens with the gonads active have been taken at Chiang Mai between December 27 and May 25, but January and February seem to be the principal breeding months there. Young birds still in post-natal molt but on the wing were collected March 30 and April 21, and others in full juvenal dress, May 24; postjuvenal molt directly into adult plumage appears in a series taken between May 20 and July 26. Postnuptial molt is shown by birds shot between May 25 and August 24. An adult male of April 22 is in body molt, but it cannot be decided whether this represents a prenuptial molt or an unusually early case of postnuptial molt.

An adult male in breeding condition had the irides dark brown; the bill black; the feet, toes, and claws black. An adult female differed in having the irides gray-brown and the basal half of the mandible plumbeous. Juveniles have the irides brown; the bill with the basal half or more bright orange and the rest horny brown; the rictus and interior of the mouth bright orange; the feet, toes, and claws brownish slate. The bill of young birds assumes the colors normal to adults during the postjuvenal molt.

The adult male has the forehead, crown, nape, back, rump, and upper tail coverts shining crimson-scarlet (with the black bases of the feathers showing through in places); the scapulars, upper wing coverts, remiges, and rectrices black, their exposed portions glossed with metallic blue; the lores, supercilium, and sides of the head, neck, and throat slaty black, paling to slate on the sides of the breast and to ashy on the flanks; the remaining underparts (including the under tail coverts) pale buff or buffy white; the under wing coverts and axillaries pure white. The adult female has the rump and upper tail coverts shining crimson-scarlet and the rectrices black, glossed with metallic blue, but the remaining upperparts dull brownish olive (more or less strongly suffused with rufescent), each feather of the forehead and crown with a minute blackish central spot; the sides of the head, neck, throat, and breast olivaceous-ashy; the remaining underparts pale buff or buffy white, suffused with olivaceous along the flanks; the under wing coverts and auxilliaries pure white. The juvenile resembles the adult female but has the rump concolorous with the mantle and the upper tail coverts dull dark orange.

D. c. siamense differs from *erythronotum* (China) by its shorter wing length and (in the female) by having the upperparts less strongly tinged with rufescent and the underparts buffy rather than olivaceous-cream. From *cruentatum* (Bengal) it differs by having the underparts in either sex less rich buff. I cannot distinguish it from *ignitum* (Malacca) by the characters relied upon by the describer but find that males of *siamense* are separable from those of *ignitum* in having the sides of the head and throat slaty black and the sides of the breast slate, instead of having these parts (as well as the upper flanks) uniformly deep black. Exceptional examples of *siamense* from the southern portions of its range are identical with *ignitum*, but such birds do not occur farther north and, in series, the two races have a quite different appearance.

DICAEUM CONCOLOR OLIVACEUM Walden

INDO-CHINESE PLAIN-COLORED FLOWERPECKER

Dicaeum olivaceum WALDEN, Ann. Mag. Nat. Hist., ser. 4, vol. 15, 1875, p. 401 (Toungoo and Karen Hills).

Dicaeum olivaceum, GYLDENSTOLPE, Kungl. Svenska Vet.-Akad. Handl., 1913, p. 46 (Phrae).

Dicaeum minullum olivaceum, GYLDENSTOLPE, Kungl. Svenska Vet.-Akad. Handl., 1916, p. 36 (Khun Tan).—DE SCHAUENSEE, Proc. Acad. Nat. Sci. Philadelphia, 1929, p. 565 (Chiang Mai, Chiang Saen).

Dicaeum minullus olivaceum, GYLDENSTOLPE, Ibis, 1920, p. 466 ("Northern Siam").

Dicaeum minullus inornatum, DE SCHAUENSEE, Proc. Acad. Nat. Sci. Philadelphia, 1928, p. 561 (Doi Suthep).

Dicaeum concolor olivaceum, DEIGNAN, Journ. Siam Soc. Nat. Hist. Suppl., 1931, p. 156 (Chiang Mai, Doi Suthep); 1936, p. 126 (Chiang Mai, Doi Suthep).—DE SCHAUENSEE, Proc. Acad. Nat. Sci. Philadelphia, 1934, p. 244 (Chiang Mai, Khun Tan, Doi Chiang Dao).—RILEY, U. S. Nat. Mus. Bull. 172, 1938, p. 518 (Chiang Mai, Khun Tan, Lampang).

This flowerpecker is not yet recorded from Mae Hong Son but may confidently be expected to occur there, since it is a fairly common resident of all the other northern provinces. It is typically a bird of the plains and lower mountain slopes, but I have frequently seen it on Doi Suthep up to 3,500 feet, and de Schauensee has found it on Doi Chiang Dao as high as 5,500 feet.

The present form appears both in gardens and in the mixed-deciduous jungle of the hills, but its favorite habitat is the dry, deciduous forest, where it finds in abundance the hemiparasitic growths of the mistletoe (*Loranthus* spp.), of which it eats the berries and distributes the undigested seeds.

A specimen from Doi San Ho, June 2, is near completion of the postnatal molt and another from Chiang Mai, November 25, is in postnuptial molt.

An adult female had the irides dark brown; the bill plumbeous-blue, with the culmen blackish; the feet and toes dark plumbeous; the claws horny black.

The plain-colored flowerpecker has the entire upperparts dull olive-green, more yellowish on the rump and upper tail coverts, each feather of the forehead and crown with a minute blackish central spot; the remiges black, outwardly narrowly edged with yellowish olive-green; the rectrices black, very narrowly edged with olivaceous-ashy; the lores olivaceous-white or olivaceous-ashy; the entire underparts olivaceous-ashy, suffused (most strongly on the abdomen) with cream; the under wing coverts and axillaries pure white.

DICAEUM HIRUNDINACEUM IGNIPECTUS (Blyth)

HIMALAYAN FIRE-BREASTED FLOWERPECKER

M[yzanthe] ignipectus "Hodgson" BLYTH, Journ. Asiat. Soc. Bengal, vol. 12, 1843, pp. 983–984 (Nepal and Bhutan).

Dicaeum ignipectus, GYLDENSTOLPE, Kungl. Svenska Vet.-Akad. Handl., 1916, p. 36 (Khun Tan).

Dicaeum ignipectus [*partim*], GYLDENSTOLPE, Ibis, 1920, p. 466 (Khun Tan).

Dicaeum ignipectus ignipectus, DE SCHAUENSEE, Proc. Acad. Nat. Sci. Philadelphia, 1929, p. 565 (Doi Suthep).—DEIGNAN, Journ. Siam Soc. Nat. Hist. Suppl. 1931, p. 156 (Doi Suthep).

Dicaeum ignipectum ignipectum, DE SCHAUENSEE, Proc. Acad. Nat. Sci. Philadelphia, 1934, p. 243 (Doi Suthep).

Dicaeum sanguinolentum ignipectus, DEIGNAN, Journ. Siam Soc. Nat. Hist. Suppl., 1936, p. 125 (Doi Suthep).

Dicaeum ignipectum [*partim*], RILEY, U. S. Nat. Mus. Bull. 172, 1938, p. 514 (Khun Tan, Doi Hua Mot, Mae Hong Son).

The fire-breasted flowerpecker probably occurs on all the northern peaks which reach elevations in excess of 4,000 feet but, in addition to the localities listed above, it is recorded until now only from Phu Kha. On Doi Suthep, where it is a permanent resident, I found it very common from 4,600 to 5,500 feet, less common as low as 4,000 feet, and occasional in winter down to 3,200 feet. The unique female taken by Smith at Mae Hong Son (January 5, 1933) is correctly identified and, if actually from so low an altitude, must represent a wanderer from one of the neighboring hills.

This tiny bird, singly or in pairs, haunts chiefly the epiphyte-burdened and rather stunted trees growing along the higher ridges of the mountains but appears also in the pinelands and in the open hill-forest of chestnut and oak; in our provinces, it is apparently the sole member of its genus to dwell in such environments. It possesses the same swift, dashing flight and clicking notes as its lowland relatives.

Two specimens collected by Smith on Doi Hua Mot, August 21, are in postjuvenal molt.

The adult male has the entire upperparts metallic blue-green (rarely metallic blue); the sides of the head and throat, neck, and breast black; the underparts buff (washed with olive-green along the flanks), with a large and not clearly defined patch of scarlet on the breast and a narrow streak of black running mesially from the lower breast to the middle of the abdomen or beyond; the under wing coverts and axillaries pure white. The adult female has the upper parts dull olive-green, brightening to golden olive-green on the rump and upper tail coverts; the rectrices black, glossed with blue-green; the sides of the head and throat, neck, and breast olive-gray; the remaining underparts buff (washed with olive-green along the flanks); the under wing coverts and axillaries pure white.

While Chasen (Handlist of Malaysian birds, 1935, p. 269) makes *D. monticolum* a subspecies of *sanguinolentum*, Stresemann avers (Journ. für Orn., vol. 88, 1940, p. 51) that "*D. celebicum* gehört der schwer zu gliedernden australisch-papuanischen Gruppe *D. hirundinaceum* an, die nur mit einem einzigen Vertreter, *D. monticolum* Sharpe vom Kina Balu, die Wallace'sche Linie westwärts überschritten zu haben scheint." Outwardly, however, *D. monticolum* seems to be no less distinct from either *sanguinolentum* or *hirundinaceum* than these latter two are from each other.

It is my opinion that conflicting views may most easily be reconciled by the acceptance of a superspecies *D. hirundinaceum*, which will then embrace all the forms treated by Chasen and Stresemann, as well as certain forms of the Philippine Islands (one of which, *D. luzoniense*, might be considered an intermediate between *hirundinaceum* and *ignipectus*!).

DICAEUM CHRYSORRHEUM CHRYSOCHLORE Blyth

INDO-CHINESE YELLOW-VENTED FLOWERPECKER

Dicaeum chrysochlore BLYTH, Journ. Asiat. Soc. Bengal, vol. 12, 1843, p. 1009 (Arakan).

Dicaeum chrysorhoeum, GYLDENSTOLPE, Journ. Nat. Hist. Soc. Siam, 1915, p. 171 (listed).

Dicaeum chrysorrhaeum [*partim*], GYLDENSTOLPE, Ibis, 1920, p. 465 ("Throughout the whole country" [*partim*]).

Dicaeum chrysorrheum chrysochlore, DEIGNAN, Journ. Siam Soc. Nat. Hist. Suppl., 1931, p. 156 (Doi Suthep); 1936, p. 125 (Doi Suthep).

An unsexed and undated specimen from "Siam," sent by Eisenhofer to Hannover and listed by Gyldenstolpe (1915), probably came from Ban Huai Hom or its neighborhood. I collected this flowerpecker in Chiang Mai, Chiang Rai, and Nan Provinces, and only in the last did I consider it to be a fairly common species; my series of eight were taken at Ban Sop Mae Chaem, Muang Fang, Chiang Saen Kao, Ban Wang Mo, and Ban Hai Huai Som. I have, in addition, four sight records from Doi Suthep: One at 3,300 feet, July 20, 1929; one at 3,600 feet, July 12, 1930; two at 3,300 feet, July 4, 1931; two at 2,200 feet, October 31, 1931.

This seems to be properly a bird of the more open lowland evergreen, although, attracted by desirable flowers or fruits, it may enter villages when these are at no great distance from the forest. To Doi Suthep, where alone I have have found it at comparatively high elevations, it seems to come only as an irregular visitor and, of the July occurrences, two certainly (the third probably) were associated with the antheses of an unidentified orange-flowered vine at the hill-residence of H. M. the late Phraratchaya Chao Dara Ratsami na Chiang Mai. Its notes and habits are those of the genus.

A male from Ban Wang Mo, March 31, had the gonads enlarged. A specimen from Ban Hai Huai Som, June 20, has not quite finished the postnatal molt, while postnuptial molt is shown by a July example from Muang Fang.

An adult male had the irides orange; the maxilla black; the mandible plumbeous, tipped black; the feet and toes slaty; the claws horny brown.

Either sex has the entire upperparts olive-golden; the remiges black, the primaries very narrowly edged with whitish, the secondaries with inwardly increasingly broad margins of olive-golden; the rectrices black; the lores white above and slaty below; a long white mustachial streak, separated from the white chin and throat by a slaty-olive stripe; the remaining underparts creamy white, boldly streaked everywhere with olive-slate or slaty olive; the under tail coverts orange-golden or golden-yellow; the under wing coverts and axillaries white.

D. c. chrysorrheum is easily separable from *chrysochlore* by its more robust bill and by having the upperparts darker and duller, the streaking below darker and bolder.

PIPRISOMA AGILE PALLESCENS Riley

INDO-CHINESE STREAKED-BREASTED FLOWERPECKER

Piprisoma modesta [*sic*] *pallescens* RILEY, Proc. Biol. Soc. Washington, vol. 48, 1935, p. 148 (Pak Chong, East Thailand).

Piprisoma squalidum, GYLDENSTOLPE, Journ. Nat. Hist. Soc. Siam, 1915, p. 171 (listed).

Piprisoma modestum, GYLDENSTOLPE, Kungl. Svenska Vet.-Akad. Handl., 1916, p. 37 (Khun Tan).

Piprisoma modestum [*partim*], GYLDENSTOLPE, Ibis, 1920, p. 466 ("Throughout the whole country" [*partim*]).

The streaked-breasted flowerpecker is apparently restricted to the districts east of (and including) the Khun Tan chain and is comparatively common only in Nan Province, whence I have three specimens: A juvenile male from Doi San Ho, June 2, 1936, and two adult males from Ban San Tha, March 31, 1937. Gyldenstolpe's example was a male collected "among the Koon Tan Hills," May 17, 1914; the one taken by Eisenhofer and listed (1915) by Gyldenstolpe seems to be no longer extant.

This is a species of the foothills and uncultivated lowlands. At Ban San Tha it occurred in small numbers at a tree laden with ripe berries, in company with no less than three other kinds of flowerpeckers. In notes and habits it is quite like the species of *Dicaeum*.

The birds of March 31 had the gonads greatly enlarged. I have noted that their irides were brown-orange.

The adult of either sex has the entire upperparts dull olive-green, rather brighter and yellower on the rump and upper tail coverts, each feather of the front and crown with a minute blackish central spot; the remiges and rectrices black, narrowly edged with yellowish olive-green; a narrow and indistinct ashy-white mustachial streak separated from the chin and throat by an indistinct dull olive-green stripe; the remaining underparts ashy white, very faintly tinged with creamy on the breast, belly, and under tail coverts, washed with olivaceous-ashy along the posterior flanks, and broadly but indistinctly streaked with olivaceous-ashy on the breast, upper abdomen, and anterior flanks. In worn plumage the upperparts become darker and browner and the underparts lose the creamy wash.

I am not prepared to believe that more than one species of this genus inhabits the Asiatic mainland and accordingly place our birds under the name *agile*.

No topotypes of *Piprisoma a. modestum* have been available, but since Hume described his race from "S. Tenasserim," which, *fide* Davison *apud* Hume (Stray Feathers, vol. 6, 1878, p. 200), means "Mergui and to the south of that place," one may assume that specimens from Trang, Peninsular Thailand, represent *modestum*. Three examples from Trang agree perfectly with two from Gunong Tahan and one from Negri Sembilan (a paratype of Robinson and Boden Kloss's *remotum*, which was described after comparison with birds from Trang believed to be *modestum* and is now synonymized with *finschii* of Java!). If *modestum* does not inhabit the *whole* of the Malay Peninsula (and Java?), one must take the improbable view that the population of Trang are in fact *finschii* (or *remotum*) and not *modestum* at all.

If I be correct in calling Malayan birds *modestum*, then a series of eight from Assam must be separated as a new subspecies; they differ in their longer wing, lighter bill, brighter and greener upperparts, and creamier underparts.

P. a. pallescens (of which I have 13 specimens, including the type) inhabits eastern and southeastern Thailand and the southern half of Indochine. It has the underparts whiter, less creamy, than any other race seen and the color of the upperparts intermediate between the bright olive-green of Assamese birds and the dark brownish olive-green of Malayan, with an ashy cast over the head and mantle.

PACHYGLOSSA MELANOZANTHA Blyth

YELLOW-BELLIED FLOWERPECKER

P[achyglossa] melanozantha "Hodgson" BLYTH, Journ. Asiat. Soc. Bengal, vol. 12, 1843, p. 1010 (Nepal).

Pachyglossa melanoxantha, DE SCHAUENSEE, Proc. Acad. Nat. Sci. Philadelphia, 1934, pp. 4, 244 (Doi Chiang Dao).

A female and an unsexed specimen, collected by de Schauensee on Doi Chiang Dao, 4,500 and 5,000 feet, January 13 and 22, 1933, are the only examples of the yellow-bellied flowerpecker yet known from Thailand. It is probably only a winter visitor.

The male of this comparatively large species has the entire upperparts, the sides of the head, throat, and neck and the greater part of the breast deep slate; the remiges and rectrices blackish, the two outermost pairs of the latter with large, subterminal white patches on the inner web; the chin and center of the throat and breast white; the remaining underparts bright yellow; the under wing coverts and axillaries white. The female has the upperparts dark olivaceous-gray; the wings and tail as in the male; the sides of the head, throat, and neck and the greater part of the breast olivaceous-ashy; the chin and center of the throat and breast ashy white; the remaining underparts yellow, overlaid with olivaceous along the flanks and sides of the abdomen; the under wing coverts and axillaries white.

Family ZOSTEROPIDAE

ZOSTEROPS ERYTHROPLEURA Swinhoe

CHESTNUT-FLANKED WHITE-EYE

Z[osterops] erythropleurus SWINHOE [*nomen nudum*], Ibis, July 1863, p. 294 ("N. China").

Zosterops erythropleura SWINHOE, Proc. Zool. Soc. London, Aug. 1863, pp. 204, 298 (Shanghai, China).

Zosterops erythropleurus erythropleurus, DE SCHAUENSEE, Proc. Acad. Nat. Sci. Philadelphia, 1929, p. 562 (Doi Suthep).—DEIGNAN, Journ. Siam Soc. Nat. Hist. Suppl., 1931, p. 154 (Doi Suthep).

Zosterops erythropleura, DE SCHAUENSEE, Proc. Acad. Nat. Sci. Philadelphia, 1934, p. 240 (Doi Suthep, Doi Chiang Dao).—DEIGNAN, Journ. Siam Soc. Nat. Hist. Suppl., 1936, p. 126 (Doi Suthep).

The chestnut-flanked white-eye seems to be a very uncommon winter visitor to our provinces, where it has been recorded only from Doi Suthep, Doi Chiang Dao, and Phu Kha, at elevations between 4,500 and 5,500 feet; the extreme dates for its stay are November 7 (1936) on Doi Suthep and April 7 (1936) on Phu Kha.

The present species usually feeds at the very tops of tall trees and probably for this reason often escapes notice; I have, however, on occasion seen it in quite low bushes, together with *Z. p. mesoxantha.*

This form is evidently very closely related to *Z. j. simplex*, from which it differs chiefly by having a broad stripe of chestnut down along either flank (largely concealed by the closed wing) and by the absence of yellow suffusion from the front and the supraloral region.

ZOSTEROPS JAPONICA SIMPLEX Swinhoe

CHINESE DARK-GREEN WHITE-EYE

Z[osterops] sinensis SWINHOE [*nomen nudum*], Ibis, 1861, p. 331, line 29 (southern China).

Z[osterops] simplex SWINHOE [*nomen nudum*], Ibis, 1861, p. 331, line 29 (southern China).

Zosterops simplex SWINHOE, Ibis, July 1863, pp. 294–295 ("Southern China, from Canton to Foochow").

Zosterops simplex SWINHOE, Proc. Zool. Soc. London, Aug. 1863, pp. 203–204, 297–298 ("China from Canton to Foochow, and perhaps a little higher").

Zosterops simplex williamsoni, DE SCHAUENSEE, Proc. Acad. Nat. Sci. Philadelphia, 1929, p. 563 (Chiang Rai) ; 1934, p. 240 (Doi Chiang Dao, Chiang Saen, "Chiengmai" [= Doi Suthep]).—DEIGNAN, Journ. Siam Soc. Nat. Hist. Suppl., 1936, p. 126 (Chiang Mai, Doi Suthep).

"Unidentified White-eye," DEIGNAN, Journ. Siam Soc. Nat. Hist. Suppl., 1931, p. 154 (Chiang Mai).

Zosterops japonica sinensis, RILEY, U. S. Nat. Mus. Bull. 172, 1938, p. 524 (Chiang Mai, Lampang, Doi Langka).

The dark-green white-eye, known from the provinces of Chiang Mai, Lampang, and Chiang Rai, is an uncommon or locally common winter visitor, recorded between November 9 (1930) on Doi Langka and March 1 (1933) on Doi Suthep. It is chiefly a bird of the plains but has been taken on Doi Chiang Dao at 4,500 feet (2), on Doi Suthep at 5,500 feet (1), and on Doi Pha Hom Pok at 6,400 feet (1); owing to the difficulty of identifying the species in life, it cannot be decided whether these examples were with others of their own kind or were merely stragglers in company with montane forms.

At Chiang Mai I saw this white-eye only in town gardens, and there the small bands fed in such fructiferous trees as the longan and the guava; at Lampang, where Smith took four specimens, November 17,

1928, it was "common in coco palms." In notes and feeding habits it does not differ from its congeners.

An example of March 1 is beginning the prenuptial molt.

A female had the irides bright brown; the bill black, with the base of the mandible bluish plumbeous; the feet and toes dark plumbeous, the soles tinged yellowish; the claws dark plumbeous.

The present species has the upperparts olive-green, rather brighter on the crown and with a suggestion of ashy on the mantle, strongly suffused with yellow on the front and especially the supraloral region, less strongly with the same color on the rump; the remiges and rectrices dull black, edged with the same olive-green as the mantle; a very conspicuous eye ring of silky white feathers, narrowly interrupted at the anterior corner of the eye by a patch of black which covers the lores and the anterior infraocular region; the chin, throat, uppermost breast, and the under tail coverts bright greenish yellow; the remaining underparts ashy, albescent on the center of the abdomen and more or less strongly suffused with vinaceous.

ZOSTEROPS PALPEBROSA MESOXANTHA Salvadori

KAREN GOLDEN-GREEN WHITE-EYE

Zosterops mesoxantha SALVADORI, Ann. Mus. Civ. Stor. Nat. Genova, ser. 2, vol. 7, 1889, p. 396 (Taho, Karen-ni).

Zosterops palpebrosa vicina RILEY, Proc. Biol. Soc. Washington, vol. 42, 1929, p. 162 (Doi Suthep. North Thailand).

Zosterops palpebrosa vicina, DE SCHAUENSEE, Proc. Acad. Nat. Sci. Philadelphia, 1929, p. 562 (Doi Suthep).—DEIGNAN, Journ. Siam Soc. Nat. Hist. Suppl., 1931, p. 154 (Doi Suthep).

Zosterops palpebrosa palpebrosa, CHASEN and BODEN KLOSS, Journ. Siam Soc. Nat. Hist. Suppl., 1932, p. 248 (Doi Suthep).

Zosterops palpebrosa cacharensis [*partim*], DE SCHAUENSEE, Proc. Acad. Nat. Sci. Philadelphia, 1934, p. 239 (Doi Suthep, Doi Chiang Dao).

Zosterops palpebrosa cacharensis, DEIGNAN, Journ. Siam Soc. Nat. Hist. Suppl., 1936, p. 126 (Doi Suthep).—RILEY, U. S. Nat. Mus. Bull. 172, 1938, p. 523 (Doi Suthep, Doi Hua Mot).

The present race of the golden-green white-eye is definitely known in our area only from those hills of the Thanon Thong Chai and Khun Tan chains (with the exception of Doi Nang Kaeo) which reach elevations in excess of 4,500 feet; on Doi Pha Hom Pok it ranges up to 6,000 feet and, on Doi Suthep, is sometimes seen (attracted by flowering trees) as low as 3,300 feet. Probably owing to the insufficient altitude, it has never been recorded from Doi Khun Tan by any one of the numerous collectors who have visited that mountain.

In large flocks, sometimes in winter accompanied by *Z. erythropleura* and perhaps also by *Z. j. simplex*, the common white-eye sweeps through bushes and trees, both high and low, at the forest's edge, busily investigating cracks in the bark and the underside of the leaves like a titmouse and constantly uttering a characteristic mewing note.

The male of a mated pair, with the gonads greatly enlarged, was taken on Doi Ang Ka at 4,500 feet, April 11. Postnuptial molt is shown by specimens collected between July 10 and September 1.

Adults had the irides gray-brown; the bill blackish, plumbeous at the base of the mandible; the feet horny gray, the toes somewhat darker; the claws horny.

This form has the upperparts golden olive-green, more strongly suffused with golden on the rump and upper tail coverts and sometimes also on the front and supraloral region; the remiges and rectrices dull black, edged with golden olive-green; a very conspicuous eye ring of silky white feathers, narrowly interrupted at the anterior corner of the eye by a patch of black which covers the lores and the anterior infraocular region and sometimes continues as a narrow line to the posterior corner of the eye; the chin, throat, uppermost breast, and the under tail coverts golden-yellow; the remaining underparts ashy, albescent toward the center of the abdomen, and always with a narrow and indistinct mesial streak of golden-yellow (or at least an indication of it on the center of the belly).

Our bird is neither *palpebrosa* (Bengal), which has the underparts vinaceous-ashy and the mesial streak of exceptional occurrence, nor *auriventer* (Tavoy), a coastal form that has the mesial streak broader and brighter and the rectrices almost without olive-green edging. The name *mesoxantha* is probably applicable to all Burmese examples called *palpebrosa* by recent authors.

ZOSTEROPS PALPEBROSA JOANNAE La Touche

Yunnanese Golden-green White-eye

Zosterops aureiventer joannae La Touche, Bull. Brit. Orn. Club, vol. 42, 1921, pp. 31–32 (Mengtz, southeastern Yunnan).

Zosterops palpebrosa joannae, Greenway, Bull. Mus. Comp. Zool., 1940, p. 190 (Doi Nang Kaeo).

I place under this name two females taken by me on Doi Chiang Dao at 6,200 feet, March 19, 1937; the two males and three females collected by the Asiatic Primate Expedition on Doi Nang Kaeo, 2,800 feet, between April 8 and 15, 1937 (examined); and, with reservations, a juvenile male from Phu Kha, 4,500 feet, April 16, 1936. On Phu Kha, at the borders of Laos, it may well be the breeding race; to Doi Chiang Dao, where *mesoxantha* also occurs, it is merely a rare winter visitor; its status on Doi Nang Kaeo is unknown but, if it occur only in winter, it is at least remarkable that not one of five specimens should belong to the resident form so common on neighboring hills.

My specimens from Doi Chiang Dao were shot from a small flock in the open forest of stunted oak, about 1,200 feet higher than the apparent upper limit of range of *mesoxantha* on that mountain.

Griswold has noted on his labels that the birds of Doi Nang Kaeo had the irides very light gray; the bill black; the feet and toes blue-gray.

As stated by Stresemann (*in epist.*), quoted by Greenway (*loc. cit.*): "*Palpebrosa* from Mengtz, called *joannae* by La Touche, is very near to *mesoxantha* Salvadori, but has the flanks a slightly darker grey and the upperside more greenish, less yellowish. The name *joannae* may stand, therefore, but the racial characters are very feebly pronounced."

A white-eye, which may be *joannae*, occurs at all seasons in the lowland evergreen of Chiang Rai Province. My memory of certain specimens from Chiang Rai Town, in Sir Walter Williamson's collection, is that they agreed perfectly with my examples of *joannae* from the heights of Chiang Dao, but his birds were perhaps merely winter visitors. Three males taken by me at and near Wiang Pa Pao, July 24 and 30, 1935, are more golden than any others seen and might be considered very worn *mesoxantha* but Salvadori's race is not otherwise known in our area from so low an elevation and there is a strong possibility that *joannae* in the same state of wear would show an equally golden hue. Because of these doubtful points and the uncertain status of *joannae* on the nearby Doi Nang Kaeo, it seems best to leave the series from Wiang Pa Pao for the present without subspecific determination.

Family PLOCEIDAE

ESTRILDA AMANDAVA AMANDAVA (Linnaeus)

INDIAN RED AMADAVAT

[*Fringilla*] *Amandava* LINNAEUS, Systema naturae, ed. 10, vol. 1, 1758, p. 180 ("in India orientali"; type locality restricted to Calcutta, by Stuart Baker, Journ. Bombay Nat. Hist. Soc., vol. 27, 1921, p. 725).

Amandava amandava amandava, DEIGNAN, Journ. Siam Soc. Nat. Hist. Suppl., 1936, p. 127 (Chiang Mai).

The occurrence of the Indian race of the amadavat at Chiang Mai is inexplicable unless the unique example be considered a genuine straggler. It was brought me, June 1, 1935, by small boys who claimed to have killed (with a catapult) one of a pair at the edge of the city. The specimen had evidently been struck by a stone only a few minutes before it came to my hands (since the blood had not yet clotted) and thus must have been feral, if not actually wild. I have never seen the

583136—45——36

species captive in northern Thailand and feel that it must be accepted as a valid addition to our avifauna.

The bird is a male, acquiring the eclipse plumage, but retaining enough of the nuptial dress to place it unmistakably with the nominate form.

It had the irides red; the bill red; the feet, toes, and claws flesh.

The nuptial male has the feathers of the upperparts brown, broadly tipped with crimson (which disappears with wear), the upper tail coverts brighter, with concealed blackish bases and each feather with a tiny white spot at the tip; the wings dark brown, each feather (including the coverts) with a round white spot at the tip; the tail black, each feather with an outwardly increasingly conspicuous white tip; the underparts crimson, changing to black on the center of the abdomen, the lower flanks, thighs, and under tail coverts (each feather of the sides of the breast and abdomen with a small white spot at the tip). The female and the nonbreeding male differ in having the crimson of the upperparts restricted to the upper tail coverts and the underparts gray-brown, changing to buffy-cream on the center of the abdomen and to whitish on the under tail coverts. Juveniles are like the female but have the upper tail coverts concolorous with the remaining upperparts.

From *E. a. punicea*, which seems to be the resident race of Central Thailand, this specimen is separable by having the wing longer (46.5 mm.), the lores black instead of red, and the white dots everywhere larger. From *flavidiventris* of Burma and the Shan States it is immediately distinguishable by having the abdomen black instead of orange-yellow.

LONCHURA STRIATA ACUTICAUDA (Hodgson)

HIMALAYAN WHITE-RUMPED MUNIA

M[unia] Acuticauda HODGSON, Asiatic Researches, vol. 19, 1836, pp. 153–154 (Nepal).

Uroloncha acuticauda, GYLDENSTOLPE, Kungl. Svenska Vet.-Akad. Handl., 1913, p. 40 (Khao Phlung); Journ. Nat. Hist. Soc. Siam, 1915, p. 170 (listed).

Uroloncha acuticauda squamicollis, GYLDENSTOLPE, Kungl. Svenska Vet.-Akad. Handl., 1916, p. 28 (Khun Tan, Pang Hua Phong); Ibis, 1920, p. 457 (Khun Tan, Pang Hua Phong).

Uroloncha acuticauda acuticauda, GYLDENSTOLPE, Ibis, 1920, p. 457 ("Throughout the whole country").

Uroloncha striata acuticauda, DEIGNAN, Journ. Siam Soc. Nat. Hist. Suppl., 1931, p. 152 (Chiang Mai, Doi Suthep); 1936, p. 126 (Chiang Mai, Doi Suthep).—DE SCHAUENSEE, Proc. Acad. Nat. Sci. Philadelphia, 1934, p. 235 (Chiang Mai, Doi Suthep).

Munia striata acuticauda, RILEY, U. S. Nat. Mus. Bull. 172, 1938, p. 528 (Doi Hua Mot, Ban Nam Khian).

The white-rumped munia is very common throughout the northern provinces, occurring chiefly in the open country of the plains but appearing also in the *pa daeng* and at clearings in the evergreen as high as 3,800 feet on Doi Suthep and 4,400 feet on Doi Ang Ka.

Its habits and notes are quite like those of the scaly-breasted munia, and the two species may frequently be observed in the same ricefields although always in separate flocks.

Gyldenstolpe states (1913) that the present form breeds in colonies and that the pear-shaped nests are nearly always attached to the branches of bamboos; it seems certain, however, that he has misidentified the nests of *Ploceus p. burmanicus*. The white-rumped munia breeds in isolated pairs and constructs the same untidy and insecure nest as *Lonchura p. topela*. I have found a partially completed nest on Doi Ang Ka (4,400 feet) as early as mid-April, but the principal breeding season falls in the early part of the rains.

Northern specimens in postnuptial molt have been taken between July 31 and August 23.

A breeding male had the irides red-brown; the maxilla black; the mandible plumbeous; the feet and toes slate; the claws dark horny brown.

The adult has the forehead brownish black, this color gradually changing to the deep brown of the crown, nape, and mantle, each feather of these parts with the shaft buffy white; the rump white, sometimes more or less sullied with brown; the upper tail coverts rufescent-brown, with pale rufescent shafts; the pointed and strongly graduated remiges black; the wings brownish black, the upper coverts with buffy-white shafts; the sides of the head, the chin, and throat brownish black; the feathers of the breast and sides of the neck deep brown, each with a buffy-white shaft and a rufescent-brown or rufescent-whitish fringe to give a scaled appearance; the upper flanks and the belly buffy white, very faintly streaked with blackish; the lowermost flanks, the thighs, and the under tail coverts rufescent-brown, the feathers with buffy-white shafts; the under wing coverts and axillaries buff. The juvenile is brown but is easily separable from the young of *L. p. topela* by its deeper color and its black remiges and rectrices.

LONCHURA PUNCTULATA TOPELA (Swinhoe)

CHINESE SCALY-BREASTED MUNIA

Munia topela SWINHOE, Ibis, 1863, pp. 380–381 (Amoy, China).

Munia punctulata topela, GYLDENSTOLPE, Kungl. Svenska Vet.-Akad. Handl., 1916, p. 27 (Chiang Rai); Ibis, 1920, p. 457 (Chiang Rai).—RILEY, U. S. Nat. Mus. Bull. 172, 1938, p. 530 (Chiang Mai).

Munia punctulata subundulata, DE SCHAUENSEE, Proc. Acad. Nat. Sci. Philadelphia, 1928, p. 559 (Chiang Mai).

Uroloncha punctulata topela, DE SCHAUENSEE, Proc. Acad. Nat. Sci. Philadelphia, 1929, p. 559 (Chiang Mai, Chiang Saen).—DEIGNAN, Journ. Siam Soc. Nat. Hist. Suppl., 1931, p. 152 (Chiang Mai); 1936, p. 127 (Chiang Mai).

Uroloncha punctulata subundulata, DE SCHAUENSEE, Proc. Acad. Nat. Sci. Philadelphia, 1934, p. 235 (Chiang Mai, "Tung Sio").

The scaly-breasted munia is an abundant bird of open country throughout the northern lowlands.

Occurring in small parties on the lawns of parks and gardens and in close flocks of hundreds in the ripening grainfields, this little weaver is one of the most familiar of Thai species. When frightened, the band arises as one bird with unusually rapid wing beats and a musical *plink-plink, plink-plink* (like the sound of tiny bells) to perch at the top of some nearby clump of bushes until it is safe to resume their gleaning. All stomachs examined by me contained the seeds of rice and other grasses.

The earliest date at which I have found the gonads active was May 8 (Chiang Mai), but most individuals breed in July and August during the heavy rains. The nest is a large, globular structure of coarse grass and lanceolate leaves with an entrance at one side, poorly made and usually much fouled by its occupants, placed at heights between five and twenty feet from the ground in shrubs, vines, and trees and so insecurely attached that any good blow may bring it crashing down; many come to grief even before the eggs are hatched and then the birds immediately begin a new home as near as possible to the old location. On July 5, 1930, one in my compound that had been fastened between the trunk of a coconut and the base of a dead frond was carried away by the falling leaf; it contained five young, one of which died during the subsequent night, but the remaining four were seen next morning fluttering about on the ground and attended by *three* adults. When the nest outlasts the rainy season, it is regularly used as a sleeping place by the family or families that have been bred therein; one in a small guava tree outside my window was so employed by six individuals at least until mid-December, at which time I removed to another part of the city. In northern Thailand, the juvenal dress seems to be regularly held through the first winter and it is therefore interesting to note that the few birds of the year seen from Bangkok are already acquiring adult plumage early in their first autumn.

Adults have the irides brownish red; the maxilla slaty; the mandible plumbeous; the feet and toes plumbeous (the soles paler); the claws plumbeous-horn.

The adult of either sex has the feathers of the forehead, crown, nape, mantle, and wings brown (brighter along the outer edges of the primaries), with fine whitish shaft streaks; the feathers of the rump more or less ashy and usually barred with whitish; the upper tail coverts and exposed parts of the rectrices dull olivaceous-yellow; the chin and throat light or dark chocolate-brown (this color sometimes invading the cheeks and ear coverts); the remaining underparts buffy white, heavily squamated with chocolate-brown on the breast and with slaty brown or brownish slate on the upper abdomen and along the flanks; the under tail coverts buffy white, sometimes streaked or barred with slaty brown or brownish slate. The juvenile differs by having the entire upperparts plain brown and the underparts rich buff with no trace of squamation.

LONCHURA FERRUGINOSA ATRICAPILLA (Vieillot)

Indian Black-headed Munia

Loxia atricapilla Vieillot, Histoire naturelle des plus beaux oiseaux chanteurs de la zone torride, Paris, 1805 [=1807], p. 84, pl. 53 ("Les Grandes-Indes"; type locality restricted to Lower Bengal, by Robinson and Boden Kloss, Journ. Nat. Hist. Soc. Siam, vol. 5, No. 3, 1924, p. 362).

Munia atricapilla, Gyldenstolpe, Journ. Nat. Hist. Soc. Siam, 1915, p. 170 (listed).

Munia atricapilla rubronigra, Gyldenstolpe, Kungl. Svenska Vet.-Akad. Handl., 1916, p. 27 (Chiang Rai, Chiang Saen); Ibis, 1920, p. 456 (Chiang Rai, Chiang Saen).

Gyldenstolpe (1916) considered the black-headed munia to be rather rare on the grassy plains near Chiang Rai and Chiange Saen. On May 6 and 8, 1936, I found it not uncommon among the scattered bushes growing behind the sand bars of the Mae Kok just opposite the town of Chiang Rai. The sole record for any part of our area outside of Chiang Rai Province is based upon an unsexed example taken by Eisenhofer in 1914 at Khun Tan and now deposited at Stockholm.

The small bands of this species occurred at the same places but not mixed together with the flocks of the more numerous *Lonchura p. topela.* Six specimens (five males, one female) collected by me all had the gonads at least slightly enlarged.

Gyldenstolpe notes (1916) that a male had the irides brown; the bill gray; the feet and toes plumbeous.

The adult of either sex has the entire head, neck, and upper breast black; the mantle, back, and wings chestnut-brown; the rump and upper tail coverts shining chestnut-maroon (the latter occasionally suffused with golden at the tip); the rectrices brown, with the exposed portions shining chestnut (occasionally suffused with golden); the remaining underparts chestnut-brown, the center of the abdomen more or less strongly suffused with dusky or black to form a broad but indistinct mesial stripe; the thighs and under tail coverts dusky chestnut or blackish.

Eight examples of *L. f. atricapilla* are easily separable from ten of *sinensis* (Malay Peninsula) by their generally deeper color above and below (without ashy tinge on the mantle) and by the stronger blackish suffusion on their abdomen, thighs, and under tail coverts.

PASSER MONTANUS MALACCENSIS A. Dubois

MALAYSIAN TREE SPARROW

[*Passer montanus*] var. *Malaccensis* A. DUBOIS, Faune illustrée des vertébrés de la Belgique, sér. des oiseaux, vol. 1, 1887, pp. 572 [*nomen nudum*], 573–574 (Malacca).

Passer montanus malaccensis, GYLDENSTOLPE, Ibis, 1920, p. 458 ("Throughout the country").—DE SCHAUENSEE, Proc. Acad. Nat. Sci. Philadelphia, 1928, p. 559 (Chiang Mai); 1934, p. 236 (Chiang Mai).—DEIGNAN, Journ. Siam Soc. Nat. Hist. Suppl., 1931, p. 152 (Chiang Mai); 1936, p. 126 (Chiang Mai).

Although few specimens have ever been taken, the tree sparrow occurs throughout the long-inhabited lowland districts of all our provinces.

In Thailand, where no form of the house sparrow is resident, the tree sparrow abounds in cities and villages, visiting the open fields only in the immediate vicinity of human settlement; the larger the town, the more numerous is the bird sure to be. The notes and habits of the species are much like those of *Passer domesticus* and thus too well known to require further comment.

The *nok chok ban* nests about inhabited houses in any recess too small to accommodate the house myna; the month of June seems to be the height of the breeding season. A pair that bred under the eaves of my veranda (in a corner where the rafters made a covered cavity) had completely filled the available space with a rude structure of dried grass and bamboo leaves, rootlets, rags, paper, string, rope, and tow, lined with feathers of domestic fowls (*Gallus* and *Numida*). I removed the nest finally (June 12), frightening out three young, able to fly well, and finding several rather large white larvae living amidst the dung and other litter on the floor of the chamber. By June 17, the birds had filled the recess with a new nest and were again breeding. A specimen of September 19 has completed the postnuptial molt except that the outermost primary is still partly ensheathed.

A female of February 25 had the irides brown; the bill black; the feet and toes dusky flesh; the claws horny brown. Juveniles and nonbreeding adults have the bill horny brown, with the base yellowish.

Adults of either sex have the forehead, crown, and nape vinaceous-chestnut; the feathers of the back and scapulars ferruginous with broad black central streaks, the median and greater upper wing coverts similar but also with buffy-white tips to form two conspicuous wing bars; the remiges blackish, conspicuously edged along the outer web with ferruginous; the rump, upper tail coverts, and rectrices buffy brown; the sides of the throat, head, and neck white, except for the lores, a narrow line passing beneath the eye and above the ear coverts, and the lower half of the ear coverts, all of which are black; the chin and center of the throat black; the remaining underparts whitish, suffused with ashy on the breast and with buffy elsewhere (the flanks and under tail coverts pure buff). Juveniles differ only in lacking the black patch on the chin and throat.

PASSER FLAVEOLUS Blyth

OLIVE-CROWNED SPARROW

P[asser] flaveolus BLYTH, Journ. Asiat. Soc. Bengal, vol. 13, 1844, pp. 946–947 (Arakan).

Passer flaveolus, GYLDENSTOLPE, Kungl. Svenska Vet.-Akad. Handl., 1916, p. 29 (Khun Tan); Ibis, 1920, p. 458 ("Northern districts").—DE SCHAUENSEE, Proc. Acad. Nat. Sci. Philadelphia, 1928, p. 559 (Chiang Mai); 1929, p. 560 (Chiang Mai); 1934, p. 236 (Chiang Mai).—DEIGNAN, Journ. Siam Soc. Nat. Hist. Suppl. 1931, p. 152 (Chiang Mai); 1936, p. 126 (Chiang Mai).

This attractive bird has been collected only as Chiang Mai, Sala Mae Tha, Khun Tan, and Phu Chae; it is, however, probably locally common in the lowlands of all the northern provinces except Chiang Rai.

On the Chiang Mai plain, the pretty olive-crowned sparrow is a well-known resident of copses and the trees and bamboo that border the ricefields; only occasionally is it seen in towns and then just at their outskirts. After the breeding season it collects in bands of 100 or more individuals (both old and young birds), which feed together in the fields and on the roads and roost together at some favored grove of trees with other similar flocks. Its song seems to be no more than a *tch'-tch*, *tch'-tch*, *tch'-tch*, and the call note a *chip*, *chip*, *chip* (rather softer than the corresponding note of the tree sparrow); at the winter roosts, however, it is a very noisy species, chattering and churring quite like other members of the genus.

In our area, *Passer flaveolus* regularly breeds in trees, leaving the cavities about buildings to the competing *P. m. malaccensis*. The breeding season at Chiang Mai runs from early in May to mid-July, by which time flocks with many juveniles are frequent about the countryside. A pair observed on May 15 were putting the finishing touches on a huge, untidy, globular nest of coarse grass (with entrance at one side), fastened in a crotch of a *mai kwao* (*Butea frondosa*) about 40 feet above ground. A similar structure, evidently holding young birds, was found July 1 in a royal poinciana (*Delonix regia*) at an elevation of 11 or 12 feet; at a distance of only a few feet was a second nest, the significance of which is unknown, since no others of the species were noted in the tree.

Nuptial males have the irides brown; the bill black; the rictus yellow; the feet, toes, and claws dusky flesh; the soles yellowish. Nonbreeding males and all females differ in having the maxilla dusky flesh and the mandible fleshy, duskier toward the tip.

The male has the forehead, crown, nape, upper back, and sides of the lower neck grayish olive-green (yellower on the forehead); the lesser wing coverts, scapulars, and middle of the back chestnut-rufous; the rump and upper tail coverts grayish olive-green; the wings blackish, the median coverts broadly tipped with grayish cream to form a bar, the remaining feathers edged along the outer web with grayish yellow; the rectrices blackish, very narrowly edged along the outer web with grayish olive-green; the lores and ocular region black; a broad band behind the eye, covering the superior ear coverts and the anterior part of the sides of the neck, chestnut-rufous; the chin and center of the throat black; the remaining underparts grayish yellow, brighter and purer yellow on the sides of the throat and the center of the abdomen. The female has the upperparts dull light brown, slightly suffused with olive on the crown and rump; a broad supercilium creamy or buffy; the underparts dull grayish yellow, rather brighter on the throat and the center of the belly.

PLOCEUS PHILIPPINUS BURMANICUS Ticehurst

Indo-Chinese Baya

Ploceus infortunatus burmanicus Ticehurst, Bull. Brit. Orn. Club, vol. 52, 1932, pp. 104–105 (Akyab, Arakan, Burma).

Ploceus passerinus infortunatus, Gyldenstolpe, Kungl. Svenska Vet.-Akad. Handl., 1916, p. 28 (Chiang Rai).—de Schauensee, Proc. Acad. Nat. Sci. Philadelphia, 1928, p. 559 (Chiang Mai).

Ploceus passerinus infortunatus [*partim*], Gyldenstolpe, Ibis, 1920, p. 456 (Chiang Rai).

Ploceus atrigula infortunatus, Deignan, Journ. Siam Soc. Nat. Hist. Suppl., 1931, p. 152 (Chiang Mai).—de Schauensee, Proc. Acad. Nat. Sci. Philadelphia, 1934, p. 234 (Chiang Mai).

Ploceus philippinus infortunatus, Deignan, Journ. Siam Soc. Nat. Hist. Suppl., 1936, p. 126 (Chiang Mai).

Ploceus philippinus infortunatus [*partim*], Riley, U. S. Nat. Mus. Bull. 172, 1938, p. 524 (Phrae).

Throughout the northern provinces, the familiar *nok chok fa* ("sparrow of heaven") is a very common permanent resident of the lowlands, except in forested areas.

Like other weaverbirds, this species subsists chiefly on seeds; after the breeding season, it occurs in enormous flocks (often exceeding 1,000 individuals) on grass-grown marshes and in the ricefields.

The remarkable nesting colonies of the baya are familiar to everyone, especially since they are seen almost as often in compounds as in the open country, Anywhere from a dozen to more than 100 pairs may breed together in a grove of palms or a clump of bamboos and normally they select trees that overhang water, whether this be a river, pond, or ditch. The body of the nest, huge in relation to the size of the builder, is a pyriform structure of tightly woven vegetable fiber, from one side of which hangs down a hollow tube of the same material; access to the chamber can be effected only by flying up this tunnel, which varies in length from a few inches to several feet. In addition to the protection afforded eggs and young by water beneath, ingenious entrance, and the astonishing strength of the woven walls, a further defense against enemies is acquired, perhaps adventitiously, from the fact that, more often than not, the colony is located in a tree which is also the home of the vicious red tailor ant, *Oecophylla smaragdina* (whose domestic arrangements, incidentally, are quite as curious as those of the bird). The polygamous males are driven to construct nests throughout the season (which, with us, runs from the beginning of April to the end of August), and among the occupied retorts hang others in all stages of development. For a full account of the extraordinary breeding behavior of the related form, *Ploceus p. philippinus*, see Ali (Journ. Bombay Nat. Hist. Soc. vol. 34, 1931, pp. 947–964).

Early prenuptial molt appears in a specimen of March 30 and in two (out of six) collected April 11; a series of seven taken between July 6 and August 4 wear full nuptial dress. Examples from Chiang Mai, April 22 and 23, are in postnatal molt; the bird of later date is probably a week or more older than the other.

A breeding male had the irides dark brown; the bill black; the rictus yellow; the feet, toes, and claws dusky flesh. A female and a nonbreeding male differed in having the maxilla pinkish brown and the mandible brownish pink. The juvenile of April 22 (mentioned above) had the entire bill yellowish horn.

The nuptial male has the forehead, crown, and nape golden-yellow; the feathers of the mantle and the upper wing coverts blackish brown, edged with rufous-buff to give a strongly streaked appearance; the rump and upper tail coverts rufous-buff, the feathers with obsolescent darker centers; the remiges and rectrices blackish brown, narrowly edged with golden-olive; the lores, cheeks, and ear coverts blackish brown, this color invading and sometimes almost covering the chin and throat; the remaining underparts deep rufous-buff, albescent on the abdomen and under tail coverts (the sides of the breast sometimes sparingly streaked with blackish brown). The female at any season and the nonbreeding male have the forehead, crown, and nape streaked with blackish brown and rufous-buff like the mantle; an indistinct rufous-buff supercilium; the ear coverts buffy brown; the chin and throat like the breast but paler.

PLOCEUS MANYAR PEGUENSIS Stuart Baker

INDO-CHINESE STRIATED WEAVERBIRD

Ploceus manyar peguensis STUART BAKER, Bull. Brit. Orn. Club, vol. 45, 1924, p. 58 (Pegu).

Ploceus manyar flaviceps, GYLDENSTOLPE, Kungl. Svenska Vet.-Akad. Handl., 1916, p. 29 (Chiang Rai); Ibis, 1920, p. 455 (Chiang Rai).

The striated weaverbird is very common on the grassy plains of Chiang Rai Province but is known from no other part of our area.

At Ban Ton Yang, a village near Chiang Rai Town, May 5, 1936, I saw numerous bands of this bird feeding in the ricefields and resting in the bamboos nearby. The common baya occurred at the same place in even greater numbers and, at this season, the flocks of the two closely related species were not intermingled. I found *peguensis* very wild, and my sole specimen, a male in late prenuptial molt, had to be taken by a chance shot from a great distance.

The example of May 5 had the gonads enlarged. Gyldenstolpe (1916) tells of seeing numbers of nests under construction about Chiang Rai at the beginning of August 1914, placed in tall elephant grass and in low trees; up to August 18, when he finally departed from this locality, he had found no sign of eggs.

The nuptial male differs from that of *P. p. burmanicus* by having the streaked upperparts generally darker, owing to the broader and blacker central markings of the feathers; the rump and upper tail coverts like the mantle but with the central streaks less distinct and the rufous-buff edgings broader; the underparts, below the blackish-brown chin and throat, pale rufous-buff, the feathers of the upper breast with broad, lanceolate blackish-brown central streaks that become narrower on the lower breast and continue down the whole length of the flanks finally to become narrow shaft streaks. The female at any season and the nonbreeding male may be distinguished from those of the commoner species by their darker upperparts, paler underparts, and streaked breast and flanks.

Family FRINGILLIDAE

MYCEROBAS MELANOZANTHOS FRATRIS-REGIS Deignan

INDO-CHINESE SPOTTED-WINGED GROSBEAK

Mycerobas melanozanthos fratris-regis DEIGNAN, Auk, vol. 60, 1943, p. 608 (Doi Suthep, Chiang Mai Province, northwestern Thailand).

Mycerobas melanozanthus, DE SCHAUENSEE, Proc. Acad. Nat. Sci. Philadelphia, 1934, p. 4 (Doi Suthep).

Mycerobas melanozanthos, DE SCHAUENSEE, Proc. Acad. Nat. Sci. Philadelphia, 1934, p. 236 (Doi Suthep).—DEIGNAN, Journ. Siam Soc. Nat. Hist. Suppl., 1936, p. 127 (Doi Suthep).

Mycerobas melanoxanthus, RILEY, U. S. Nat. Mus. Bull. 172, 1938, p. 533 (Doi Hua Mot).

The grosbeak of Thailand has until now been found only on Doi Suthep and Doi Hua Mot; at the former locality it has been seen at 5,300 and 5,500 feet. It is a permanent resident and may be expected to occur also on other mountains of the northwestern provinces.

On Doi Suthep it was noted in small bands containing individuals of both sexes, both in the pines and in berry-bearing trees at the edge of adjacent evergreen. The song of the male, which I heard in May, was a soft, whistled *phew—phew-phew-phew* (*-phew*), with the first note stressed.

An almost adult male had the irides dark brown; the maxilla slaty; the mandible plumbeous; the feet and toes plumbeous; the claws dark brown.

The old male has the entire head and neck (to the upper breast) and all the remaining upperparts deep slaty; the inner primaries white at the base and outwardly very narrowly edged with white near the tip, the inner greater upper coverts and the inner secondaries with a large, apical yellowish-white spot on the outer web; the remaining underparts lemon-chrome; the feathers of the thighs mixed black and yellowish white. The adult female has the upperparts olivaceous-slaty, the feathers of the head, nape, and mantle with yellow or yellowish-white bases and edgings to give a strongly streaked appearance; the wings as in the male; a broad slaty streak from the base of the bill, through the eye, to the shoulder, edged above and below by yellow; the entire underparts yellow, almost every feather (except those of the throat and the under tail coverts) with a bold black guttate spot.

CARPODACUS ERYTHRINUS ROSEATUS (Blyth)

INDIAN COMMON ROSEFINCH

Pyrrhula roseata "Tickell" BLYTH, Journ. Asiat. Soc. Bengal, vol. 11, 1842, p. 461 (Calcutta, Bengal).

Carpodacus erythrinus, GYLDENSTOLPE, Journ. Nat. Hist. Soc. Siam, 1915, p. 170 (listed).

Carpodacus erythrinus roseatus, GYLDENSTOLPE, Ibis, 1920, p. 457 (Khun Tan).—DE SCHAUENSEE, Proc. Acad. Nat. Sci. Philadelphia, 1929, p. 560 (Chiang Saen); 1934, p. 236 (Doi Chiang Dao).

Carpodacus murati, RILEY, U. S. Nat. Mus. Bull. 172, 1938, p. 534 (Doi Ang Ka).

The rosefinch, recorded from Doi Ang Ka, Doi Chiang Dao, Khun Tan, Doi Langka, Doi Nang Kaeo, Ban Pang An, Pang Makham Phong, Ban Muang Sum, Chiang Saen, and Phu Kha, seems to be merely a winter visitor to our provinces; the extreme dates shown by the series before me are December 3 (1928) on Doi Ang Ka and

April 9 (1936) on Phu Kha. I have found it both in semicultivated lowland districts and on the hills to 5,000 feet (Phu Kha and Doi Chiang Dao).

This species avoids the centers of population but profits by a small degree of cultivation and especially by the conditions which follow its abandonment. On Phu Kha and on Doi Chiang Dao, I found it numerous at illicit gardens of the opium poppy (*Papaver somniferum*), keeping to the ground beneath the plants, where it fed on seeds dropping from the dehiscing capsules; at these places it was accompanied by *Emberiza pusilla*. Near the primitive settlement of Ban Muang Sum, where, late in December 1936, a locally abundant species of bamboo had burst into spectacular bloom, it occurred in extraordinary numbers along with *Emberiza rutila* and *E. a. ornata*. I suspect that the flocks wander widely in search of such bounty and that they may accordingly appear wherever, in sufficiently wild country, the suitable conditions temporarily prevail. The usual notes in winter are a conversational twittering but, during the first two weeks of April, on Phu Kha, the males were already rendering a soft, sweet, whistled song from low trees at the edge of the plantations.

No sign of molt is shown by my specimens, and Smith's bird from Doi Ang Ka, if correctly sexed, is the only male wearing a dress like that of the female.

De Schauensee has noted (1934) that his examples had the irides dark brown; the bill horny gray or plumbeous-horn; the feet, toes, and claws brown.

The old male, in winter plumage, is somewhat variable but ordinarily has the forehead, crown, nape, rump, and upper tail coverts carmine-rose; the feathers of the mantle maroon, inconspicuously edged with olivaceous-brown; the feathers of the wings and tail deep brown, their exposed parts very narrowly edged with a brownish pink, the upper wing coverts also broadly tipped with the same color to form two inconspicuous wing bars; the underparts rose (often somewhat mottled with carmine on the chin, throat, and upper breast), this color paling posteriorly to become almost white or pale buff in the region of the vent and on the under tail coverts. The adult female has the entire upperparts brown, more or less strongly suffused with olivaceous-buff, each feather of the crown and mantle with an ill-defined blackish center to give a broadly streaked appearance; the feathers of the wings and tail deep brown, their exposed parts very narrowly edged with olivaceous-buff, the upper wing coverts also broadly tipped with buff or buffy white to form two bars; the underparts brownish buff, albescent on the center of the throat and lower abdomen and on the under tail coverts, the feathers of the chin, throat, breast, and upper abdomen with broad but indistinct dark brown central streaks.

CARPODACUS ERYTHRINUS ERYTHRINUS (Pallas)

West Siberian Common Rosefinch

Loxia erythrina Pallas, Novi commentarii Academiae scientiarum imperialis Petropolitanae, vol. 14, pt. 1, 1770, pp. 587–588, pl. 23, fig. 1 ("ad Volgam et Samaram"; type locality restricted to "Wolga, als erstgenannter Fundort," by Hartert, Vögel der paläarktischen Fauna, vol. 1, 1910, p. 106; here further restricted to Kuibishev [Samara], at the junction of the Volga and Samara Rivers).

An adult male rosefinch, taken by my collectors on Doi Langka, March 4, 1937, is indistinguishable from specimens of *C. e. erythrinus;* unless this example be an aberrant individual of *roseatus*, we must assume that the highly migratory Siberian race at least occasionally reaches northern Thailand. It is interesting, in this connection, to note that Ticehurst states (Ibis, 1938, p. 615): "More than one form, I think, occurs in Burma, one of which is, no doubt, *roseatus*, but one obtained by Mr. Stanford I cannot separate from *erythrinus*."

It is probable that my bird was in company with a flock of *roseatus*, of which a specimen was collected at the same locality just one day earlier.

From the old male of *roseatus*, that of *erythrinus* (at least in winter) differs in having the carmine-rose of the plumage everywhere paler (more rose, less carmine) and in having the roseate hue beneath scarcely extending beyond the upper abdomen. Females of the two forms are apparently identical.

EMBERIZA FUCATA FUCATA Pallas

Siberian Gray-hooded Bunting

Emberiza fucata Pallas, Reise durch verschiedene Provinzen des russischen Reichs, vol. 3, 1776, pp. 237, 698 (at the Onon and Ingoda rivers, southeastern Siberia).

Emberiza fucata fucata, Deignan, Journ. Siam Soc. Nat. Hist. Suppl., 1936, p. 170 (Ban Bu, Ban Tong Yang).

I have collected one female at Ban Bu (Nan Province) and another at Ban Tong Yang (Chiang Rai Province), April 21 and May 4, 1936; these are still the only examples known from our area but specimens were also taken, April 25 and 29, 1936, at Ban Din Tok and Ban Na Ban, localities in French Laos only a few miles from the borders of Thailand.

I found this shy species in small numbers, feeding among the stubbles of fallow ricefields in company with the commoner *Emberiza a. ornata*.

The male late in spring has the forehead, crown, nape, and sides of the neck ashy gray, each feather with a black central streak (the streaks less distinct on the nape and obsolescent on the sides of the neck); the mantle dull chestnut-rufous, the feathers with broad black central streaks; the rump chestnut-rufous; the upper tail coverts dull grayish rufous, with deep brown central streaks; the lesser wing coverts chestnut-rufous to form a shoulder patch, the remaining feathers of the wing deep brown or black, edged along the outer web with dull grayish rufous (the median and greater coverts narrowly tipped paler to form two indistinct bands); the central pair of rectrices dull grayish rufous with blackish along the shaft, the remaining pairs blackish (the outermost largely white, the penultimate pair merely tipped with the same color); the ear coverts chestnut, bordered below by a white mustachial line; the chin, throat, and breast white, with a necklace of black streaks across the upper breast and continued along the sides of the throat to the base of the bill; a broad and indistinct band of chestnut between the breast and abdomen (often broken in the middle); the remaining underparts pale rufous (albescent on the center of the abdomen), the feathers of the lower flanks with blackish central streaks. The female is similar but rather paler and duller and has the chestnut breast band merely indicated. In autumn the ashy gray of the hood is concealed by dull chestnut-rufous tips to the feathers; these tips are gradually lost by abrasion.

EMBERIZA AUREOLA ORNATA Shulpin

Ussuri White-shouldered Bunting

Emberiza aureola ornata Shulpin, Ann. Mus. Zool. Acad. Sci. URSS, vol. 28, 1927 [= 1928], p. 401 (mouth of the Suifun, environs of the village of Tavritchanka, South Ussuri-land).

Emberiza aureola, Gyldenstolpe, Journ. Nat. Hist. Soc. Siam, 1915, p. 171 (listed); Kungl. Svenska Vet.-Akad. Handl., 1916, p. 30 (Tha Chomphu); Ibis, 1920, p. 458 ("Different parts of the country").—Deignan, Journ. Siam Soc. Nat. Hist. Suppl., 1936, p. 127 (Chiang Mai).—Riley, U. S. Nat. Mus. Bull. 172, 1938, p. 536 (Phrae).

The elegant white-shouldered bunting is a rather common winter visitor to the lowlands of every one of the northern provinces; it has been found from October 13 (1936) at Thattafang to May 8 (1936) at Chiang Rai.

This species appears in October in flocks composed of hundreds of individuals and, at first, keeps almost entirely to the flooded marshes and the adjacent stands of grain but later, in smaller bands, spreads across the ripening fields or gleans among the stubbles. At Chiang Mai I have never noted it after mid-December, but, in moister districts, it is numerous all through the cold weather and often accompanied by the other lowland buntings. Stomachs examined by me contained only rice.

An adult male had the irides brown; the maxilla dark horny brown; the mandible horny brown, fleshy beneath; the feet, toes, and claws fleshy brown.

Spring males have the front and forecrown, lores, ocular region, ear coverts, chin, and upper throat black; the remaining upperparts chestnut, most of the feathers fringed with ashy buff (some on the mantle with black central streaks); the median upper wing coverts white to form a conspicuous shoulder patch, the greater coverts chestnut, broadly tipped with white to form a bar; the remiges blackish brown, the primaries narrowly edged with ashy buff, the secondaries broadly edged and tipped with chestnut or chestnut-rufous; the rectrices blackish brown, the central pair edged with chestnut, the remaining pairs with ashy buff, the outermost pair largely white (the penultimate pair with a narrow white streak on the inner web); a narrow chestnut gorget separating the throat from the breast (the feathers fringed with ashy buff); the remaining underparts yellow, albescent in the region of the vent and on the under tail coverts, boldly streaked with deep chestnut or black along the flanks. The adult female in winter has a broad black stripe at either side of the crown; the center of the crown and the remaining upperparts ashy brown, the feathers of the mantle with black central streaks, those of the rump often partly chestnut; the median upper wing coverts tipped with buffy white, the greater coverts with ashy buff, to form two inconspicuous wing bars; the feathers of the wings and tail otherwise like those of the male but the chestnut replaced by pale rufous; a buff supercilium; the ear coverts brownish buff, edged all around by a narrow black line; the entire underparts yellow (becoming buffy cream on the under tail coverts), washed with vinaceous-buff on the breast and upper flanks, streaked with black along the flanks. First-winter males at first resemble the female, and in any flock will be seen many intermediate stages of plumage.

EMBERIZA RUTILA Pallas

CHESTNUT BUNTING

Emberiza rutila PALLAS, Reise durch verschiedene Provinzen des russischen Reichs, vol. 3, 1776, pp. 210, 698 (at the Onon River and toward the frontiers of Mongolia).

Emberiza rutila, GYLDENSTOLPE, Kungl. Svenska Vet.-Akad. Handl., 1913, p. 41 ("Between Denchai and Pak Pan"); Ibis, 1920, p. 458 (Den Chai).—CHASEN and BODEN KLOSS, Journ. Siam Soc. Nat. Hist. Suppl., 1932, p. 248 (Doi Suthep).—DEIGNAN, Journ. Siam Soc. Nat. Hist. Suppl., 1936, p. 127 (Doi Suthep).—DE SCHAUENSEE, Proc. Acad. Nat. Sci. Philadelphia, 1934, p. 236 (Doi Suthep).

The chestnut bunting, while nowhere really common, is found in all our provinces in winter; occurring chiefly on the mountains (3,300 to 5,500 feet), it is seen also in uncultivated districts at the level of the plains. It has been noted in our area from November 23 (1936) on Doi Chiang Dao to April 5 (1929) near Wiang Pa Pao.

The species is not recorded from the Chiang Mai plain, but, on Doi Suthep, small parties appear sporadically in the more extensive forest clearings and the lalang stands and then vanish again; all such observations have been made between February 13 (1932) and March 12 (1932). The irregularity of its occurrences here and elsewhere leads me to believe that like some others of the family the bird wanders widely over the country in search of food and that an unusually large gathering may represent the total population of an extensive territory. Unlike the white-shouldered bunting, it avoids the cultivated lands, preferring the lalang, bamboo, and other weedy growth that follows the abandonment of agriculture at whatever elevation.

Fine-feathered spring males have the whole head and neck (including the upper breast) and the entire upperparts (including the wing coverts) rich chestnut-rufous; the remiges and rectrices blackish, narrowly edged with yellowish ashy, except for the inner secondaries, which are largely chestnut-rufous; the remaining underparts creamy yellow, broadly streaked along the flanks with olive-slate (and sometimes with chestnut-rufous as well). Earlier in the season, each feather of the chestnut-rufous areas is more or less broadly fringed with ashy. First-winter males resemble older males but have the feathers of the crown and mantle with broad olivaceous-brown tips and black central streaks (very conspicuous on the latter part). The only female I have examined (a worn specimen) differs from the old male in having the center of the crown and nape ashy brown, the feathers with narrow black central streaks; the mantle ashy brown, each feather with a rufous-edged black central streak; an indistinct ashy-buff supercilium; the sides of the head ashy brown; the chin and throat creamy buff; the remaining underparts cream, broadly streaked along the flanks with olive-slate.

EMBERIZA PUSILLA Pallas

LITTLE BUNTING

Emberiza pusilla PALLAS, Reise durch verschiedene Provinzen des russischen Reichs, vol. 3, 1776, pp. 697–698 (Davurian Alps, southeastern Siberia).

Emberiza pusilla, DE SCHAUENSEE, Proc. Acad. Nat. Sci. Philadelphia, 1934, pp. 4, 236 (Doi Chiang Dao, Doi Suthep).—DEIGNAN, Journ. Siam Soc. Nat. Hist. Suppl., 1935, p. 66 (Doi Ang Ka); 1936, p. 127 (Doi Suthep).

The little bunting is a decidedly uncommon winter visitor, recorded in our provinces only from certain high peaks of the Thanon Thong

Chai range and from Phu Kha, at elevations between 3,000 feet (Doi Suthep) and 6,000 feet (Doi Ang Ka). The extreme dates for its stay with us are unknown; my own observations of it run from January 9 (1937) on Suthep to April 9 (1936) on Phu Kha.

I found this species solitary or in pairs, feeding on the ground beneath the bracken or along the trails through the lalang on Doi Suthep, with rosefinches gleaning the poppy seeds on Phu Kha. It is shy and, when flushed, seeks refuge at once in some high tree. The only note I have heard is a soft *chip*.

The adult male, as seen in Thailand, has the crown and nape black (the feathers fringed with rufous), with a broad rufous mesial stripe (the feathers fringed with ferruginous); the remaining upperparts ferruginous, the feathers with rufous-margined black centers (most conspicuous on the dorsum) to give a boldy streaked appearance; the wing feathers dark brown, outwardly margined (more broadly on the secondaries) with rufous, the coverts also narrowly tipped with pale rufous or rufous-white to form two bars; the rectrices dark brown, the outermost pair largely white; the lores, anterior half of the supercilium, ocular region, and ear coverts ferruginous, the last outlined above, behind, and below by a narrow black line; the posterior half of the supercilium ferruginous-white, connected with a whitish band that runs down the side of the neck behind the ear coverts and then forward beneath them to the base of the bill; the entire underparts white (usually more or less sullied), boldly but narrowly streaked with black at the sides of the throat, across the breast, and down along the flanks. The female is similar but has the markings about the head rather paler and thus less conspicuous. The feathers of the crown gradually lose their pale fringes by abrasion, with the result that the head stripes become much more obvious toward the end of the winter.

MELOPHUS LATHAMI LATHAMI (Gray)

CHINESE CRESTED BUNTING

Emberiza Lathami GRAY, Zoological Miscellany, No. 1, 1831, p. 2 ("China and India"; type specimen from Canton, *fide* Ticehurst, Bull. Brit. Orn. Club, vol. 53, 1932, p. 16).

Melophus melanicterus, DE SCHAUENSEE, Proc. Acad. Nat. Sci. Philadelphia, 1929, p. 560 (Chiang Rai, Chiang Saen).

Melophus malanicterus, DEIGNAN, Journ. Siam Soc. Nat. Hist. Suppl., 1931, p. 153 (Doi Suthep).

Melophus lathami, DE SCHAUENSEE, Proc. Acad. Nat. Sci. Philadelphia, 1934, p. 237 (Doi Suthep).—DEIGNAN, Journ. Siam Soc. Nat. Hist. Suppl., 1936, p. 127 (Doi Suthep).—RILEY, U. S. Nat. Mus. Bull. 172, 1938, p. 535 (Doi Ang Ka).

The crested bunting is a winter visitor to northern Thailand, where it has been recorded only from the provinces of Chiang Mai and Chiang Rai. On the grassy plains of the latter district I found it

583136—45——37

plentiful in April, 1929, at Wiang Pa Pao, Chiang Rai, and Chiang Saen; in Chiang Mai, it is known from Doi Ang Ka (where it was not uncommon at 4,000–4,200 feet in April, 1931) and from Doi Suthep (where it is a rare visitor between 2,700 and 5,500 feet). The extreme dates for its occurrence on Doi Suthep are December 30 (1931) and April 2 (1931).

This striking species is normally a bird of the grasslands, whether cultivated or wild; on the mountains it is found both at abandoned *hai* and in the lalang beneath oak and pine. The song, heard in April, is a series of sweet whistles.

An adult male (Doi Ang Ka, April 6) had the irides brown; the maxilla horny brown, blackish along the culmen; the mandible horny brown, fleshy at the base; the feet fleshy brown, the toes darker; the claws horny brown, paler at the tip.

The old male has the entire head (including the long, pointed crest) and body, above and below, black (slightly glossed with blue), each feather more or less broadly fringed with ashy buff; the upper and under tail coverts mixed black and chestnut-rufous; the wing feathers (including the upper and under coverts) chestnut-rufous, the primaries and outer secondaries tipped with black, the inner secondaries almost wholly black; the rectrices chestnut-rufous, tipped with black, most broadly on the central pair and scarcely at all on the outermost pair. The adult female has the entire upperparts dull olivaceous-brown, the feathers of the crown and mantle with broad blackish-brown centers; the wings much as in the male but with deep brown and rufous in place of chestnut-rufous and black; the rectrices deep brown, the outermost pair largely rufous; the underparts brownish buff (brighter on the center of the throat and abdomen), the sides of the throat, the breast, and flanks indistinctly streaked with blackish brown. A first-winter male (Doi Ang Ka, December 3) resembles the female but has the wings and tail of the adult male.

INDEX

○

BIBLIOTHÈQUE VANIER
UNIVERSITÉ D'OTTAWA
Échéance
Celui qui rapporte un volume
[illegible] la dernière date timbrée
[illegible]ous, devra payer une
[illegible] de [illegible], plus deux
[illegible]

VANIER LIBRARY
UNIVERSITY OF
OTTAWA
Date due
For failure to return
or before the last dat[illegible]
below there will be [illegible]
cents, and an ex[illegible]
[illegible]